NATURAL COMMUNITIES

NATURAL COMMUNITIES

By
LEE R. DICE

Ann Arbor

THE UNIVERSITY OF MICHIGAN PRESS

PREFACE

The purpose of this book is to describe the more important methods and concepts of one division of biology, that dealing with natural communities. If the reader gains a better understanding of the importance of ecologic communities to the world of life, I shall be pleased. It is my earnest hope, moreover, that this exposition may stimulate further investigation in this complex and as yet little understood field of biology.

The method of presentation is that of a condensed summary of what is known about those ecologic principles which apply to communities as they exist in nature. Numerous references to previous publications are given, so that the student can secure additional information about those particular topics in which he is interested. No attempt is made, however, to supply a complete bibliography of this very extensive subject.

It is presumed that the reader is already acquainted with the general principles of biology and that he has some acquaintance with living plants and animals. If he is not already somewhat acquainted with the principles that govern the relations between individual organisms and their environments, it will be desirable for him to read several of the references given at the end of Chapter V. In order to hold the book within a reasonable number of pages it has been necessary to condense very greatly certain sections. This has been particularly true of the section dealing with the effects of physical factors on communities.

Human communities are most interesting and at the same time most complex communities. It was my initial plan to include a chapter on human communities in this book. It soon became apparent, however, that any adequate treatment of this subject required more space than could be allotted to it in the present volume. It is my plan, therefore, to present a discussion of human communities from the ecologic viewpoint in a later work.

ACKNOWLEDGMENTS. Special thanks are due Carlton W. Angell, artist in the University of Michigan Museums, whose lively pencil sketches do so much to make the book attractive and greatly aid in the illustration of certain ecologic principles. Francis C. Evans has kindly read the entire manuscript, and his criticisms and suggestions have been of great value. S. A. Graham has also given helpful criticism. The skill of F. Ridlen Harrell, associate divisional librarian in the University of Michigan Library, has been of frequent service in locating obscure or rare references. The Laboratory of Vertebrate Biology of the University of Michigan has assisted in the preparation of the manuscript in many ways, not the least of which has been the service rendered by its excellent reprint library. Most of the charts were drawn by technical assistant John A. King.

The Izaak Walton League of America has kindly allowed the printing in Chapter I of a quotation from Aldo Leopold which first appeared in *Outdoor America*. The University of California Press has granted permission to quote in Chapter X from an article by Joseph Grinnell, which appeared in the *University of California Chronicle*. A quotation from Robert M. Yerkes in Chapter XII is reproduced from the book *Chimpanzees; a laboratory colony,* by permission of the Yale University Press. Through the courtesy of the Ontario Department of Lands and Forests I am permitted to quote in Chapter XIV from a paper by S. Charles Kendeigh, which was published in their *Biological Bulletin*. The Carnegie Institution of Washington has permitted the use in Chapter XVI of certain quotations from their *Publication,* Number 242. In Chapter XVI also there is reprinted by permission of Forrest Shreve a statement originally published in *Ecology*. Duke University Press, publisher of *Ecological Monographs,* has permitted the reprinting of several tables and figures. The use of other copyrighted material is acknowledged where it is presented.

The data for Table VII were collected during a study supported by the Kansas Agricultural Experiment Station and the Division of Forage Crops and Diseases, United States Department of Agriculture.

In addition to the use of materials from books and other sources for which credit is specifically given in the captions, I have copied numerous figures, tables, and quotations from the periodicals *American Naturalist, Auk, Condor, Ecology, Ecological Monographs, Journal of the American Society of Agronomy, Journal of Forestry, Journal of Mammalogy, Journal of Wildlife Management, University of California Chronicle, Wilson Bulletin,* and *Zoologitsheskij Journal*. Without the help of such technical journals science could not advance. To the numerous authors whose figures have been copied, data used, or words quoted, I am most grateful. In each case the name of the author is given at the appropriate place in the text.

ANN ARBOR, MICHIGAN
   October, 1949.

CONTENTS

ILLUSTRATIONS

NATURAL COMMUNITIES

I

COMMUNITY ECOLOGY

DEFINITION OF COMMUNITY ECOLOGY. The division of ecology that treats of communities may be called community ecology as contrasted with the individual ecology of single organisms. Community ecology (Adams, 1913: 5) is also sometimes called synecology, and individual ecology then is called autecology, but these are special terms that will not easily be remembered. Community ecology deals with the relations between individuals and between species, both of plants and of animals, and also with the relations between communities and their physical environments. Actually, there is no clear distinction between community ecology and individual ecology. Information about the functional anatomy, physiology, reactions, and habits of each individual plant and animal is necessary to an understanding of its ecologic position in every community of which it forms a part.

RELATION TO OTHER BRANCHES OF BIOLOGY. The ecologist must of necessity utilize the methods and concepts of many diverse branches of biology and, indeed, of science in general. This has led certain biologists to the opinion that ecology is not a separate science, but is mainly a point of view. Ecology does, it is true, have a somewhat different point of view from that of other branches of biology. In addition, many of its problems, concepts, and methods are different from those of other subdivisions of biologic science (Kashkarov, 1938: 33). This is especially true of community ecology, concerned as it is with the organization into communities of individuals belonging to different species. For example, the relations between the several species within a community which together form a food chain is the special concern of ecology rather than of any other branch of science. It seems logical to conclude, therefore, that ecology, at least in its community aspects, represents a distinct subdivision of biology.

PROCEDURES FOR THE STUDY OF COMMUNITIES

The necessary steps to be taken in any scientific investigation are: first, the accumulation of accurate information derived from observation and experimentation; second, the classification of this information; and third, the attempt to discover the causes of the phenomena observed (Fig. 1).

The student of communities will accordingly be concerned with these 3 types of procedure in his investigations. The emphasis to be accorded to each step will necessarily vary with the subject of the investigation.

DESCRIPTION. Among the features of communities about which information is desired are lists of the kinds of plants and animals which are associated, their absolute and relative numbers, their variations in abundance from time to time, their distribution locally over the area occupied by the community, their structures and activities, and the effects of each kind of organism on its associates. In the first part of any investigation the emphasis must be on the identification and enumeration of the organisms that are present, the description of the habitat and of its variations, and the ascer-

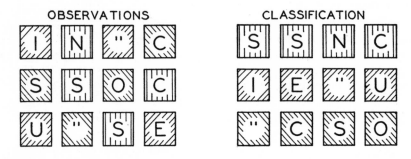

FIG. 1. The method of science. This imaginary group of related but random observations of particular letters and patterns can be classified according to the pattern of the background. This helps in deducing the hypothesis of "Succession," in which all the observations take their proper places.

tainment of the relations between the several elements of the community and its habitat. It is most important that the information recorded shall be fully accurate and shall be as complete as possible. Insofar as may be possible, this information should be gathered in quantitative form so that it may later be tabulated and evaluated.

MEASUREMENTS. Accurate measurements are necessary in ecology, just as they are in every other science. One of the reasons why ecology has developed slowly is the difficulty of devising measurements of ecologic relations. Steady progress now is being made in the development of methods for estimating the populations of the various kinds of organisms. Much less progress has been made in untangling, measuring, and evaluating the interrelations of the several associated members of a community.

CLASSIFICATION OF DATA. The second step in the study of a given community or of a group of communities will usually be the classification of the data into convenient form so that each item can readily be found when needed and so that the several items can be compared and analyzed.

MATHEMATICAL TREATMENT OF DATA. Community interrelations are nearly always extremely complex, and therefore it should occasion no surprise that their exact expression frequently involves various branches of higher mathematics. Fortunately for one who is not especially adept in mathematics, very valuable studies of ecologic communities can be made which require only simple computations. It is evident, however, that as community interrelationships become more precisely known, mathematics must play an increasingly important part in expressing these relations.

A word of caution is offered here in regard to the use of numerical data in ecology. Every community is tremendously complex in its organization, and no community ever remains the same from moment to moment. Any adequate description of even a minor community would require very accurate counts and measurements of a large number of species and of numerous physical factors in the habitat, including their normal fluctuations. It is obvious that such a body of measurements is at present impossible and that the measurements which can be taken are too few, too limited in scope, and cover too brief a period of time to permit a description or explanation of the community in any mathematical notation.

Most of the figures are approximate only or are the mean of a scanty number of inexact measurements. No mathematical treatment can make these figures any more exact than they already are. This does not argue against the use of quantitative data in ecology. In fact, much more use of quantitative methods is needed. But at the present stage of development these methods have their limitations. The unintelligent use of mathematical statements based on inexact observations of ecologic relations in nature may be positively misleading (Uvarov, 1931: 174).

EXPLANATIONS. The third and most important step in the study of a community will be the attempt to discover the factors that are responsible for the origin and for the continued existence of the community. It is especially important to know what laws govern the relationships between each organism and its environment and what enables all the individuals that make up a community to thrive together as an ecologic unit.

Knowledge about ecologic processes and evolutionary trends may be deduced from various types of evidence secured from observations and from experiments. Observations alone will usually prove inadequate to disclose the factors responsible for the evolution of any community or to explain the causal mechanisms which control its continuing existence. This knowledge must be secured by experiment. Some experiments can be conducted in the field; more frequently, however, the organisms will have to be brought into the laboratory, where the environmental factors can be more completely controlled.

HYPOTHESES. The most powerful tool of modern science is that of multiple working hypotheses. Each possible explanation that can be invented to explain some body of facts is called a hypothesis. Then, by the collection of further information and, if possible, by experimentation the validity of each possible hypothesis is tested. Those hypotheses that do not fit the facts at hand must be modified or discarded. If several hypotheses explain a set of facts equally well, additional information must be accumulated to prove which is the best. If no hypothesis is adequate to fit all the known facts, then all the old hypotheses must be modified or new ones must be invented.

THEORIES AND LAWS. When a particular hypothesis explains the facts at hand with reasonable certainty and with few known possible exceptions it is called a theory. An explanation which has stood the test of repeated study and which is in general accord with all the known facts is called a natural law. Every natural law is based only on evidence of various sorts, and no law can ever be completely and irrevocably proved to be true.

PREDICTIONS. The great value of hypotheses, theories, and laws is that they enable one to make more or less dependable predictions about future events. If, for example, the general trend of succession for a given ecologic community is known, it is possible to predict with some degree of certainty what the characters of the community will be next year or 10 years hence. In making such predictions it must be assumed, of course, that the surrounding conditions will remain normal or average. It is possible also to make predictions about the character of a particular community during an especially dry year or following a fire.

Far too little is known about biological processes in nature and about communities in particular to enable dependable predictions to be made at present concerning the results that might follow many types of possible alterations in natural conditions. For instance, the introduction of a foreign species of plant or animal into a region often causes profound changes in certain communities, perhaps even the local extirpation of certain native species. The ecologic relations of the various species that make up a community are, however, so extraordinarily complex and so little understood that no ecologist is able to predict accurately the probable outcome of the introduction of any given alien species. Notwithstanding this situation, many sportsmen clamor for the introduction into their communities of foreign species of game animals. Many such ill-considered introductions of foreign species have in the past resulted in far more harm than good.

Fortunately for the investigator, the considerable body of scientific information already available in published form will aid in the solution of many of the problems that he may wish to study. There will also usually be available various hypotheses about the causes of the phenomena. Some of these hypotheses may already have been tested and found fairly adequate.

The first step, therefore, in any ecologic study will usually be the classification of the information already available and the examination of the various hypotheses that have been proposed to explain the phenomena. The scientist should never allow himself to be too easily convinced of the validity of any particular hypothesis. If the observations are inadequate to make a choice between contradictory hypotheses possible, then it will be necessary to gather more data, through either observation or experiment. For greatest efficiency these new data should be gathered in such a way that they will serve to verify or to disprove a particular hypothesis. The field and laboratory studies will, therefore, need to be carefully planned in advance. A combination of field and laboratory studies will often provide the best method for testing a given hypothesis.

CONCEPTS. It should be emphasized that ecology, like every other science, is made up of an accumulated and classified body of facts, of numerous kinds of working methods, and of numerous concepts. The concepts are the most important part of any science. Every science progresses by the continual development of new and fruitful concepts (Conant, 1948: 78). Although facts are important, not all are equally important. The student can spend too much time in the accumulation of facts which do not bear on any particular problem in ecology. In this book, therefore, particular attention will be given to concepts as expressed in hypotheses, theories, and natural laws. Facts will in general be used only to illustrate concepts. The description of working methods will receive considerable attention, for the ecologist must be familiar with the means of testing hypotheses and of discovering new ecologic relations within communities.

THE PROBLEM OF ADAPTATION

INDIVIDUAL ADJUSTMENTS. The central problem of ecology, as of all biology, is adaptation. Every organism, in order to live effectively, must be able to adjust itself to the constantly changing conditions of its environment. This was pointed out long ago by Herbert Spencer in his *Principles of Biology*. Some environments do not change much from month to month or from year to year, and accordingly the inhabitants need have little power of adjustment. Parasites within the body of a warm-blooded vertebrate, for instance, may be supposed to have a relatively uniform environment; but the organisms that live in certain other situations must meet rapidly fluctuating conditions of life, which may change from season to season, from night to day, and sometimes almost from moment to moment. Every individual organism, if it is to continue to exist, must be able to adjust itself to each change of its environment.

ADAPTATIONS FOR REPRODUCTION. To ensure the continued presence of life on the earth it is not sufficient that each individual be able to adapt itself tolerably to its environment. Every individual will in time die. If the species is to continue to exist, at least a few individuals during their lifetime must produce others of their own kind. The process of reproduction demands special adaptations by the individual beyond those necessary for its own survival. Furthermore, the process of sexual reproduction, at least in most animals, implies social relationships between 2 or more individuals of the same species.

ADAPTATIONS FOR SOCIAL LIFE. The social relations among the individuals of many kinds of species include other aspects of behavior and of survival besides those concerned with reproduction. Thus, the individuals of a particular species of animal may associate themselves for greater efficiency in securing food, for escaping enemies, or for building a home. Numerous kinds of animals are, in fact, so dependent upon the societies in which they live that the individuals are unable to exist alone.

ADAPTATIONS FOR COMMUNITY LIFE. Individual organisms live in association not only with members of their own species, but also with members of other species. The individuals of the several species that live together in any community must continually adjust themselves to the presence of one another. Many species exhibit special adaptations of structure and of behavior that fit them for the particular niche they occupy in the community. Some, for example, are herbivores, some are predators, others are parasites or saprophytes, while the green plants serve as the primary food basis for the community.

Every individual, then, must continually adjust itself not only to the inanimate features of its environment, but also to all its living associates, both of its own and of other species. Furthermore, the reactions of each individual of each species must vary from time to time in accordance with changes in its age class, life-history stage, and reproductive activity. Its reactions vary also with fluctuations in the activity of the other members of its community and with variations in the features of its physical habitat.

THE COMMUNITY CONCEPT

Life on the earth may accordingly be said to be organized at 3 most important levels: (1) the individual, (2) the species or the society, and (3) the ecologic community. The community is the highest level about which life is organized according to this classification, and the community, therefore, deserves especially careful study.

No species of either plant or animal is uniformly distributed over the earth or even over its own geographic range. On the contrary, each species usually occurs in more or less discontinuous patches, between which the species is often rare or absent (Diver, 1938a). The kinds of plants and animals which have ecologic relations with one another tend to recur together, and thus communities are formed.

NUMBER OF ASSOCIATED SPECIES. The number of diverse kinds of plants and animals that are associated to form a community may be very great. This is true both of the number of individuals and of the number of species. It has been estimated, for example, that in a gram of rich topsoil there may be as many as 100,000 algae, 1,000,000 molds and other fungi, 15,000,000 actinomycetes, and perhaps several billion bacteria. The total weight of living matter, including plant roots, in an acre of topsoil may be placed at 5,000 pounds at least, and in many soils 2 to 4 times that amount may be present (Lyon and Buckman, 1937: 13).

Invertebrate animals may be especially numerous in soil that is moist and well supplied with organic debris. On a cultivated and manured plot in England the total number of soil-inhabiting invertebrates per acre has

TABLE I

ABUNDANCE OF LIFE WITHIN A COMMUNITY

Invertebrates living in the soil on the Duke Forest, Durham, North Carolina (data from Pearse, 1946).

Animals	Estimated Numbers Per Acre
Mites	89,602,920
Collembolans	28,052,640
Thysanopterans	1,437,480
Insect larvae	888,224
Ants	662,112
Proturans	601,128
Iapygids	546,417
Chelonethids	518,364
Symphylans	414,142
Insects, various	409,464
Diplopods	387,972
Spiders	372,177
Pauropods	176,853
Chilopods	138,085
Earthworms	90,604
Termites	44,779
Snails	19,166
Nematodes	3,332
Phalangids	797
Total	124,366,656

been calculated to be nearly 15,000,000, not including the protozoa (Waksman, 1927: 357). Many of these soil-inhabiting animals are small and secretive forms that escape observation unless special search is made for them.

From a study of the fauna of the forest floor in a part of Panama it was estimated by E. C. Williams (1941: 108) that the average number of individual animals per acre was approximately 40,000,000. At least 294 and probably over 400 different species were present, and this did not include the protozoa nor any of the bacteria, fungi, or other plants. It has been estimated by Pearse (1946: 131) that in the Duke Forest of North Carolina nearly 125,000,000 invertebrates per acre live in the surface soil (Table I).

In many aquatic communities also the number of kinds of organisms and their density may be enormous. In some fresh-water lakes the bacteria per cubic centimeter of water may number several millions. The annual production of plankton in Lake Mendota, Wisconsin, for example, has been estimated at 12,000 kilograms of dry organic matter per hectare (10,700 pounds per acre) of water surface (Welch, 1935: 253, 265).

Not all ecologic communities are by any means as crowded as those mentioned. Nevertheless, the number of species and of individuals that are associated to form most communities is much greater than might be expected by one who has not investigated the subject.

HISTORY OF THE COMMUNITY CONCEPT

That many kinds of animals and plants are restricted to particular types of habitat must have been noted by primitive man, for his very life depended upon a knowledge of where to find his food and where to be on the lookout for dangerous beasts. That the plants and animals which live together in a particular place have interrelated activities must also have been discovered in ancient times. Early pastoral and agricultural man certainly knew something about the relations of his domestic animals to their food plants and of his crops to the various pests with which they had to contend. The early naturalists noted the relationships between certain species of organisms and between various organisms and their habitats, and in their writings they published many details of these relationships.

HUMBOLDT. The first scientist to give a name to a group of associated species of organisms seems to have been the German scientist Humboldt (1805), who wrote about "associations" composed of several species of plants. Humboldt did not describe these associations in much detail, nor did he perceive clearly the relations between the several associated species.

GRISEBACH. The term "formation" (*Pflanzengeographische Formation*) was proposed by Grisebach (1838), a German botanist, for plant communities of geographic extent which are distinguished by their physiognomy.

MÖBIUS. The clear recognition that all the organisms which live together in a particular habitat form an interrelated community was delayed until 1877, when Karl Möbius, another German investigator, described the community that occupies an oyster bank (Möbius, 1883: 723). Although Möbius did not describe this community in very much detail, he did appreciate the fact that the various organisms composing it were ecologically interrelated and that the community formed a more or less self-regulating unit. To designate such a community he proposed the term "biocoenosis" (*biocönoze*).

EARLY PLANT ECOLOGISTS. During the latter part of the nineteenth and the early part of the twentieth century the plant ecologists took the lead in developing the concept of plant communities and in discovering the laws that govern them. Deserving of special mention among these pioneers are Schimper (1903), Warming (1909), Cowles (1901a), and Raunkiaer (1909).

EARLY ANIMAL ECOLOGISTS. The zoologists for a time lagged far behind the botanists in their study of communities. So far as the communities on land are concerned, this lag was perhaps to be expected because plants dominate and control most terrestrial communities. The lag of the zoologists in the recognition of aquatic communities is more difficult to explain because in aquatic habitats the plants seldom are in complete control.

Although the zoologists did not progress as rapidly as did the botanists in the study of communities, nevertheless many important studies of the animal components of communities were made by early investigators. In a study of the waters of Vineyard Sound off the coast of Massachusetts, Verrill as early as 1873 listed the species that live in each kind of marine habitat. Forbes (in 1887 and later) made many contributions to the ecology of the terrestrial and fresh-water communities of Illinois, though he made little effort to describe or to classify the individual communities. The oceanographers described numerous types of marine communities, but seldom made any attempt at an ecologic classification.

SOME RECENT COMMUNITY ECOLOGISTS. The more recent studies of communities have dealt mostly with terrestrial areas. Among notable workers in this field may be mentioned especially C. C. Adams, Frederic E. Clements, H. A. Gleason, Victor E. Shelford, and A. G. Vestal in North America; Charles Elton and A. G. Tansley in England; J. Braun-Blanquet, of France; and A. N. Formozov and Daniel Kashkarov, of the U. S. S. R.

AQUATIC COMMUNITIES. Far less study has been given to aquatic communities than to those on land. Many aquatic environments are difficult of access to the ecologist. Also many kinds of aquatic communities, such as those in a muddy stream or on a shifting shoal, are unstable in their position and in their limits. Nevertheless, ecologic communities exist both in fresh-water and in marine environments, and a considerable number have been described by various authors (Murray and Hjort, 1912; Petersen, 1914 and later; Allee, 1934; MacGinitie, 1935; Clements and Shelford, 1939: 294-353). In recent years such limnologists as Birge and Juday (1922), Thienemann (1926), and Wesenberg-Lund (1930) have made many notable studies of fresh-water communities.

The great importance to man of aquatic and especially of marine communities is apparent when one considers that plankton makes up a large part of the organic world (Coker, 1947: 237). This is true because of the much greater area of the earth covered by the oceans than by land. Marine and fresh-water communities, therefore, deserve careful study no less than do terrestrial communities.

PLANT AND ANIMAL COMMUNITIES NOT DISTINCT

The earlier students of ecologic communities usually described only the plants or only the animals, depending upon whether the particular investigator happened to be a botanist or a zoologist. Often, indeed, only certain kinds of plants or animals were considered. Many descriptions of plant communities, for example, failed to take into consideration the nonflowering plants. Descriptions of animal communities often dealt with only 1 class, order, family, or smaller taxonomic group of animals, as for example, birds, rodents, or tiger beetles.

It is now generally recognized by ecologists, however, that all the organisms, both plants and animals, that are associated in a situation constitute an interrelated community (Shelford, 1913; Vestal, 1913, 1914; Phillips, 1931a; W. P. Taylor, 1935b; Kashkarov, 1938; Clements and Shelford, 1939). Although an ecologist may give special attention to some one group of plants or animals, he should always keep in mind that his favorite forms make up only a part of the whole natural community. It is no more possible to consider the plants separately from the animals that feed upon them, pollinate them, and transport their seeds than it is to consider the animals apart from the plants that provide them with food and shelter.

MODIFIED AND ARTIFICIAL COMMUNITIES

The community concept is useful not only for the study of undisturbed natural conditions but also for the study of the more or less artificial communities produced by man. The agriculturalist and the forester, especially, must deal with these artificial communities. Attempts to convert natural communities directly to man's use have in the past often met with failure due to a lack of understanding of ecologic principles.

EFFECTS OF MAN'S ACTIVITIES. The characters of many natural communities have been greatly changed through the activities of man. Through the clearing of forests, draining of swamps, plowing of fields, irrigating of lands, polluting of streams and lakes, killing of the native plants and animals, introducing of foreign species, the building of habitations, roads, and canals, and through other means, man has completely altered the face of nature. Modified or entirely artificial communities now cover a considerable part of the land area of the earth. These man-made communities are of very great importance for the welfare of man.

Violence to a community may produce unfavorable effects that persist long after the visible effects of the original damage have disappeared. Thus, Aldo Leopold (1942) described a hardwood forest on the north flank of the Alps, of which one-half has never been slashed and has given sustained cuttings since 1605. "The other half of this forest was slashed during the 1600's, but has been under intensive forestry during the last 150 years." Nevertheless, "the old slashing now produces only mediocre pine, while the unslashed portion grows the finest cabinet oak in the world. . . . On the old slashings the litter accumulates without rotting, stumps and limbs disappear slowly, natural reproduction is slow. On the unslashed portion litter disappears as it falls, stumps and limbs rot at once, natural reproduction is automatic." The inferior performance of the old slashing is attributed by Leopold to its depleted underground community of bacteria, molds, fungi, insects, and burrowing mammals. This soil biota "constitutes half the environment of a tree."

NEED TO PRESERVE NATURAL COMMUNITIES. Natural or nearly natural communities usually furnish the best situation for studies designed to disclose the processes that govern communities. In most parts of the world, unfortunately, the native conditions are rapidly being altered by man. In many regions of intensive agriculture or of industry practically all the natural communities already have been greatly altered or destroyed, with hardly a trace remaining. In some districts it is now impossible to find even a small sample of unmodified habitat. It is urgent, therefore, that sample areas of each important type of community occurring in any part of the world be preserved in parks, wildlife refuges, or study areas. Accordingly, a broad program must be developed for the selection and preservation of samples of those natural areas that are still in good condition.

HUMAN COMMUNITIES

Man is completely dependent on plants and on other animals for his food and for many other essentials for his existence. He cannot live except as a member of some "ecologic" community. Man affects in many ways all those natural and artificial communities of which he is a member. Certain members of these human communities in their turn have important effects upon the life of man. For example, the presence of a parasite, such as the Plasmodium which produces malaria, in a community where man lives may have drastic effects on his health and well-being. Likewise, a herbivore, predator, or parasite which attacks an organism that is an important source of human food may seriously disrupt the economy of a human society.

The term "community" is frequently applied by sociologists and anthropologists to a human society alone, not including the other associated animals and plants. To distinguish clearly this kind of community from the community that includes all the associated plants and animals, the latter may be called an "ecologic" community, even though the adjective "ecologic" is redundant. In this book the term "community" will always be used in its broader sense to refer to a whole group of associated species of organisms.

The communities which are dominated by man, even those most highly organized, are subject to many of the same ecologic laws that control natural communities. Ecologic regulatory mechanisms operate to control human populations, just as they do the populations of other animals and of plants. The ecologic interrelations within human communities are often extraordinarily complex. Because of its great importance for human welfare, the ecology of man's interrelations with his plant and animal associates deserves special attention.

In his conceit man is inclined to think of himself as the most important of living organisms. Yet, from the ecologic point of view the several kinds of plants and animals that together constitute a community are all to a greater or lesser extent essential to the well-being of one another. Each species serves some biologic function in the community. The loss of any species would change to a slight extent or perhaps upset the whole community organization (Gabrielson, 1941; 107). From the point of view of many other kinds of animals, man would be considered a dangerous and perhaps unnecessary species.

CO-OPERATION IN RESEARCH

The science of ecology has been developed by the labors of many men, as have all other sciences. The names of some of these investigators are listed in the Literature Cited at the end of this work. For every one there listed dozens more have had to be ignored, though they may have made equally important contributions to an understanding of communities. It is true that the teachings and publications of different men are not all equally important, nor are all their contributions important in the same way. Some investigators are painstaking, persistent observers or experimenters; others are imaginative and original, able to devise new methods and to combine observations into logical systems. All are servants of science, so long as their work is honest and their reports thorough and unbiased. Many important observations have been made by men who are relatively untrained in biology. The most valuable scientific contributions, however, will always be made by men who are well trained in the methods and concepts of their particular branch of science.

COMPLEXITY OF ECOLOGIC DATA. In the early days of science it was possible for one man to know and to comprehend many sciences. Leonardo da Vinci, who lived from 1452 to 1519, made important contributions to our knowledge of anatomy, medicine, and engineering and in addition was an outstanding artist. At the present time the amount of factual data accumulated by the several sciences is so tremendous, the concepts are so numerous and so diverse, and the interrelations of the various parts of knowledge are so complex that seldom can 1 man be competent in more than 1 small division of 1 branch of science.

In no division of science are the accumulated data greater in amount or the complexities of nature more evident than in ecology. The student of communities must be familiar with the kinds of plants and animals that live in the communities that he studies and he must be able to identify at least the more important species with certainty. He must have a considerable knowledge of the morphology and the physiology of these forms and of the way they react to the conditions of their habitats. He must have some comprehension of the psychologic basis for the behavior of the various kinds of animals that live together in the communities under investigation. The heredity of the various species must not be neglected, for heredity forms the basis for much of the variability in the physiology, psychology, and morphology of the species. The role of the evolutionary tendencies present in every species must be kept in mind, for every species is the result of past evolution and most forms are probably in process of evolution at the present time. To compare and to evaluate his data properly, the ecologist must treat his measurements statistically and must therefore be a biometrician of no small ability.

TRAINING FOR ECOLOGY. The associational ecologist, therefore, must have extensive and intensive training in many branches of biology. He must also be able to describe and to measure the environments of the species and communities that he studies. To this end he must have training in geography, geology, meteorology, climatology, and soil science. These subjects demand a broad background training in physics and chemistry.

A fully trained ecologist, accordingly, has to be well trained in practically all the major branches of science. Even astronomy and anthropology cannot be neglected, for they may help to explain fluctuations in certain populations and to clarify the past history of certain communities. Furthermore, because the results of scientific studies are published in many languages, the ecologist must be a linguist. He should be able to read with fair facility English, German, French, and Russian. A knowledge of Spanish and of several other languages will often be helpful.

Obviously, no one man can acquire or can retain in his mind all this diverse information. Yet to investigate communities adequately requires full use of the technics and accumulated wisdom possessed by almost every branch of science.

RESEARCH TEAMS. The solution of this dilemma lies in co-operation in research. The modern trend in scientific investigation is for a group of several persons, each trained in a special field of science, to co-operate in order to solve a particular problem that no one of them would be competent to attack alone. Co-operation in research is especially desirable in ecology because of the complexity of the problems and the number of fields of science included.

Even the amateur who lacks intensive training in any field of science can often fit into a co-operative research project, if only he is intelligent, honest, persistent, and willing to contribute regularly a part of his time. In order that the amateur may be able to make worth-while contributions to science, however, he must nearly always associate himself with some individual scientist or group of investigators who can help him plan his program of observations and of record keeping and who can assist him in properly filing or publishing his results. Should the interested amateur not be able to find such scientific help in his own community, he can perhaps secure advice by writing to his state university, college, or museum, or to the appropriate national scientific society.

One great difficulty in the study of communities, either natural or modified by man, is the amount of time and effort required to secure an adequate basis of data for the drawing of satisfactory conclusions. Investigations made at only 1 season or in only a single year cannot possibly give a complete description of the fluctuations that continually take place in the composition of every community. Only through well-planned, long-continued, and comprehensive studies by a research team can the processes that go on in even a single community be learned, and the agencies that keep the community in balance with its changing environment be discovered.

The individual ecologist by spending his week ends, his summers, or perhaps a sabbatical year now and then in study can make important contributions to the knowledge of particular communities. Many of the more complex problems of communities, however, cannot be solved in the time left over from a busy life filled with teaching or with other duties. To secure the services of the needed research team will require the setting up of special projects with adequate staffs and with suitable financial support. It is heartening to note that the federal government and occasionally a state government has supported particular comprehensive projects for the study of certain problems of wildlife or forestry. Very rarely, however, has the full complexity of the ecologic problems involved in any of these projects been appreciated. Usually, the projects have been too temporary, have employed too few investigators, and have considered too few of the associated species of plants and animals. It is to be hoped that the need for long-continued and comprehensive studies of particular communities will soon be generally recognized.

SELECTED REFERENCES

Braun-Blanquet, J., George D. Fuller, and Henry S. Conard. 1932. Plant sociology: the study of plant communities. New York and London: McGraw-Hill Book Co. Chaps. 1-4.

Clements, Frederic E., and Victor E. Shelford. 1939. Bio-ecology. New York: John Wiley and Sons. Chap. 1.

Elton, Charles. 1927. Animal ecology. New York: Macmillan Co. Chaps. 1-2.

Kashkarov, D. N. 1938. Principles of animal ecology. Moscow and Leningrad. Chap. 5. (In Russian.)

Möbius, Karl. 1883. The oyster and oyster-culture. Rept. U. S. Fish. Comm., 1880, Pt. 8: 721-29.

Weaver, J. E., and Frederic E. Clements. 1938. Plant ecology. 2d ed.; New York: McGraw-Hill Book Co. Chap. 3.

II

SOME IMPORTANT KINDS OF COMMUNITIES

Definition of Ecologic Community

An ecologic community is an assemblage of ecologically related organisms composed of 2 or more species. Such a community may be of any ecologic rank and may include any number of associated individuals. An assemblage of individuals all of the same species is not a community, but is a society.

According to the definition given above, the minimum membership in any community is 2 associated individual organisms, each belonging to a different species. For example, a single cottontail rabbit and the blackberry bush under which the rabbit is sitting form a community (Fig. 2). At the other extreme, all the plants and all the animals of the whole earth, considered together, constitute an immense world community. Between these extremes in size of communities are many intermediate grades. The term "community," therefore, has very broad applications.

The rabbit and the blackberry bush in the example given above are ecologically related because the bush provides shelter for the rabbit and perhaps some food also. The feces and urine of the rabbit form fertilizer for the plant. It is, however, not usually necessary to ascertain the precise ecologic relations between the several animals and plants that live together in an aggregation in order to consider them all members of the same community. It may nearly always be assumed with confidence that any 2 species which live in the same habitat must have direct or indirect ecologic relations with each other.

Certain kinds of communities are actual concrete assemblages of organisms (Fig. 3). Other kinds are abstractions only.

Biotic Province and Regional Community

All the plants and animals that live on a large land area, such as a continent, together constitute an immense community. Over any large area, however, the distribution of the organisms is never uniform. Certain regions may be well watered but cold, some regions may be warm but arid, while other regions may have different kinds of climate. Certain species of plants and animals likewise will live in the cold and wet tundras, others in the hot and arid deserts, and still others in the various intermediate climates. The communities of plants and animals must, accordingly, differ from region to region in correspondence with the regional distribution of climate and of the other features of the physical habitat. Each major ecologic division of a continent that covers a continuous geographic area may be called a biotic province (Dice, 1943). The plants and animals that live within a biotic province or within one of its major subdivisions may be called a regional community. The aquatic communities of the world have been much less studied than have the terrestrial communities, but there is good evidence that biotic provinces and regional communities can also be recognized in the oceans.

FIG. 2. A simple ecologic community composed of a single rabbit sitting under a single blackberry bush. (Drawing by Carlton W. Angell.)

Association

Each biotic province contains a number of diverse types of communities, such as forest, swamp, marsh, prairie, meadow, or dune. An association is a type of community that in the aggregate covers an important part of the area of a biotic province. Associations nearly always are distributed in irregular patches which are more or less isolated from one another. The several associations that occur within a biotic province are consequently interspersed to form a mosaic.

FIG. 3. Concrete communities which may occur within a small area. The Bonito Valley 5 miles northwest of Lincoln, New Mexico, showing the stream, gravel-bar, cut-bank, nogal (walnut), short-grass, cultivated-field, pinyon-cedar, and other communities. (Drawing by Carlton Angell from a photograph by L. R. Dice taken July 5, 1937.)

The concept of association which is defined above is the one which is used by most ecologists, though certain others use the term for a very different concept. I shall discuss the classification and terminology of communities in Chapters XIX and XX.

Stand

A stand may be defined as a local example of an association composed of those individual plants and animals that live together in a particular situation (Braun-Blanquet, Fuller, and Conard, 1932: 23). The stand then is a concrete community in which the member individuals are directly or indirectly associated. All the stands of the same type that occur within a biotic province together form an association. It is to be noted that the term "stand" is applied only to a concrete community which is an example of an association. Other kinds of concrete communities which are not stands will be described later.

In the past the term "stand" has been applied mostly to examples of various kinds of forests. It is entirely proper, however, to apply the term to an example of an association dominated by organisms of any kind, whether these be bulrushes, water lilies, or even oysters.

Care should be taken not to confuse the term "stand," when applied to a whole local community, with other usages of the word. Thus, in the expressions "pure stand" or "mixed stand" attention is directed chiefly to one or to several of the most conspicuous species. The community which is called a stand, however, includes not only the conspicuous species which may give the stand its name, but also all the associated plants and animals.

None of the several organisms that compose a stand need be stationary in position, in spite of an implication to that effect in the term. In an open-water habitat, for example, all the plants and animals making up a particular stand may be free-floating or swimming, with the result that no member of the stand is stationary.

Stratum

Most stands, and therefore most associations, are made up of several layers or strata. A stratum may be defined as a horizontal or nearly horizontal division of a stand or association. Strata are particularly evident in forest communities, where 5 or even more layers may sometimes be distinguished (Colquhoun and Morley, 1943: 75). In stands where the growth of vegetation is low, there will probably be few strata. On a bare rock surface, for example, there may be only a single stratum. In almost all terrestrial associations, however, at least 2 strata are present: soil surface and a subterranean layer. In aquatic associations, also, several strata may often be distinguished. Thus, on a shoal in Douglas Lake, Michigan, Moffett (1943) noted that the water above the shoal was inhabited mostly by plankton organisms similar to those occurring elsewhere in the surface waters of the lake, but that the bottom stratum was inhabited by an assemblage of burrowers characteristic of shallow depths.

Microstand

Numerous kinds of concrete communities are not of sufficient extent or importance to be considered stands, but nevertheless they may require description and discussion. For each such minor community I here propose the term "microstand." An example of a microstand that frequently recurs in a forest association is the assemblage of plants and animals that live in and upon a decaying log (S. A. Graham, 1925). Such a microstand may pass through several successional stages and ultimately may disappear completely. Other examples are the microstands that exist in heaps of animal dung or decaying animal carcasses. Still another type of microstand is centered around the nests of animals, notably the nests of the social insects. Numerous kinds of microstands are formed by clumps or small patches of herbs or shrubs together with their associated organisms.

Microassociation

Many kinds of microstands recur frequently in the stands of a given association. Each group of recurrent microstands of similar type may be called a microassociation. A microassociation, then, is a community composed of a group of microstands of similar type which occur within a particular association. Within an ant nest, for example, the ants together with their symbionts compose a microstand. All the microstands (nests) formed by this particular kind of ant within the limits of 1 association constitute a miscroassociation.

Seasonal Aspect

The character of a given community at a particular season of the year is its aspect. Almost every community changes its character from season to season in greater or lesser degree. In the terrestrial communities of the North Temperate Zone, for instance, relatively few organisms are active in winter. At that season the annual plants exist only as seeds and the deciduous plants are bare of leaves. Certain animal species have migrated to the south, while others have become dormant. In spring most of the dormant forms become active again, and the migratory species return. In each of these seasons, accordingly, any given community exhibits different aspects. Special aspects are characteristic of each of the other seasons.

The several species of plants differ in the seasons at which they bear leaves, flowers, and fruits. The species of animals differ in the periods during which they mate, bear their young, migrate, and become dormant. In describing any community, care should be taken to include an account of its various aspects, or if only 1 aspect is described, the season should be precisely stated. Strata and microstands as well as stands may change their aspects at successive seasons.

The 4 most important seasonal aspects of a community lying in a temperate or frigid zone are designated vernal (spring), estival (summer), autumnal (autumn), and hiemal (winter). Other terms may be used where the seasons do not progress in a regular manner or where additional aspects appear. The aspect of the arid foresummer on the Arizona desert before the beginning of the summer rains, for example, may thus be called pre-estival. The late summer aspect of the Illinoian biotic province is called serotinal (Weese, 1924: 23).

Community Type

Certain of the ecologic communities that occur in widely separated regions may be more or less similar in general appearance and perhaps also in the adaptations of their members, but may differ from one another, at least in part, in the species of plants and of animals which compose them. Some of the grassland communities of the North American Great Plains, for instance, look superficially very much like certain grassland communities on the steppes of the U.S.S.R. and also like others in Australia. In spite of their similar appearance these communities on the different continents may be composed of wholly different species. Likewise, some of the minor communities of widely separated areas may be similar in appearance and in the behavior of their members, even though none of the component species is common to the several areas. For example, the several microassociations of small organisms that attack and consume decaying animal carcasses in various regions of the world have much in common ecologically, but the species that form these communities are likely to differ in each region. Such apparently similar communities may be grouped to form community types. A community type, then, is a group of communities that have a similar physiognomy, however widely they may differ in taxonomic composition and however widely they may be separated geographically.

Ecotone

Between adjacent communities there often is a more or less intermediate transitional strip. Such a strip is called an ecotone. Ecotones may be narrow or broad and they may connect communities of any rank. Along the border between a deciduous forest grove and the adjacent prairie, for example, there is often an ecotone of bordering shrubs (Shelford, 1913: 262), which will in this instance be a distinct community. An ecotone is called a tension zone because here 2 adjacent communities come into competition with each other.

Environment

Environment includes all the organic and inorganic features that surround and affect a particular organism or group of organisms. It includes, therefore, the associated individuals of the same and of different species, as well as the physical factors of the habitat. If it is desired to distinguish between the living and nonliving parts of the environment, these may be designated, respectively, the biotic environment and the physical environment.

Habitat

The word "habitat" has been used with various meanings by different biologists. It is necessary, therefore, to define the term carefully. As used here, the habitat is the situation in which or on which any community, species, or individual lives. Any consideration of a given habitat must obviously include the climate as well as all the other features of the situation.

The habitat of a community usually consists only of the physical features of the environment, for the organisms are all included in the community. An exception must be made, however, wherever a microstand is resident in or on an individual plant or animal, which therefore forms part of its habitat.

The habitat of a particular species of either plant or animal may include other species of organisms in addition to the purely physical features of the environment. Thus, the grassy plains of part of North America are the habitat of the pronghorn antelope. The grasses are, in this example, an important feature of the habitat of the pronghorn.

The habitat of an individual plant or animal, particularly of the smaller forms, is especially likely to include other individual organisms. A caterpillar may spend its whole larval existence on the particular plant on which it feeds. Likewise, a parasite may spend all of 1 stage in its life history in or on 1 particular individual host. The assorted individuals of the same species also constitute an important feature of the habitat of individual organisms. This is particularly obvious with such social forms as the ants.

Although, as has been pointed out, other organisms often form essential elements in the habitats of species and of individuals, nevertheless, the greater emphasis in the description of a given habitat is often on the physical conditions of the situation.

Habitats, like communities, may vary in size and in rank. The habitat of a single unicellular organism may occupy only a very tiny space. Although it is correct to speak of the habitat of a single individual, the habitat of a small individual organism or of a microstand is more commonly called a microhabitat. The habitat of a regional community may cover many square miles of territory. In the widest sense of the term the whole world forms 1 immense habitat for living beings.

Ecosystem

An ecologic community together with its habitat constitutes an ecosystem (Tansley, 1935; Lindeman, 1942: 400). This term covers both the living and the nonliving elements that are associated in a given situation, whereas the term "community" by definition applies only to the living organisms (Fig. 4). The term "ecosystem" corresponds with community and with habitat in scope and may be applied to an ecologic unit of any rank or size.

According to this definition each biotic province is an ecosystem. The word "province" carries implications of the physiography, climate, and other physical features of the regional habitat as well as of the biota. All the communities that occur within a biotic province make up a regional community. A regional community and the regional habitat in which it occurs together comprise a regional ecosystem. The biotic province, therefore, is a particular kind of regional ecosystem.

FIG. 4. A community and its habitat together constitute an ecosystem.
(Drawing by Carlton W. Angell.)

In any comprehensive consideration of an ecologic community the ecologist must of necessity have the ecosystem in mind. It would always be most satisfactory if a study could be made of ecosystems rather than of ecologic communities alone (Egler, 1942: 249). Unfortunately, however, no one person can ever have adequate training in all the fields of science that must be included in the consideration of even a single ecosystem. Consequently, it becomes a matter of practical necessity to divide the ecosystem into several parts for study. It is for this reason that the plants in a given community often are considered separately from the animals and that the climate and the soil often are given only scant attention. The animal ecologist, in fact, must usually be a specialist on some one type of animal, sometimes covering only a single family. Nevertheless, the organisms that are described do not, strictly speaking, form a plant community, insect community, or bird community, but are only plant, insect, or bird parts of the whole community.

Furthermore, the whole community forms only a part of the larger unit, the ecosystem.

Succession of Communities

Many communities have only a more or less temporary existence, after which they are replaced by communities of a different type. The replacement of one community by another is called succession. In each climatic region, however, there is a climatic climax type of community, which under stable conditions of climate and of physiography is not in process of further succession. Special conditions of the soil or of the physiography, nevertheless, may prevent a particular type of community from progressing toward the climatic climax. In such a case there may be formed a temporary edaphic climax controlled by the soil or a physiographic climax controlled by the physiography. These matters will be discussed in more detail in Chapter XVI.

Community Nomenclature

Community nomenclature applies to the names by which communities are to be called. Various methods for naming communities have been proposed by ecologists, but complete agreement on this subject is still lacking.

To designate certain kinds of associations, plant ecologists sometimes add the Latin suffix *etum* to the generic name of the principal plant. Thus, a *quercetum* is a community made up principally of oaks (*Quercus*). Literally, *quercetum* means in Latin "a thing with oaks," or, in other words, an oak forest. Some ecologists go further and add the specific name of the plant in the Latin genitive in order to indicate its special dominance in the community named. Such a practice is incorrect in Latin (Bartlett, 1933) and is difficult to apply because in most communities there is more than 1 important species of organism.

The best name for any community is generally agreed to be one that is descriptive, distinctive, and not overlong. The names applied by ecologists usually are derived from the language of the country in which the communities are located. Frequently, the name used refers to 1 or more of the conspicuous plants or animals making up the community. Other names of communities, however, are based on the type of vegetation and still others on the character of the physical habitat, wherever this exercises a controlling effect on the occurrence of the community.

The name used by the first author who clearly describes a given community should continue to be used if it is appropriate. It is generally agreed by ecologists, however, that no system of strict priority can be applied to the names of ecologic communities (Flahault and Schröter, 1910: 23). It is, therefore, proper for the ecologist to reject a prior name, if it is deemed unsatisfactory for a given community, in favor of a better name proposed at a later date.

SELECTED REFERENCES

Braun-Blanquet, J., George D. Fuller, and Henry S. Conard. 1932. Plant sociology: the study of plant communities. New York and London: McGraw-Hill Book Co. Chap. 2.

Dice, L. R., and Philip M. Blossom. 1937. Studies of mammalian ecology in southwestern North America, with special attention to the colors of desert mammals. Publ. Carnegie Inst. Wash., 485: 45-74.

Nichols, G. E. 1923. A working basis for the ecological classification of plant communities. Ecology, 4: 11-17; 154-67.

Shelford, Victor E. 1913. Animal communities in temperate North America as illustrated in the Chicago region. A study in animal ecology. Chicago: Univ. Chicago Press.

III

METHODS FOR DESCRIBING AND MEASURING COMMUNITIES

More adequate descriptions of the communities of all parts of the world are greatly needed. Quantitative measurements of the population density of each component species and of the distribution of the individual organisms over each ecosystem are especially desirable. Information about the variability between stands and microstands of the same types from place to place is now mostly lacking. For no part of the world are the available descriptions fully satisfactory even in regard to the climax associations. The microassociations and successional associations in most areas are still very imperfectly known. A wide field in descriptive biology is here open to those persons with some training in ecologic methods who may have time to devote to field study in their localities.

There is no known mechanical method for the selection of those communities that it may seem desirable to describe. The decision as to which communities are of sufficient importance to merit description and measurement must be made by the ecologist on the basis of his knowledge and previous experience. The value of the resulting descriptions will depend in part on the competence of the ecologist who makes this original decision.

GEOGRAPHIC RELATIONS

STATEMENT OF GEOGRAPHIC LOCATION. As a basis for the description of any community it is necessary to have an accurate statement of its precise geographic location. Unfortunately, many of the descriptions of communities published in the past by ecologists have failed to indicate the precise local area under consideration.

DESCRIPTION OF CONCRETE COMMUNITIES. Most kinds of communities occur in more or less isolated stands or microstands which are repeated again and again in the regional community. The several concrete units which make up a given association or microassociation, of course, differ more or less from one another. The amount of variability among the units of the same community type is a matter of much ecologic interest. The most satisfactory kind of community description, therefore, is one which de-

25

scribes in detail 1 or more of the stands or microstands, as the case may be, and then compares these with other units of the same association or micro-association in order to indicate the amount of variability among the several units.

STATION. Each particular situation that is described in detail is a station. The area included within a given station may be of any size, but preferably should not be larger than the observer can adequately describe. A station may comprise only a part of a particular stand or it may include an entire isolated stand. Several microstands may be included within the limits of 1 station. In an area of intermediate conditions a single station may include parts of 2 or more associations.

In describing a station one will, of course, include statements about the physiography, soil, and local climate of the site. The term "station" implies the ecosystem, rather than the community alone.

PHYSIOGNOMY

The simplest description of any particular situation is given in terms of its general ecologic character or physiognomy. In those terrestrial communities in which plants are conspicuous, and this is true of most of them, vegetation type usually determines the physiognomy. For example, the physiognomy of many areas is characterized by forest, grassland, or marsh. In certain littoral marine ecosystems, however, various attached animals, such as corals or barnacles, may be the most conspicuous elements in the physiognomy. In still other ecosystems, such as those characterized by sand dunes or rock cliffs, the physical factors of the habitat may be most prominent.

LIFE FORM. The physiognomy exhibited by a growth of plants or animals will depend in considerable part upon the ecologic structure or life form of the individuals. Many attempts have been made to classify plants (Raunkiaer, 1934; W. G. Smith, 1913; Gams, 1918; Tansley and Chipp, 1926: 19-24) and animals (Hesse, 1924) according to their life forms. Plants, for instance, may be classed as annuals, biennials, herbaceous perennials, and woody perennials, and these classes may be further subdivided if desired. The distinctions among the several classes and subclasses of the life forms (growth forms) of plants, however, are not always clear. These terms are useful in the description of individual species of plants and sometimes of groups of species, but attempts to describe a whole community according to such terms are not satisfactory.

Animals do not lend themselves well to classification according to life form, though the body forms of animals seem always to be adapted to the habitat (Hesse, Allee, and Schmidt, 1937; E. H. Graham, 1944: 28). The animal body, however, is so varied in form in the various phyla and classes, and the types of physiologic responses by animals are so diverse that no practical classification of the life forms of animals has been devised or seems possible (Clements and Shelford, 1939: 48-50).

LISTS OF MEMBER SPECIES

The characters of every community are determined by those of the several species that together compose it. Any full description of a community, therefore, must include a list of at least the more important of the member species. This list should contain not only those species of plants and animals which are most easily observed, but so far as possible should also include all those forms that play any significant role in the functioning of the community.

RATING OF ECOLOGIC IMPORTANCE. A bare list of the component species making up a community, however, is insufficient. Certain species are very abundant or for other reasons may play an important role in the control of the characters of a given community. On the other hand, many of the rarer species play only an insignificant role in community life. The ecologist's statement of his general impression of which are the most important species in the community is useful, but it is not enough. Quantitative measures of the actual abundance of each of the several species are needed and also an analysis of the functions that each of these species performs in the organization of the community.

SAMPLING METHODS

A complete inventory and set of measurements of the individual plants and animals that comprise even a small community is nearly always impracticable because of the enormous number of individuals involved. A very accurate description of the community can be obtained, however, from counts and measurements of samples taken in a suitable manner.

SAMPLE PLOTS. The samples taken as an aid in the description and measurement of a community may be of several kinds. Many of the samples employed by ecologists are taken from sample plots or sample transects. A sample plot may be defined as any area which is examined as a representative of a particular ecosystem. A square sample plot is called a quadrat.

The sample plots taken for the study of particular features of community composition or activity may be of several special kinds. On a list quadrat the species are listed, and the individuals of each form present are counted. A chart quadrat is one on which the position of each plant or of each permanently attached animal under consideration is accurately plotted on a chart or map. A permanent quadrat has its position marked so that it may be studied at successive intervals of time to discover the changes that take place in community composition. A denuded quadrat is one from which the vegetation and perhaps certain of the animals have been removed, so that the stages in succession beginning with bare soil may be observed (Weaver and Clements, 1938: 29). Other special types of plots may be established for particular purposes (Hanson and Love, 1930).

SAMPLE TRANSECTS. A belt transect is a sample plot that is considerably longer than it is broad. A line transect has a specified length but no breadth. Measurements or counts are made only lengthwise along this kind of a transect. In recent years the line transect has been increasingly employed in ecologic surveys. Line transects may be used as a basis for the calculation of density index, relative frequency, coverage, and other ecologic statistics.

A stratum transect cuts vertically across the strata and produces a profile of the community showing, for example, the relative heights above the ground of the various kinds of plants in the community. A bisect is similar to the stratum transect, except that it includes the subterranean strata and, therefore, includes the plant roots as well as their above-ground parts (Tansley, 1946: 131).

SELECTED SAMPLES. If only a simple description of a community is desired and if no statistical treatment of the data is planned, the sample plots or transects which are to be examined may be located at places selected by the investigator as typical of the community. If the community varies somewhat from place to place, as is usual, then the sample plots may be selected to include the range of variation within the community.

RANDOM SAMPLING. Statistical treatment of the data secured by the counts or measurements, however, is always desirable; therefore it is usually best to take the samples at random and to avoid their selection by the investigator. Unfortunately, some of the methods for locating sample plots used in the past by ecologists have given biased samples (Hasel, 1941). There is a very great difference between the haphazard selection of plots and random sampling.

The best method for locating sample plots at random is first to decide upon the size of the sample plots which are to be examined. Next, the whole area of the community concerned is divided into units, each the size of a single sample plot. Then, by some random method, such as throwing dice or drawing cards, the plots to be examined are located. Should the same sample unit be drawn twice, this duplicate drawing is discarded and another number drawn to replace it. The essential feature in random sampling is that every individual in the population being sampled must have exactly the same chance of being chosen in each sample that is taken.

In locating the positions of sample plots or transects in the field, extreme accuracy will not, as a rule, be necessary. The plots will usually be located with sufficient accuracy if the distances are measured by pacing and if the directions of the lines or boundaries are determined by use of a compass. In order to avoid any possible bias in the selection of the locations for the sample plots, one may, by pacing or by some other rough method, locate a point near the spot desired and then by exact measurement from this spot with a steel tape or other dependable instrument locate the precise corner of the plot or beginning point of the line transect (Canfield, 1941). One should always mark the boundaries of each sample plot with precision and should measure the area of the plot accurately.

If the ecosystems that are to be studied are rectangular in outline, they can readily be divided into regular square or rectangular sampling units. The boundaries of most communities, unfortunately, are irregular in outline. Such communities, nevertheless, can also be divided for sampling into units of any standard size desired. Among the various possible methods for taking samples at random from an ecosystem which has an irregular outline, one of the simplest is illustrated in Figure 5.

RANDOMIZED BLOCK SAMPLING. The community to be described often is not uniform over its whole extent and, therefore, a few samples taken at random may not give all the desired information about the distribution of

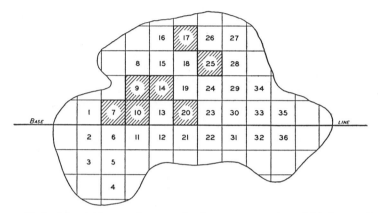

FIG. 5. Method for taking random samples from an ecosystem which has an irregular outline. A base line is first drawn across the area, preferably across its longest axis. A surveyor's tape makes a good base line for a small area. Measuring from this base line, the area of the ecosystem is next divided into uniform plots, each the size of the sampling unit to be used. Those plots which lie wholly inside the boundaries of the area are next numbered serially. Those marginal plots that lie partly outside the boundary are omitted from consideration. Then, by drawing at random one number at a time from a set of numbered cards, or in some other random manner, the location of each sample plot is found. In this figure 7 sample plots thus drawn at random have been marked by shading.

the several associated species. Under these conditions the method of randomized block sampling will give a better basis for quantitative description. This method is sometimes also called representative or stratified sampling. By this method the area to be sampled is first divided into several large blocks, which may be either equal or unequal to one another in size. Each of the blocks is next divided into subunits, each subunit having the size of a single sample plot (Fig. 6). Then from each block 2 or more subunits are drawn at random as samples (Schumacher and Chapman, 1942: 61). The computations will be simplified if the proportional number of sample units taken from each block, as compared to the total possible number of units in that block, is the same.

It may, for example, be desirable to ascertain the variation in the population density of a given species among the several blocks of a community, such as that illustrated in Figure 6. The mean population density per sample can be calculated for each block. The significance of the differences among the means of the several blocks can then be determined. A general mean per sample for the whole community can also be computed by taking the average of the block means. Should there be much variation from block to block, the mean computed in this way will be more accurate than the mean computed from samples taken at random over the whole area. Another method of treatment would be to subject the data to analysis of

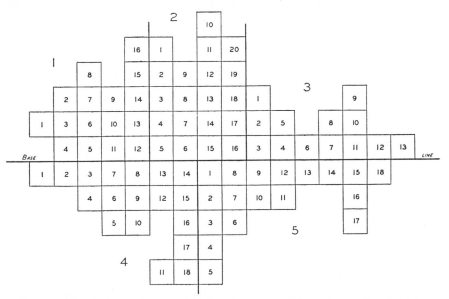

Fig. 6. Randomized block sampling of an ecosystem of irregular outline. The heavy lines mark off the ecosystem into 5 blocks. Each of the blocks is further subdivided into sampling units of uniform size. In order to provide a basis for statistical calculations 2 or more units should be taken at random as samples from each block.

variance in order to discover whether the amount of variability among the blocks is greater than the variability within the blocks. For more details about methods of mathematical treatment the reader is referred to Schumacher and Chapman (1942).

RANDOM TRANSECTS. Belt transects may be taken at random by the same methods that are used for taking square plots at random. The area to be sampled is first divided into sampling units, each having the width and length of a single belt transect. Then in some random manner the units to be taken as samples are selected. If the problem does not require the measurement of the whole area of the community, belt transect samples may be taken at random by using the method illustrated in Figure 7.

For locating line transects at random one can use much the same methods as for belt transects. In order to avoid crossing one another the line transects over a given area should all run in the same direction. To locate them at random, then, it will be necessary to locate only their beginning points. Inasmuch as a line transect has no breadth, there is theoretically an infinite number of them possible on any given area. Without producing any serious bias in the data, however, it may be assumed that no 2 line transects will be located closer together than the width of the smallest of the individual plants or animals to be counted or measured. If this width is taken as a unit together with the length of the transect, the area may be

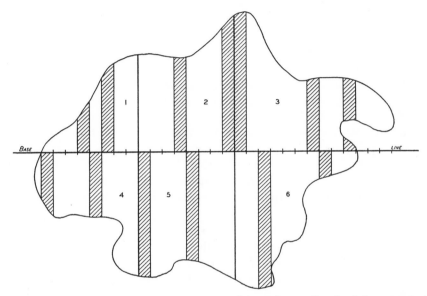

Fig. 7. Method for sampling an ecosystem of irregular outline by belt transects in randomized blocks. A base line, either imaginary or real, is first drawn across the area. This base line is marked off in units each the width of a belt transect. The area is then divided into blocks, the boundaries of which coincide with the belt-transect units. Next, from the number of belt-transect units in each block 2 or more are drawn at random. In the figure, the shaded transects indicate those that have thus been drawn. Since transects vary in length, each one examined must be measured. The median length of the transect times its width will give the area sampled by that transect.

laid off into sampling units, the desired number of which may then be drawn at random for examination.

SYSTEMATIC SAMPLING. Although random sampling will usually be most desirable for ecologic studies because of the possibility of measuring the sampling error, nevertheless, in some instances systematic sampling may be preferred, in which method the samples are taken evenly, at specified distances apart over the area rather than at random. Systematic sampling usually gives a more accurate mean of the population density than random sampling of equal intensity (Osborne, 1942) and is, therefore, to be

preferred in many practical ecologic surveys, such as resource surveys
(Blythe and Pechanec, 1943: 415). As an example of such a survey the inventory of the wildlife of Young County, Texas, made by Ben Osborn (1943),
may be mentioned.

In systematic sampling special care should be used not to take samples
from adjacent plots, which naturally tend to be more nearly like one
another than are widely separated plots and thus do not give a reliable
sample of the whole area (G. E. Blackman, 1935: 760). An especially inefficient method of sampling is to divide a selected part of the area into subplots and then to treat each of these subplots as a sample. For the same
labor far more reliable information would be obtained from sample plots
taken at random from the whole area of the community under investigation.

SAMPLE-PLOT SHAPE. The shape of the sample plots, whether square, rectangular, or of some other form, is largely a matter to be determined by
the special problem under investigation and by the convenience of the field
worker. Square plots are usually employed. It has been shown by Clapham
(1932), however, that long, narrow plots, with length as much as 16 times
the breadth, sample the plants of an area more efficiently than square plots.
A difficulty in long plots (belt transects) is that the plot boundary is longer
in proportion to the area of the plot than in round or square plots. Long
plots, accordingly, give an increased chance of error per unit area in determining whether individuals on the edges of the plots are inside or outside the boundary.

Circular plots can sometimes be marked out more easily than rectangular plots. They have the serious disadvantage, however, that if they are
taken at random, some parts of the area may be excluded from being sampled. Plots that are to be used for random sampling should, as a rule, have
straight sides.

SAMPLE-PLOT SIZE. The size of the sample plots to be employed in any
ecologic study must be adjusted to the size, mobility, and abundance of the
organisms that are to be observed. Sample plots of diverse sizes are difficult
or impossible to compare statistically. So far as possible, therefore, sample
plots of some standard size should always be used.

For the measurement of the ecologic distribution of plants in grassland
or in other types of herbaceous vegetation, quadrats 1 meter or 1 yard
square are commonly employed. Also, for animals of small size, slight activity, and moderate abundance this size of plot may be satisfactory. For
the study of very small or very abundant plants, such as mosses or lichens,
or of very small animals, such as mites or minute insects, a square-meter
quadrat may be impracticably large, and smaller plots, perhaps as small as
1 square decimeter, must be employed. When large plants, such as shrubs or
trees, are present, the sample plots must be of large size (Weaver and Clements, 1938: 11; Vestal and Heermans, 1945). A sample plot area of 1 acre
is probably as small as should be used if large trees are to be enumerated.
For studies of large mobile animals, such as deer or geese, the sample plots

may need to have areas of 1 square mile or more. It is evident, therefore, that no one size of sample plot is equally suited for the study of all the organisms that make up a community. Plots of 2 or more sizes may be required in many studies.

MARKING THE PLOT BOUNDARIES. When the size and position of a given sample plot have been determined, it is usually necessary to mark the boundaries in some manner. The simplest way to mark large plots is to drive metal or wooden stakes at the corners. Cords, tapes, or wire cables may then be stretched between the stakes, or strips of wood or metal may be laid on the ground connecting them. A small plot is often delimited by a frame of wood or metal of the proper size, which is laid on the ground or driven into it. A circular plot may be marked by a center stake, about which a wooden or metal strip or a tape of proper length is swung as a radius.

Metal or wooden rules or tapes should always be used in locating sample plots, for cloth tapes often are very inaccurate. Metal tapes vary slightly in length depending upon the temperature, and wooden rules are affected by moisture. Variations in length due to weather conditions, however, are usually slight, and in ecologic field work correction for these factors seldom needs to be made.

NUMBER OF SAMPLES TO BE TAKEN. The number of samples to be taken or of sample plots to be examined for the study of any particular ecologic community depends both on the accuracy desired in the computations and on the time and amount of assistance available for the field work. The description of a single sample is seldom convincing, no matter how carefully it is selected as representative of the community under consideration. At least 2 samples should be taken in every community studied. More than 2 samples will always be desirable in order to show the amount of variability within the community.

The inexperienced student should be cautioned not to embark on an overambitious program that cannot be satisfactorily completed. One is apt to underestimate greatly the time that will be required for the field and laboratory measurements. In general, it may be said that dependable measures will nearly always be obtained if the combined area of the samples examined constitutes 5 to 10 per cent of the total area of the community under consideration and that a total sampling area of considerably less than 5 per cent may often be satisfactory.

The reliability of any mean, standard deviation, or other statistic increases with the number of samples on which it is based. The increase in accuracy, however, is not directly proportional to the number of samples, but only to the square root of their number. Thus, 400 samples give only twice the accuracy, measured by the standard error, of 100 samples of the same size.

For the calculation of mean density alone, 10 or even a smaller number of samples may give a useful measure if the amount of variability in the community is relatively low. About 25 samples will usually be the minimum number required if a reliable measure of variability is desired, assuming a moderate amount of variability. For studies that include the accurate computation of frequency index or of association index, 100 or more samples will often be needed.

The labor required in measuring a large number of samples is so great that it will seldom be practical to examine a large number except where the samples are very small and counts or measurements are to be made of only 1 or of a very few species. The ecologist must, therefore, often be content with calculations based on a smaller number of samples than he might desire. More dependable statistical results will in general be secured from measurements made on a considerable number of small random sample plots rather than on a small number of larger plots of the same total area. It is, furthermore, always better to gather as extensive field data as possible rather than to expend great effort on the elaborate statistical treatment of an inadequate number of samples.

OTHER KINDS OF SAMPLES. Another important kind of sample often used in ecologic field studies does not come from an exactly limited unit of space but consists of a collection of individuals taken in the community in some other standardized manner. A single sweep of an insect net of a specified size, if swung in a particular manner, will collect a certain number of insects and other invertebrates and will constitute a sample of the invertebrate population from that part of the community. Similarly, a single haul of a townet or dredge of a specified kind, when drawn through the water at a given speed for a given period of time, will secure a sample of the organisms in an aquatic community. Another kind of sample can be secured by counting the organisms of a particular kind seen or collected in a specified period of time under uniform working conditions. Certain kinds of animals can be attracted by lights or baits to traps or to places in which they can easily be collected. Various other special methods have been devised for securing samples of particular kinds of organisms. Some of these methods are described in Chapter IV.

POPULATION DENSITY

Population density is indicated by 3 methods of statement: relative abundance, mean number of individuals per unit area, and density index.

Relative Abundance

The population density of a given species in a community or region has in the past often been stated roughly in terms of estimated relative abundance. Frequently, a scale of abundance having 5 levels is employed. Terms commonly used are: rare, scarce or few, numerous or frequent, common, and abundant. In this scale a rare species is one of which only a very small number of individuals is encountered per year. At the other extreme, an abundant species is one that is observed in numbers every time search is made for it in the proper habitat. Qualifying terms, such as "very" common, "not" numerous, or "extremely" rare, are sometimes used, but add little in precision.

The statement of population density by means of these relative terms usually is based only on the general impression of the observer. Since observers differ in amount of field experience and in point of view, any 2 persons are likely to disagree on the term to be used for any particular density of population. Furthermore, the same observer will of necessity use different scales of abundance for dissimilar species. For instance, an average density of 1 per square mile might be called abundant for the wolf or bear, but rare for a species of moss or of insect. These relative terms of abundance, therefore, are at best only rough indications, yet they are of value when no more precise measure of population density can be obtained.

Mean Number of Individuals per Unit Area

The population density of any given species is best stated as the average number of individuals per unit area. The unit of area employed varies with the type of organism and with the problem being studied. For small organisms the statement of density is often made in numbers per square meter or per square yard. In the United States the statement of density on large areas usually is made in average numbers per acre or per square mile. In countries where the metric system is used for geographic measures the statement for large areas is usually in average numbers of individuals per hectare or per square kilometer. The student is cautioned not to assume that a figure given for mean density in any way implies a uniform distribution for the individual organisms over the area described.

A complete or nearly complete count of all the individuals of a given species present in a particular stand or on any limited area is called a census. Unfortunately, it is rarely practical to make a complete census of any species, even for a small community. Accordingly, estimates of population density are nearly always based on counts made on sample plots. The best size of sample plot for the calculation of mean population density is the one that is most practical for making accurate counts of the number of individuals present.

RELIABILITY OF ESTIMATES. Any estimate of population density that is based on sample counts is liable to errors of 2 principal kinds. There are, first, errors that are due to the inaccuracies of counting. Certain individuals on the sample plots may escape being counted, and others by error may be counted more than once. If the inaccuracy of the counts is known to be a fairly regular percentage of the number counted, allowance can be made in the estimates for this inaccuracy. It would be far better to improve the accuracy of the counts so that the actual numbers counted can be employed in the calculations. Unfortunately, it is seldom possible to secure completely accurate counts of populations in nature. Estimates of natural populations, therefore, are usually to be taken as useful approximations whose reliability depends very largely on the competence of the observer.

The second source of error in the calculation of population density comes from errors of random sampling. Should the counts on the several sample plots be known to be accurately made and should they all be of nearly the same magnitude, then it is evident that there can be only a slight amount of variability in population density over the area sampled. Any plot or set of sample plots that might be chosen would give a fairly reliable estimate of the mean density. On the other hand, if the counts on the several sample plots differ considerably from one another, then it is indicated that there is considerable variability in population density from plot to plot within the community. Thus, if only a few samples are taken, they may not give a very accurate estimate of the average density over the whole area of the community.

STATISTICAL DIFFICULTIES. Here I must insert a word of caution concerning the application of the usual statistical formulas to measures of wild populations. Most of the commonly used statistical formulas assume random distribution and a normal curve. Organisms in nature, however, often are not distributed at random and their curves of distribution are rarely of normal type (Michael, 1916; Clapham, 1932, 1936; Ashby, 1935; G. E. Blackman, 1935).

Many kinds of organisms live in clumps or social groups. This is particularly true of forms that reproduce by asexual means, but it is true also of many sexually reproducing organisms, such as the social insects. A number of other kinds of organisms, because of intraspecific competition or for other causes, tends to be distributed more evenly than they would be at random. Many forms are greatly affected in their distribution by the local habitat, which often varies in character from place to place within the ecosystem. All these factors prevent the members of a community from being distributed at random.

The difficulty of nonrandom distribution in nature would be overcome in calculations if a sufficiently large number of random samples could be taken. Unfortunately, the labor of collecting samples is usually so great that the samples obtained must be held to a low number; therefore, the likelihood of the nonrandom distribution of the population must always be considered.

POISSON SERIES. By statistical methods it is possible to determine whether the distribution of the individuals in any given series of samples is approximately at random. If the distribution is at random, then the number of samples in which 0, 1, 2, 3, 4, and so on, individuals of the species concerned are counted will fall into a Poisson series. The Poisson series expected for any given number of samples and for any given mean number of individuals per sample may easily be calculated (Table II or Snedecor, 1946: 440-44). The significance of the deviation of the actual sample series from the distribution expected in a Poisson series may then be tested by means of chi-square. This test will be most efficient if the samples are so small that a part of them (preferably about 20 per cent) fails to include any representative of the species.

TABLE II

EXAMPLE OF CALCULATION OF POISSON SERIES EXPECTED FOR A GIVEN NUMBER OF SAMPLES AND A GIVEN MEAN PER SAMPLE

Fruit stocks of yarrow (*Achillea*) on square-yard sample plots on Edwin S. George Reserve, near Pinckney, Michigan, Sept. 10, 1947. Plots examined, 100 (= n).
Mean plants per plot, 1.10 (= m).

Stocks per Plot (Class)	Symbol	Logarithm	Expected Number of Plots (Antilogarithm)
0	$n = 100$ $e^m = (.434295)(1.10)$ n/e^m	$= 2.000000$ $= \underline{.477725}$ (subtract) $= 1.522275$	33.29
1	$m = 1.10$ nm/e^m	$= \underline{.041393}$ (add) $= 1.563668$	36.62
2	$m = 1.10$ 2 $nm^2/2e^m$	$= \underline{.041393}$ (add) 1.605061 $= \underline{.301030}$ (subtract) $= 1.304031$	20.14
	Subtotal of plots in classes 0, 1, and 2		90.05
3 and up			9.95
		Total plots	100.00

TABLE III

EXAMPLE OF CALCULATION OF THE CHI-SQUARE OF THE DEVIATION OF SAMPLE COUNTS FROM A POISSON SERIES

Fruiting stalks of yarrow (*Achillea*) on square-yard sample plots on Edwin S. George Reserve, near Pinckney, Michigan, September 10, 1947.

Plants per Plot	Frequency (Number of Plots)	Frequency Expected in Poisson Series	Deviation from Expected	(Deviation)^2 Expected (X^2)
0................	68	33.29	+34.71	36.191
1................	7	36.62	−29.62	23.958
2................	6	20.14	−14.14	9.927
3 and up........	19	9.95	+ 9.05	8.231
Totals.........	100	100.00	.00	78.307

Degrees of freedom $= 4 - 2 = 2$.
Total chi-square $= 78.307$ (very significant).

The method of calculation of chi-square for a Poisson series is illustrated in Table III. The chi-square of the deviation in the example totals 78.307. The number of classes is 4 and the number of degrees of freedom is 2 less than this, or 2. From a table of chi-square, such as is presented by R. A.

Fisher (1936) or by Snedecor it is evident that this amount of deviation from a Poisson series is highly significant statistically. These data, therefore, indicate that the distribution of this species of plant over the area sampled is not random. In setting up a table for the calculation of chi-square, attention should be given to the rule that in no class should the expected number be less than 5.

Organisms occur in nature as individual units, rather than in a continuous series; therefore, their frequency of occurrence in a series of random samples forms a binomial rather than a normal curve. Actually, the frequency curve is often strongly skewed and, as already stated, tends to follow a Poisson series. This is illustrated in Table IV, in which the proportional

TABLE IV

EXAMPLES OF POISSON DISTRIBUTIONS

Samples expected to contain each given number of individuals in a series of 100 samples, when the distribution is random.

Classes of Samples According to Number of Individuals in Each	Mean Number of Individuals per Sample						
	0.5	1.0	1.5	2.0	2.5	3.0	4.0
0.................	60.65	36.79	22.31	13.53	8.21	4.98	1.83
1.................	30.33	36.79	33.47	27.07	20.52	14.94	7.33
2.................	7.58	18.39	25.10	27.07	25.65	22.40	14.65
3.................	1.26	6.13	12.55	18.04	21.38	22.40	19.54
4.................	.16	1.53	4.71	9.02	13.36	16.80	19.54
5.................	.02	.31	1.41	3.61	6.68	10.08	15.63
6 and up...........	.....	.06	.45	1.66	4.20	8.40	21.48
Total............	100.00	100.00	100.00	100.00	100.00	100.00	100.00

number of samples containing each given number of individuals is calculated for various means per sample. More complete tables of Poisson series are given by Karl Pearson (1924) and by Molina (1942). It will be noted that as the mean number of individuals per sample is reduced the amount of skewness is increased. Comparison with Table IV will enable a rough estimate to be made of whether or not a particular series of sample counts falls into a Poisson series.

The standard deviation of the strongly skewed Poisson distribution obviously will not give the same information about a population that it would give if the curve were normal. For instance, in a normal curve it is expected that 34.13 per cent of the population will fall in the range between the mean and a point one standard deviation above the mean, and that 34.13 per cent will fall in the same interval below the mean. In a Poisson distribution, on the contrary, these proportions are not expected to hold.

The standard error of the mean of a series of samples, however, is often fairly dependable, particularly if the population density per sample plot is high, even though the curve of distribution is skewed. When the counts of the individuals of the particular species under consideration average 50 or more per sample plot, the curve of distribution may usually be assumed to be approximately normal. With fewer than 50 individuals per plot, the distribution is likely to be noticeably of the Poisson type (Snedecor, 1940: 378). For practical purposes the standard error will be fairly dependable in most cases where the number of individuals averages 10 or more per sample plot. When the number of individuals per sample plot runs fewer than 10, however, it will be unwise to depend upon the standard error of the mean or upon fiducial limits calculated from formulas based on the normal curve.

COMPARISON OF THE MEANS OF POISSON SERIES. Means from 2 series of samples having Poisson distributions usually cannot be compared by the methods used for comparing the means of populations that have normal curves. Means of such samples may properly be compared by the method of chi-square.

As an example of the chi-square method of comparison, a series of sample plots may be assumed on which a total of 250 individuals of a certain species is counted. In another series containing the same number of sample plots and the same area 150 individuals of the species may be counted. Is the population density significantly different in the 2 series of samples? The mean of the 2 sample series is $(250+150)/2 = 200$ individuals per series. The deviation of each series from the mean of the 2 series is 50. The sum of the squares of the deviations, therefore, is $(50)^2 + (50)^2 = 2500 + 2500 = 5000$. The chi-square of the difference is this amount divided by the mean, or $5000/200 = 25$. This with one degree of freedom is a very significant amount. The difference between the population densities of the 2 hypothetical sample series, therefore, is not likely to be due to chance. In making this calculation one should be very careful to use the full number of individuals in each sample series and not the mean per sample.

DENSITY INDEX

Actual counts of the population of any given species even on a small sample plot are always laborious and often are impracticable with the time and labor available. In such cases an index of the population density may serve. A density index is a mathematical indication of the abundance of a particular species of organism that does not involve an estimate of the actual number of individuals present per unit area or per unit volume.

Density indexes are utilized especially by wildlife managers for ascertaining the relative numbers of a particular species in successive years, in separated areas, or under differing conditions of management. Although a density index cannot be directly converted into exact numbers per unit area, a series of density indexes taken at successive intervals of time will often indicate whether or not a given species is decreasing or increasing in abundance. By the comparison of density indexes taken on comparable areas it also may be possible to ascertain whether the numbers of a species are greater or lesser in one place than in another. Density indexes are, in fact, nearly as useful for many practical purposes as are exact counts of the number of individuals per unit area.

SUITABLE SAMPLES. The method to be employed for securing a density index for a given species at a given place and time must vary with the habits of the species concerned, with the conditions of the habitat, and with the amount of time the observer can devote to the task. Often a count will be made of the number of individuals present in samples of some sort. These samples may be of various kinds. In general, they may be classified as either space units or time units, though often they are defined in terms of both space and time.

SPACE UNITS. An instance of a suitable space-unit sample from which to compute a density index is a townet haul taken in a pelagic community. If the townet is of a specified construction, of a particular size of mesh, with an opening of a given diameter, and if it is drawn through the water at a given speed for a specified time, then the number of individuals of each species secured will give an index of the abundance of each form under the conditions of time of day, season, water temperature, and other environmental factors at the time the sample was secured. A similar sort of sample of certain of the organisms living on the ocean bottom will be obtained if a dredge haul is made, again under exactly specified conditions.

A specified number of sweeps of an insect net of given size, of particular size of mesh, and swung in a standardized manner will also produce a sample which may be used as a basis for computing a density index. Many kinds of insects may be caught in traps or attracted to lures. If the conditions for setting the traps are fully standardized, the counts of individuals taken may form a satisfactory sample for the computation of a density index.

In fisheries studies a density index is often obtained through calculations based on the return per unit of fishing effort. In the marine fisheries a statement of fishing effort may be given in terms of the number of days per fishing-boat operation (Herrington, 1947). With game fishes a density index may be calculated from a "creel census" of the number of fishes taken by each fisherman per hour of fishing in a particular area of lake or stream.

Still another kind of density index makes no attempt to count the individual animals, but, instead, counts only the signs of their presence in selected space units. The number of nests, burrows, trails, droppings, or other signs of the presence of a species may be counted on sample plots of specified size or along transects of specified length. From these counts a density index may then be computed.

A transect gives an especially valuable sample for the computation of density index because the transect crosses a variety of local conditions and secures an average of the population over a considerable linear section. The townet and dredge hauls previously mentioned actually are a special kind of transect. Another common type of transect is made by the observer walking across a community and recording all the individuals of a particular kind of animal, such as a certain species of bird, seen within a specified distance from his trail. It is a common practice of mammalogists to set a line of traps to secure a sample of the mammal population, and from the number of individuals taken per line to compute a density index (Dice, 1941: 404). A density index for certain species of plants may also be obtained from counts made along a transect (Marks, 1942). It is important that the length of each transect should be measured and standardized; otherwise it will be impossible to compare one sample with another or to combine them to form a mean density index.

TIME UNITS. Time units as well as space units may be used as a basis for the calculation of density indexes. Time units have been used particularly for securing indexes of bird abundance (Grinnell and Storer, 1924; Kashkarov, 1927; Linsdale, 1928; Dice, 1930; Lay, 1938). It is important that during the unit time of observation the speed of travel of the observer be held nearly constant (Colquhoun, 1940). When the observer travels at a given rate of speed for a specified time, he will tend to travel a uniform distance. There is, therefore, not a great deal of difference between time units and distance units used for the purpose of securing a sample count from which a density index may be computed. The time unit has the advantage that under usual field conditions time is generally more easily measured than distance.

Density indexes for certain invertebrates can also be obtained from time units. An estimate of the abundance of slugs, for example, has been based on the number of each species collected with the aid of an electric torch in 30-minute periods on nights favorable for slug activity (Barnes and Weil, 1944). A density index for surface isopods and diplopods has been obtained by Herold (1928, 1929) from counts made during a search period of definite length, usually 30 minutes. Rogers (1942: 15-16) has devised a scale of the abundance of crane flies based on the numbers obtained per hour of intensive collecting. Colquhoun (1942b) has secured an index of ladybird beetle populations by counts of the number of beetles seen during 15-minute periods. An index of the number of cabbage butterflies based on counts of the number of eggs laid per unit of time has been suggested by O. W. Richards (1934). Any of these methods should give density indexes of value if the environmental conditions during the periods of counting are uniform.

UNIT OF STATEMENT FOR DENSITY INDEX. Each density index can best be stated in terms of the sample units from which it has been derived. Thus, if the number of birds or other animals of a particular species seen from an automobile is counted, the resulting density index should be stated as the number of individuals seen per mile or per kilometer of road traversed (Bennett and Hendrickson, 1938; Randall and Bennett, 1939; Hiatt, 1942; Allan and Sime, 1943). For counts of kangaroo-rat mounds the density could be stated in the average number per acre or per mile of transect. If time units rather than space units are used in the counting, the result should be stated in terms of the number of individuals observed per time unit employed.

The temptation to convert a density index into an estimate of the number of individuals per unit area should be stubbornly resisted by every ecologist who values his reputation for accuracy. It may be possible in a certain situation to make an accurate census of the population density on the same area for which a density index has been obtained and then to derive a coefficient for converting one into the other. In other situations, at other times, and for other species, however, this relationship between density index and population density will certainly vary. It will always be best, therefore, to let each density index stand on its own merits and not to attempt to estimate actual population densities from such data.

The conditions on which any density index is based should always be clearly stated. It is well known that the activity and conspicuousness of many kinds of animals are greatly affected by the weather, time of day, season, stage in life history, age, and other environmental and physiologic factors. All these factors, therefore, may affect the counts on which the density index is based. When counts made at diverse places are combined to form a mean density index, special care must be used to make sure that the conditions under which the several counts were made are fully comparable.

RELATIVE FREQUENCY

The proportion which the individuals of a given species form of the total aggregation of individuals of a certain type in a particular area constitutes its relative frequency.

INDEX OF RELATIVE FREQUENCY. The index of relative frequency of a given species is derived by dividing the number of its individual members by the total number of individuals of all species of the type under consideration in the area. If, for example, all the individuals counted happened to be of the same species, its index of relative frequency would be 1.00.

A simple field method for ascertaining the relative frequencies of certain kinds of organisms is to count the first 100 individuals of the type under consideration as they are encountered, recording them by species. The proportion represented by each species in the total count is then its relative frequency. For example, along a trail through a mature mixed forest in the province of New Brunswick, about 20 miles west of Matapédia (Quebec), I counted the first 100 trees observed that had trunk diameters of 6 inches or more at breast height and that were within about 25 feet of the trail (Table V). Beech evidently was the most abundant large tree in this forest, and hard maple was next in frequency. Yellow birch was slightly more abundant than balsam fir, while white spruce was represented by only 2 small individuals.

It is obvious that this method for estimating relative frequency can be employed only for organisms that are equally easy of detection and of identification. The method cannot be used for secretive organisms or for those whose identification in the field cannot be made readily and with certainty.

Usually, only those species that have a somewhat similar life form are compared in calculating their relative frequency. For example, one might compute the relative frequencies of the trees that grow in a particular forest stand or of the birds that live in that stand but would not usually attempt to secure a combined relative frequency for the trees and birds. Neither would one attempt to compare the relative frequency of birds and insects. Relative frequency, therefore, is a measure which can be used to compare only a part of the members of a community.

TABLE V

RELATIVE FREQUENCIES OF FOREST TREES IN A NEW BRUNSWICK FOREST

Sample of 100 trees with trunk diameters of 6 inches or more at breast height (original data, 1936).

Species	Individuals Counted	Index of Relative Frequency	Maximum Trunk Diameter in Inches (d.b.h.)
Beech..........	37	0.37	14
Sugar maple.....	26	0.26	15
Yellow birch.....	19	0.19	30
Balsam fir.......	16	0.16	8
White spruce....	2	0.02	6
Totals........	100	1.00	

FREQUENCY INDEX

The frequency index is another useful statistic for describing ecologic distribution in quantitative terms (Raunkiaer, 1909; W. G. Smith, 1913; Gleason, 1920).

COMPUTATION OF FREQUENCY INDEX. In order to compute frequency index the presence or absence of the particular species under consideration in each of a series of samples is recorded. Then:

$$\text{Frequency index} = \frac{\text{Number of samples in which the species is present}}{\text{Total number of samples examined}}.$$

The frequency index, therefore, is a statement of the proportion in which a given species appears in a series of samples taken in a standard manner. For example, if 50 sample plots of a given size should be examined and a certain species should be recorded on only 2 of the plots, then its frequency index would be $2/50 = 0.04$.

FREQUENCY PERCENTAGE. Frequency of occurrence is sometimes expressed in percentage rather than as a decimal; if that is done, it should be called frequency percentage rather than frequency index. The decimal form is preferred by mathematicians and, therefore, it is adopted here.

ABSENCE INDEX. In a few types of computations the absence index is used rather than the frequency index. The absence index shows the proportion of samples of a given series in which a particular species does not occur. It may either be calculated directly or obtained by subtracting the frequency index from 1.00.

SUITABLE KINDS OF SAMPLES. Kinds of samples other than sample plots may be used as a basis for the calculation of frequency index. Records taken on a series of standardized transects, for instance, provide a fully satisfactory base. Records taken in a series of standard time units may also be employed. Any series of collections or other samples taken in a standard manner may, in fact, be used as a base for the calculation of frequency index. For example, Michael (1916:xx) took each haul of a marine dredge as a sample unit and from records of the occurrence of the several species of organisms in a series of hauls made under a particular combination of environmental conditions he calculated their frequency indexes. The indexes thus obtained may be compared with indexes obtained from other series of dredge hauls made under somewhat different environmental conditions.

It is not even necessary that any individual of the species concerned be actually observed in order that its presence on a series of sample plots may be recorded and its frequency index computed. The nests, trails, or other evidence of the presence of the species is sufficient, so long as the identification of the form can be made with certainty and so long as the same field methods are used for all the samples.

The samples from which a frequency index is to be computed may be taken either in some systematic manner or at random. Random sampling will in general give the more useful information, for then the results may be treated statistically.

RELATION OF FREQUENCY INDEX TO SAMPLE SIZE. The frequency index is affected seriously by the size of the samples employed. The larger the sample, the greater is the chance of a given species occurring in each sample. If the samples are very large plots, a considerable proportion of the species in the community will appear on every plot. The frequency indexes of even some of the rarer forms will in that case be relatively large. If the sample plots are very small the frequency indexes of even the commoner forms will tend to be low. In this case many of the rarer forms will not appear at all, unless a very large number of samples is examined.

When the frequency indexes of several species in a community are to be computed from plots of the same size, it will be desirable to select a plot size such that no species greatly exceeds an index of 0.80, which will give the most efficient index (R. A. Fisher, 1941, sec. 17). It is evident, moreover, that all the sample plots, transects, or samples on which any frequency index is to be based must be of the same size. Frequency indexes computed from samples of dissimilar size cannot be directly compared (Romell, 1930).

If the frequency index of a species is known for a given size of sample plot, if the distribution of the species is at random, and if the sample plots are taken at random, then it is possible to calculate what the frequency index would be for any other sample plot of given size (G. E. Blackman, 1935: 762). If F_a is the frequency index of a species on sample plots of area a, then the frequency index F_b of the same species on sample plots of area b will be given by the formula:

$$F_b = 1.00 - \left(1.00 - F_a\right)^{\frac{b}{a}}.$$

For example, if the frequency index of a randomly distributed species is 0.64 when determined on sample plots of an area of 1 square meter, then on sample plots that are 0.5 square meter in area the expected frequency index will be:

$$1.00 - \left(1.00 - 0.64\right)^{\frac{0.5}{1.0}} = 1.00 - 0.36^{\frac{1}{2}} = 1.00 - \sqrt{.36} = 1.00 - 0.60 = 0.40.$$

RELATION OF FREQUENCY INDEX TO POPULATION DENSITY. A species that is abundant in a given community will appear in a greater proportion of the random samples taken there than will a species that is rare. The frequency index of any species is related, therefore, to its population density. The relationship between frequency index and population density is, however, logarithmic rather than directly proportional (Kylin, 1926; G. E. Blackman, 1935; Ashby, 1935). The mathematics of such a relationship has been considered by R. A. Fisher (1941, sec. 17).

If the individuals of a species can be assumed to be distributed at random over a given area, then the mean density per sample plot may be calculated from the frequency index. A simple method of making this calculation is here presented. In making the calculation one will actually use the number of plots on which no example of the species is recorded (absence index) rather than the frequency index.

In a Poisson series, which obtains when the distribution is at random, the first term, being the number of samples in which no individual is expected, is given by the formula:

$$A = \frac{N}{e^m}.$$

Here A represents the number of samples containing no example of the species under consideration; N is the total number of samples examined; e is the base of the natural logarithm; and m is the mean number of individuals per sample. Then:

$$\log A = \log N - m(\log e)$$
$$m(\log e) = \log N - \log A$$
$$m = \frac{\log N - \log A}{\log e}.$$

The value of $\log e$ (base 10) may be taken to be 0.434295 and is a constant. The formula, therefore, becomes:

$$m = \frac{\log N - \log A}{0.434295}.$$

This formula is based on the fact that *A,* the number of samples in which no example of the species is present, forms the first term of a Poisson series composed of the given number of samples and having the unknown mean. If the number of samples is known and also the first term *A* of the corresponding Poisson series, then the mean per sample can be calculated from the formula given. It will be noted that the formula gives the mean density per sample directly and not the logarithm of the density.

The population density per sample expected for several frequency indexes is presented in Table VI. In making up this table, random distribu-

TABLE VI

Average Population Density Corresponding to a Given Frequency Index

Random samples and random distribution assumed.

Frequency Index	Density per Sample	Frequency Index	Density per Sample
.01	0.010	.55	0.799
.02	0.020	.60	0.916
.03	0.030	.65	1.050
.04	0.041	.70	1.204
.05	0.051	.75	1.386
.10	0.105	.80	1.609
.15	0.163	.85	1.897
.20	0.223	.90	2.303
.25	0.288	.95	2.996
.30	0.357	.96	3.219
.35	0.431	.97	3.507
.40	0.511	.98	3.912
.45	0.598	.99	4.605
.50	0.693	1.00	Approaches Infinity

tion of the individuals and random sampling have been assumed. It is evident that for the lower values of the index, under these assumptions, density per sample corresponds rather closely to the frequency index. The density per sample, however, rises more rapidly then the frequency index and ultimately approaches infinity. The most rapid rise in estimated density occurs after the frequency index has become greater than 0.90.

The calculation of the population density of a species from its frequency index is impossible if the index is either 1.00 or 0.00. The results may not be accurate if the index approaches 1.00 closely. No error is introduced by a close approach to zero so long as that point is not reached, but at low values the collection of sufficient samples to supply an adequate basis for the calculation of the frequency index will be laborious. The calculation will be most efficient if the size of sample is adjusted to give a frequency index of approximately 0.80 (R. A. Fisher, 1941, sec. 17). The most dependable results will be obtained when the number of samples is large, preferably 50 or more. Furthermore, the computation will be reliable only when the individuals of the species concerned are distributed at random over the area from which samples are drawn, unless the samples are very small.

EFFECT OF NONRANDOM DISTRIBUTION ON FREQUENCY INDEX. Unfortunately for the ecologist who may wish to use the frequency index for the computation of population density, most kinds of organisms living in nature seem not to be distributed at random (Cole, 1946a). When a species is distributed over an area in a nonrandom manner, the calculation of its population density from its frequency index may give a very erroneous estimate (Dice, 1948) unless the density per sample is very low. In other words, the frequency index is affected by the spacing of the individuals as well as by their density.

Actually, it is possible to use the frequency index as a basis for calculating the population density of any species, whether or not its distribution is at random. Where nonrandom distribution is known or suspected, the proper procedure is to reduce the size of the samples until only rarely will more than 1 individual of the species under consideration be taken in any sample. Then by taking a large number of samples at random a satisfactory basis for the calculation of population density will be obtained. Because this method lacks efficiency, it may be necessary to examine a considerable number of the possible sample units in order to secure an adequate representation of the abundance of the species. Enough samples should be examined so that at least 10 will contain examples of the species concerned. With such small samples the frequency index nearly always will be low and, therefore, it usually will coincide closely with the population density per sample unit (Table VI), so that often no computation will be needed to obtain the population density per sample unit.

COMPARISON OF FREQUENCIES. The frequency of occurrence of a particular event in 2 comparable series of samples may be compared by means of chi-square. In making the comparison one must go back to the original counts instead of using the frequency indexes. If, for instance, a samples in series A and b samples in series B contain 1 or more individuals of a particular species and if c samples in series A and d samples in series B contain no example of this species, then we may test the significance of the difference of the frequencies in the 2 series by the chi-square of a 2 by 2 table:

$$\chi^2 = \frac{n\,(ad-bc)^2}{(a+b)\,(c+d)\,(a+c)\,(b+d)}.$$

There is 1 degree of freedom. An example of the application of the formula is given in Table VII, where the frequency with which the species of flea infested the individuals of the red-backed vole was significantly higher than was the frequency for the wood mouse.

USE OF FREQUENCY INDEX AS A DENSITY INDEX. The frequency index often makes a very useful index of population abundance. As a density index the frequency index is most valuable for comparing the relative abundance of a given species at different places or in successive years, rather than for comparing the abundance of dissimilar species. One can often assume that each species will have much the same type of distribution at any given season wherever it occurs; therefore, any variations in its frequency index from place to place should indicate somewhat similar variations in its population density. On the other hand, dissimilar species will likely have somewhat different patterns of distribution, and accordingly a comparison of their frequency indexes might not give reliable results. Likewise, the frequency indexes of certain species may be comparable only at equivalent seasons because their patterns of distribution vary at different seasons.

TABLE VII

EXAMPLE OF COMPARISON OF FREQUENCIES

Comparison of proportion of red-backed voles (*Clethrionomys glareolus*) and of wood-mice (*Apodemus sylvaticus*) infected with fleas of the species *Ctenophthalmus agyrtes* in Bagley Wood, Berkshire, England, 1938-39 (original data from F. C. Evans and R. B. Freeman).

Host Species	Number of Hosts		
	Infected	Not Infected	Total
Clethrionomys............	148 (*a*)	177 (*b*)	325
Apodemus	265 (*c*)	465 (*d*)	730
Total...............	413	642	1055 (*n*)

Index of infected *Clethrionomys* ....148/325 = .46.
Index of infected *Apodemus*..............265/730 = .36.
χ^2 of difference in frequencies = 8.055, with 1 d.f. (highly significant).

The frequency index is especially useful as an index of the densities of those species whose presence is not difficult to detect, but whose actual numbers are for one reason or another difficult or impossible to count on sample plots. Plants or marine animals that grow in dense colonies are often difficult or impossible to count individually, though their presence or absence on a given sample plot may often be readily ascertained. In a meadow with a closed sod the individual grasses are very difficult to count, especially when they are not in flower or fruit, but the presence of the species will often be obvious.

The frequency index may also be used as a density index for those animals whose numbers are impracticable to count, but whose presence may be detected from their characteristic homes or signs (Dice, 1931a). Ben Osborn (1943) has, as a very practical method, used a frequency percentage obtained from observations on sample plots, making no distinction between actual observations of the living animals and evidence of their presence given by their signs.

Plants which grow in clumps or animals which live in bands necessarily have a nonrandom distribution. The distribution of the signs of the presence of particular animals also tends to be nonrandom because many species have the habit of living in individual home ranges. Accordingly, it will be necessary for the frequency indexes of such forms to be based on a large number of random samples, each of relatively small size, if they are to constitute reliable density indexes. For most accurate comparison the size of the samples should be made so small that in a majority of them no example of the species under consideration appears.

"LAW OF DISTRIBUTION OF FREQUENCIES." A relationship between the frequency indexes of the several species making up each ecologic community, discovered by Raunkiaer (1918: 21), was called by him the "law of the distribution of frequencies." On sample plots of a given size the species of least frequence, as measured by their frequency indexes, are by far the most numerous; the number of species having medium indexes is much smaller; but the number of species having the highest frequencies is slightly greater than that having medium frequency, though by no means so great as the number with low frequencies. Such a relationship has been shown to hold for a considerable variety of communities (Kenoyer, 1927). This distribution of frequencies, however, is not based on any peculiarity of organization of the community, as was at one time erroneously supposed, but is inherent in the mathematical relationship between the frequency index and the relative size of the sample plots employed (Gleason, 1929a; Ashby, 1935; G. E. Blackman, 1935).

SPACING OF THE INDIVIDUALS

The spacing of the individuals of a species over a given stand or microstand is of much significance to the organization of the community. The individuals of certain species are distributed at random, those of other species tend to occur in aggregations, while those of still other species tend to be very evenly spaced.

ASCERTAINMENT OF TYPE OF DISTRIBUTION. The type of distribution of the individuals of a given species over a particular community can be ascertained from counts of the number of individuals of the species concerned on each of a series of sample plots taken at random over the area to be studied. The sample plots should all be of uniform size, and the usual precautions for random sampling should be observed. The number of sample plots examined should be sufficiently great to give a reliable basis for calculation, preferably at least 40, and if possible 100 or more. The sample plots should, furthermore, be of a size sufficiently small so that on some of them, preferably at least 20 per cent, no example of the species under consideration will occur.

RANDOM DISTRIBUTION. If the distribution of the individuals over the area studied is at random, then, as already pointed out, the counts of the numbers of individuals in the samples should fall into a Poisson series, based on the mean number of individuals per sample and on the total number of samples. The Poisson series has the unique peculiarity that its variance is equal to its mean. A method for calculating the variance of a series of sample counts is illustrated in Table VIII. In calculating variance the sum of the mean squares of the deviation from the mean should be divided by n, rather than $n-1$. Care should be taken not to assume that a variance which exactly equals the mean thereby proves that the distribution is random. In certain types of nonrandom distribution the variance may be equal to the mean. Furthermore, where the number of individuals per sam-

TABLE VIII

CALCULATION OF VARIANCE OF COUNTS ON SAMPLE PLOTS

Fruiting stocks of yarrow (*Achillea*) on square-yard sample plots on Edwin S. George Reserve, near Pinckney, Michigan, Sept. 10, 1949. Total plots (n), 100.

Plants per Plot (X)	Plots (f)	Plants (fX)	(fX^2)
0	68	..	..
1	7	7	7
2	6	12	24
3	6	18	54
4	3	12	48
5	4	20	100
6	4	24	144
7	..	..	...
8	1	8	64
9	1	9	81
Sums (S)	100	110	522

$$\text{Variance} = \left[S(fX^2) - (SfX)^2/n \right]/n = \frac{522 - 100^2/100}{100} = \frac{522 - 12100/100}{100}$$

$$= \frac{522 - 121}{100} = \frac{401}{100} = 4.01$$

ple is very small, a Poisson distribution of the samples may be approached, even though the individual organisms are loosely clumped.

CONTAGIOUS DISTRIBUTION. Should the variance of the counts made on the sample plots be greater than the mean per plot, this will indicate a tendency for the individuals to occur in aggregations. A tendency for such grouping constitutes a contagious distribution. In certain species a contagious distribution results from a tendency for the offspring to remain near the place of their birth or origin. Thus, the seedlings of a plant that has heavy seeds spring up around the parent plant and form a family or clan. Among animals the social habit causes the individuals of many species to live together in social groups.

As a theoretical example of a contagious distribution, it may be assumed that all the individuals of a mobile species living in a given stand are gathered into a single band. It may be assumed further that the members of this band all occur within the limits of 1 of the sample plots into which the stand is divided. If the plots of this stand are examined, a high concentration of individuals on a single plot will be noted, while all the other plots contain no example of the species. The mean density per plot will be the number of individuals in the band divided by the total number of plots. The variance will be very high and will greatly exceed the mean. Should, for instance, the number in the band be 50 individuals and the number of plots examined be 100, then the mean would be 0.5 individual per plot and the variance would be 25.00. In this example the fact that the variance is much greater than the mean indicates that there is a strong clumping of the individuals.

EVEN SPACING. Should the variance of a series of counts on sample plots be less instead of greater than its mean, this will indicate that the organisms are more evenly spaced than would be expected on the basis of chance. For example, those animals that defend breeding territories tend to approach a uniform spacing. Plants growing in a pure stand of a single species under conditions of severe competition for light or for soil moisture also tend to be evenly distributed. The creosote bushes growing on the deserts of southwestern North America, for example, are usually very evenly spaced because of the severe competition of their roots for soil moisture. In a thick forest of trees of the same age the individual trees likewise tend toward a uniform distribution because of the competition of their crowns for light.

As an extreme example of even spacing one may assume a situation in which on a series of sample plots each plot contains only a single example of a given species. Such a situation would be present in an orchard if the sample plots were of the same length and width as the spaces between the trees. In such a distribution the variance would be zero because no plot would contain a number of individuals differing from the mean of 1.0. Zero variance, therefore, is the extreme indication of even distribution.

EFFECT OF HABITAT IRREGULARITY. The examples given above of nonrandom distribution produced by aggregation and by even spacing are both assumed to take place in a habitat which is uniform throughout. Many nonrandom types of distribution, however, are produced by irregularities in the habitat and are not due to any special type of behavior by the species concerned. Thus, the local distribution of red-backed voles (*Clethrionomys glareolus*) in 1 part of England is reported by F. C. Evans (1942) to be nonrandom because these voles are more abundant in patches of bracken than in areas where this cover is lacking. The bracken is not uniformly distributed, and accordingly the voles also are not distributed at random. In this case, therefore, the nonrandom distribution of the voles is related to the irregular distribution of an important feature of the animals' habitat. Methods will be given in Chapter XIII for comparing statistically the amount of association between the distribution of 2 species such as these.

DEGREE OF DEPARTURE FROM RANDOMNESS. Various coefficients, ratios, and indexes have in the past been suggested for the measurement of the degree of nonrandom distribution of a species over its habitat (Arne Fisher, 1915: 117-26; Beall, 1935; Clapham, 1936; Cole, 1946a). Unfortunately, none of these suggested measures is adequate to take account of the various combinations of factors that in a natural community may affect the distribution of the individuals. The chi-square test is suitable for determining whether or not any given deviation from the expected Poisson distribution is statistically significant. No mathematical treatment is now available, however, to measure in any simple way the extent to which any particular type of distribution departs from randomness.

As an example of the possible development of mathematical methods for the statement of nonrandom distribution, attention is called to the treatment developed by Neyman (1939) and by Bliss (1941) for 1 kind of contagious distribution. In this particular type of distribution the individual organisms spread out from a number of local centers. If, for example, a species of insect deposits its eggs in masses and the larvae disperse at a uniform rate from these local centers, this kind of contagious distribution will result. Similarly, many kinds of plants spread out from centers represented by the seed parents (Fracker and Brischle, 1944). The numbers of individuals expected to be taken in a series of random samples of a species with such a contagious distribution may be calculated, and the significance of any deviation from the expected numbers may be estimated. In making these calculations it is important to take into account the ages of the individuals (Beall, 1940). Unless all the individuals considered in the calculations are of the same age, that is, unless they began to spread out at the same time and at the same rate from their respective local centers, the computations become too complex to be practical.

The distribution of any species of plant or animal in a fully random manner over its habitat seems to be relatively rare, to judge from the inadequate data at hand (Cole, 1946b). Spacing that is more uniform than that of random distribution seems also to be somewhat uncommon. Most organisms seem, in fact, to occur in groups of one kind or another or to be irregularly distributed.

DIRECT MEASUREMENT OF SPACING. All the methods so far described for the analysis of the spacing between the individuals in a population are based on counts of those individuals that occur on sample plots. Any such analysis is bound to be affected by the size of the plots employed. One can avoid this difficulty by measuring the actual distances between the individuals.

Individuals which are evenly spaced over a plane surface and which are packed as densely as possible will fall into a triangular pattern (Fig. 8). If any individual is taken from this population at random as a point of origin and 6 sextants are laid out around it, the distances to the nearest individual in each of the 6 sextants are equal. There is, consequently, no variance in the measurements of spacing of an evenly spaced population when taken in this manner.

In a random distribution, however, the distances to the nearest individuals in each of the sextants around any individual taken as the point of origin are variable. When plotted, these measurements form a skewed curve. If, however, these measurements are transformed by taking their square roots, they will then fall into an approximately normal curve. Variances, standard errors, and other statistics, therefore, can be calculated from these transformed measurements. The reason why a square-root transformation is necessary for these measurements of spacing, in order to secure a normal curve, is that, as one goes away from any point of origin, the possible number of points at which other individuals of the same kind can occur increases as the square of the distance.

Should the individuals of any population which occupies a plane surface tend to occur in clumps, then the measurements of spacing between them,

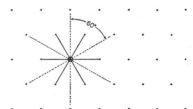

Fig. 8. Method for measuring the distance between any individual taken as a point of origin and the nearest individual in each surrounding sextant. In this example all the individuals are spaced an equal distance apart.

taken by sextants and transformed into square roots, will form an irregular curve. Should the clumps be regularly spaced, then the curve will be bimodal, one of the modes indicating the mean spacing between individuals within clumps, the other mode indicating the mean spacing between the nearest individuals in adjacent clumps. Should the spacing both within and between clumps be irregular, then the curve will be irregular and the statistical treatment of the measurements becomes more difficult (Dice, in press).

PRESENCE

The regularity with which a species occurs in the individual stands of a given association is called its presence. Presence, therefore, is similar in concept to frequency, but differs in that it compares the composition of separated examples of an association rather than that of samples taken within a stand (G. E. Nichols, 1930; Braun-Blanquet, Fuller, and Conard, 1932).

MEASUREMENT OF PRESENCE. The presence of a given species can most simply be expressed as the percentage of the stands of a particular association in which that species is present. Such a statement would, of course, apply only to the particular region considered.

A serious difficulty in the measurement of presence is that the number of species making up a stand is affected by the area which the stand covers. This is demonstrated by species-area curves, such as those presented by

Braun-Blanquet, Fuller, and Conard (1932) and by Cain (1938, 1943).
Species-area curves usually are constructed to illustrate the relationship
between number of associated species and size of sample plot. A similar
relationship, however, undoubtedly holds also for stands. The smaller the
area of any stand or microstand, the fewer the number of species which
may be expected to form the community. Only in those rare conditions in
which stands of exactly the same size can be compared will it be possible
to measure presence without making allowance for variations in the areas
covered by the stands.

A partial solution of the difficulty of comparing stands of different sizes
has been obtained through the use by certain plant ecologists of small
sample plots. By examining in each stand a standardized sample plot which
is smaller in area than any single stand, the effect of the size of the stand is
in part eliminated. When presence is determined in this way on a small
sample rather than on the whole stand, it is called constancy (Braun-
Blanquet, Fuller, and Conard, 1932).

When animals as well as plants are considered members of the community, however, it may be doubted that the occurrences of species on small
sample plots of uniform size are actually comparable if the stands in
which the plots are located vary in area. Certain species characteristic of
large stands may be completely absent from smaller examples. This is particularly true of such mobile animals as birds and large mammals. Many
kinds of plants likewise fail to appear regularly in stands which have less
than a certain minimal area.

A still further difficulty in the measurement of presence lies in deciding
just which stands are to be included in the measurements. If only mature
and normal stands are to be included, as recommended by Braun-Blanquet,
Fuller, and Conard (1932: 53), the judgment of the field worker will inevitably color the results. Workers will certainly vary in their opinions as to
which stands are typical of any given association. Field workers are likely
to vary also in their opinions as to which stands actually are independent
of one another.

For these reasons the statement of presence is subject to much error and
none of the methods so far proposed for its measurement has come into
general use.

EXCLUSIVENESS

The degree of restriction of a species to a particular kind of community is
called its exclusiveness (Tansley and Chipp, 1926; G. E. Nichols, 1930) or
fidelity (Cain, 1932: 497). A certain species, for example, may in a given
region occur only in one particular kind of association, while another
species may be distributed widely in many types of communities.

Five grades of exclusiveness have been recognized by certain plant ecologists (Braun-Blanquet and Pavillard, 1930; Cain, 1932). The exclusiveness

with which any species is restricted to a particular association or micro-association, however, will depend upon the degree of subdivision to which the communities of the area under consideration have been subjected. Because of this dependence of the concept on the classification adopted for the local communities, it is difficult to establish any usable scale of exclu-siveness. The concept, nevertheless, has considerable descriptive value for indicating the degree of limitation of species to particular community types.

COVERAGE

The proportion of the area of a stand or microstand covered by a particular species of plant or attached animal is called its coverage. The proportional areas covered by mobile animals or by free-floating plants can seldom be accurately measured. Coverage is of especial importance in studies of the competition for sunlight among plants, but it is also of significance in esti-mating the amount of shelter provided for animals by plants. The several species of plants that compose a given stand or microstand may vary greatly in the proportional areas that they cover, as is illustrated in the chart of a quadrat given in Figure 9.

COVERAGE INDEX. Coverage is most simply expressed as an index, ob-tained by estimating or measuring the area covered by the species under consideration and dividing by the total area examined:

$$\text{Coverage index} = \frac{\text{Area covered}}{\text{Total area examined}}.$$

The maximum possible coverage index will therefore be 1.0.

For many types of field studies an approximate estimate of coverage will be sufficient. With practice estimates of coverage can be made rather rapidly and with a satisfactory degree of accuracy (G. E. Nichols, 1930). In forests the total coverage index may be roughly estimated by looking up at the forest crown and calculating the proportion of area covered by the foliage. The index may best be expressed as .9, .7, .5, .1, and so on.

Coverage can be measured very accurately from aerial photographs (Haugen, 1942b: 239). Certain precautions, however, must be taken in using aerial photographs for this purpose because (1) the perspective varies from the center to the edge of each photograph, and (2) the scale of the photo-graph varies over areas that are not level (H. Jensen, 1947: 199). Closely similar types of vegetation often are difficult to discriminate in photographs. Furthermore, the ground cover is often obscured by the presence of trees and shrubs. For the accurate measurement of coverage, ground surveys, therefore, are nearly always required in addition to aerial photographs.

For any accurate measurement of coverage on small areas the ecologist must usually utilize sample plots or transects. The area of the plot covered by each plant is measured, whether or not the stem originates on the plot (G. E. Nichols, 1930). If part of a plant extends outside the plot, only that part inside the plot is measured. If the coverage index of each species of plant on a plot is calculated separately, and if certain plant individuals overlap one another, these indexes when added may give a total coverage index that exceeds 1.0. This is true because some plants are able to grow in the partial shade of other plants. In any estimate of coverage, therefore, it will be advisable to measure the total coverage on each plot in addition to the coverage of each species.

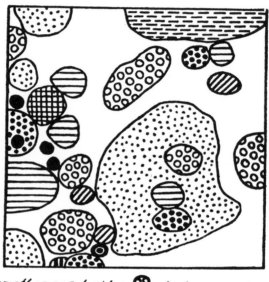

FIG. 9. Coverage pattern of the plants on a square meter of St. Johns fine sand in a flatwoods community, Welaka area, Putnam County, Florida. (After Laessle, 1942, by permission of Univ. Fla. Press.)

The amount of area actually covered by a plant is nearly always difficult to measure accurately. If an outline is drawn around the plant connecting the tips of its most widely extending parts, there will be included many vacant spots that are not covered by foliage. This is particularly true when the plant is made up of narrow segments, such as the leaves of a grass, or when a plant has small leaves that fail to overlap completely. Furthermore, the coverage of most kinds of plants varies greatly from time to time, being affected by the growth of the leaves and branches, by grazing, and by accidents of various kinds. At best, therefore, the measure of coverage must be only approximate.

BASAL COVERAGE. Because of the difficulty of accurately measuring the spread of the outside foliage of most plants, it has become the practice in grazing studies to measure the spread of forage plants at 1 inch above the ground, which is assumed to be the height of usual utilization by grazing animals (Hanson and Love, 1930: ₋736). The method is illustrated in Figure 10. This measure is called basal coverage. The basal coverage index is the proportion of area covered by a single species as compared to the total area measured.

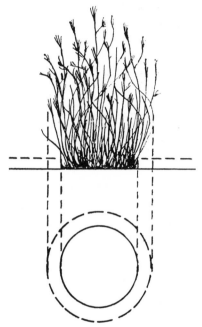

FIG. 10. Method of measuring basal coverage. The area covered by the plant mat at a level of 1 inch above the ground is outlined by the inner circle in the figure. (After Cain, 1932.)

BASAL AREA. Foresters sometimes employ another measure of coverage called basal area. Basal area is the sum of the cross sections of all the tree trunks per unit area measured at breast height ($4\frac{1}{2}$ feet above the ground) (D. M. Brown, 1941). Basal area is usually expressed in square feet per acre.

USE OF LINE TRANSECTS. Line transects are considered by many field ecologists an easier and quicker measure of coverage than sample plots, while the results are not less accurate (Canfield, 1941; K. L. Anderson, 1942). The method is illustrated in Figure 11. Although the line transect itself has no breadth, measurements of the coverage of the several species of plants along its length are proportional to the areas covered by each species concerned. For example, if in a transect 100 meters long a particular species of plant intersects the transect along a total of 27 meters, its coverage index will be 27/100 or 0.27.

As an example of the calculation of the basal coverage index from line transects one may use the data obtained by K. L. Anderson (1942) in a study of pasture vegetation near Manhattan, Kansas (Table IX). The basal

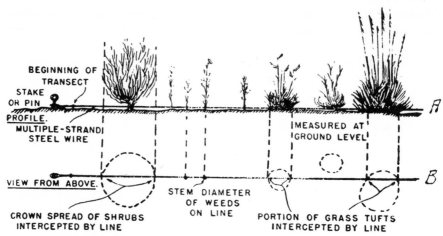

FIG. 11. Method for measuring crown spread of shrubs and basal coverage of grasses and similar plants by use of a line transect. (After Canfield, 1941.)

TABLE IX

COMPUTATION OF BASAL COVERAGE INDEX

Basal coverage on a pasture near Manhattan, Kansas. Based on measurements along seven 10-meter line transects (data from K. L. Anderson, 1942, Table 5, Pasture I).

Species	Mean Length along 1000-cm Transect	Basal Coverage Index
Andropogon furcatus.........	21.6	0.0216
Andropogon scoparius........	6.8	0.0068
Panicum virgatum...........	0.5	0.0005
Sorghastrum nutans..........	1.6	0.0016
Bouteloua curtipendula.......	21.5	0.0215
Bouteloua hirsuta............	1.8	0.0018
Bouteloua gracilis............	2.4	0.0024
Buchloë dactyloides..........	19.5	0.0195
Sporobolus heterolepis........	0.2	0.0002
Sporobolus asper.............	1.2	0.0012
Sporobolus cryptandrus.......	7.5	0.0075
Chloris verticillata...........	3.1	0.0031
Poa pratensis................	0.4	0.0004
Other perennial grasses.......	1.6	0.0016
Annual grasses...............	7.6	0.0076
Sedges......................	3.6	0.0036
Annual weeds................	2.2	0.0022
Perennial weeds.............	3.3	0.0033
Total....................	106.3	0.1063

coverage of each kind of plant was measured in 1 cm. units along a 10-meter transect. The 10 meters of the transect therefore covered a total of 1,000 cm. Any stem or clump that touched the wire used for marking the line transect was recorded as a minimum of 1 cm. Open spaces between the plants less than 1 cm. across were ignored. In one pasture the grass *Andropogon furcatus* covered an average length of 21.6 cm. along the line transects measured. The basal coverage index of this species, therefore, was 21.6/1000 or 0.0216. The total basal coverage index of all the species of plants on the area was 106.3/1000 = 0.1063. This low index shows that there were many bare spaces between the clumps of vegetation.

TABLE X

COMMUNITY COVERAGE

Based on line transects along highways; original readings to 0.1 mile by automobile speedometer (data from Dice, 1938*b*).

Vegetation Type	Community Coverage Index	
	Canadian Province: 10-20 Miles North of North Bay, Ontario (10 Miles of Transect)	Hudsonian Province: Cochrane to Swastika, Ontario (94.7 Miles of Transect)
Sugar-maple, yellow-birch, and white-pine forest...............	.72	...
Black-spruce bog...................	.22	.49
Jack-pine forest...................	...	.11
Aspen............................	...	.26
Mixed types of forest.............	.06	.11
Clearings........................	...	.03
Total........................	1.00	1.00

COMMUNITY COVERAGE. The area covered by a given association or micro-association may be called its community coverage. The community coverage index is then the proportional area covered by a particular type of community as compared to the total area included in the region studied.

Line transects are especially useful for calculating the relative coverage of each of the several types of communities that occur in a given region (Hasel, 1941). A simple method for making such a transect is to drive an automobile along a road and to record the distances along the sides of the road covered by each type of community. These distances can be read to tenths of a mile on the automobile speedometer.

As an example of such a measure of community coverage there is presented in Table X the community coverage indexes of the more conspicuous communities in 2 parts of northern Ontario. Along a transect through a part of Ontario lying in the Canadian biotic province the area covered by sugar-maple, yellow-birch, and white-pine forest had a community coverage index of 0.72, while along a transect through a part of the adjacent Hudsonian province this forest type was not seen. In the Canadian-province transect also the community coverage index for black-spruce bog was 0.22, while in the Hudsonian transect its index was 0.49. These differences in community coverage indexes show the considerable differences in community types between the 2 biotic provinces.

Errors in the calculation of community coverage indexes, however, may result from the use of line transects located along roads. Roads as a rule do not cross the more difficult mountains, cliffs, bogs, swamps, rivers, and lakes. Community coverage indexes based on measures taken along a road, therefore, may be too low for certain types of communities. Houses, farm-yards, and towns are usually concentrated along roads and thus may show too high a community coverage index. If any statistical computations are to be based on community coverage indexes derived from line transects, the transects must, of course, be taken at random. When roads are used for making line transects, this may not be possible, and consequently the derived measurements may not be a satisfactory basis for statistical computations.

MAPPING METHODS

Maps of various kinds must be made at one time or another by every field ecologist. Most frequently a map is needed which will show the distribution of one or more particular types of communities over a given area. In constructing any kind of an ecologic map it is desirable to start with the most accurate base map obtainable. Topographic maps, which have been published for many parts of the United States, are usually the best and may be purchased from the United States Geological Survey, Washington, D. C. Should a topographic map not be available, one must use some other kind of base map. The supervisor of each national forest can supply a base map of his forest. Each county surveyor can often supply a map which gives section lines and roads. The department of conservation and the agricultural experiment station of the state concerned will be able to furnish information about certain other kinds of maps that may cover the chosen area.

For suggestions about the mapping of vegetation the student is referred especially to Tansley (1946). For the mapping of cover types reference is made to Wight (1939, Chap. III). Most ecologic maps will be based to a very large extent on transects made at specified distances apart across the area to be mapped. The location of every community boundary encountered will be marked at the appropriate place on the map. The distance the transects are spaced apart will depend upon the accuracy desired in the map and the time available for the survey. A forester's compass will be of much value in keeping each transect line straight. Counts of paces will usually give sufficiently accurate measures of distances, but for greater accuracy a steel tape may be employed. The use of a steel tape necessitates the services of 2 persons.

An aerial photograph often is of great assistance in the preparation of an ecologic map. On such a photograph appear not only the streams, lakes, roads, and other features, but also the vegetation. Considerable experience, however, is needed in order to interpret the distribution of the vegetation correctly from an aerial photograph (H. A. Jensen, 1947). Additional cruising over the area will nearly always be needed.

MEASUREMENT OF THE AREA COVERED BY A STAND

The total area covered by a particular stand often needs to be known. Usually, the boundaries of each stand are irregular in outline and, therefore, the direct measurement of the area covered is difficult to secure. If a real or imaginary grid can be set up to divide the area into a series of quadrats of uniform size, however, then the area covered by the stand may readily be estimated. The quadrats used in this computation may be the same sample units that are employed for securing information about the composition of the community. Count is made of all the quadrats which the given stand completely covers and also separately of all the borderline quadrats in which the stand is represented. The average area covered by the community in the quadrats in which it appears but which it does not entirely cover will approach one-half a quadrat as a limit. The total area covered by a given stand, therefore, will be approximately the number of quadrats which it completely covers, plus one-half the quadrats in which it appears but which it does not entirely cover. Thus, in Figure 5, 36 quadrats are entirely within the stand outlined, while 41 are cut by the boundary so that they are only partly covered by the stand. The total area of the stand may, therefore, be estimated to be $36 + (41/2) = 36 + 20.5 = 56.5$ quadrats.

SELECTED REFERENCES

Braun-Blanquet, J., George D. Fuller, and Henry S. Conard. 1932. Plant sociology: the study of plant communities. New York and London: McGraw-Hill Book Co. Chaps. 3 and 4.

Cain, Stanley A. 1932. Concerning certain phytosociological concepts. Ecol. Monog., 2: 475-508.

Gates, Frank C. 1949. Field manual of plant ecology. New York: McGraw-Hill Book Co.

Schumacher, F. X., and R. A. Chapman. 1942. Sampling methods in forestry and range management. Bull. School Forestry, Duke Univ., No. 7.

Snedecor, George W. 1946. Statistical methods applied to experiments in agriculture and biology. Ames: Ia. State Coll. Press.

Tansley, A. G. 1946. Introduction to plant ecology; a guide for beginners in the study of plant communities. London: George Allen and Unwin.

Weaver, J. E., and Frederic E. Clements. 1938. Plant ecology. 2d ed.; New York: McGraw-Hill Book Co. Chap. 2.

IV

METHODS FOR THE ESTIMATION OF POPULATIONS

In order to describe any community in quantitative terms it is necessary first of all to be able to identify with certainty the individuals of those species that are of ecologic importance. The number of individuals of each important form must then be counted or their abundance estimated in some manner. It is often difficult to discriminate between closely related species, especially if certain of the individuals are immature or are represented in the samples by their early life-history stages. Furthermore, the taking of adequate samples of the several populations and the counting of the individuals in the samples will often require special technics.

TAXONOMIC IDENTIFICATIONS

The field ecologist is urged to become familiar with all the more important species in the communities that he plans to study. Obviously, it will be impossible for any one person to become equally proficient in the recognition of all the diverse kinds of plants and animals that may live on a given area. Nevertheless, it is possible without undue effort to become acquainted with at least the more conspicuous plants and animals in a given region.

The ability of the ecologist to discriminate between closely related species depends largely on the experience he has acquired in the taxonomic identification of the group of organisms under consideration. In general, it will be easier to identify the species of flowering plants and of vertebrates than of nonflowering plants or of invertebrates. This results from the fact that few manuals and keys for identification are available for the lower forms of life. The taxonomy of many of those lower organisms that are not of special economic importance to man is still only imperfectly known. It will often be impossible, therefore, for the field ecologist to identify certain individual specimens.

No person should consider himself a qualified field ecologist until he can recognize with certainty the organisms that he is trying to enumerate. This requirement means that seldom can one person be competent to carry out ecologic studies on a wide variety of organisms. Only rarely will an ecologist have the time and facilities to become fully familiar with the taxonomy of more than a few groups of animals or of plants. Especially fortunate, then, is the ecologist who is able to enlist the co-operation of his taxonomically trained friends to assist him with the identification of those organisms with which he himself is not well acquainted.

The ecologist himself should be fully competent to identify the group of organisms which is receiving most of his attention in the field. Familiarity with this group will greatly improve the quality of the field work; consequently only debatable specimens need be referred to the specialist.

Many kinds of plants are very difficult for even a specialist to identify when they are not in flower or in fruit. Certain field studies may possibly be timed to take place at the season when the individuals can be most readily identified. In order to make identifications at other seasons it will usually be possible to discover diagnostic characters in the vegetative parts of the plants.

Keys for the identification of the eggs, larvae, and young of many kinds of animals have not yet been prepared. Especially among the invertebrates the identification of the early stages of many species is difficult or impossible. The eggs, larvae, pupae, or young of certain kinds of animals may be reared to maturity in the laboratory in order to obtain the adults for identification (Baweja, 1939), but this is a laborious process not well adapted to quantitative field studies. For critical studies the ecologist must perforce often construct his own keys to the several species he may encounter.

PRESERVATION OF SPECIMENS. A set of specimens representing each of the species encountered during the field study should always be preserved. Such collections are especially important if the biota of the region has not already been well described. These specimens should later be checked by taxonomists who are competent in the groups represented. The names of the taxonomists who make the identification should, of course, be given in any publication, so that the authorities for the scientific names employed will be known.

Certain ecologists have incurred ridicule by publishing erroneous identifications of species. No species should be recorded as a member of a particular community without a fully reliable taxonomic identification supported by a preserved specimen. The specimens which thus serve to verify published records should always be deposited in a natural history museum, where they may be consulted at any later time by anyone who is inclined to question the record.

LUMPING OF SPECIES BY GENERA OR FAMILIES. The invertebrates are represented in most ecologic communities by so many types that in extensive field studies the separate enumeration of each species is laborious. A summary by Elton (1946) shows that in some communities it is not uncommon for a genus to be represented by 2 or more species. In certain field studies, in order to conserve effort, the species have been treated in groups by genera or even by families or by orders. Such lumping must ignore and obscure many details of ecologic significance. Species belonging to the same genus often have very dissimilar physiology and habits and they may occupy very different niches in the community. It is questionable, therefore, whether the lumping of species in the description of communities actually furnishes information of any considerable ecologic value. It would seem better in most field studies for the ecologist to confine his attention to those species which he can identify with certainty, rather than to attempt a more extensive and less accurate enumeration. He will then be able to discuss with confidence and with adequate detail the ecologic relationships of each of those forms which he describes.

GENERAL FACTORS AFFECTING THE ESTIMATION OF A POPULATION

DEFINITION OF AN INDIVIDUAL. In any quantitative study of the organisms which compose a community careful attention must be given to the definition of the word "individual" as used for each of the species to be counted. This is particularly true for those species of plants and of animals in which certain individuals may be produced by asexual division and may remain for a time attached to the parent. With grass, for instance, it is often considered that each stem bearing a flowering head constitutes an individual. With shrubs it is usually considered that each crown constitutes an individual, even though more than one stem may arise from the same crown. Field biologists, however, do not always agree on what constitutes an individual organism of a given species. Seeds, spores, mycelia, eggs, larvae, pupae, and dormant individuals are likely to cause especial difficulty. In every case of possible doubt, therefore, the ecologist should specify what definition of individual he is using for each species that he discusses.

SIZE CLASSES AND AGE CLASSES. In the enumeration of plants and animals it often is desirable to distinguish between the size classes or age classes and possibly also between the several life-history stages.

Plants usually are classed according to size. The size of a tree is customarily stated by foresters in terms of the diameter of the trunk at the breast height of a man. Breast height is taken to be $4\frac{1}{2}$ feet above the level of the ground. In the United States the diameter of the trunk at breast height (d.b.h.) is stated in inches.

The size of shrubs is sometimes stated in terms of the diameter of each stem at breast height (Cahalane, 1941). Another method of describing the size of shrubs is by stating the maximum diameter of the area they cover (Hardy, 1945). Maximum height is probably the best measure of the size of grasses and other herbs.

Very accurate determinations of the ages of many kinds of trees can be made by tree-ring counts, the samples being taken by an increment borer. The method, however, is laborious. Certain kinds of trees, especially the conifers, have a regular system of annual branching, which provides a simple but rough estimate of their age.

Animals are classed when possible according to age, sex, or life-history stage, as well as by size. A simple classification may consider only the immature and the sexually mature (adult) stages. When age classes are recognized, the divisions are usually according to years of age. With the teleost fishes, for example, the age of individuals can be determined by examination of the scales. With certain kinds of mammals the approximate age can be determined from the sequence of replacement of the teeth. With many kinds of animals, however, the age of individuals cannot be accurately determined, and the best that can be done is to group them according to size classes.

DIFFICULTIES OF CENSUS TAKING. The taking of a census of the individuals of those species and subspecies that make up a given stand or microstand is always laborious. It often involves special difficulties in distinguishing and in counting the individuals of the several species that may be present. The operations of the census taker may also be interfered with by the terrain, by thickets of vegetation, by noxious insects or other animals, and by winds, waves, unfavorable air or water temperatures, rain, snow, or similar hazards of weather.

DIFFICULTIES OF RANDOM SAMPLING. Estimates of population density must usually be based on samples of some kind, as has been pointed out in Chapter III. As a basis for statistical calculations these samples should for greatest reliability be taken at random. Unfortunately, in nature it often is impractical to apply the usual methods of random sampling. On mountainous terrain, for example, it may be impossible, with any reasonable expenditure of time and effort, to lay out a given area in equal-sized sample plots. Even if it should be possible to divide such an area into sample plots, the ecologist might have very great difficulty in carrying out any studies at all on certain of the plots selected by chance. In aquatic communities, also, it may be impractical to mark out sample areas that will be clearly delimited from their neighbors. In many situations, therefore, special methods for the sampling of populations must be used.

MOBILE ORGANISMS. Mobile organisms are considerably more difficult to count accurately than are those forms that are stationary. Many kinds of animals have some degree of mobility, and numerous forms are able to move rapidly from place to place. A number of kinds of plants also, such as the diatoms and certain algae, are free-floating and are moved about from place to place by currents of water. These mobile organisms are difficult to census accurately, and for certain forms no precise enumeration is practical.

SECRETIVE FORMS. Another difficulty encountered in an attempt to find and to count animals is that of discovering those forms which live in burrows or inhabit other secluded places. Many kinds of animals are nocturnal in habit, which makes them particularly difficult to count. Furthermore, many animals are shy, and some of them may retreat out of the census area as soon as the observer appears.

VARIATION IN INDIVIDUAL ACTIVITY. The number of individuals of a given species recorded in a sample count often depends in part on the degree of activity of the individuals at the time the count is made. Nearly all kinds of animals are more active at certain times than at others. Counts of individuals made on sample plots at different times of the day (Hovanitz, 1948), at different seasons, under different weather conditions, or in different types of habitat, therefore, may not be fully comparable. There is often a great difference between the number of individuals present on a sample plot (absolute abundance) and the number recorded in a given sample count (recorded abundance), as has been emphasized by D. E. Davis (1945: 263). Whenever sample counts are combined to calculate a mean population density or mean density index, therefore, a full statement should be given of the conditions under which the sample counts were taken.

MOVEMENTS OF INDIVIDUALS WITHIN THEIR HOME RANGES. Any estimate of population density which is based on trapping records may be seriously affected by the movements of the individual animals within their home ranges. Certain individuals which are trapped near the edge of a sample plot may have home ranges that extend beyond the plot boundaries. Likewise, individuals whose homes are outside the plot may have home ranges which extend into the census area. An outside individual thus has some chance of being caught in a trap, in which case he is counted in the census. Only in those situations where the census area is delimited by boundaries over which the organisms to be counted cannot pass, will it be possible to set precise limits to the area. With animals that live in relatively stable home ranges, the actual range of the population living within any given trapping plot extends beyond every side of the area containing the traps, for a distance equal to one-half the average diameter of a home range (Fig. 12) for the age class and sex of the species concerned (Dice, 1938a). Due allowance for this fact must be made in any calculation of population density based on trapping records or on records from marked individuals.

In this method of estimating the area covered effectively by traps it is assumed that there is no diminution of trapping effectiveness because of the absence of traps in the area outside the trap plot. In other words, it is assumed that the catch is independent of the density of the traps and that any animal whose home range includes a single trapping station is as likely to be caught as one whose home range includes 2 or more trapping stations. Such an assumption is probably justified in those cases where the animals are attracted to the traps from some distance because of the presence of the bait. It is presumably justified also in those instances in which the traps are kept in operation for a sufficient period of time to allow every animal a chance to come into contact with a trap.

ISOLATION OF THE CENSUS AREA. In certain types of habitat it may be possible to isolate each sample area during the period of counting so that none of the inhabitants can escape and no others can enter. Then all the individuals of the species under consideration may be collected or directly counted. Actual counts, for example, can sometimes be made of all the fishes in a small tide pool along the ocean shore.

Unfortunately, however, very few sample areas can be so completely fenced off during the period of counting that the ingress or egress of all individuals is prevented. Yet the counting or collecting operations can seldom be carried out instantaneously and, therefore, the movements of mobile animals out of or into the census plot may cause a serious error in the counts. Also, an individual animal that moves about inside the plot during the progress of the counting operations may escape being counted or may be counted 2 or more times. Often it is difficult to define and to maintain the boundaries of the sample plots during the period when the counts are being taken. The boundaries of a sample plot are especially diffi-cult to define in a body of water or in the air above the ground, as, for in-stance, in a shrub stratum.

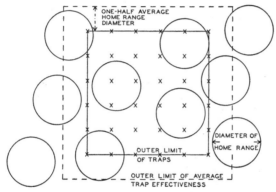

FIG. 12. The area effectively trapped extends outside the setting of traps a distance equal to one-half the average width of a home range of the species being trapped. In the figure all the home ranges are arbitrarily given a circular shape and the same diameter. The area effectively trapped, therefore, will on the average include all that lies within the broken line, although the setting of traps is confined within the area outlined by the solid line. The corners of the rectangle enclosed by the broken line are not rounded, as they theoretically should be, because of the greater ease of calculating the area of a perfect rectangle. The error so introduced is slight when compared with the error of estimate of the average diameter of a home range.

RELEASE OF MARKED ANIMALS

In many studies of animal populations the capture and removal of those individuals which are counted may cause a disturbance which seriously interferes with further studies at that locality. Should the counting continue over a number of days, as would be true of certain types of trapping, the removal of part of the population may create a vacancy, thereby possibly inducing the immigration of outside individuals. Such an immigration will not only produce an alteration in the community, but may lead to an exorbitant estimate of the population density of the species which is being trapped.

CAPTURE OF THE ENTIRE POPULATION. In order to avoid removal of the animals of the kind under study, the individuals may be trapped alive, given distinctive recognition marks, such as colored bands placed on the legs of birds, and then released. When no more unmarked individuals are encountered in the census area, the whole population has been marked, and accordingly a count of its numbers has been obtained. This method is especially useful for secretive forms that are difficult to enumerate directly on each sample plot.

The chief difficulty with the trapping and marking method, besides the labor and equipment required, is that, if the marking operations cover any appreciable period, certain individuals that have been marked and therefore counted will probably move off the area or will die. Likewise, certain individuals trapped in the later part of the trapping operations may be newcomers to the plot. There is a tendency, therefore, for this method to give too high an estimate of the population.

PROPORTIONAL METHOD. A proportional method that also employs marked individuals is frequently used for estimating animal populations. The first suggestion of this method seems to have been made by Petersen (1896: 21), who did not actually apply it to a particular population. This method of calculation is sometimes called the Lincoln index (Lincoln, 1930), but the term "index" is inappropriate, because the figure obtained is an estimate of actual population size rather than an index.

In the proportional method a number of individuals in the given area are captured, marked, and released during a preliminary trapping period. Thus, the number of marked individuals present on the area is known. In a second trapping period the number of previously marked and also the number of unmarked individuals taken are counted. From the proportion of marked individuals among the total number taken in the second period and the known number of marked individuals present, the total population may be computed:

$$\text{Total population at conclusion of preliminary trapping period} = \frac{Tm_1}{m_2}.$$

In this formula T is the total number of marked and unmarked individuals taken during the final trapping period on a particular area; m_1 is the number of marked individuals released during the preliminary trapping period; and m_2 is the number of marked individuals taken during the final trapping period. The calculation of population size applies to the preliminary trapping period rather than to the final trapping period, and the method, therefore, does not make allowance for reproduction nor for mortality which may have occurred between the 2 trapping periods.

As an example of the application of this formula one may use the data collected by Green and Evans (1940: 223-24) on the abundance of snowshoe hares during 1932-33 in a section of Minnesota. During a precensus period 948 hares were trapped and released alive on an area covering approximately 5 square miles. During the final census period a total of 421 hares was taken, of which 167 were previously marked individuals. Then, according to the formula, the total population $= (421 \times 948)/167 = 399108/167 = 2390$ hares.

If the trapping and marking operations are continued for more than a single day, it is possible, by use of the formula, to calculate the population present on each day of trapping except the final day. More detailed statistical treatments of the records obtained by the proportional method have been developed by Schnabel (1938), Jackson (1939), Dowdeswell, Fisher, and Ford (1940), Ricker (1942), and others.

The assumptions made in using the proportional method of estimating population density are (1) that during the interval between the preliminary marking period and the final census period there is (a) no unrecognized reproduction on the area, (b) no differential mortality between marked and unmarked individuals, (c) no immigration into the area, and (d) no differential emigration of marked and unmarked animals from the area, and (2) that the chances for every individual to be trapped are wholly at random in both trapping periods.

If reproduction occurs on the area during the period of counting and if the investigator is not aware of it, an error is introduced. There will always be some mortality and this will usually be greater the longer the interval between the trapping periods. Mortality that affects the marked and unmarked individuals equally, however, will not affect the calculations. The marking operations may handicap the animals and thereby produce a differential mortality between marked and unmarked individuals after their release (Lagler and Ricker, 1943: 64-65).

There will probably be some immigration or emigration, except on completely isolated plots. Emigration that is not differential between marked and unmarked individuals will not affect the computations, but the immigration of individuals does introduce an error. The method, accordingly, is particularly adapted for estimating fish populations in isolated ponds or pools. It is not so well suited to situations where the habitat is continuous over extensive areas.

In order to secure random samples, the traps must be set at random over the area in both trapping periods. It cannot be assumed that the individual animals will be distributed at random when first trapped, nor that they will distribute themselves at random over the area after they are marked (Lagler and Ricker, 1943: 63). The location of the traps should be changed between the first marking period and the final trapping period unless the whole area under consideration is covered by traps. The habit of many kinds of animals to live in home ranges may interfere seriously with the random distribution of the individuals. Unfortunately, very few of the investigators who in the past have used this proportional method as a basis for estimating populations have actually used fully random samples.

The proportional method, nevertheless, is one of the best methods so far developed for estimating animal populations, when it is used with due allowance for possible errors. Much less labor is required for its operation than for trapping and marking every individual in the census area. As a basis for a reasonably reliable estimate, the proportion of individuals which are trapped and marked should be fairly large, preferably 10 per cent or more of the total population.

SPECIAL METHODS FOR PARTICULAR KINDS OF ORGANISMS

The methods to be employed for making counts or measures of the individuals on sample plots or in other types of samples must obviously vary with the kinds of organisms being studied. It is evident that the methods used for counting trees must be different from those used for counting diatoms, birds, or earthworms. The several kinds of animals in a community are especially likely to differ in their size, habits, and microhabitats. For this reason it is often necessary to use a special census technique for each species of animal. Rarely will it be practical for the ecologist to count all the microscopic and macroscopic plants and animals present in a given sample. Usually, only certain groups of organisms will be counted and sometimes only a single species.

Space will not permit the giving here of detailed instructions for counting or measuring the abundance of each special kind of organism. The following discussion, therefore, will be confined to brief descriptions of certain methods that are of wide application. The inexperienced student should learn the methods employed by investigators who previously have worked with the same kinds of plants or of animals that he desires to count. Often, however, new methods will need to be devised for the particular problem under investigation. No practical methods have yet been devised for estimating the population densities of many kinds of animals.

Aquatic Organisms

The student of aquatic communities is under a severe handicap in his attempts to ascertain the numbers and interactions of the associated organisms because man is not well adapted for life in water. Except in very shallow water or with special diving equipment the observer is unable to see directly the plants and animals that make up the community. The information, therefore, must usually be obtained indirectly through the use of nets, dredges, scoops, bottom samplers, and other special instruments (Shelford, 1929: 47-49; McLean and Cook, 1946; Welch, 1948). It is especially difficult to secure counts of such highly mobile aquatic forms as the fishes and certain of the crustaceans. The mechanical difficulties increase rapidly with the depth of the water.

PLANKTON. Free-floating or feebly swimming organisms, such as bacteria, diatoms, protozoa, rotifers, and similar forms are usually collected in dip nets or townets. Nets cannot be made fine enough to capture many kinds of the smaller "plankters," and special methods for centrifuging or otherwise concentrating measured samples of the water must often be employed (Welch, 1948). For the bacteria it may be necessary to make cultures from samples of the water. From counts made of the organisms in the samples, measures of the relative abundance of the several plankton species may then be computed. It usually is difficult, however, from such data to arrive at any accurate statement of the actual abundance of the individuals of the several species in terms of a unit area of water surface or of a unit volume.

ATTACHED AQUATIC PLANTS. Attached aquatic plants can sometimes be counted and measured on sample plots by much the same methods employed for the census of terrestrial forms, except that the presence of the water makes the field work more difficult. From sample plots located in shallow water all the vegetation may be collected, dried, and then weighed to secure a measure of the total forage (Rickett, 1921; Heady, 1942). It is still better to measure the quantity of each species of plant present, if the vegetative stages of the several species can be distinguished.

ATTACHED AQUATIC INVERTEBRATES. The attached aquatic invertebrates growing in shallow water also can be enumerated on sample plots. Because many of the lower invertebrates are colonial in habit, a clear definition must be established of what is to be considered an individual. In deep water information about invertebrate populations must usually be secured from dredge hauls. Underwater photography, now being explored by a few investigators, offers promising possibilities here.

BURROWING AQUATIC FORMS. Those aquatic organisms that burrow into the substratum present great difficulties to the census taker. Many clams, for example, burrow deep into the sand of the ocean shore. In shallow water a few kinds of these burrowing animals may be counted if sample plots are excavated. It may also be possible under certain circumstances to enumerate the individuals of such forms as clams by counts of the extended siphons. Those organisms that hide in the crevices of the rocks or which burrow into the rock itself offer special problems. In deep water the problem of counting such animals is very serious because dredges seldom are able to penetrate the ocean bottom sufficiently far to secure all the burrowing animals that are present (MacGinitie, 1939).

FISHES. Because of their mobility, fishes are particularly difficult to count accurately. Rarely will it be possible to count these animals by direct observation. Certain kinds of fishes may be secured by traps, nets, or hook and line. A few kinds also may be speared. These methods, however, are usually selective and tend to take certain species and certain size classes more readily than others. Although such methods may give information about the kinds of fishes present in the community and may also provide usable density indexes, they often fail to give accurate information about actual population densities and population structures.

The complete seining out of the fishes in a particular pool or pond is a useful method for securing a count of the total population. If handled carefully and quickly the animals should, for the most part, escape serious injury and may be returned to the water. If it is desired, the individuals may be marked so that when captured again in later studies they can be identified. Unfortunately, many small bodies of water contain rocks, vegetation, or other kinds of obstructions that make fully effective seining impossible. Furthermore, many ponds and pools are too large or too deep for seining, or they may lack a shore suitable for landing the seine.

In very small ponds or pools the entire fish population may be poisoned by the addition of derris root (Ricker, 1942) or other poisons to the water; then the number of dead individuals of each species may be counted. If there is an outlet to the pool it is sometimes possible to construct a temporary dam so that the effect of the poison is concentrated in the selected area. The use of poison has, of course, the objection that the population is destroyed in being counted and that continuing studies are thereby made impossible. Devices have been recently constructed for paralyzing the fishes within a small area by means of an electric shocker (Shetter, 1947). This method promises to be a valuable addition to the technics for estimating populations of fishes. If the strength of the shock can be standardized and the location of the device set at random, each shock discharge should provide a random sample of the population in the area sampled.

The populations of migratory fishes in a particular stream system may be estimated by counts made during migration at a properly located counting station, such as a specially constructed weir. In small ponds or pools the fish population may be estimated by the proportional method previously described, in which a certain number of the animals are marked and then released for later recapture. This proportional method, unfortunately, will usually be impractical in large bodies of water.

DEEP-SEA FORMS. With increasing depth of water the difficulties of making counts of the organisms present also increase, as has already been pointed out. The difficulties in deep water of capturing fish and other mobile organisms or of obtaining burrowing forms are especially great. Mobile organisms avoid the dredge by rapid evasive action. The dredge, furthermore, is unable in most cases to extract the burrowing forms from their burrows and thus brings up a preponderance of those species that live on the surface of the ocean floor. These are scraped up from a considerable, but usually unmeasured, length of transect.

Terrestrial Organisms

Terrestrial organisms, as compared to aquatic forms, are generally much easier to enumerate. Many of the terrestrial forms can be counted directly.

This is particularly true of the plants. Often also the spacing of the individuals can be observed and the relationships between individuals of the associated species evaluated. Nevertheless, the difficulties in making accurate census counts of many terrestrial forms are great. The high mobility of many land animals requires the employment of special technics for estimating their numbers. The tendency of many animals to be secretive in habit and of others to be active only at night imposes further difficulties.

LAND PLANTS. Methods for the field study of terrestrial plants have been described by many authors, including Weaver and Clements (1938), G. E. Nichols (1930), Cain (1932), McLean and Cook (1946), and Tansley (1946). Ecologists have in the past given most attention to the green plants and especially to the flowering plants. Much less attention has been given to the development of methods for the calculation of the abundance of the fungi and of other more simple types of plants.

When individual plants on a sample plot are counted, a practical difficulty may arise in regard to those individuals that overlap the plot boundaries. The general practice of ecologists is to count all the individuals with stems which arise within the plot, whether or not the stems or the foliage extend beyond the plot boundaries. On the other hand, no plant is counted whose stem arises outside the plot, even though its foliage may overhang the plot. Should a plant stem arise directly on the boundary line, the plant should be counted if one-half or more of the stem lies inside the plot, but ignored when the greater part of the stem is outside.

MATS OF VEGETATION. An interlaced mat is often formed by the stems and roots of grasses and other plants that grow closely associated with one another. Examples of such mats may be found in every meadow, marsh, and bog. In such a living mat it is often wholly impractical to identify or to count the individuals. If, however, the individuals are actually independent of one another, it may be possible to take up the mat piece by piece and, after soaking it well in water, to pull the roots and stems apart and thus to separate the individuals. If, on the contrary, some of the individual plants are attached to one another, it may be impossible to disentangle the mat without destroying the relationships between the individuals.

SOIL BACTERIA, PROTOZOA, AND FUNGI. The counting of the soil protozoa requires special technics (A. Dixon, 1939), and it is recommended that only a person specially trained in this difficult field should make the attempt. The same advice is offered in regard to the soil bacteria (Conn, 1928) and the soil fungi (Brierley, Jewson, and Brierley, 1928).

TERRESTRIAL INVERTEBRATES. The terrestrial invertebrates form a numerous and highly varied assemblage of animals, exhibiting many diverse habits and occupying many dissimilar kinds of local habitats. Because of the special economic importance of the insects many estimates of the density of insect populations have been attempted, and many methods have been employed for making the estimates (Hyslop, Webster, and Hinds, 1925). Nevertheless, the technics so far developed for making estimates of the population density of most terrestrial invertebrates are far from satisfactory.

For the enumeration of the soil-inhabiting invertebrates certain investigators mark out each sample plot with a wooden or metal frame, either round or square in shape, and then carefully search and sift the materials within the enclosure to some standard depth, identifying and counting all the animals discovered or preserving them for later taxonomic identification (McAtee, 1907; Weese, 1924; Shelford, 1929; Wolcott, 1937; E. C. Williams, 1941; Eaton and Chandler, 1942). Frequently, the leaf litter, or perhaps the whole quantity of soil within the sample plot, is taken to the laboratory and there sifted and examined. Various special methods are employed to find all the organisms and to prevent the escape of the more active forms. Treatment of the collected soil and debris in a heated Berlese funnel may assist in driving out certain kinds of animals from the soil (Jacot, 1936; Eaton and Chandler, 1942). Washing the collected materials in water also may aid in the recovery of certain kinds of animals. By the flotation method, whereby the specific gravity of the water is raised by the addition of certain salts, such as Epsom salts, most of the organisms can be made to float. They can then easily be collected and counted (Fenton, 1947).

Small sample plots may be most conveniently marked out by driving a proper-sized metal frame into the ground to a satisfactory depth (Jacot, 1935; Glasgow, 1939; Brady, 1943). The materials within the frame may then be dug up in layers as desired, or the whole frame and its contents may be lifted out of the ground with a spade. If the ground is not firm it may, however, be necessary to close the bottom of the frame while it is being removed from the soil.

The biota of the soil varies greatly according to depth from the surface. In collecting the samples, therefore, it is important that the organisms taken at each successive depth of the soil be kept separate. If there is a layer of plant and animal debris lying on the surface of the ground, the biota inhabiting this litter is likely to differ from that of the lower soil levels.

The more active soil animals are likely to escape from the sample plot before they can be counted. To avoid this possibility, Weese (1924: 10) placed the soil debris in boxes and etherized the animals before sorting them. Sanders and Shelford (1922: 308) pressed an inverted bucket into the soil; after this was in place they introduced through an opening in the bucket a chemical which killed or stupefied the animals.

Those invertebrates that live in strata above the ground are often even more difficult to count than those that live in the soil. Only a few kinds of animals, such as the chinch bug (Shelford and Flint, 1943), potato beetle, certain kinds of caterpillars, and snails are sluggish enough in their movements and sufficiently conspicuous to be directly counted. Many kinds of invertebrates, on the contrary, are quick in their movements, and the flying forms are especially difficult to count on sample plots. Butterflies in flight, however, may in certain situations be counted with great accuracy by a skilled observer (Hovanitz, 1948).

Traps of various kinds are often employed to collect insects and other terrestrial invertebrates (Phillips, 1931b; Shelford, 1929). Usually the traps are baited with a substance attractive to the species being sought (Patterson, 1943; Hubbell, 1936). Other kinds of traps make use of the attraction that light has for certain nocturnal species (Shelford, 1929: 42). It is evident that the distance from which the animals come to the traps will rarely be known and that counts of the number of individuals taken at traps can usually give only a density index rather than an estimate of population density per unit area of habitat. Such light traps are of course highly selective and capture only those nocturnal animals that are positively phototropic.

THE SWEEP-NET METHOD. For securing a density index of the populations of certain insects, spiders, and other invertebrates that inhabit herbs and shrubs, the sweep-net method is simple and usually effective (Weese, 1924: 10; Shelford, 1929: 45-47; Lowrie, 1942: 181). An entomological sweep net of standard diameter, made of standard materials and provided with a handle of standard length, is used. A specified number of sweeps of this net is taken in a regular manner in the part of the community to be sampled, each sweep covering a previously undisturbed spot. The animals collected are then identified and counted. It is important to standardize all the operations so far as possible.

Although the sweep-net method gives reliable information about the presence of certain species of invertebrates in the herb and shrub strata, it does not always secure representatives of all the species present, and it often fails to secure the individuals in direct proportion to their abundance. The numerous kinds of invertebrates vary greatly in their habits and accordingly in the ease with which they are taken in the net. Furthermore, the same species varies in its reactions and in its location in the habitat depending upon such factors as its age, the time of day, and the weather conditions (Romney, 1945). Field men also differ in their manner of swinging the net. It is impossible to standardize the methods of sweep-net collecting, even when field conditions are fairly uniform.

The sweep-net method, therefore, may give useful density indexes for certain species, but it cannot be depended upon to provide a reliable estimate of the actual number of individuals of any species per unit area, nor can it be used for the critical comparison of the relative abundance of diverse kinds of species (Phillips, 1931b: 638; O. W. Richards, 1934; Rogers, 1942: 15-16; Cantrall, 1943: 20-21). Nevertheless, this is one of the most useful methods for securing information about the relative abundance of those invertebrates which live in certain strata of terrestrial communities (Carpenter and Ford, 1936).

SOCIAL INSECTS. The populations of social insects, such as ants, termites, or bees, can seldom be accurately estimated from counts made on small sample plots. The activity of these forms is greatly affected by the time of day, by the weather, and by biological factors. Also, their numbers are usually greatly concentrated near their nests and along their pathways or flightways. Any accurate estimate of the population density of these forms at a given spot, therefore, would require an impractically large number of small samples taken at random in regard to both space and time. The population density of a colonial insect over a general area can, it is true, be estimated from counts of the population of each colony, but this estimate will not give a good indication of the population density of the form in any given minor community.

REPTILES AND AMPHIBIANS. Few quantitative studies seem to have been made of the populations of reptiles or amphibians. Many of the methods used for counting terrestrial birds and mammals, however, should prove useful for the terrestrial forms of amphibians and reptiles. The populations of the aquatic larvae of amphibians can be estimated in the same manner as those of other aquatic organisms. Andrushko (1936) has used a modified transect method for counting desert reptiles. Time of day, weather conditions, and mating habits influence the activity of these animals and accordingly may be presumed to affect the counts. The low density of most kinds of snakes in terrestrial habitats makes quantitative field studies of those animals very laborious.

BIRDS. The methods commonly employed for the estimation of bird populations have recently been reviewed by E. M. Nicholson (1931, Chap. 3), by Kendeigh (1944), and by Lack (1937). Birds are in general somewhat easier to count than reptiles or mammals because most birds are diurnal in habit and many species are more or less conspicuous. Attempts to estimate entire populations of birds by the general reconnaissance method have been most successful with waterfowl, many of which breed in large colonies or congregate during winter in large flocks.

Actual counts of certain kinds of birds on sample plots may be made by several observers walking abreast across the area and recording all individuals observed (Forbes, 1907a; Lack and Lockley, 1935; Lay, 1940). The counts made by a single observer who travels back and forth across the area in a specified pattern (Kendeigh, 1947) are liable to the error that individual birds, because of their movements over the area, may escape the count or may be counted twice. Even with a line of observers errors of counting are likely to occur. The single observer has the advantage that he will be more uniform in his operations and recordings than will the members of a group (E. M. Nicholson, 1931).

The number of birds detected on a given area varies with the weather, time of day, and other factors that influence bird activity (Dice, 1921). In thick cover it is very difficult to make sure that every individual bird has been observed (Glading, 1941). Counts of shy birds are accordingly most dependable in winter when the leaves are off the deciduous trees and shrubs.

Because of their shy and secretive habits many kinds of birds are extremely difficult to count accurately, especially in thick cover (Udvardy, 1947). It must be admitted, therefore, that many bird "censuses" are at best only crude estimates of the actual population densities.

Estimates of bird populations are most commonly made during the breeding season from counts of the males, which then usually are in song or otherwise are conspicuous (May T. Cooke, 1923, 1927; Silloway, 1923; Saunders, 1936). The computation of the adult breeding population is usually made by multiplying the number of males by 2, under the assumption that all the males are mated. It has been shown, however, that not all the males of certain species actually are mated. On the other hand, a few of the males may already have stopped singing, or for other reasons may be overlooked at the time the count is made (Kendeigh, 1944: 90). A count of singing males therefore gives an unreliable census (E. M. Nicholson, 1931: 107).

A modification of the male-count method is to count occupied nests (Yapp, 1934; Beck, 1942). Many species of birds, however, conceal their nests so well that accurate counts of them are impracticable (Cramp and Ward, 1934). In spite of these difficulties and inaccuracies, counts of singing males and of nests are the simplest methods of estimating most bird populations during the breeding season.

The most accurate counts of bird populations undoubtedly are made by trapping and banding all the birds within a given area. If the birds are given distinctively colored bands, it will be possible to determine the population at any given time with considerable accuracy. One of the best studies of this kind is that by Mrs. Nice on the song sparrow (M. M. Nice, 1937).

Because of the difficulties of securing accurate counts of bird populations, ornithologists often make use of density indexes. As a matter of fact, most estimates of bird populations actually are density indexes rather than dependable estimates of population density per unit area. Density indexes of bird populations often are based on counts made on sample plots or along transects (Bennett and Hendrickson, 1938; Davison, 1940a; McClure, 1939). Samples based on time units also are sometimes used as a basis for the calculation of bird-frequency indexes (Grinnell and Storer, 1924: 22-35; Kashkarov, 1927: Linsdale, 1928: 3-24; Dice, 1930: 22-24; Lay, 1938: 254-56; Colquhoun, 1940: 53-67).

Counts of birds made either on sample plots or along transects are seriously affected by the amount and kind of cover, the light conditions, the alertness and experience of the observer, and the degree of activity of the animals. The activity of the animals in turn is affected by many conditions, such as time of day, season, temperature, humidity, rainfall, dewfall, and other conditions of weather, amount of light, sexual cycle, age, time of feeding, abundance of food, presence of enemies, and numerous other factors. These variables introduce so much error into the calculations that

Fisher, Hiatt, and Bergeson (1947), after a careful study, reached the conclusion that roadside counts of the introduced ringneck pheasant give very
unreliable estimates of population density.

The bird lists that are made with so much enthusiasm by amateur ornithologists have very little biological value. Such lists could, however, be
made of very considerable value if they were taken in a standardized manner, on definite plots or transects, in clearly described types of ecologic
communities, and at regular intervals. Density indexes could then be calculated for each form, and the migratory movements and yearly fluctuations in
numbers of the several species could be accurately recorded.

MAMMALS. The methods generally employed by mammalogists for estimating populations of mammals have been summarized by Dice (1941) and
by Rasmussen and Doman (1943). Direct counts of living mammals are
seldom practical. For large mammals the general reconnaissance method is
widely used by wildlife managers, but the results, while fairly reliable for
certain species in particular places, often are very unreliable for other species or in other situations (Rush, 1942). Drives, during which the individuals on measured areas are counted, are useful for counting certain
species, but are not practical for most forms.

For counting small mammals it is sometimes possible to capture all the
individuals present on specified sample plots (Kalabukhov, 1937) by intensive trapping, by excavation of burrows, or by flooding. These methods,
however, are practical only for small plots, both because of the labor required and because of the damage usually caused to the community and
to the habitat.

Trapping methods of some kind must usually be employed as a basis
for estimating the population densities of most kinds of small mammals
because of the nocturnal habits of these animals. In any trapping operation,
however, it is important to know the average diameter of the home ranges
of the individuals in order to be able to calculate the distances from which
the animals come to the traps. The proportional method of estimating
population density, based on marking and releasing and later recapturing
certain individuals, is difficult to apply to mammals because sufficiently
isolated areas of a given type of habitat are seldom available.

Because of the difficulty of securing actual counts of most kinds of
mammals, density indexes of various kinds are widely employed. Unfortunately, these density indexes have sometimes erroneously been used as a
basis for the estimate of population density per unit area.

A commonly employed density index for small mammals is based on
the number of individuals taken per "trap night." A "trap night," however,
does not give as reliable a density index as the number of individuals
taken per measured length of trap line (Dice, 1941), provided a sufficient
number of traps are set to trap all the individuals resident along the line.
Even the trap-line index gives only a rough measure of abundance because

of variations in the "trapability" of the individuals, in the efficiency of the traps, in the activity of the animals, and in other relevant factors.

It is the practice of many mammalogists to leave their traps set for a period of 3 nights. In thinly populated areas, however, a single night's trapping may often capture the entire population living along the route of the trap line. On the other hand, a period of 3 nights may fail to capture the whole resident population of a densely populated habitat.

Useful density indexes for certain kinds of mammals may be obtained also by counts of the number of tracks, nests, burrows, droppings, or other signs observed along a given length of transect, or on sample plots of specified size. A density index for certain forms may also be calculated from the number of individuals counted per unit of time under specified conditions of travel by the observer (Colquhoun, 1942c; Hicks, 1942).

SELECTED REFERENCES

Dice, Lee R. 1941. Methods for estimating populations of mammals. Journ. Wildlife Manag., 5: 398-407.

Kendeigh, S. Charles. 1944. Measurement of bird populations. Ecol. Monog., 14: 67-106.

Phillips, John F. V. 1931b. Quantitative methods in the study of numbers of terrestrial animals in biotic communities: a review with suggestions. Ecology, 12: 633-49.

Rasmussen, D. I., and Everett R. Doman. 1943. Census methods and their application in the management of mule deer. Trans. N. Amer. Wildlife Conf., 8: 369-86.

Ricker, William E. 1942. Fish populations of two artificial lakes. Invest. Ind. Lakes and Streams, 2: 255-65.

Shelford, Victor E. 1929. Laboratory and field ecology; the responses of animals as indicators of correct working methods. Baltimore: Williams and Wilkins Co. Chap. 2.

V

PHYSICAL FACTORS OF HABITATS THAT AFFECT COMMUNITIES

The physical factors of the environment play a very important role in determining the kind of ecologic community that can exist at any given site. Only to a very limited extent can the organisms that compose any community modify the raw habitat and thereby manufacture their own environment.

THE TERRESTRIAL HABITAT

The physical factors in terrestrial habitats differ greatly from those in aquatic habitats, and these 2 types of habitats must, therefore, be considered separately. Terrestrial and aquatic habitats, however, are not always completely distinct, for intermediate conditions often exist, particularly along shores and in riparian situations.

Climate and Weather

Climate includes the conditions of temperature, precipitation, air humidity, sunshine, wind movement, and other atmospheric phenomena characteristic of a given area, together with their changes from hour to hour, from day to day, from season to season, and from year to year. Weather, on the other hand, consists only of the combination of meteorological factors occurring at a particular place at a given moment. The sum of the weather conditions at any given place over a long period of time is its climate. The weather is extremely variable on many parts of the globe, but the climate changes only slowly over long periods of time.

The weather as well as the climate directly affects communities. Any statement of climate that is to be of value to the ecologist must, therefore, include a description of the variability of the weather.

TEMPERATURE. The various kinds of plants and animals thrive at different temperatures. Certain organisms thrive best at warm or even hot temperatures, others at moderate temperatures, and still others at cool temperatures. Certain forms succeed best under fluctuating temperatures, but others prefer uniformity.

For measuring air temperatures it is the practice of the United States Weather Bureau to use the Fahrenheit scale, but many ecologists prefer the Centigrade scale. The highest temperature recorded within a 24-hour period by a maximum thermometer is the daily maximum; the lowest temperature recorded in the same period by a minimum thermometer is the daily minimum. The daily mean is usually taken to be the mean between these 2 readings, but this fails to give full consideration to the fluctuations in temperature that may occur during the course of each day.

Biotic provinces may differ greatly from one another in their mean daily temperatures, as is shown in Figure 13, which compares the monthly mean

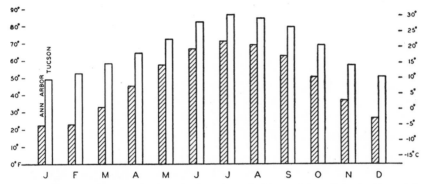

Fig. 13. The monthly means of temperature in a deciduous forest climate at Ann Arbor, Michigan (shaded), and in a desert climate at Tucson, Arizona (unshaded). (Data from United States Weather Bureau.)

temperatures of Ann Arbor, Michigan, and Tucson, Arizona. Such monthly means, however, fail to show the amount of daily variability in the weather and, therefore, are not fully suited for the use of ecologists (Daubenmire, 1947: 193).

FROST. Many types of organisms are injured or killed by freezing temperatures. Frost, therefore, is a good indicator of possible damage to cold-sensitive plants or animals. Freezing may occur, however, without the formation of frost if the air is so dry that it does not become fully saturated with moisture when its temperature is lowered to 0° C. The period between the last killing frost in spring and the first killing frost in autumn at any given place is called the frost-free season. The length of the frost-free season, of course, varies from year to year.

The actual effect of frost on plants is a complex matter, even for frost-sensitive forms. Most plants and animals native to regions subject to freezing temperatures are little injured by ordinary frosts; if they were, they would be eliminated. Only for domestic crops, therefore, need we be particularly concerned with the statistics of the frost-free season (Daubenmire, 1947: 202).

The first killing frost of autumn is, nevertheless, a most significant annual event for most cold-climate communities. Many of the annual plants are killed by the first severe frost, though the several species vary considerably in their ability to withstand freezing. The above-ground vegetation of many perennials and the leaves of many shrubs and trees also are killed. Likewise, many of the summer insects and other invertebrates are eliminated or are induced to retire to their winter quarters. The aspects of many communities, therefore, are greatly changed by the advent of the first killing frost of autumn.

PRECIPITATION. Precipitation is the amount of water that falls on a given station during a specified period. In the United States the rainfall gauge is usually calibrated in inches and hundredths, but certain investigators use

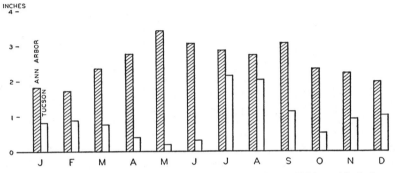

FIG. 14. The monthly means of precipitation at Ann Arbor, Michigan (shaded), and at Tucson, Arizona (unshaded). (Data from United States Weather Bureau.)

millimeters instead. The gauge is read once per day or sometimes after every heavy rain. Precipitation that falls as snow is melted into water or its weight is used in computing the equivalent depth of water. In addition, a record often is made each day of the depth of snow covering the ground on a level area. In any description of the rainfall of an area, it should be stated whether in the various seasons the water falls in gentle rains or in torrential storms.

The amount of precipitation that falls during the year and its distribution from season to season controls to a large degree the types of communities that can exist in a given region. In a region of heavy precipitation the climax association is likely to be a dense growth of forest, while in regions of scanty rainfall desert conditions usually prevail (Fig. 14). Precipitation that falls in the season when plants are dormant, however, is not so effective for promoting the growth of vegetation as that which falls in the growing season. In regions where high temperatures or strong winds prevail, desert conditions may exist unless the precipitation is sufficiently great to counterbalance the high rate of evaporation.

AIR HUMIDITY. Air humidity is the amount of water vapor present in the air. Relative humidity is the percentage of saturation of the air. The higher the temperature of the air, the more water vapor it can absorb. It will readily be understood, then, that if a body of air having a given relative humidity is heated, the relative humidity is lowered. Similarly, if a body of air is cooled its relative humidity is increased. When the relative humidity is increased to nearly 100 per cent the excess moisture falls as rain or snow, depending on the temperature. Should the vegetation be cooled at night by radiation so that the adjacent air reaches a relative humidity of 100 per cent, the excess moisture will be deposited on the vegetation or ground in the form of dew or frost, according to the temperature.

Air humidity is usually measured by a psychrometer, which is composed of a pair of thermometers, the bulb of one of which is surrounded by a wet cloth. The evaporation of moisture from this wet cloth lowers the reading of the "wet-bulb" thermometer. The maximum decrease in reading is proportional to the air humidity. The air humidity then is read from a psychometric table which gives the relative humidity corresponding to each dry- and wet-bulb reading of the pair of thermometers. Air humidity may also be calculated from a dew-point apparatus, which cools the air on a silvered surface until dew forms.

VAPOR-PRESSURE DEFICIT. Because relative humidity is dependent upon temperature, it cannot be treated statistically to obtain a mean. In order to state the average amounts of water vapor in the air, one may either calculate the actual weight of water present in a given volume of air or he may calculate the vapor-pressure deficit. Either may be calculated from proper tables by using the readings from wet- and dry-bulb thermometers. Vapor-pressure deficit has the advantage that it is more readily translated into terms of evaporation tension than is actual weight of water vapor.

WIND MOVEMENT. Rate of wind movement in the United States usually is recorded in miles per hour. Strong winds may directly damage certain plants and animals. Winds also may aid the dispersal of pollen, of many kinds of seeds, of certain insects, and of other kinds of animals. The direction of wind movement may be important in its effects on the dispersal of pollen and of individual organisms.

The rate of wind movement often has very important indirect effects upon certain of the physical factors of the habitat. The relationship between the rate of wind movement and the rate of evaporation of water has already been mentioned. A high rate of wind movement may cause the rapid removal of moisture from the soil, with consequent unfortunate results for certain plants and animals. In exposed situations the actual shape of some plants is in part controlled by the wind.

RATE OF EVAPORATION. The rate of evaporation of water from any given surface depends upon the barometric pressure, upon the amount of water vapor in the air, upon the temperature, and upon the rate of wind movement. The evaporation rate increases with increase of temperature and with decrease in air humidity (increase in vapor-pressure deficit). It increases also with increase of wind movement up to a certain point, beyond which increase of air speed causes little if any increase in evaporation rate. Rate of evaporation is also greatly affected by the surface from which evaporation occurs. Calculations of evaporation rate are almost always based on the amount of water evaporated from a free water surface or from a free film of pure water.

Various types of instruments have been used to measure evaporation rate directly. Probably the best known are the atmometer cups described by Livingston (1908). These devices require considerable care in their operation. Dust, microorganisms, and other substances often interfere with the efficient operation of the apparatus. The instruments may absorb moisture that falls as rain or forms as dew; consequently they may give erroneous readings unless special precautions are taken. Very few of these devices can be operated when the temperature falls below freezing, a circumstance which greatly limits their usefulness.

Rate of evaporation has especial importance for the existence of plants and animals. Those species that live in habitats where the evaporation rate is high must have adaptations to prevent the individuals from drying out. For example, many plants and animals have thick bark or skin to prevent dessication. Certain forms also have a covering of hair or of other material to prevent the free circulation of air next to the skin, and they thereby further reduce evaporation.

SOLAR RADIATION. The radiation received from the sun makes possible photosynthesis by plants and provides sufficient heat for the existence of life in earthly habitats. Solar radiation is, therefore, the basis for the existence of every community. The measurement of solar radiation is a complicated process, which will not be attempted by field ecologists except for very special studies. Some indication of the amount of solar radiation received by any given habitat may be obtained from the measurement of the incident light intensity. Light intensity may be measured most simply by a photographic exposure meter. Most of these exposure meters are calibrated in foot-candles and the light intensity may, therefore, be read directly. In those situations where the light intensity is too great for the range of the meter, a metal mask containing a small hole or series of holes of known size may be placed over the sensitive cell to reduce the light intensity. Another method is to read the amount of light reflected from a sheet of white paper.

The photoelectric cell in the exposure meter unfortunately is not equally sensitive to all the wave lengths of visible light, and it is relatively insensitive to radiant heat (infrared). The light in a forest, after passing in part through the green leaves, is much greener in character than light in an open field. The light of early morning and late afternoon, on the contrary, is much redder than that of the middle of the day. In winter the light at noon in the northern latitudes is more reddish than in summer. The exposure meter, therefore, can at best give only a rough summary of the light intensity. Furthermore, not all meters are accurately calibrated.

PERCENTAGE OF SUNSHINE. The possible amount of sunshine per day in a particular month at any given locality is determined by its latitude. The actual amount of sunshine, however, is never equal to the possible amount because of the presence of clouds or of dust on certain days. Sunshine may be measured by an automatic sunshine recorder, and from this the proportion of actual to possible sunshine can be calculated.

AIR PRESSURE. Air pressure has an important effect on the distribution and survival of high-mountain forms of life. Air pressure is also related in an important way to the periodic storms that occur in many parts of the globe.

WEATHER VARIABILITY. In many parts of the world and especially in the temperate zones there is considerable variability in weather from day to day and from week to week. The degree of this variability in any given region is itself an important feature of the climate. For instance, the frequency with which rain falls and the length of the intervals between rains may control the type of vegetation that can exist at a given site. There is at present no good way of measuring or classifying weather variability, though undoubtedly such measures could and should be devised. The usual measurement of climate in terms of means and normals has the unfortunate result that the variability of weather is ignored and obscured (Cain, 1945).

SUMMARIES OF METEOROLOGIC DATA. Measures of temperature, precipitation, and other meteorologic factors usually are summarized for the several months and for the year. For a subdivision of a month the 10-day period, approximately one-third of a month, is often useful. The calendar week is not a good unit to use for the purpose because of its changing position in the year.

For each measurement of a meteorologic factor it usually is desirable to state at least its mean, mean minimum, mean maximum, and mean range for the station and interval under consideration, based on the whole period of observations at that station. Other computations will be needed for special studies. Sometimes, for example, the average monthly precipitation for the growing season only may be the item of most importance. In another study the absolute maximum temperature within the last few years may shed light on the distribution of a particular heat-sensitive species.

Climatic data pertaining to a particular region may be presented graphically by charts of various kinds. Monthly means of temperature, precipitation, and other climatic factors may be presented in simple diagrams (Figs. 13 and 14). Other more complex types of charts are sometimes used, such as the hythergraph (Fig. 15), which combines the monthly means of temperature and of precipitation (Griffith Taylor, 1919; Shelford, 1929: 18).

Summaries of the climates of the various parts of the United States are published from time to time by the United States Weather Bureau. Data on the observations currently taken are published in the periodical called *Meteorological Data*. The Weather Bureau in the state concerned will supply the latest records for a given region. Excellent summaries of the climates

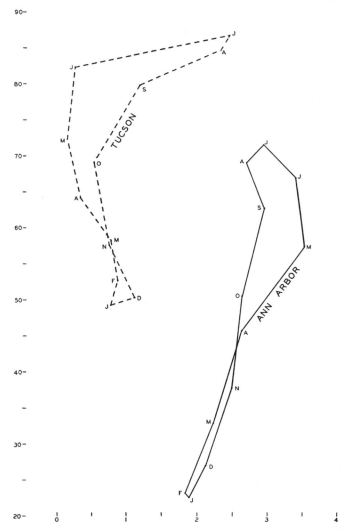

FIG. 15. Hythergraph comparing the monthly means of temperature and of precipitation at Tucson, Arizona, and at Ann Arbor, Michigan. (Data from United States Weather Bureau.)

of the several states and territories are given also in the *Yearbook* of the United States Department of Agriculture for 1941, entitled "Climate and Man."

The weather of most parts of the earth is so variable that any correct statement of the climate of a given area or of a particular habitat requires many years of careful instrumental observations. Rarely will it be practical for the ecologist himself to attempt to gather this kind of data. There is so much daily, seasonal, and annual variation in the meteorologic factors of most habitats that a brief series of observations will usually have little ecologic value. Except for very special studies, therefore, the ecologist working in the United States should depend upon the excellent summaries of climate made by the Weather Bureau.

MICROCLIMATES. Most of the meteorological records secured in the United States are taken in standard Weather Bureau stations. Sometimes such a station on the top of a building in a city may be a considerable distance from the habitat being investigated by the ecologist. Although the trends of weather and of climate recorded in the Weather Bureau stations undoubtedly parallel in a general way those in the habitats of the same region, these Weather Bureau records cannot be taken to represent the conditions in any particular habitat.

The peculiarities of weather and climate that distinguish local areas may have important effects on the local communities. For instance, a community that occupies a "frost pocket" may be very different from that of the surrounding area (Hough, 1945). The progression of the seasons and the changes in the microweather also are known to differ in each microhabitat (Wolfe, Wareham, and Scofield, 1943). Precise information about the meteorological conditions in any particular habitat, therefore, can be obtained only from a battery of instruments located in that situation. Fortunately for the ecologist, such detailed meteorologic information is essential only for special kinds of investigations.

ZONES OF CLIMATE. The climates of the world have a zonal arrangement around the globe (Fig. 16). Around the middle of the earth and extending on each side of the equator is an equatorial zone characterized by high temperatures and by the convectional rise of moisture-laden air, resulting in heavy afternoon showers. On each side of the equatorial zone, to the north and to the south, near the latitude of 30°, is a zone characterized by generally high temperatures, low humidity, and slight precipitation. These zones, called horse latitudes, have a hot and arid or semiarid climate. North of the horse latitudes (south of them in the Southern Hemisphere) is a polar-front climate zone of highly variable weather. Here there is a rapid succession of wet and of dry spells and of strong temperature contrasts. Surrounding the north and south poles, respectively, are the north-polar and south-polar zones, which are characterized by their cold and arid or semiarid climate (Rossby, 1941: 612-13).

Well-marked subdivisions of the major climatic zones occur in many parts of the earth. These subdivisions vary considerably from place to place, depending on local conditions. The presence of oceans or of smaller bodies of water, of land masses, and of mountains often have a great influence on the local climate, either directly or through their interference with wind movements. The result is that a considerable variety of climates may be represented within the limits of a single major climatic zone.

CLASSIFICATION OF CLIMATES. Various methods have been proposed for classifying the numerous types of climates of the world and of particular continents (Livingston and Shreve, 1921; Köppen, 1936; Thornthwaite,

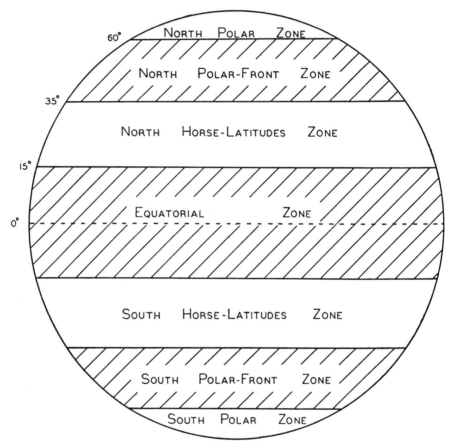

FIG. 16. Major climatic zones of the earth. The shaded zones have mostly moist climates, while the unshaded zones have arid or semiarid climates. (Redrawn from a figure by Blumenstock and Thornthwaite in the 1941 *Yearbook* of the U. S. Dept. of Agric.)

1931, 1933, 1941). In general, the best index to the climate of any given area is the type of vegetation that grows there. The climatologist can accurately measure the various climatic factors within a particular habitat and can calculate their means, extremes, and variabilities, both from time to time and from place to place. Little is known as yet, however, about the particular climatic factors and their combinations that limit the growth and distribution of the many diverse kinds of plants and animals. It seldom is possible, therefore, to correlate the available meteorological measurements with the occurrence or with the success either of particular species or of communities.

Physiography

In describing the physiography of any region special note should be made of its general type of relief, whether flat, rolling, or mountainous. The type of relief will depend in part on the geologic structure of the region and on its geologic history. The development of drainage systems and of certain other features of physiography, however, depends not only on the geologic structure and history, but also on the past and present climate. The amount of slope of the land surface and the direction of its exposure to sun and to wind are often of great importance in determining the type of community that can exist at a given locality.

Soil

Soil may be defined as the more or less solid material covering the surface of a terrestrial habitat, which is capable of supporting the growth of plants. At certain places the soil may be in great part composed of large boulders or coarse gravel, but in most situations it is composed of more or less finely divided mineral particles intermingled with organic materials.

The soil plays a very considerable role in controlling the development of most kinds of communities (Hardy, 1945). The character of the soil governs the local topography, the rate of runoff of water, the amount of moisture available to plant roots, the ease with which burrowing animals are able to excavate their tunnels, and the color of ground-dwelling animals. In these and many other ways soil affects the community. Because of the control which soil exercises over the habitat, a community may remain for a long time at a particular stage of development. Thus a temporary edaphic climax is formed. On sandy soil, for example, the plants of the regional climatic climax may be unable to establish themselves, at least for a time, with the result that an edaphic climax community adapted to the sandy soil may persist for a long time without succession toward the climatic climax.

Any complete analysis of the soil at a given site requires special technics and special training. Fortunately for the ecologist, the soils of most parts of North America have been fairly well described. Detailed soil surveys have been made of many counties in the United States by the Department of Agriculture and by the state agricultural experiment stations. Unfortunately, many areas of much ecologic interest have not yet been surveyed, and in such areas the ecologist, if he attempts to describe the habitat adequately, must draw up his own description of the soil.

PEDOLOGY. The important relation of soil to the growing of agricultural crops, to pastures, to forests, and to organic life in general has resulted within recent years in the elevation of the study of soils to the rank of a distinct subscience, which is called pedology.

FORMATION OF SOIL. The character of newly formed soil is at first closely dependent upon the nature of the parent materials. All soils, however, become altered in time by further decomposition of the minerals present, by the addition of plant and animal detritus, by the leaching of soluble materials, and by other processes (Shaler, 1892). The ultimate character of soil is often determined more by the climate of the area and by the resulting growth of vegetation than by the character of the underlying rocks or other materials (Glinka, 1935).

SOIL TEXTURE. Soil texture is largely dependent upon the size of the soil particles. The size of the particles in any given soil may be ascertained by shaking a dried and weighed sample through a succession of sieves of progressively smaller standard-sized meshes. The amount of the whole sample that has passed each of the sieves is then weighed and the proportion which it forms of the whole sample is calculated. Soil particles that have diameters greater than 2 mm are called gravel; those between 2.0 and 0.05 mm are said to be sand; those between 0.05 and 0.002 mm are silt; and those less than 0.002 mm in diameter are called clay (Rice and Alexander, 1938: 893).

Soils which are made up of large particles, and which, therefore, have an open texture, are more easily penetrated by the roots of plants than are those composed of very fine particles. Animals also can more easily burrow into the loose-textured sands and loams than into the firmer-textured clays. Some of the clays are almost impenetrable when they are dry. The texture of the soil also influences the rapidity with which rainfall is absorbed, the rate of evaporation from the soil surface, the water-retaining power of the soil, the height to which water will rise in the soil by capillary action, and the rate at which oxygen and carbon dioxide diffuse through the soil. All of these features affect the kind of community that can exist on any given site.

HUMUS. One of the most important constituents of the soil from the point of view of the plants is humus. Humus is composed of plant and animal materials which are undergoing decomposition in the soil. These decomposing materials enter into a very complex relationship with the inorganic soil materials to form a substance which is partly colloidal in physical structure and which is a storehouse of the chemicals that are essential for plant growth. These chemicals include especially carbon and nitrogen and, to a lesser extent, phosphorus, calcium, iron, and manganese. Soils containing considerable amounts of humus favor the growth of vegetation by continually releasing plant nutrients. Such soils also tend to retain the plant nutrients and to prevent their rapid leaching into the subsoil. The presence in the soil of decomposing organic materials in the form of humus, therefore, is very important for the plant growth (Waksman, 1936).

The amount of humus varies greatly in different kinds of soil. In grassland soils there may be as much as 600 tons of humus per acre, but in forest soils the amount is usually less than 50 tons per acre (Daubenmire, 1947: 27). In desert soils the amount of humus may be very slight, as is shown by the usually pale color of such soils.

Soil Profile. Mature soils ordinarily exhibit several layers which together form a soil profile (Fig. 17). The layers are grouped by pedologists into 4 major soil horizons (Rice and Alexander, 1938: Fig. 1). Horizon A

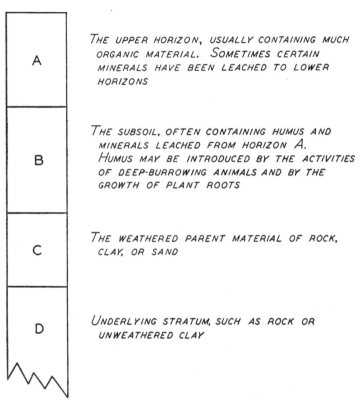

FIG. 17. A soil profile, showing the horizons A, B, C, and D. The subdivisions of the horizons are not indicated.

includes the surface soil. This horizon often contains much organic debris, but its soluble materials tend to be leached to lower horizons and its colloidal clay also has often been extracted. Horizon B includes the subsoil. Here is usually the maximum accumulation of soluble materials and of colloidal clay extracted from Horizon A. Horizon C consists of the weathered, but otherwise little altered, parent materials of the soil. The underlying stratum of rock, clay, or sand forms Horizon D. Subdivisions of the horizons are usually designated by numerical subscripts, such as A_1, A_2, B_1.

Depth of Soil. The depth of the soil at a given situation has an important effect on the type of ecologic community that may be able to develop. If bare rock alone is present, then only the hardiest pioneer plants, such as the lichens, will be able to exist. In shallow soils a somewhat richer vegetation will develop. On deep soils the vegetation should be able to progress to the climatic climax unless prevented by adverse factors. Soil depth, therefore, is an important environmental factor which should be stated in any complete description of a habitat.

SOIL MOISTURE. The amount of moisture present in the soil directly and indirectly controls the type of community that can exist at any given site. Plants and animals vary in their ability to endure very wet and very dry soil. A soil that is filled with moisture will be occupied by marsh or swamp plants and animals, whereas a very dry soil can support only organisms that are adapted to xeric conditions. The water-retaining power of the soil depends upon the size and type of the soil particles, upon the arrangement and compactness of the particles, and upon the amount of organic matter in the soil.

The amount of moisture in the soil may be ascertained by taking a sample, usually with a soil borer, by weighing, and then by drying this sample in an oven at 105° to 110° C. until it ceases to lose weight. The amount of weight loss divided by the dry weight of the sample and multiplied by 100 will give its original water content in percentage of dry weight.

The amount of water present in a soil does not directly indicate the amount available to plants. The roots of no plant are able to extract all the moisture from the soil. Plants differ in their ability to extract water from soil, and therefore the proportion of available water in any given soil must be calculated separately for each species (Vestal, 1931: 233). The relation of plants to soil moisture is, in fact, extremely complex (Daubenmire, 1947: 122-34).

WATER TABLE. In well-watered regions the soil moisture penetrates to bed rock, and a water table is formed at a greater or lesser distance below the ground surface. The height to which water rises in a well usually indicates the approximate level of this water table except in artesian wells, in which the water is under pressure. If the water table reaches the surface of the ground, the water will emerge as a spring. By capillary action water rises through the soil layers for some distance above the water table. The precise distance water may thus rise and become available to the plants depends upon the character of the soil.

The depth of the water table below the surface of the ground is of much importance in controlling the type of community at a given site. If the water table is near or above the soil surface, a marsh or swamp may be formed, but if the water table is deep, the water from this source can have little or no effect on the growth of vegetation. The depth of the water table, however, often varies from season to season and sometimes from year to year, depending upon the steepness of the slope, amount of runoff, rate of

evaporation from the soil surface and from the vegetation, and retentive-
ness of the soil. In very arid regions there may be no water table except in
the beds of washes or in enclosed basins. In the Palusian biotic province of
southeastern Washington and adjacent Oregon and Idaho, for instance, the
water that falls as precipitation seldom penetrates the soil to a depth of
more than 4 to 6 feet. The available water then is stored only in the upper
soil layers. Below this depth the soil is almost perfectly dry, and no water
table is formed except in the valleys.

The amount of moisture in the soil affects the distribution of practically
all terrestrial plants. The species of plants vary greatly in the amount of
water they require for existence and also in the quantity of water they will
tolerate around their roots. Plants which are adapted to arid conditions are
able to live for considerable periods of time in local habitats that have very
little soil moisture, but many of these plants cannot endure any lack of soil
drainage. Plants adapted to wet situations, on the contrary, must be able to
tolerate a considerable concentration of soil moisture, but they may not be
able to live in dry soil.

SOIL SOLUTION. The chemicals dissolved in the water which is present in
the soil control to a very large extent the character of the community that
can exist in that situation. From this soil solution the plants must secure
the water and nutrients that enable them to grow. The chemical character
of the soil solution also determines the kinds of bacteria, fungi, protozoa,
and other simple organisms that can live in the soil. The soil and soil solution form an extremely complex chemical system, and the absorption of
nutrients by a plant is far from being a simple process (Daubenmire, 1947:
40-45).

In regions of very heavy rainfall the water that penetrates the soil usually
leaches away the soil nutrients as fast as they are formed, and thus the soil
is impoverished. In arid regions, on the contrary, there may be insufficient
rainfall to leach out harmful salts. The region most favorable for plant
growth, therefore, is one in which the effective rainfall entering the soil is
adequate to dissolve harmful chemicals, but not so great as to carry away
also the plant nutrients held in the soil solution.

SOIL ACIDITY. The acidity or alkalinity (pH) of the soil solution is
another important factor that controls, both directly and indirectly, the
growth of plants (Daubenmire, 1947: 45-55). Soil acidity is measured on a
scale of which pH 7.0 indicates a neutral condition. A pH lower on the
scale than 7.0 indicates an acid condition, while one higher than 7.0 indicates an alkaline condition. A rough measure of soil acidity can be made
by any of several portable indicator sets which may be purchased. For a
more accurate determination of pH an electrical apparatus equipped with a
glass electrode may be employed (Truog, 1938).

Plants vary greatly in their tolerances to the various levels of soil acidity.
Bog-inhabiting plants must be tolerant of acid conditions, while the plants

that live on certain alkaline soils in the desert must be able to tolerate a pH considerably above the neutral point. Certain plants are able to grow in a very limited range of pH values, while others are very tolerant and are able to thrive in a wide range of acidities or alkalinities.

The acidity of the soil solution affects the roots of plants not only directly but also indirectly. The availability of the several plant nutrients is controlled to a considerable degree by the pH of the soil solution. The pH of the soil also affects the lives of the soil animals (Morgan, Gourley, and Ableiter, 1938). Earthworms, for instance, seem unable to survive in soils that have a pH other than 6 or 7 (Arrhenius, 1921).

The nature of the vegetal litter that covers the soil surface and which eventually becomes incorporated into the topsoil has a direct relationship to soil acidity (Tansley, 1946: 214). The litter falling from conifer trees tends to be of an acid type which is called "mor." Mor soils have in general a poor fauna, but an abundant flora of fungi. The litter from most deciduous trees forms a less acid type of soil than that from conifers and is called "mull." Mull tends to have a rich soil fauna, but few fungi (Romell, 1935). The leaves of such trees as the oaks form a more acid soil than those of the beech or maple.

SALTS. Many soils contain salts that are more or less detrimental to certain plants. Along the shores of the ocean and of salt lakes, common salt (NaCl) and other salts may inhibit the growth of all plants except those that are especially tolerant. In arid regions evaporation from the soil surface often causes salts of various kinds ("alkali") to accumulate near or at the surface of the ground. The presence of any considerable concentration of these salts in the soil solution may control the kinds of plants that can grow in the habitat (Daubenmire, 1947: 56-65).

HARDPAN. The concentrations of chemicals that may be deposited at or near the surface of the ground especially in arid regions often cement the soil particles to form impervious layers of "hardpan" or "caliche." Such a hardpan layer interferes with the penetration of rainfall into the soil, with the rise of soil moisture from below, with the growth of plant roots, and with the activities of burrowing animals.

COLOR OF THE SURFACE SOIL. Ground-dwelling animals tend to match the color of the surface soil of their habitat (Dice and Blossom, 1937). In certain ecologic studies a description of the color of the surface soil is consequently essential. Such a description will be most accurate if it is based upon actual colorimetric measurements. A sample of approximately a pint of the surface soil may be collected in a cloth bag, thoroughly dried, and then preserved in a clean tin can or jar. In the field an empty and clean soup or vegetable can makes a suitable shipping container if the open end is stopped by a tightly wedged wad of crumpled newspaper. It is desirable to collect several such samples in each habitat, preferably 10 or more, taken at random. Later, in the laboratory, the color of the samples is analyzed with a reflection type of photometer.

In collecting a sample of the surface soil care should be taken to secure the actual soil surface, rather than the subsoil. Living vegetation should be avoided, but if dead leaves or leaf mold forms the soil surface these should be included. Small rocks or pebbles lying on the surface often have their upper surfaces weathered to a color different from their undersides. When color readings of such materials are made, care should be used to place them in the same position that they occupied in nature. Most soils are darker when they are moist than when they are dry. In order to obtain comparable readings of soil color, therefore, it has been my practice to measure the color of the samples in air-dry condition.

SNOW. Snow often covers the ground during the winter and sometimes at other seasons in the cold-temperate and frigid zones. The layer of snow temporarily constitutes the upper stratum of the soil. The presence of a snow cover modifies the habitat in a number of ways (Morgan, 1939; Formozov, 1939). The depth of the snow cover attained and its duration, therefore, is an important feature of those terrestrial habitats in which snow is of occasional or regular occurrence.

DEPENDENCE OF SOIL ON THE CLIMATE. The character of the soil is controlled to a very considerable extent by the climate. In part this relationship is a direct one through the agencies of water, frost, and wind in forming the soil; in part also it is indirect through the control that climate has over organic life. The kind and luxuriance of plant and animal life have much to do with the kind of soil that is formed at any given location. The vegetation also to some degree controls the microclimate in its immediate vicinity. In these and in many other ways climate and soil influence each other.

CLASSIFICATION OF SOILS. Soils are classified by soil scientists according to soil series and soil class (Baldwin, Kellogg, and Thorp, 1938). The soil series classification is based on the kind of soil profile present at the locality being studied, without regard to surface materials. All the soils of a given series have developed from parent materials of similar character. Each series is given a locality name, which usually is taken from the place in which the series was first identified. The soil class is based on the size of the soil particles in the surface layer. It receives such names as gravel, sand, silt, or clay. A particular class of soil in a given series is called a soil type.

Many different kinds of soil are found in the world. In North America the soils range from the peaty soil of the tundra in the North to the desert soils of the Southwest and to the lateritic soils of the southeastern states. A few of these kinds of soil will be described briefly.

PODZOL. Podzol is the kind of soil that is formed under coniferous forests in cool-temperate zones having a moderate amount of rainfall. The soil reaction is somewhat acid. In undisturbed situations the podzols have a surface mat of partly decayed fragments of wood and of decaying conifer needles. Below this thin surface layer is a very light gray, highly siliceous, leached layer a few inches or more thick. From this pale layer the clays and iron compounds have been dissolved, to be redeposited in a lower soil horizon. The B horizon is dark because of the deposition of materials leached out of the A horizon. The podzols often are shallow. The subsoil is in general much less suitable for plant growth than is the surface soil. Any erosion that removes the surface layer of such a soil, therefore, seriously lessens the productivity of the habitat.

BROWN FOREST SOIL. Under deciduous forests in cool-temperate zones having medium to moderately heavy rainfall the soils are often brown or grayish brown. In contrast to the podzols, which usually have a rather heavy layer of leaf litter on the surface, the brown forest soils usually have only a thin surface layer of scattered organic litter, beneath which is a thick brownish layer containing much mixed organic debris and humus. This brownish layer merges gradually into the subsoil. The great depth of the humus layer in the deciduous-forest soils is due to the activities of burrowing animals, both invertebrate and vertebrate. The humus layer in the brown forest soils usually is neutral or somewhat basic in reaction (Fenton, 1947: 79-80). Most of the deciduous-forest soils of the United States are classed by the Bureau of Soils as "podzolic" soils of several types (*Yearbook*, U. S. Dept. Agric., 1938).

CHERNOZEM. The prairie soils or chernozems are developed in temperate, subhumid grasslands. This kind of soil is dark brown to black in its upper 2 to 4 feet. It contains much organic material and is naturally very fertile. A distinguishing feature of the chernozems is an accumulation of carbonates, principally lime carbonate, in a lower level of the soil. Erosion that removes the layer of topsoil will, of course, seriously lower the value of chernozem soil for plant growth.

The chernozems illustrate soil construction at the maximum and soil destruction at the minimum. In the areas in which they are developed the rainfall and temperature are adequate to allow an extensive accumulation of clay in the soil. The minerals are more finely broken down than in most other kinds of soils, and the more soluble elements have been leached out, leaving only the stable compounds. The clay is in an active state capable of holding and of exchanging the chemicals essential for plant growth. There remain in the soil enough minerals other than quartz to serve, when later broken down, as a reservoir of plant nutrients. The highly productive soils of this type, unfortunately, cover only limited areas of the world. In the United States the distribution of the chernozems is closely delineated by the wheat belt (Albrecht, 1944: 23-24).

DESERT SOIL. On the desert, organic materials are so scanty that they have little effect on soil formation. Mechanical disintegration of the rocks, on the other hand, is energetic. Because of the dry condition of the surface soil and the general lack of binding vegetation, the finer soil materials tend to blow away to surrounding regions, leaving the soil surface composed mostly of coarse sand and gravel (Glinka, 1935). Distinct soil horizons are for the most part lacking in the desert, and the surface soil is not appreciably different in character from the subsoil. Erosion has, therefore, little effect on the quality of desert soils.

OTHER SOIL TYPES. A more complete classification of the soils of the United States and further information about soil structure and about the process of soil formation are given in the *Yearbook* of the Department of Agriculture for 1938. In other parts of the world, especially in the tropics and in the arctics, numerous other kinds of soil occur besides those found in the United States.

THE AQUATIC HABITAT

The aquatic habitat differs from the terrestrial habitat in a number of ways that are of importance to communities. Water is a much heavier medium than air, and many organisms are able to float in it. On the other hand, water in motion is a much more effective agent of destruction than is air, and accordingly aquatic organisms that are exposed to moving water must have special characters to enable them to avoid or to endure these mechanical effects. The oxygen available in water is much less concentrated than that in the air. For this reason aquatic animals and those aquatic plants that are unable to manufacture their own oxygen must have special adaptations for extracting it from the water. Furthermore, water is an excellent solvent for many chemicals. Some of these chemicals when in solution in certain concentrations are beneficial, while others are injurious to aquatic organisms. For all these and many other reasons aquatic communities are strikingly different from terrestrial communities.

Precise measurements of the several factors that compose an aquatic habitat are often difficult to make. This is especially true of the deeper waters and of the bottom conditions at considerable depths. In spite of the difficulties, limnologists and oceanographers have devised a considerable number of apparatus and of technics for studying the aquatic habitat. The student is referred to such general works as those by Welch (1935, 1948) and Sverdrup, Johnson, and Fleming (1942) for a description of these methods.

As an environment for living organisms the aquatic habitat has many favorable features. Water carries in solution such necessary gases as oxygen and carbon dioxide and the several mineral substances that are essential for the life of plants and animals. Water itself is an essential element in the make-up of all organisms. The high heat capacity of water and its high latent heat of evaporation also are important in maintaining fairly uniform temperatures in aquatic environments.

Among the more important of the physical factors of aquatic habitats that control the occurrence and distribution of particular communities may be mentioned the temperature of the water and its changes during the course of the year, the salinity and other chemical and physical qualities of the water, the movements of the water, the quantity and quality of the light, the depth of the water, and the character of the bottom (Petersen, 1914: 34-35).

A few kinds of aquatic habitats are made up of water only and include no contact either with the more solid substratum or with the atmosphere. Most aquatic habitats, however, do include contacts with the soil under the water, with the air that lies above it, or with both.

The Aquatic Medium. The aquatic medium itself is affected by many variable physical factors (Welch, 1935; Sverdrup, Johnson, and Fleming, 1942). Its temperature varies from time to time and from place to place. The gases and other chemicals that the water holds in solution are variable in their concentration, and this affects the salinity, the acidity (pH), and the ability of the water to support life. Nearly all natural waters also hold a variable amount of inorganic and organic materials in suspension. In some mountain lakes the amount of suspended substance may be so slight that the water is very transparent, but a muddy stream may carry a heavy load of suspended materials.

Sea water has the special property that it is a buffered solution, and for that reason changes in acidity or alkalinity are resisted. The high specific gravity of sea water gives it a buoyant effect that enables many kinds of organisms to float in it without special effort on their part. Furthermore, since the minerals dissolved in sea water are present in nearly the same concentrations as in the body fluids of most marine invertebrates, there is no tendency for osmosis to destroy those organisms which are immersed in the water. All these features make the marine habitat an especially favorable one for the existence of organisms (Sverdrup, Johnson, and Fleming, 1942: 268).

Dissolved Chemicals. Water that falls as rain or snow is practically free of dissolved minerals, though it contains certain dissolved gases. A few streams and lakes that are fed by melting snow or that occur on areas where the rocks are only slightly soluble in water may retain much of their original purity. Most natural waters, on the contrary, contain variable amounts of dissolved minerals as well as of gases. In the oceans and in lakes that have no outlet these dissolved minerals become concentrated by the evaporation of the water, until in some bodies of water complete saturation may be reached and deposition of one or more minerals may occur. In lakes and streams there is marked variation from place to place in the kinds and amounts of chemicals in solution. In the ocean also there is a certain amount of variability from place to place in the concentration of the several chemicals, but, except near the mouths of rivers or in partially landlocked bays, the chemical content of sea water is remarkably constant compared to that of inland lakes or streams.

Suspended Materials. Materials suspended in the water have a particular importance to aquatic communities because of the reduction they cause in light penetration. Microorganisms floating in the water operate in the same manner to decrease the penetration of light as do inorganic particles. In water containing any considerable amount of suspended materials photosynthesis can occur only near the surface. In very muddy water few aquatic plants can exist, and accordingly only a meager community can be supported.

WATER PRESSURE. Water pressure becomes very great in the depths of the ocean. This is also an important factor in the life of certain inhabitants of fresh water. Many aquatic organisms, nevertheless, are able to perform vertical migrations of considerable magnitude. The individuals of certain species make daily movements over a vertical distance as great as 400 meters (Sverdrup, Johnson, and Fleming, 1942: 273). Most kinds of organisms, however, live within a fairly narrow vertical range, though it is probable that the limits of this range are often controlled by light and by environmental factors other than pressure.

WATER TEMPERATURE. The temperature of the water varies in different aquatic habitats from scalding in certain hot springs to freezing in frigid situations. In shallow lakes in the Temperate Zone the temperature may vary from warm in summer to freezing in winter. There may also be considerable variation in temperature during the course of a single day. Besides the direct effect which water temperature has on organisms it indirectly affects certain floating and swimming forms by changing the water density and viscosity (Welch, 1935: 31-34).

THERMAL STRATIFICATION. In large bodies of water the deeper levels often are colder than the surface, and there is accordingly a thermal stratification. Thus, in the depths of the oceans, even in the tropics, the temperature usually is somewhat below the freezing point of fresh water. On the other hand, shallow lakes whose water is continually stirred to the bottom by the waves do not exhibit thermal stratification. When such lakes are covered by ice in winter, however, and also under certain other conditions, they may become stratified. Some types of fairly deep inland lakes exhibit a special kind of thermal stratification in summer which includes the development of a thermocline (Welch, 1935: 45-57). Above the level of the thermocline the water is continually mixed by the waves and, therefore, is of generally uniform temperature. Below the thermocline, however, the water is stagnant and is much colder than at the surface (Fig. 18). In the water below the thermocline the dissolved oxygen often becomes exhausted during the course of the summer and only a few anaerobic organisms are able to persist.

MECHANICAL ACTION OF WATER. The water, which is so important an element in every aquatic habitat, is often in motion. The rate of this motion has very important consequences for the organisms that make up the aquatic community. Those organisms that are free in the water will be carried from place to place by the motion of the water. Accordingly, if the water is moving very slowly and at an even rate over a considerable area it may transport a whole local community without any particular disturbance in its organization. If the water is in rapid motion it will continually rearrange the assemblages of individuals and may prevent the formation of a well-organized community. The movements of water also may carry organisms from situations where the habitat is suitable to them to other localities in which they are unable to exist. Thus, a river emptying into the ocean carries countless numbers of fresh-water organisms to their destruction. The motion of water may be of benefit to certain individuals, bringing them fresh and oxygenated water and perhaps also carrying food materials within their reach.

Water in motion may, through the force it exerts, severely damage delicate organisms. If its rate of motion is high, it may even damage robust and strongly protected forms. Streams tend to erode their channels; they move

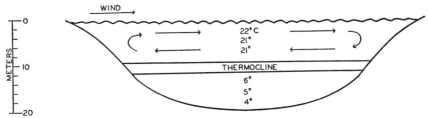

Fig. 18. Thermal stratification during summer in a temperate lake of the second order. The water below the thermocline is not involved in the circulation of the lake water by the wind; its oxygen becomes depleted and only a few types of animals are then able to exist in the bottom of the lake. The autumnal storms break up the thermocline and until the next summer the water circulation in the lake involves the lower as well as the upper layers. (Modified from a figure in *Limnology* by Paul S. Welch; by permission of McGraw-Hill Book Co.)

materials from place to place and often wash away rooted plants. Floods may even destroy whole communities. Along the shores of large bodies of water the waves constantly erode the land. The materials carried in suspension by moving water, both in streams and in waves, assist in the erosional process. When water that is carrying a heavy load of suspended material slows its motion, the suspended materials are deposited, thereby often considerably altering the habitat concerned and sometimes burying individual organisms or whole communities.

COVERING OF ICE. The surface of the water may be covered by ice during part of the winter in cold-temperate and frigid climates. The icy covering interferes with the movements of those animals that live at the water surface or at the water margins. A covering of ice also interferes with the interchange of oxygen and other gases between the water and the atmosphere. It may happen in winter that under a covering of ice and snow which hinders photosynthesis most of the oxygen in a small lake is consumed by the aquatic organisms, with the result that many of the animals die of asphyxiation (Greenbank, 1945).

The ice that covers a lake or river may be of benefit to certain of the organisms making up the aquatic community. Under the ice the temperature does not go lower than freezing so long as any free water is present. Often the water level falls slightly after the ice is formed, thus leaving a free air space under the ice and above the water. Semiaquatic mammals, such as the muskrat, beaver, mink, and otter, often spend much time in this open space under the ice, where they are protected by the ice against extreme cold and against nonaquatic predators.

DEPTH OF THE WATER. The depth to the substratum beneath the surface of the water has a direct effect on the growth of many kinds or organisms. Rooted plants, such as water lilies, whose leaves must reach the water surface obviously cannot grow in water that is deeper than the length of their petioles. No attached plant that requires sunlight can grow in water at a depth to which light cannot penetrate effectively. In this case the maximum allowable depth of the water is dependent also upon its transparency. Animals that feed upon or live among plants also are limited to the shallow depths at which these plants can live. Animals that live upon dead organic debris, however, can live at greater depths.

The depth of the water has another important effect on the character of the bottom community through its relation to wave action. In shallow water wave action is likely to be severe and only large rocks or coarse gravel may make up the bottom if all the finer materials have been washed away; in deep water, where the strength of wave action is diminished, fine materials may be deposited on the bottom. In protected bays or coves, where wave action is absent or slight, fine materials may be deposited at shallow depths.

CHARACTER OF THE BOTTOM. The character of the materials of which the bottom is composed also greatly affects the type of community that can exist in such a habitat. If the bottom is composed of fine sand or mud, many kinds of organisms will be absent because they would be smothered by this fine material. If the bottom is composed of hard clay or of rock, certain burrowing forms of animals may be unable to excavate their homes. The amount and kind of organic detritus in the bottom materials also determine the kinds and numbers of bottom-feeding animals that will be able to exist. Very dissimilar kinds of communities therefore are found on muddy, sandy, gravelly, and rocky bottoms (Verrill, 1873).

EFFECT OF THE BOTTOM ON SURFACE COMMUNITIES. The depth of the water in a given situation may also affect the character of the community that inhabits the open water above. Many of the organisms that make up the bottom communities, both the burrowing and the attached forms, have larvae that are free-swimming and which form part of the adjacent open-water community. Open-water communities that overlie water so deep that few bottom animals are present will, therefore, be of somewhat different composition from open-water communities that occur over shallow water.

EFFECT OF THE ATMOSPHERE ON AQUATIC ECOSYSTEMS. The air that lies above an aquatic habitat may affect it in several ways. It may, by conduction, raise or lower the temperature of the water. The extent to which the air transmits the rays of the sun also determines the quantity of light and of heat that the aquatic habitat receives. Clouds or dust in the overlying atmosphere, therefore, may seriously reduce the photosynthesis of aquatic plants and the temperature of the aquatic habitat. The air also has an important mechanical effect on the aquatic habitat through its production of waves and of currents in the water.

EFFECT OF ADJACENT LAND. The physical and biotic conditions of aquatic communities are often much modified by the presence of adjacent land. This is especially true of small bodies of water. In particular, the water temperature and salinity of aquatic habitats may be modified by fresh water discharged by rivers or flowing as runoff from the land. This fresh water tends to make the habitats that it enters warmer in summer and cooler in winter. The sediments brought into aquatic habitats by rivers or eroded from the shores affect the light transmission of the water. Adjacent land masses also influence the climate of aquatic habitats by their partial control of the prevailing winds and by cooling the air in winter and heating it in summer.

RELATION OF COMMUNITIES TO THE PHYSICAL FACTORS OF THEIR HABITATS

Very accurate quantitative measurements can be made of certain physical factors of habitats, both in terrestrial and in aquatic situations. For example, air and water temperature, precipitation, air humidity, water salinity, wind movement, evaporating power of the air, light intensity, and many other factors can be measured very precisely. On the other hand, numerous factors, such as soil humus or the materials suspended in water, can be evaluated only in rough terms that the ecologist has not as yet been able to make precise.

It is seldom possible to estimate the exact effect of the various intensities of even those physical factors of the habitat that can be measured precisely on the activities and success of each of the several kinds of organisms that make up a given community. Far too little is yet known about the relations between organisms and their environments to enable one to predict how any individual is going to react to any particular combination of physical factors (Daubenmire, 1947). The range of physical factors under which any particular species can exist is not definitely known. With the present meager information it is, therefore, usually impossible to ascertain in more than a general way how the innumerable possible combinations of these physical factors may affect the characters of any community.

The community ecologist, therefore, would be wise not to spend too much time in taking very precise measurements of the temperature, humidity, wind movement, soil moisture, salt concentration, and other physical factors of the habitat in every community that he encounters. Each of the physical factors of the habitat undoubtedly plays an important role in controlling the associated community. Until more is known about the physiologic responses of individual organisms and of diverse species to the constantly fluctuating conditions of their environments, however, much of the detailed instrumental data cannot be interpreted. There is great need for detailed studies of the responses of every species to the fluctuations in the more important physical factors of the environment.

SELECTED REFERENCES

Braun-Blanquet, J., George D. Fuller, and Henry S. Conard. 1932. Plant sociology: the study of plant communities. New York and London: McGraw-Hill Book Co. Chaps. 5 to 10.

Chapman, Royal N. 1931. Animal ecology. New York and London: McGraw-Hill Book Co. Chaps. 2 to 6.

Daubenmire, Rexford F. 1947. Plants and environment: a textbook of plant autecology. New York: John Wiley and Sons.

Kittredge, Joseph. 1948. Forest influences. New York, Toronto, and London: McGraw-Hill Book Co.

Lutz, Harold J., and Robert F. Chandler, Jr. 1946. Forest soils. New York: John Wiley and Sons.

Sverdrup, H. U., Martin W. Johnson, and Richard H. Fleming. 1942. The oceans: their physics, chemistry, and general biology. New York: Prentice-Hall. Chaps. 3, 6, and 8.

Weaver, J. E., and Frederic E. Clements. 1938. Plant ecology. 2d ed.; New York: McGraw-Hill Book Co. Chaps. 11 to 16.

Welch, Paul S. 1935. Limnology. New York: McGraw-Hill Book Co. Chaps. 3 to 5.

Yearbook United States Dept. Agric., 1938. Soils and men. Parts 4 and 5.

Yearbook United States Dept. Agric., 1941. Climate and men. Parts 4 and 5.

VI

EFFECTS ON COMMUNITIES OF FLUCTUATIONS IN THE PHYSICAL CONDITIONS OF THEIR HABITATS

Every community is affected directly or indirectly by the changes that are constantly taking place in the physical factors of its habitat. The activity of every organism is to a large extent controlled by the daily alternation of night and day, by the progression of the seasons, and by changes in the weather. At night, for example, photosynthesis stops and diurnal animals become quiescent. During darkness, conversely, the nocturnal animals are active, and the blossoms of certain plants open. In winter many plants and animals become dormant and the annuals die. From year to year many communities also vary because of fluctuations in sunshine, temperature, precipitation, and other habitat factors. The whole character of most communities, therefore, changes from day to night, from season to season, and often also from year to year.

Fluctuations occur constantly in nearly all the physical factors of both terrestrial and aquatic habitats and may sometimes be very great. Temperature, humidity, light, wind movement, and barometric pressure all vary from hour to hour. In exposed situations, for example, the light intensity may change during the course of a 24-hour day from intense sunlight to nearly complete darkness. Likewise, the temperature in certain habitats may vary by 60° F. or more during a period of 24 hours. The several physical factors acting in a given habitat, furthermore, often change independently of one another, so that new combinations of these factors continually arise.

The fluctuations in the physical factors of the habitat may recur in a regular rhythm or may be more or less irregular. The distinction between regular and irregular fluctuations is not always sharply marked. In certain parts of the world, for example, a fall of snow is a very unusual occurrence, but in other regions snow falls every winter. Even in a given region the regularity of occurrence of certain phenomena may vary from time to time. Thus, in southern Michigan a thunderstorm in winter is a rare event, but in summer one or more of these storms may be expected nearly every week.

RHYTHMIC CHANGES IN THE HABITAT

Recurrent cycles of certain combinations of physical factors are character-istic of most habitats. The 2 cycles in physical factors which are most impor-tant for nearly all communities have periodicities of 24 hours and 12 months, respectively. A lunar rhythm of a little over 29 days is also of significance in many marine communities.

DAILY RHYTHMS. The rotation of the earth on its axis produces in most habitats a daily cycle of daylight and darkness, which often is accompanied by temperature and humidity cycles also. Only in the extreme polar regions, in caves, and in the abysses of the oceans and of deep lakes is this daily cycle unimportant or absent.

The daily alternation of daylight and darkness controls the activi-ties of many organisms. Green plants are able to manufacture food only during the hours when the sun shines. The flowers of many species of plants are open only at particular hours of the day or night. Some animals also have a 24-hour rhythm of activity that can be changed only with difficulty. Others seem not to have such a rhythm at all, but exhibit short irregular periods of activity alternating with periods of rest throughout the day and night. The shrews and moles, for example, may be active at short intervals any time during the whole 24 hours. The daily rhythms of activity exhibited by animals have been well summarized by Calhoun (1944-46).

INTRADIEL PHASES. The term "diel" may be used to designate the 24-hour period of day and night (J. R. Carpenter, 1934, 1935, 1939). The group of organisms present and active in a community at any particular time of day may then be called an intradiel phase. Carpenter listed the intradiel phases as auroral, diurnal, vesperal, and nocturnal. These pertain, respectively, to dawn, full daylight, dusk of evening, and night. Animals that are mem-bers of both the auroral and vesperal intradiel phases are said to be crepus-cular in habit.

The activity of many kinds of animals is controlled by the light intensity. Blair (1943a) has shown this to be true, for instance, for the deermouse (*Peromyscus maniculatus*). This animal is so sensitive to light that it tends to avoid even the intensity provided by the full moon. Other environmental factors, especially temperature, also affect animal activity. Park, Barden, and Williams (1940) suggested that relative humidity, in addition to temperature and light, may affect the daily periodicity of animals. The daily activity of the cotton rat (*Sigmodon hispidus*) and of the prairie vole (*Microtus ochro-gaster*) is controlled not only by light intensity, but also by temperature, relative abundance of food, breeding activity, age, population density, and other factors (Calhoun, 1945). The diurnal movements of certain aquatic organisms are controlled by light intensity, temperature, intensity of wave action, and perhaps by other factors (Dice, 1914).

Those organisms that together constitute a particular intradiel phase often have special adaptations for one another. Thus, certain flowers open only during the hours when the particular insects that pollinate them are active. Those predators, such as the owls, that prey upon nocturnal mammals have special adaptations of vision and of hearing to enable them to capture their prey at night. The rattlesnake, which in the warm season of the year is often nocturnal, has special sense organs (pits) for detecting the proximity of birds or mammals through the heat given off by their bodies.

LUNAR RHYTHMS. Lunar rhythms are especially evident in those littoral marine communities which are subject to the effects of the tides. Marine organisms that live in situations subject to tidal action must adjust their activity to conform to the tides. Thus, the animals living in the intertidal zone are usually active when covered by the tide, but may be inactive when they are exposed by its ebb.

A lunar rhythm appears also in the time of reproduction of certain marine animals. For example, in Holland the swarming of the larvae of the oyster (*Ostrea edulis*) reaches its maximum about 10 days after the full or new moon. The evidence indicates that the spawning of this species reaches its maximum at about the time of the spring tides (Korringa, 1947). Many other mollusks, fishes, and annelids have breeding seasons related to the phases of the moon. It seems likely, however, that in all these relationships the influence of the moon is exerted through the tides rather than through its reflected light.

SEASONAL RHYTHMS. The annual revolution of the earth in its orbit around the sun produces the ecologically important progression of the seasons. Seasonal rhythms are most conspicuous in the plants and animals of the temperate and frigid zones. The temperature of the habitat in those zones is an especially important factor in determining the time at which plants flower and animals breed.

Variations in the physical habitat produced by the progression of the seasons cause an important sequence of changes in the composition and structure of practically every community, often resulting in a succession of aspects. In certain parts of the tropics the seasonal changes are very slight, but in most parts of the world seasonal variations in the characters of communities are profound.

The most obvious seasonal change in the temperate zones is the presence of an abundance of succulent green vegetation in summer and its general absence in winter. Even in the cold-temperate zones, however, many conifers and other plants are evergreen. In the colder parts of the world the ground may be solidly frozen to a considerable depth during winter. At that season the surface of the ground may also be covered with snow, which forms a surface very different in color and in other characters from the soil surface in summer. The water of the lakes and streams in these cold regions is frozen in winter, at least on the surface. The covering of ice seriously affects the lives of all aquatic plants and animals.

Seasonal rhythms occur also in many parts of the Tropical Zone, even in places where there is no pronounced seasonal variation in temperature. Alternations in the amount of rainfall, in the direction and strength of the prevailing winds, in the amount of cloudiness, and in other meteorological factors may in such situations produce seasonal rhythms of abundance in various types of organisms. In certain parts of the tropics, for example, the arrival of the rainy season stimulates growth of plants and initiates the reproductive cycle of such animals as the amphibians.

The reproduction of both plants and animals is confined in many parts of the world to the warmer seasons of the year. Great seasonal fluctuations accordingly take place in the population densities of many species, especially of those forms that live less than a year. Many plants and also many invertebrates exist during winter in forms different from those which they assume in summer. Annual plants, for instance, usually pass the winter as seeds, and certain invertebrates have winter stages to carry them over the cold season. The various kinds of plants, moreover, produce their flowers and fruits at diverse seasons; some in early spring, some in summer, and some not until fall.

Certain animals also vary in their life-history stages in successive seasons. The insects and other invertebrates are particularly subject to fluctuations in abundance and in life-history stage from season to season.

The changes that take place in the composition of a particular community during the growing season may be very considerable. For instance, certain open fields studied by Pickwell (1931: 114) near Evanston, Illinois, were utilized by the horned lark for breeding during March and April. With the vernal growth of the vegetation these situations had become suitable in May for the breeding of the vesper sparrow. With the continued growth of the vegetation the habitat had by June become unfavorable for both the horned lark and the vesper sparrow, and they had gone elsewhere. In their place the dickcissel was breeding in considerable numbers.

PHYSIOLOGIC RHYTHMS. Many of the daily and seasonal cycles of activity of plants and animals are in part produced by physiologic rhythms which operate within each organism concerned (Shelford, 1918: 147). Thus, many organisms have internal physiologic rhythms corresponding to the 24-hour cycle of daylight and darkness. Man has such a rhythm, which is in part independent of the actual daily light cycle. Proof of the existence of this internal 24-hour rhythm is given by the fact that man does not find it difficult to adjust to a daily period of activity in which he sleeps during part of the daylight hours and works or plays during part of the night, but adjusts with much difficulty to any longer or shorter period than 24 hours.

Similar physiologic rhythms presumably produce the seasonal periods of activity of many organisms and also control at least in part such cyclic processes as molt and reproduction. Thus, for those migratory birds that spend the winter in the tropics, the initial stimulus to migrate northward in the spring and to prepare for breeding can hardly be received from the immediate environment. On the contrary, it seems certain that these animals must have some internal physiologic rhythm which initiates the annual reproductive cycle. Good evidence for such a rhythm is contained in the study by Blanchard (1941) of the reproductive cycle of the white-crowned sparrows of the Pacific seaboard.

The presence of a physiologic rhythm in any given species does not in any way diminish the importance of the environmental factors in controlling the exact time of reproduction or of other activities. During unfavorable weather the expression of a physiologic rhythm may be delayed for a time, or in especially favorable weather the time of breeding may equally well be accelerated. Periodicities of reproduction and of other activities, therefore, often seem to be due to the operation of an innate physiological rhythm, the expression of which is controlled in part by regular or irregular fluctuations in the environmental factors.

The amount of control that the physical factors of the environment can exert over a physiologic rhythm, however, is usually decidedly limited. In very few, if any, species do the physiologic activities seem to be entirely under the control of the environment. Variations in the normal rhythm of the environment may speed up or slow down the time of appearance of various rhythmical types of physiologic activities, such as sleep, dormancy, migration, feeding, and reproduction, but only to a limited extent. In no case can the environment induce a physiologic response by an organism unless the tendency to that type of response is already potential in the individual. One may then think of fluctuations in the physical environment as affecting to some degree the time of appearance of the physiologic activities, but not as being in complete control.

The several physiologic rhythms which most organisms possess are in general adapted to the cycles in physical factors that regularly occur in their habitats. In the North Temperate Zone, for example, the time when plants come into leaf and into flower is attuned to the arrival of spring or summer. The science of the correlation of season and weather with the time of appearance of the various life-history sequences of organisms is called phenology. Certain phenological data have been summarized for North America by Hopkins (1938).

PHOTOPERIODISM. Often a physiologic rhythm in a given kind of organism is initiated by a change in some physical factor of the environment. A change in the length of day, for example, has been discovered to be related to the growth and to the production of flowers and fruit by many kinds of plants (Garner and Allard, 1920; Garner, 1936). Certain fall-flowering plants, such as the chrysanthemum, come into flower only when the days become shorter in fall following the longer days of summer. Advantage may be taken of this fact to produce the flowers of such species earlier than usual by artificially lengthening and then shortening the number of hours of light to which the individual plants are exposed. The reproductive season, migration, and other physiologic processes of certain animals also are controlled at least in part by the length of day (Rowan, 1926; Bissonette, 1938; Blanchard, 1941). Organisms of which the seasonal activities are in part controlled by length of day are said to be photoperiodotropic.

Rhythmic changes in other physical factors of the environment in addition to light almost certainly affect the physiologic processes of many kinds of organisms. Thus, for example, seasonal changes in temperature undoubtedly affect the breeding season, time of molt, time of migration (Southern, 1938), rate of growth, and other features of the life cycle of many animals. This is a field, however, which has as yet been very imperfectly explored.

EFFECT OF SNOW COVER. As an example of the effect on the community of a seasonal environmental factor, the influence of a snow cover in winter may be mentioned. The important ecologic effects of a snow cover have been well discussed by Formozov (1939, 1946). Many mammals and birds burrow into the snow and thus escape the cold wind and the more extreme temperatures above the snow. The snow also is eaten to provide drinking water. A few forms of animals visit snow fields in summer to escape bloodsucking insects. On the other hand, snow impedes the locomotion of most mammals and birds, it hides many types of food, and it makes feeding on some kinds of food difficult or impossible.

Special adaptations for life in snowy regions have been evolved by many species of both mammals and birds. These adaptations include for various forms a protective white coloration, structures for walking on the snow, and structures and habits for burrowing into the snow both for protection and to secure food. Should a crust form on the snow through a fall of freezing rain or from some other cause while the animals are burrowed beneath the surface, they may be unable to force their way out and may perish. Such conditions sometimes produce widespread mortality in the ptarmigan and other northern species of birds. Species that are not adapted for life in the snow must either hibernate or migrate southward in winter; otherwise they will be excluded from living in those areas where snow covers the ground at any time.

A cover of snow also forms a protection against temperature changes or frost heaving that might injure plants. If, in any winter, the snow covering in a northern region is slight or absent, severe injury to certain kinds of plants may result. The melting snow also is an important source of soil moisture. In some regions a considerable proportion of the annual precipitation falls as snow.

IRREGULAR CHANGES IN THE HABITAT

In addition to the regular cycles of alternation in the physical habitat from day to night and from season to season, there are irregular changes that are of much significance to every community.

FLUCTUATIONS IN WEATHER. Among the types of irregular variation that occur in the physical habitat, the changes in weather are of most widespread importance, especially for terrestrial communities.

In a few parts of the world the weather is rather uniform from day to day. In other parts of the earth, especially in the cyclonic belts, there may be frequent changes. During these changes in weather there may be rapid alternation from warm to cold temperatures, from clear to cloudy skies, from dry to moist air, from absence of rain to heavy precipitation, from still air to strong winds, and in winter from bare ground to a cover of snow. Correlated with these variations in the local weather the character of the surface soil may change from warm to cold and from dry to wet or the converse. Likewise, the concentration of the soil chemicals in solution may change greatly from day to day. Changes in the weather, therefore, directly and indirectly affect the activities and the lives of the plants and animals of every terrestrial community.

In aquatic habitats likewise the temperature of the water may fluctuate during a 24-hour period from warm to cold, the concentration of the various chemicals in solution may be considerably altered, and the amount of photosynthesis may be greatly increased or decreased.

Even temporary weather conditions may have a very considerable effect on the activities of plants, both in terrestrial and in aquatic communities. On cloudy days photosynthesis by plants is reduced, and the plants accordingly do not grow so much as on sunny days.

The character of the weather also affects the activities of animals. At the beginning of the breeding season for North American sunfishes, for example, bright sunshine induces nest building and other breeding activity, but when the sky becomes cloudy these activities cease (Breder, 1936: 3). On cold days the growth rate both of plants and of cold-blooded animals is necessarily slower than on warm days.

FLUCTUATIONS FROM YEAR TO YEAR. In addition to seasonal changes in weather, the earth is subject to fluctuations from year to year in the physical factors of its habitats. Very rarely are the same amplitude and sequence of weather variations experienced in any given habitat for 2 successive years. On the contrary, there are usually at least slight annual fluctuations in all factors. Sometimes these fluctuations, especially in the temperate zones, may cover a considerable amplitude. Alternations of wet and dry years and of hot and cool summers have occurred within the memory of most persons. Severe fluctuations in the climatic factors are especially characteristic of deserts. In the Mohave Desert of California, for example, the amount of annual precipitation is highly variable (Fig. 19).

CLIMATIC CYCLES. Many of the annual fluctuations in climatic factors occur more or less irregularly, but certain of them seem to fall into cycles covering periods of several years. A climatic cycle approximately 11 years in length and dependent upon the sunspot cycle has been postulated by many students. Still shorter cycles are sometimes reported. A cycle covering a 33-year period and even longer cycles are also sometimes suggested. There is as yet, however, no general agreement by meteorologists on the types of climatic cycles to be recognized nor on the length in years of each type. Neither is there agreement on the basic causes of climatic cycles. The climatic fluctuations of the earth are undoubtedly produced by the complex interaction between variations in the output of heat energy by the sun and variations in the ability of the earth to receive and retain this radiant heat, as well as by changes in the atmospheric and oceanic circulations on the earth (Huntington and Visher, 1922).

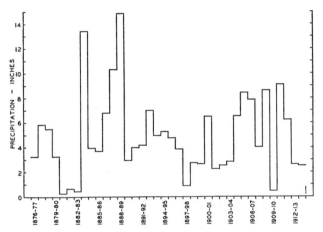

Fig. 19. Variability of annual precipitation at Mohave in the Mohave Desert of California from 1876 to 1913. (Data from the U. S. Weather Bur.)

The annual fluctuations in many animal populations are known to be irregular in the number of years that elapse between the peaks (Allee, 1943a). Also, a widespread population does not everywhere increase or decrease at the same time. A given species may be increasing in numbers in one part of North America and simultaneously decreasing in other parts of the continent (MacLulich, 1937; Chitty and Chitty, 1941). The hypothesis that the sunspot cycle is primarily responsible for cyclic variations in the numbers of animals has accordingly been abandoned by most biologists (Elton, 1942: 160).

The presence in Canada of 10-year, approximately parallel cycles of abundance in the muskrat, snowshoe hare, lynx, and New Brunswick salmon, nevertheless, affords strong evidence for the existence of a controlling climatic factor of some kind (Elton and Nicholson, 1942a, 1942b). The precise factor or factors responsible for these cycles have not yet been identified. Fluctuations from year to year in the numbers of the roseate spoonbill in southeastern North America also are sometimes synchronous in widely separated colonies, likewise suggesting some broad controlling climatic influence (R. P. Allen, 1942: 31-33).

Among the most important effects of year-to-year fluctuations of climate are those that result in the droughts that afflict considerable parts of the earth in certain years. A drought in the year 1925 in the southern Appalachian region of North America, for example, resulted in widespread damage to the forest. Many trees, especially those on shallow soils, were damaged or killed (Hursh and Haasis, 1931). Droughts are most noticeable in areas of normally scanty rainfall. The great drought from 1933 to about 1940 in middle North America wrought great changes in the vegetation and fauna as well as in the economic status of the human inhabitants. Certain species of pasture grasses were much reduced in abundance, while species that were better able to withstand xeric conditions increased (Weaver and Albertson, 1943). Drought years in the U.S.S.R. that lower the water levels of the lakes where flamingos breed cause the migration of many of these birds to near-by or to distant regions, where many of them perish because of their failure to find habitats suitable for their existence (Issakov and Formozov, 1946).

Variations in amount of rainfall from year to year particularly affect the communities of streams and fresh-water lakes and also the adjacent riparian communities. In years of scanty precipitation the streams are reduced and the smaller and less permanent ones may completely dry up. The lakes fed by these streams become reduced, their more shallow parts emerge, and even a whole lake may become dry land. Under these conditions all the aquatic communities become greatly altered. Many plants are injured or destroyed, and many animals are killed, exposed to predation, or forced to migrate to other areas.

Riparian communities usually are largely dependent upon soil moisture derived from adjacent streams or lakes. When the water level is lowered, the vegetation in these communities may be injured or killed and the environmental conditions so greatly altered that many of the animals also suffer. Thus, during a drought year in western Siberia the areas covered by the lakes became greatly reduced and the water birds suffered very severely (Formozov, 1934a and 1937). Likewise, during a series of drought years in Iowa the muskrat population suffered great reduction (Errington, 1939).

Years of more than usual precipitation produce equally striking changes in aquatic and in riparian communities. At such times the streams and the lakes overflow their normal banks and flood the adjacent areas. The floating vegetation and free-swimming animals suffer least from these alterations. Many of the attached plants, especially of the riparian communities, are killed or injured by the flooding, and many of the animals are drowned or driven from their homes. These displaced animals are particularly subject to predation. Many are killed also by unfavorable physical conditions in the neighboring habitats into which they migrate.

CATASTROPHIC CHANGES IN THE HABITAT

Certain variations in the physical habitat are more or less catastrophic in their occurrence. A severe windstorm, for example, may seriously damage the vegetation and injure or kill many animals in certain exposed communities. Floods likewise may be very destructive to low-lying communities. Landslides may locally produce serious damage to communities lying in their paths. A severe freeze may destroy certain kinds of organisms. A volcanic eruption may not only overwhelm the near-by communities, but may fill the upper atmosphere with dust and thereby reduce the amount of solar radiation received by the earth. Such a reduction in the receipt of solar energy may be sufficient to cause cool summers over the whole globe for several subsequent years. It is impossible to list here all the possible catastrophic changes that may affect a community, but it is obvious that every community is affected more or less frequently, sometimes only slightly but sometimes severely, by these vicissitudes of nature.

SOIL EROSION. The washing away or blowing away of the top layers of the soil usually has an especially serious effect on the characters of the community which occupies the habitat (E. H. Graham, 1944). Erosion occurs to some extent in all types of soil, but varies in amount, depending on the character of the soil, on the steepness of the slope, on its exposure to wind, on the character of the covering vegetation, on the type of rainfall, and on other factors. Erosion is likely to be especially severe during heavy rainstorms. When erosion is severe many individual organisms, both plants and terrestrial animals, may be washed away and lost to the community. The destruction of the surface soil may result in retrograde succession with the consequent establishment of a community lower in scale of organization than the one destroyed. Even where erosion is only mild, it may result in considerable alteration in the characters of the community concerned.

FIRE. Fire is one of the most frequent causes of catastrophic changes in communities. Fires may be light or severe. A severe fire may entirely destroy a community, so that it can be restored only through succession. Even a light surface fire, however, may do great damage to the more tender plants and to the ground-dwelling animals. Many fires are started either intentionally or accidentally by man. Lightning starts many forest fires. It is possible also that occasionally a fire may be started by the spontaneous combustion of decaying organic debris.

DIFFERENTIAL EFFECTS OF FLUCTUATIONS IN PHYSICAL FACTORS

The regular and irregular variations that constantly occur in the physical factors of the habitat may produce numerous diverse effects on each of the several kinds of animals and plants which compose any given community. In particular, the several member species respond differently to the daily cycle of light and darkness, to the progression of the seasons, and to the annual fluctuations in temperature, in precipitation, and in other physical factors. A wet year, for instance, may result in an increase in herbaceous vegetation and a consequent increase in large herbivorous mammals. At the same time the numbers of ground-nesting birds and burrowing mammals may decrease (Gabrielson, 1941: 102).

As a result of the fluctuations in the physical factors of the habitat, therefore, certain species may be increasing in abundance at the same time that other members of the same communities are decreasing. Certain species likewise may be increasing their rate of activity at the same time that other species are decreasing their activity or even tending to become dormant. The composition of every community consequently changes from moment to moment.

SELECTED REFERENCES

Calhoun, John B. 1944-46. Twenty-four hour periodicities in the animal kingdom. Journ. Tenn. Acad. Sci., 19: 179-200, 252-62; 20: 228-32, 291-308, 373-78; 21: 208-16, 281-82.
Shelford, Victor E. 1929. Laboratory and field ecology; the responses of animals as indicators of correct working methods. Baltimore: Williams and Wilkins Co.
Welch, Paul S. 1935. Limnology. New York: McGraw-Hill Book Co. Chaps. 6 to 13.

VII

FOOD RELATIONS WITHIN COMMUNITIES

Energy is expended by every organism in the process of living. Even when it is completely at rest or dormant, each organism requires energy for its metabolic and digestive processes. When an organism moves about, its use of energy is greatly increased. Reproduction also demands extra energy.

As the energy which supports each living organism is supplied by its food, every individual must be provided with an adequate source of food. The energy supplied to the individual organisms by food enables the community to exist.

PRIMARY SOURCE OF FOOD

The animal life of the earth is dependent, directly or indirectly, upon food produced by plants, which, in their turn, are dependent upon the energy received from the sun for their ability to produce food. All animals, with a few disputed exceptions, feed on plants or on other animals that have directly or indirectly derived their food from plants. The possible exceptions are certain chlorophyll-bearing 1-celled organisms, such as volvox, which zoologists classify as animals, though botanists consider them plants. Not all kinds of plants, however, contain chlorophyll. Many kinds obtain their food from other plants, either directly as plant parasites or indirectly as saprophytes.

CHLOROPHYLL. When chlorophyll is acted upon by sunlight under proper conditions of temperature in the presence of suitable concentrations of carbon dioxide, nitrogenous compounds, water, and certain other chemicals, free-living plants are able to synthesize certain food elements. The necessary carbon dioxide is obtained from the air. A few simple plants also obtain their nitrogen indirectly from the air. All the other necessary plant-food materials are obtained from the soil solution. Oxygen is a by-product of the process and is liberated.

At least one kind of diatom is able to synthesize food by using carotenoid pigments in addition to chlorophyll (Dutton and Manning, 1941), but so far as is now known most plants lack this ability. A few types of bacteria also are able without photosynthesis to build inorganic materials into food for their own use, but these types of bacteria are not important in most communities. It may be stated, therefore, that practically all life on the earth, both plant and animal, is dependent upon the activity of chlorophyll (Gabrielson, 1941: 6).

BASIC FOOD PLANTS. The basic food plants in terrestrial communities are the flowering plants, ferns, mosses, liverworts, and their allies. Most of these plants are of good size and some of them, such as certain kinds of trees, may be relatively enormous.

In aquatic communities the basic food plants usually are very small, most of them being single-celled, microscopic forms, such as diatoms and algae of various kinds. Certain kinds of marine algae, the seaweeds, are large, but these are mostly confined to the ocean margins and are not so largely fed upon by animals as are their microscopic relatives. Aquatic flowering plants of various kinds are also important producers of food, especially in fresh-water communities. Nevertheless, these aquatic flowering plants in the aggregate produce only a relatively small amount of food compared to the enormous productivity of the myriads of unicellular plants over the vast expanses of the oceans.

FOOD-PRODUCING STRATA. The production of food in the oceans by plants is confined in general to the upper 100 meters of water. The energy of the sun does not penetrate effectively much beyond that depth. Actually, the effectiveness of penetration by sunlight decreases rapidly below the surface, especially in water that contains any appreciable amount of suspended organic or inorganic materials. The whole life of the sea, therefore, is dependent upon the activity of the organisms that live in the upper strata (Coker, 1947: Chap. 14). The aquatic organisms that live in the deeper strata depend basically for their food on the remains of organisms that have sunk down from the upper strata or on organic debris washed in from the shores and adjacent land.

Terrestrial organisms also are dependent basically for their food on the photosynthetic activity of plants within a shallow stratum. The plants growing on a prairie or meadow, for example, seldom grow more than a few feet in height. Even a forest community performs photosynthesis for the most part in its upper stratum. Making allowance for the small amount of photosynthesis that takes place on the ground stratum under the shade of a forest, the total depth of the plant layers active in elaborating food is very small compared to the size of the earth. Yet it is within this thin layer that all the food of terrestrial communities is manufactured.

Classification of Organisms According to Food Source

Green plants manufacture their food directly from fairly simple chemical substances through photosynthesis. Chlorophyll-bearing plants that are not dependent on other green plants for their food are said to be free-living. A plant is considered free-living even if it secures some of its nitrogenous food elements through the help of nitrogen-fixing bacteria. A saprophyte is a plant that secures its food second hand from dead organic material. A plant-food parasite secures part or all of its nourishment from another living plant.

Animals that eat plants are herbivores, those that eat other animals are carnivores, and those that eat either plants or animals are omnivores. Carnivores or omnivores that attack and kill other living animals for food are predators, and the individuals they attack are their prey. Special terms are sometimes employed for animals that eat special kinds of food. An insectivore, for instance, is an animal that feeds mostly on insects. A scavenger is an animal that feeds on the dead bodies of animals that it has not itself killed. There are also numerous kinds of animal parasites that secure their food from other living animals (see Chap. XIII).

Food Chain

The food relationship of a series of plants, herbivores, carnivores, and other kinds of food-using organisms is often spoken of as a food chain (Elton, 1927: 68). One may define a food chain as a sequence of species within a community, each member of which serves as food for the species next higher in the chain.

In terrestrial communities certain food chains may be very simple. A herbivorous animal, for example, such as a bison, may be preyed upon directly by a large carnivore, such as a wolf. A wolf will seldom be eaten by any other carnivore and, if one ignores the wolf parasites, the food chain from plant to wolf could be composed of only 2 animal species and perhaps in some situations of only a single plant species. Another simple food chain is the one that leads from the plants through the herbivorous rabbit to the fox (Fig. 20).

FIG. 20. A simple food chain involving only 3 links.

Other food chains, on the contrary, may be very long and they may also be extremely complex. This is most likely to be true when the primary herbivore is an invertebrate. As a hypothetical case, an insect larva may feed on the green leaves of some herb or shrub. This larva is likely to be parasitized by some other insect, which, in turn, may be parasitized by still another insect. The final parasite, when it emerges as an adult, may happen to be caught and its juices sucked out by a spider. The spider will possibly be collected by a wasp to serve as food for its young. When the young wasp emerges it may be eaten by an insectivorous bird. The bird in its turn may fall a victim to a predaceous bird or mammal. This food chain, though imaginary, is not impossible. It is probable that many food chains actually contain a greater number of steps between plant food and ultimate large carnivore than does this hypothetical chain.

Food chains, in fact, often are extremely complex, principally because many predaceous animals are very adaptable in regard to the kinds of food species they prey upon. A predaceous form which feeds on 1 species of

animal may, in some other stage of its life history or in certain special conditions, find itself preyed upon directly or indirectly by its erstwhile prey
species. Certain species vary also in their food requirements during successive stages of their life history. The sparrows, for instance, are mostly herbivorous when adult, but insectivorous in their nesting stage. Within any
given community the food relations of the several associated species of animals may accordingly be extremely involved.

Many attempts have been made (see Woodbury, 1933: 232) to illustrate graphically the interrelations of the various organisms within a community in regard to food. The food relationships within most communities,
however, are much too complex and too greatly subject to change with
season, stage in life history, and other factors to be classified or illustrated in
any simple manner.

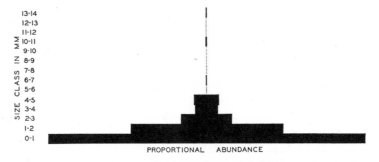

FIG. 21. Pyramid of numbers of the invertebrates inhabiting the forest floor in the
rain forest on Barro Colorado Island, Panama. Proportional numbers in the several size
classes. (Redrawn from Williams, 1941, by permission of the Chicago Academy of Sciences.)

PYRAMID OF NUMBERS. Because all animals derive their food ultimately
from plants, it is obvious that plants must in general be more numerous
than herbivores and that herbivores must generally be more numerous than
carnivores. Each herbivore may consume every day a considerable number
of small plants. Each carnivore likewise may consume during its life a considerable number of herbivores (Elton, 1927: 69).

This relationship between the numbers of organisms and their position
in the food chains of the community has been called the pyramid of numbers (Fig. 21). The pyramid of numbers is especially evident in aquatic
communities, where the basic producers of food are mostly 1-celled plants.
In terrestrial communities, on the contrary, it often happens that certain
herbivores are actually smaller and more numerous than the plants upon
which they feed. This is true, for example, of most of the herbivorous insects. The numerical relations of the organisms in a food chain or in a
series of parallel food chains, therefore, may not always form a pyramid.

Those species of animals that are small in body size usually occur in
greater numbers than species of larger size (E. C. Williams, 1941: 109). Size

alone, nevertheless, is not a criterion of the position of an animal in a food chain. Some herbivorous ungulates, for example, are many times larger than certain invertebrate carnivores. Parasites are often very much smaller and more numerous than their hosts. Also, some kinds of animals that operate in social groups, such as ants and wolves, are able to overcome and to feed upon prey much larger than themselves. In view of these variations in the relations between the relative sizes and numbers of predators and their prey, it is evident that the concept of a pyramid of numbers is not always fully applicable in natural communities.

Circulation of Matter

The food cycle in a community is not complete when the food materials elaborated by a green plant have been transformed into the flesh of a large carnivore. Each individual plant and each animal ultimately must die. When an organism dies from any cause, its tissues are then utilized by other forms of life. Scavengers of various kinds, including the bacteria and fungi, ultimately consume every bit of dead organic material. Nothing goes to waste. Furthermore, the nitrogenous wastes and the feces of most animals contain a considerable amount of food material that is utilized by the lower forms of life. Certain of the organic chemicals which result from the decomposition of plant and animal tissues become important elements of food for green plants.

The passage of food materials from link to link in the various food chains, the re-use of dead organic material, and the ultimate incorporation again of the decomposed organic compounds into the stream of life may be called the circulation of matter (Lotka, 1925: 209; Thomson and Geddes, 1931: 107). The amount of re-use of dead organic material is astounding. The debris on the floor of a forest is passed and repassed through the alimentary tract of many successive kinds of small animals (Eaton and Chandler, 1942), and the last possible calorie of energy is extracted.

In aquatic communities many kinds of fishes and of invertebrates are bottom feeders which pick up mud and ooze and pass it through their digestive tracts. Very little energy can be left in some of this bottom material, but nevertheless many kinds of animals live wholly upon it. In the abysses of the oceans green plants are absent because of the lack of sunlight. All the nourishment available in these depths must sink from the surface waters in the form of organic debris. There is a steady rain from the surface stratum of the dead bodies of plants and animals, most of them microscopic in size. The remains of organisms that grow along the ocean shores are distributed widely by waves and currents and serve as food for many bottom-dwelling animals (Petersen and Jensen, 1911; P. B. Jensen, 1915).

When organic material has been reduced to a state in which it no longer can serve as food for animals, it may retain sufficient energy to support a host of bacteria, molds, and other microorganisms. After these microorganisms have extracted all possible energy from a given bit of organic material, the residual chemical compounds may serve as food for green plants. The circulation of matter, therefore, is a cycle that leads from raw chemical compounds, through a sequence of green plants, animals, and microorganisms, back to the same simple compounds (Fig. 22).

The constant transformation, through the activities of microorganisms, of organic debris into nutrient elements needed for plant life is essential

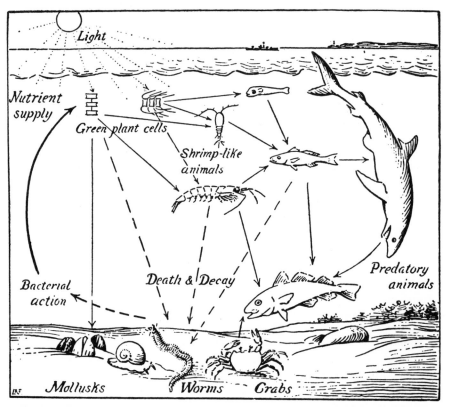

FIG. 22. Circulation of matter in a marine community. (Reprinted from a chapter on sea life by G. L. Clarke, 1943, in *Science from Shipboard;* by permission of Science Service.)

for the continued existence of life on the earth. Carbon is made available as carbon dioxide, nitrogen as ammonia, phosphorus as phosphate, sulfur as sulfate, and so on. If it were not for the continual activities of microorganisms, the limited supplies of these essential chemicals on the earth would soon become locked up in living and dead organisms and in various derived compounds, and no further production of living beings would be possible (Waksman, 1945: 341).

CARBON CYCLE. The carbon cycle (Fig. 23) well illustrates the circulation of matter and also demonstrates the close relationship that exists among the several kinds of organisms which make up each ecologic community. The sugar produced by photosynthesis may be used by the plant to build up its own tissues through growth or it may be stored in a form such as starch or fat. Herbivores devour the plant tissues and utilize the stored sugars, starches, and other foods as the source of their energy. In the animal body carbohydrates obtained from the plants are in part oxidized and thereby their energy is released. In this process oxygen is absorbed from the atmosphere, from the surrounding water, or from the organism itself, and carbon dioxide is liberated. Thus, the carbon cycle typically involves both animals and plants. Those plants that do not contain chlorophyll are unable to synthesize their own food, but are dependent directly or indirectly upon the food elaborated by green plants. In the carbon cycle the fungi and similar kinds of plants occupy, therefore, much the same position as the animals.

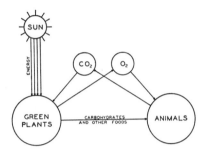

Fig. 23. The most essential parts of the carbon cycle through green plants and animals.

NITROGEN CYCLE. The role of nitrogen in the circulation of matter is of particular significance for living beings (Fig. 24). Nitrogen is of fundamental importance to all organisms because protein, which is essential for all living cells, is made up in part of this element. Although nitrogen is present in abundance in the air and occurs in solution in water, it cannot be utilized directly by most plants. A few types of bacteria that grow in the soil and a number of blue-green algae are able to take nitrogen directly from the air and transform it into compounds usable by other plants (Daubenmire, 1947: 35).

Many of the legumes, such as beans, clovers, and peas, obtain nitrogen through a symbiotic relationship with particular kinds of nitrogen-fixing bacteria that grow in nodules on their roots. The legumes play an especially valuable role in nitrogen fixation in the poorer soils, where the nitrogen supply tends to be low. On such soils a crop of a legume, aided by its symbiotic nitrogen-fixing bacteria, may add as much as 400 pounds of nitrogen per acre per year to the ecosystem (Waksman, 1927: 523). The nitrogen-fixing bacteria, therefore, constitute a most important link in the nitrogen cycle (Waksman, 1945: 341).

Most plants, other than the nitrogen-fixing bacteria and the legumes, are dependent for their source of nitrogen on animal excretions or on the compounds produced by the decomposition of plant and animal bodies.

Only small quantities of ammonia and other nitrogenous compounds usable by plants are produced by inorganic agencies.

The actual chemical processes involved in the nitrogen cycle are very complex (Lotka, 1925: 229-45; Sverdrup, Johnson, and Fleming, 1942: 913-16). Only rather simple nitrogenous compounds can be utilized by plants. The complex proteins that make up the bodies of plants and animals and also those that occur in animal excretions must consequently be broken down before they can be utilized. The decomposition of these complex compounds occurs in a series of steps controlled in large measure by the activities of bacteria. In the first stages of protein decomposition amino acids and ammonia are among the products which are formed. These compounds may in part be utilized directly by plants, but for the most part they are still further changed by bacterial action. Ammonia is changed to nitrites by the action of certain kinds of bacteria. Nitrates are formed from the

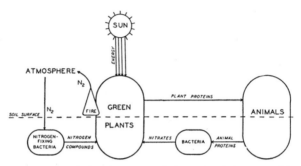

FIG. 24. Part of the nitrogen cycle in terrestrial communities.

nitrites by the action of still other bacteria. The nitrates can be utilized directly by green plants. Certain nitrate-reducing bacteria are able to reverse the process and to convert nitrates to nitrites. Denitrifying bacteria may carry the process a step further and reduce the nitrites, with the consequent liberation of free nitrogen. The liberation of nitrogen to the atmosphere, of course, constitutes a loss from the nitrogen cycle. In most situations the denitrifying process seems fortunately to be of minor significance and the main trend of the nitrogen cycle is toward the use over and over again of the supply of fixed nitrogen present in the ecosystem.

The important thing about the nitrogen cycle from the viewpoint of the community is that in suitable habitats there tends to be an accumulation of nitrogenous compounds in forms available for the use of plants, and that this in turn results in an enrichment of the whole community. The general scarcity of available nitrogen in pioneer communities is undoubtedly one of the reasons why such communities usually consist of only a few unusually adaptable species.

OTHER CYCLES OF MATTER. Cycles of matter similar to those described above for carbon and for nitrogen operate for water, phosphorus, chlorine, sodium, potassium, and other chemicals (Lotka, 1925). Many of these chemicals have direct relationships to the production or to the assimilation of food by plants and animals.

QUANTITY OF FOOD IN THE ECOSYSTEM

In recent years much attention has been given to the ascertainment of the kinds and amounts of foods available in certain ecosystems. Such an ascertainment is not only of value to the theoretical ecologist, but is of particular importance to such practical ecologists as range managers, wildlife managers, and aquatic biologists.

Measures of Available Food

Any precise consideration of the food relations within an ecosystem must include a measurement of the kinds and amounts of food which are present at each season. Special attention must be given to the fluctuations in the kinds and amounts of food available. Dissimilar kinds of organisms, of course, require dissimilar kinds and amounts of food. Often the requirements of a given individual may vary with age, with life-history stage, and with season. The food requirements for plants are very different from those of most animals. Accordingly, there must often be separate measurements of the foods available in the ecosystem at each season of the year for each age class and sex of each species under consideration.

AN EARLY STUDY. A pioneer study of the bird food available on and in the surface soil of a terrestrial ecosystem was made by McAtee (1907). This study included the counting in November and in March of the invertebrates, including adults, larvae, cocoons, and eggs, and of the plant seeds. The area studied was a plot covering 4 square feet, near Washington, D. C. An interesting result of the study was the finding of a number of dead but apparently uninjured insects, indicating that not all the insect food available was being utilized by insectivorous animals.

PLANT FOODS. The food of free-living plants is in general fairly simple inorganic and organic material. The concentration of most of the necessary chemicals in the water or soil can be measured with considerable accuracy. All the chemicals, however, that are essential for the growth of each kind of plant are not yet known. Recent studies indicate that many free-living plants thrive best if they are provided with small quantities of certain trace elements and with certain complex chemical compounds, some of which may be called vitamins. Additional studies are needed to identify all the chemicals which are required by plants for food and to determine the quantities of each compound necessary for each kind of plant at its various stages of growth and in each of the seasons of the year.

CLIP QUADRATS. Herbage suitable for consumption by animals usually is spoken of as forage. One method of estimating the amount of forage available in a given ecosystem is to clip the edible parts of the plants from

sample plots of measured size, dry the food samples in air at room temperature, and then weigh them. The weight of air-dry forage per unit area may
then be calculated (Schwan and Swift, 1941). Sample quadrats from which
the vegetation has been cut near the surface of the ground and completely
removed are called clip quadrats.

The available forage of each species of plant, or of each group of closely
related species, must be calculated separately because the food values of the
several food species may vary. The several species of herbivores also may
vary in their food preferences and in their ability to utilize certain foods.
For instance, sheep utilize a somewhat different kind of forage from that
preferred by deer.

The time of year when the vegetation is to be clipped to secure an estimate of the available forage has not been fully agreed upon, nor is there
yet any standard practice for the number of times per year clipping is to be
done. It is obvious that the forage available will not vary much from time
to time during winter, nor at other seasons when there is no active growth.
On the other hand, the amount of certain kinds of food available will be
much greater when shrubs and trees are in leaf than when they expose only
bare twigs. Also, green herbage is usually more suitable for food than dried
grass and weeds. Furthermore, growing plants when carrying fruits or seeds
are often much richer in food value than they are earlier in the season.

Clipping of the forage of some kinds of plants early in the season before
they have produced their seeds induces further growth; consequently, the
total production of certain kinds of food may be increased. This is taken
advantage of by farmers to secure several cuttings of hay from a field each
season. Natural grazing or browsing must often have the same effect. Too
early or too frequent clipping, however, may injure certain kinds of plants
and decrease their productiveness or may even kill them (Sampson, 1914).
Clip quadrats, while they are of great value for the estimation of the
amounts of food available, do not fully simulate grazing conditions, and
proper allowance for this weakness must be made (Culley, Campbell, and
Canfield, 1933).

ESTIMATES OF FORAGE. Actual measurement of the forage available on
particular areas is often impracticable, either because the resulting damage
to the vegetation would interfere with long-continued studies or because
of the great labor required for extensive sampling. For practical range management sufficiently accurate estimates of available forage may sometimes
be made by the careful scrutiny of well-trained observers working on sample
plots. The observers must have been previously trained on other plots in
the same general region by measuring, clipping, and weighing the forage
from individuals of the species concerned (Pechanec and Pickford, 1937a,
1937b).

SEEDS AND FRUITS. The quantities of fruits, seeds, or grains available for
the food of animals at any given time may be estimated by harvesting the

crop on sample areas and measuring or weighing the materials obtained. By harvesting each species of plant separately the quantity of each kind of food may be calculated. Furthermore, it is possible by this method to collect and to measure the quantity of seeds or of dried fruits available during each month of winter (Baumgras, 1943). Measures of the seeds that have fallen to the ground and of roots, bulbs, tubers, and other plant materials in the ground can be obtained by sifting the surface soil from sample plots (Dalke, 1935b). Such work is of necessity laborious. A method for estimating water-fowl foods in aquatic habitats has been developed by Low and Bellrose (1944).

A rapid method developed by Bishop and Skinner (1946) for estimating the quantities of seeds produced by certain weeds may prove to be widely applicable. By this method the number of fruiting stems of each species of plant concerned is counted on a series of sample plots and the average number of stems per plot computed. The average production of seeds per stem is also measured. A sufficient number of samples must be taken to secure reliable averages both of the number (or weight) of seeds per stem and of the number of stems per plot. The average production of seeds per plot may then be calculated.

OTHER SPECIAL FOODS. Measures of the quantity of insects and other invertebrates present in the soil may be made by the methods described in Chapter IV. The quantities of mammals, birds, insects, and other mobile animals available in particular communities as food for carnivores can likewise be calculated from counts taken in some standard manner on sample plots.

BIOMASS. The total quantity of living material present at a given moment at a particular situation is the biomass (Demoll, 1927: 462). Biomass usually is stated in weight per unit surface area of the habitat (Zenkevich, 1931: 2; Bogorov, 1934: 585), but volume or weight per unit volume is sometimes given instead. In calculating the biomass no allowance is made for the weight of the shells, skeletons, or other nonnutritious parts of the organisms concerned.

Calculations of biomass have in the past been confined mostly to plankton. A few estimates, however, have been made of the biomass of certain of the components of terrestrial communities. W. H. Brown (1919, Tables I and II), for example, has estimated the volume per unit area of certain trees in Philippine forests; Pickles (1937) has estimated the biomass of certain kinds of ants in a part of Yorkshire, England. E. C. Williams (1941: 108) has calculated the weight of invertebrates living on the floor of the rain forest on Barro Colorado Island, Panama; and Mohr (1940) has estimated the weights per unit area of the several kinds of mammals in Illinois.

STANDING CROP. The total quantity of a particular kind of organic material which is available at a given time and place constitutes the standing crop. This term differs from biomass in that it usually is applied only to the usable part of the individuals of 1 or of a few ecologically related species in the community. In forestry, for example, standing crop refers to the quantity of lumber or of other timber products available in a given stand of timber. In aquatic ecology the term may be applied to the total quantity of plankton existing per unit area at a given time and place (Pennak, 1946: 351) or to the quantity of 1 particular species only (G. L. Clarke, 1946: 324). One may also estimate the standing crop of such a species as a food fish of which only certain of the larger age classes are to be harvested. Standing crop refers only to the quantity of organic individuals or materials of a particular kind existing at a given instant and place and does not indicate the total productivity of a community per season or per year.

Water as a Food

Water is a most important food item for all organisms. Aquatic organisms, as a rule, have no difficulty in securing an abundant supply of water. In fact, special devices must be used by most fresh-water organisms to prevent the absorption of too much water. In highly saline waters, on the contrary, special precautions must be taken to prevent dehydration through osmosis into the surrounding medium. Terrestrial plants secure most of their needed water by absorption through their roots from the soil solution. Terrestrial animals secure water either directly by drinking or indirectly from their food.

Most animal foods, even those air dried in the desert, contain a certain amount of moisture. Succulent foods, such as green herbage, may contain a large percentage of water. Animals that feed on such succulent materials may not need any other water. Thus, E. L. Sumner (1935: 192) noted that during winter and spring the California Valley quail secure their necessary water from the green vegetation which they eat, but that during the dry summer months when succulent vegetation is not available they go several times a day to water holes to drink. Animal tissues contain a considerable amount of water, and therefore many flesh-eating animals are able to obtain all their necessary water from food.

Certain kinds of animals, notably the birds and the reptiles, may excrete uric acid rather than urea. This allows a reduction in the amount of water lost from the kidneys. Uric acid is not toxic when concentrated and requires, therefore, no water for its elimination, while urea must be dissolved in water.

The amount of water required for the maintenance of life varies greatly among the species of animals. It varies also with age, with life-history stage, and with numerous other factors. Many species that inhabit moist meadows, such as the voles (*Microtus*), require each day considerable quantities of water, most of which they secure from their succulent food (Dice, 1922). The raccoon, which usually lives near streams or lakes, also requires an abundance of water (Stuewer, 1943: 236). Many desert animals can exist for long periods of time without any other water than that obtained from their air-dry food.

METABOLIC WATER. A small amount of water is obtained by animals as a by-product of metabolism, through the oxidation of the hydrogen contained in their foods. By means of this chemical action protein foods may produce an amount of water equal to as much as 70 per cent of the dry weight of the food, and carbohydrates and fats may produce an amount of water equal to their dry weight or even greater (Babcock, 1912). In any estimate of the amounts of water available in a particular ecosystem, therefore, account must be taken of the metabolic water which may be obtained from the food.

Metabolic water is extremely important to the existence of the animals of many communities, especially of those in arid regions. Pocket mice and kangaroo rats, for example, are able by careful conservation of this metabolic water to live for several years in the laboratory on a diet composed solely of air-dry seeds, though they cannot be said to thrive on this diet. In nature, however, these rodents obtain some water also from succulent foods. No mammal, so far as is known, can exist indefinitely on dry food alone (Bailey, 1923).

Some insect larvae, as those of the clothes moths and the meal worms, are able to live and to grow on food which is completely air dry. These larvae, of course, are using not only metabolic water, but also the small amount of moisture held by their air-dry food. When meal worm larvae are kept in artificially dried air and fed on meal dried at 105° C., they lose weight and die, but when fed air-dry meal which contains approximately 12 per cent of moisture, they gain in weight and increase their total water content (Berger, 1907).

Variations in Available Food

The amount of any particular food available in a given ecosystem varies from time to time, depending on fluctuations in food production, deterioration, and utilization. Nearly all plants and animals have more or less fixed seasons for reproduction and growth. During the season of activity of each species there will be a rapid increment of the food materials that it produces. On the other hand, during its inactive season a species may produce little or no food.

SEASONAL VARIATIONS. The seasonal variations in community activity result in fluctuations not only in the amounts but also in the kinds of food available to animals. In cold climates, for instance, the green, lush vegetation of summer gives place in winter to much more barren conditions. Annual plants pass the winter, as a rule, only in the form of seeds. Many animals pass the winter as eggs or larvae. Other animals during winter are inactive in hibernation or have burrowed into the soil, where they are not available as food to passing carnivores. The maturation of seeds and fruits

at varying times of the growing season likewise produces considerable variation in the kinds of food available.

ANNUAL VARIATIONS. Variations from year to year in the kinds and
amounts of available food also are characteristic of many ecosystems. Thus,
in a relatively cold or relatively dry year the vegetation may grow much less
luxuriantly than in a moist and warm year. On some parts of the San
Joaquin Experimental Range in California, for example, it is estimated
that nearly twice as much forage is produced in some years as in others. A
still greater fluctuation in forage yield has been described for the southwestern part of the San Joaquin Valley between the very dry year 1934 and
the very rainy year 1935 (Talbot and Biswell, 1942: 32-33). It is estimated
that the production of herbage on certain experimental plots in that area
was approximately 193 times greater in 1935 than in 1934 (Talbot, Biswell,
and Hormay, 1939: 402).

Variations in Nutritive Value of Foods

The foods produced by plants nearly always pass through a cycle of changing nutritive values. Rapidly growing tender shoots and leaves may be more
edible, but perhaps contain fewer food values, in their early than in their
later stages of growth. As the seeds and fruits of a plant ripen, its nutritive
value may for a time increase very rapidly. Increasing evidence is accumu-
lating that the nutritive values of plants are in part dependent on the
quality of the soil on which they are grown. Plants grown under poor conditions, such as on relatively sterile soil, may be lacking not only in energy-
producing foods, but also in certain of the chemicals essential for animal
growth (Albrecht, 1944).

The nutritive values of many animals also vary from time to time, depending upon the proportion of the body that is composed of internal
skeleton, exoskeleton, scales, hair, feathers, and other largely indigestible
materials. The amount of fat accumulated in the animal body may likewise
greatly affect its food value. The fecundity of both males and females may
be reduced when animals are fed on plants grown on soils of poor quality.
The animals as well as the plants of a community, therefore, thrive best
when the soil of the habitat is highly fertile.

DETERIORATION OF FOOD. Many kinds of foods deteriorate slowly; others
deteriorate rapidly after they have been produced. Green and soft plant
tissues in time dry and harden. Certain plant tissues may retain their nutritive values when they are dry, but others become inedible. Fruits decay
rapidly or dry. Seeds become stale or, if they lie in moist soil, they may mold.
Although certain kinds of seeds may deteriorate rapidly, others may on the
contrary remain edible for years. Animal carcasses decay rapidly in warm
weather, but in cold weather they may remain usable, at least by certain
scavengers, for a long period of time.

Different parts of a food plant or a food animal may deteriorate in nutritive value at different times. Thus, the stems and leaves of a food plant may be growing tough and inedible at the same time that the fruits or seeds are increasing in food value.

Food Storage

Foods stored by plants and animals themselves often provide an important reserve supply, especially during seasons when food productivity is low. These stored foods may at certain seasons form a large proportion of the total food available in the ecosystem.

Plants store much food and water in their own tissues. These reserves enable many species to exist in an ecosystem which may be unfavorable for them during a certain season of the year. The food often is stored in the plant in the form of starch, but may also be conserved as sugar, fat, protein, or some other type of organic compound. Food may be stored in almost any part of the plant, but special storage structures, such as bulbs or tubers, often are developed. By drawing on their stored food, plants are able to make rapid growth or to produce their seeds or fruits quickly during a short growing season. Such biennials as carrots and beets store up food in their roots during one year and the following year are able quickly to produce an abundant crop of seeds.

Most animals carry a small reserve of stored food and water within their bodies. These reserves of food are most frequently in the form of fat, but carbohydrates, such as glycogen, are sometimes stored. In time of urgency even the proteins making up the body may be drawn upon. Several kinds of ants utilize certain specialized individuals, called "repletes," for the storage of food (Wheeler, 1910: 361-77). The abdomens of the repletes become greatly distended with a sweetish liquid, which they regurgitate when food is needed by the other members of the ant colony.

Many species of animals are able to survive unfavorable seasons by utilizing food which they themselves have previously stored outside their own bodies. The pikas (*Ochotona*) that live in the high mountains of western North America and in some parts of Asia, for example, during summer gather the stems, leaves, and flowers of a variety of plants and dry these in the sun to form hay. The hay is stored under the rocks in the talus-slope habitat of the animals and furnishes their winter food (A. H. Howell, 1924: 5). The tree squirrels also are notable for their storage of nuts, acorns, and other seeds (Cahalane, 1942).

KINDS AND AMOUNTS OF FOOD CONSUMED BY EACH SPECIES

The kinds of food consumed by each animal species within a particular ecosystem will depend upon its food preferences, its specialization for food type, and the kinds of food available to it. The amounts of food consumed by each species will depend upon its population density, upon its population structure according to age classes, sex ratio, and life-history stages, upon the size of the individuals, the degree of their activity, the relation of their body temperature to that of the surrounding air or water, the availability of suitable food, and the temperature and other environmental conditions in the habitat.

Specialization for Food Type

The kinds of animals vary greatly in their ability to utilize the various kinds of food that may be present in a given ecosystem. Some animals are omnivorous in their food habits and are able to eat and to digest a wide variety of foods. Other kinds of animals, on the contrary, are specialized to use only particular kinds of foods. Thus, a highly specialized carnivore, such as a cat, is well adapted for capturing living prey and for cutting up and digesting their bodies, but is unable properly to chew or to digest coarse plant foods. A specialized herbivore, such as a horse, can thrive on coarse herbage, but is not equipped to capture living animals or to digest flesh. Many animals have highly specialized adaptations for securing and for digesting particular kinds of food. Certain kinds of insects, for example, are able to feed on only 1 particular kind of plant. As an extreme specialization one strain within a single species of herbivorous insect may feed on 1 kind of plant, while another strain of the same species may be restricted to a very dissimilar food species (Brues, 1946, Chap. III).

The basis for the variations in the dietary needs of diverse kinds of animals lies in part in their varying ability to synthesize particular amino acids and vitamins. The ruminants, for example, are able to synthesize, with the help of their associated intestinal biota, most of the essential amino acids, the vitamins of the B-complex, and also vitamin K. Man and the other anthropoids, on the contrary, are unable to synthesize any of these substances or vitamin C, all of which, therefore, must be present in their food. Individuals of the same species of animal, furthermore, often vary in their dietary needs and accordingly they vary in their dependence upon certain classes of foods (Brody, 1945: 741-43).

SPECIALIZATION FOR SIZE OF FOOD. Almost all predaceous animals are to some degree specialized for using food animals falling within certain maximum and minimum size limits. Most predators feed on organisms smaller than themselves, sometimes much smaller. On the other hand, some predaceous animals attack and eat other animals that are larger than themselves. Each species of predator is especially adapted for capturing and devouring its prey which, in general, falls within a fairly well-circumscribed size class. In time of food shortage, however, prey of a size smaller or larger than usual may be utilized.

As an individual predator grows, the size of its food species also tends to become correspondingly larger. Very old predators or those weakened by disease or parasites, however, may not be able to subdue as large prey as younger and more vigorous individuals. They may, therefore, be forced to feed on prey which is smaller and weaker than the size of the individual predator would indicate.

Herbivores also are often especially adapted for food of certain sizes. Thus, those birds that have large beaks may be able to crack large seeds, while species with smaller beaks must confine their attention to smaller seeds.

ADAPTABILITY TO DIVERSE FOODS. Notwithstanding the food specializations which all animals exhibit to some degree, most species can utilize at least a small variety of food materials. Many kinds of animals, in fact, are able to thrive on a wide diversity of foods. The deermouse (*Peromyscus maniculatus*), for example, utilizes many kinds of seeds, nuts, fruits, buds, bark, succulent vegetation, insects, spiders, and other plant and animal materials. For many species a varied diet may promote health. The actual amount of adaptability in regard to food, however, varies greatly among the species of animals.

The ability to utilize a variety of food confers certain obvious advantages on an animal species. An adaptable species can occupy a diversity of habitats. During times of food scarcity it may be able to survive when other more specialized species starve.

A species, such as the horse, that is specialized in its food habits likewise has certain advantages. It has special structures and types of behavior for securing particular food and it has a specialized digestive apparatus for handling this food. It may, therefore, be able efficiently to secure and to digest types of food that could not be utilized by those species which have more generalized food habits.

VARIATIONS IN DIET. The diet of many kinds of animals varies considerably from season to season and often from year to year. This is due to variations in food preferences and in requirements at successive life-history stages, at successive ages, and at various seasons, but is especially governed by variations in the kinds of food available. The California quail, for example, feeds principally on green vegetation in the winter and spring (Fig. 25), but in summer and fall, when its food plants usually are dried up, it feeds for the most part on seeds (Glading, Biswell, and Smith, 1940). Only a relatively few kinds of animals subsist on a single kind of food which is available at all times in sufficient quantity for their needs.

Very striking changes in diet correlated with changes in life-history stages are exhibited by many kinds of animals. Young mammals are nourished by milk, a totally different kind of food from that used by most adults. Many birds feed their nestlings on a very different diet from that which the adults use. Changes in food habits with life-history stage are also conspicuous among those insects which have complete metamorphosis and among those invertebrates which have alternation of generations.

ASCERTAINMENT OF FOOD CONSUMPTION

DIRECT OBSERVATION. The food consumption of a few kinds of animals can be ascertained by direct observation in nature. By this method J. S. Dixon (1934: 108), for example, secured valuable information about the foods utilized by the mule deer in California. The food brought by parent birds

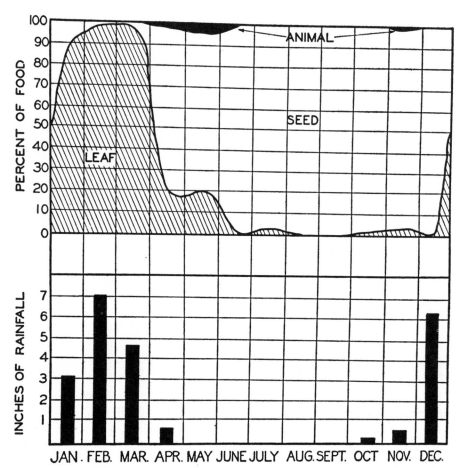

FIG. 25. Variation by months of the leaf, seed, and animal materials in the food of California Valley quail on the San Joaquin Experimental Range during 1937. Food is represented as percentage by bulk. (After Glading, Biswell, and Smith, 1940.)

to their young in the nest gives important clues to the kind of foods consumed by the species. Detailed information about the food of the catbird was thus obtained by Gabrielson (1913) through observations made from a blind. Due allowance, however, must be made for the fact that the young of many kinds of animals may be fed a different kind of food from that preferred by the adults.

Observations made in nature are almost the only practical method for ascertaining the foods of certain kinds of animals, as, for example, those that feed upon nectar or plant juices. The foods taken by many kinds of insect larvae also can best be ascertained by direct observation. Observations on the natural method of feeding, the feeding periodicity, and the other food habits of a given species are always essential to an understanding of its food niche in the community. Such information may often be best secured by direct observations.

FOLLOWING ANIMAL TRAILS. Authentic information about the feeding habits of certain animals may be obtained by following their trails in snow,

TABLE XI

MEASUREMENT OF FOOD PREFERENCE

Relative frequency of several species of plants in a given area compared to their relative frequency in piles of cuttings made by the prairie vole (data from Jameson, 1947, by permission of the Museum of Zoology, University of Kansas).

Plant Species	Relative Frequency	
	Growing in the Field	In Piles of Cuttings
Quack grass (*Agropyron repens*).........	.30	.13
Spear grass (*Poa annua*)...............	.01	.00
California brome (*Bromus carinatus*)......	.01	.04
Smooth brome (*Bromus inermis*).........	.01	.00
Alfalfa (*Medicago sativa*)...............	.25	.73
Peppergrass (*Lepidium densiflorum*).......	.02	.00
Cleavers (*Galium aparine*)..............	.15	.01
Wild lettuce (*Lactuca scariola*)..........	.25	.09
Total......................	1.00	1.00

sand, or mud. Adolph Murie (1936) has written a delightful account of the feeding habits of the red fox in southern Michigan as deciphered from its trails in the snow. Information about the food habits of the timber wolf in northern Michigan has been secured in the same manner by Stebler (1939).

A similar but indirect method for ascertaining food preferences has been employed by Jameson (1947: 133) in a study in Kansas of the prairie vole (*Microtus ochrogaster*). These voles, like many other microtine rodents, secure the tender heads of grasses and other herbs by cutting the stems off at the base, then making repeated cuts of the stem until the head is brought down within reach. Jameson identified the plant species represented in 10 heaps of such cuttings and calculated the relative frequency of occurrence of all the species of plants found. The relative frequency of alfalfa in these piles of cuttings (Table XI) was .73, while in the area concerned the relative frequency of alfalfa was only .25. Although the observations are too few and have not been treated statistically, it is likely that under the conditions of observation alfalfa was the most preferred food of these voles.

Direct and indirect observations, however, are rarely adequate to provide accurate measures of the foods consumed by a particular species. The feeding habits of nocturnal and of very shy animals are particularly difficult to observe. Furthermore, it is difficult to secure by direct observation quantitative data on the foods eaten. Cowan (1945: 112), for instance, noted that estimates of the food preferences of black-tailed deer on Vancouver Island, British Columbia, based on direct observations were erroneous when checked by stomach analyses. Field observations alone, therefore, may give an inadequate measure of food consumption and should if possible be supplemented by other technics.

LABORATORY TESTS. The foods chosen by animals when they are kept under laboratory conditions give important clues to their food requirements (Stegeman, 1937; Arnold, 1942). Studies of captive individuals are valuable, in addition, because of the useful information they yield about the feeding habits of the species. In interpreting the results of laboratory studies due consideration, however, must be given to the fact that wild animals usually require more energy and consequently more food than captive animals, both because of their necessarily greater activity and because of their greater exposure to the elements. Also, the range of choice offered to an animal under laboratory conditions must usually be much narrower than that available to him in nature. For this reason the captive animal may possibly eat or at least nibble foods in the laboratory that the wild animal would refuse.

DIGESTIVE-TRACT ANALYSES. Analyses of the remains of food found in the digestive tracts of the species under study provide valuable indications of food consumption. Analyses of the contents of the crop and stomach are of especial value for ascertaining the foods consumed by those animals, such as birds, reptiles, and fishes, that swallow their food whole or in large masses. The results of these digestive-tract examinations may be expressed in a number of ways, of which the following are especially useful:

NUMBER OF FOOD ITEMS PER DIGESTIVE TRACT. A record of the number of individual items of each food species present in each digestive tract examined gives information about the food habits of the form under investigation. The mean number of items of each food species per digestive tract in the series examined may then be calculated.

Unfortunately for the investigator, most kinds of food disintegrate rapidly when acted upon by the digestive enzymes. Only those food items that contain relatively indigestible bones or other hard parts, therefore, may reliably be counted from their remains. Moreover, many kinds of animals tear or chew their food into small bits before swallowing it. For these and other reasons, it often is impossible or impractical to identify and to count the number of food items present in each digestive tract examined. Even when the numbers of the several kinds of food individuals eaten can be accurately estimated, it will be misleading to compare food species which differ considerably in size.

FREQUENCY INDEX OF FOOD ITEMS. The number of digestive tracts examined that contain a particular food species divided by the total number of digestive tracts in the series examined gives a frequency index of food items. There will be a separate frequency index for each food species identified in any given series of digestive tracts.

The frequency index of each food species provides a useful and simple measure of food preference. In fact, in those studies in which it is impossible or impractical to measure the volume or to count the numbers of each food species present in each digestive tract the frequency index may be the best method for indicating the foods actually consumed.

VOLUMETRIC METHODS. Experience has demonstrated that volume often is the most practical measure of the relative abundance of the several food items which occur in digestive tracts. Measurement may best be stated in terms of the mean volume of each food item found in each individual digestive tract and also of the maximum volume found in any tract. It is customary to lump some of the food items that are difficult to identify under general headings, such as "insects" or "plant material."

INDEX OF TOTAL VOLUME is a statement of the proportional volume that each particular food item represents in the digestive tracts examined as compared to the total volume of all the food items present in the same series of samples. If this proportion is stated in percentage, it become percentage of total volume. For further information about methods of digestive-tract analysis the student is referred to McAtee (1912), C. Cottam (1935), Wight (1939), Davison (1940b), Salyer and Lagler (1940), and Martin, Gensch, and Brown (1946).

The volume of remains of a given food species present in a particular digestive tract has an evident relation to the number of individuals eaten at the last meal of the herbivore or carnivore and to the size of the bodies of the food species. This is true because it takes more individuals of a small than of a large food species to make up a given volume of food. For any given food species the average size and volume of the individuals can usually be ascertained. If the average volume per individual of a given food species is known, then it should be possible to estimate the number of individuals of that species represented in any given volume of food found in the stomach of a predator or a herbivore.

This calculation will be possible if each prey individual is entirely eaten. If, on the other hand, only a part of each prey animal or food plant is eaten at a meal, then this calculation cannot be made. Nor will it be possible to calculate the number of prey individuals represented in a given volume of digestive-tract contents if any appreciable amount of digestion has occurred. Herbivores rarely eat the whole of any plant, and carnivores in general digest their food rapidly. The calculation of the number of individuals eaten from the volume of that food item in any given digestive tract, therefore, will seldom be possible.

FECES ANALYSIS. The analysis of animal feces ("scats") is another practical method for ascertaining the kinds of food eaten by certain species. The method has yielded results of great value in the study of the food of mammal predators (Olaus Murie, 1935b; Adolph Murie, 1936) and to a lesser extent has been used for rabbits (Dusi, 1949), for birds (Dalke, 1935a) and for other land vertebrates. The analysis of the pellets regurgitated by owls gives similar information.

TABLE XII

RESULTS OF DIGESTIVE-TRACT ANALYSIS

Early spring food of otters in Michigan. Based on contents of 95 stomachs (761.8 cc) and 133 intestines (data from Lagler and Ostenson, 1942).

Food Item	Stomachs			Intestines		
	Individuals of Each Item Eaten	Percentage of Total Volume of Food	Percentage Frequency of Occurrence	Individuals of Each Item Eaten	Average Estimated Percentage of Food by Bulk	Percentage Frequency of Occurrence
Game and pan fishes..	..	22.7	27.4	...	16.3	45.9
Trout............	19	....	....	45	....	....
Bullheads.........	5	....	....	9	....	....
Northern pike.....	2	....	....	7	....	....
Perch............	4	....	....	26	....	....
Bass and sunfish....	17	....	....	36	....	....
Forage fishes.......	..	35.9	63.2	...	21.1	69.2
Suckers..........	16	....	....	40	....	....
Minnows.........	51	....	....	158	....	....
Mad toms........	..	....	....	1	....	....
Mud minnows.....	81	....	....	72	....	....
Darters..........	22	....	....	5	....	....
Muddlers.........	69	....	....	99	....	....
Sticklebacks.......	25	....	....	41	....	....
Fish remains.......	..	3.9	34.7	...	14.0	49.6
Amphibians........	23	25.2	21.1	32	6.4	21.8
Other vertebrates....	3	4.5	3.2	1	0.7	0.8
Insects............	16	0.4	10.5	61	3.7	26.3
Crayfishes..........	48	7.4	42.1	132	37.8	54.9
Snails.............	..	....	....	2	Trace	0.8

INADEQUACIES OF DIGESTIVE-TRACT AND FECES ANALYSES. False conclusions about food habits may easily be drawn from the examination of feces or of the contents of digestive tracts. Clarence Cottam (1935) especially has urged the necessity of field studies to aid in the interpretation of digestive-tract analyses. Olaus Murie (1935b), for example, found remains of black bear in the stomachs of 2 coyotes taken in Yellowstone Park, but he did not draw the conclusion that the coyotes concerned had killed and eaten a bear. Almost certainly the bear was carrion. Similarly, the remains of domestic stock found in the digestive tracts or feces of predators often represent carrion.

That the several possible methods for measuring food consumption do not always give the same answers is evident from Table XII, in which the food taken by the otter in early spring from trout waters in Michigan is analyzed. It will be noted that for such food items as "forage fishes" and "crayfishes" very different figures are obtained for the percentage of total volume of food in the stomachs and for the percentage frequency of its occurrence. A different indication of food preference is given also by the remains in the intestine from the indications given by the remains found in the stomach.

Although analyses of digestive-tract contents and of feces furnish a useful list of the types of food taken by a given species and may provide some indication of the relative proportions in which the several food items are taken, the method does not give a direct measure of the food preferences nor does it give a satisfactory basis for the estimation of the quantities of each kind of food consumed. Certain foods digest more quickly and more thoroughly than others (Hess and Rainwater, 1939), and some food remains are more readily identified than others. Since most mammals grind up their food to at least some degree, a considerable proportion of their stomach contents often is unidentifiable. Even when all the kinds of food eaten can be identified, it will still rarely be possible to ascertain the relative quantities of each of the several food species. As proof of this may be cited the careful study by Norris (1943) which demonstrated that stomach analyses of sheep are of limited value in measuring forage consumption.

The evidence about food habits obtained from the remains present in a given digestive tract or in feces applies, of course, only to the season, locality, and particular ecologic community in which the animal concerned obtained his last meal. There are undoubtedly variations among the individual members of most species in their food preferences. Variations in the kinds and quantities of foods actually consumed may be related to such factors as the season, the ecologic community, the age of the consumer, and availability. Care must be taken, therefore, not to draw sweeping conclusions from specimens which may not be fully representative of the variety of conditions under which the species being studied actually lives in nature.

Food Preferences

Practically every study that has been made of the food habits of a particular species of animal has shown that certain foods are taken in greater abundance than other foods that are available in equal quantity. Most kinds of animals exhibit food preferences. The larvae of the butterfly *Papilio ajax*, for example, feed readily on a number of species of Umbelliferae, but in the laboratory most larvae refuse to eat *Hydrocotyle americana* (Dethier, 1941: 63). For another example, the social vole (*Microtus socialis*) of the U.S.S.R. was kept in captivity by Voronov (1935) and was offered 144 diverse species of plants, with the result that 43 of these species of plants were completely eaten or nearly so, 65 species were eaten with more or less relish, 23 species were eaten only a little, and 13 species were either refused or eaten to an extent too slight for recognition.

Certain of the food preferences of animals may be correlated with the nutritive values of their foods, but this is certainly not always true. Animals, like man, have food prejudices. For instance, the Malemute dogs of interior Alaska are nearly always hungry and will devour almost anything remotely edible, including boots or harness carelessly left within their reach. From my own observations, however, I can certify that these dogs can hardly be starved into eating any part of a duck or goose. Seton (1912: 162) reported that the husky dogs of northern Canada likewise refused to eat a pelican. Little is known about other possible food prejudices that wild animals may have. It seems incredible that a wild animal could afford to ignore any nutritious food available. Nevertheless, a strong preference for certain foods, such as is exhibited by many animals, must necessarily be correlated with a prejudice against other kinds of foods.

BASIS FOR FOOD PREFERENCES. The basis of their preference for particular types of food is known for only a few kinds of animals. Man chooses foods in considerable part because of their pleasant odor, flavor, or texture. He may also avoid certain foods because from previous experience he has learned that they are difficult to eat or because they produce undesirable consequences. It is probable that animals also choose their foods at least to some extent for these same reasons.

The chemical composition of the food undoubtedly plays a large role in its palatability. For example, Lyford (1943) ascertained from a careful laboratory study that the leaves of certain tree species are more palatable than others to 1 species of millipede (*Diploiulus londonensis caeruleocinctus*) and that the palatability is correlated with the calcium content of the leaves. The precise relationship between the chemical composition of foods, the degree to which they are essential to the body, and their palatability to animals is, however, little understood.

Certain odorous essential oils have been shown to be the basis for the selection of their food plants by a few kinds of insects. Thus, the cabbage butterfly (*Ascia rapae*) is attracted to the food plants of its larvae by the odor of the "mustard oils" which these plants give off (Brues, 1946: 119).

EMERGENCY FOODS. At those times when their preferred foods are unobtainable, most kinds of animals will turn, though doubtless with reluctance, to other food substances. Thus, it was noted by Bellrose and Low (1943: 180) that during a flood in the Illinois River Valley the muskrats, whose usual food had been river bulrush, pickerelweed, and marsh smartweed, turned to coontail, duckweeds, duck potato, and the twigs and bark of buttonbush and willow.

The foods eaten by animals during food emergencies often fail to be sufficiently digestible to supply the proper nutriments and the accessory food elements essential for continued health. Animals may in fact starve while their stomachs are full of materials that they have eaten. Certain materials eaten by desperate animals may actually be harmful to them. Many conifers, for instance, contain indigestible resins and other substances, some of which may be injurious when taken in quantity.

POISONOUS FOODS. A few kinds of plants, such as the larkspur, that are sometimes eaten by animals for food, may at certain seasons contain active poisons. Cattle, sheep, and other domestic animals are sometimes killed by eating poisonous plants (Stoddard and Smith, 1943, Chap. 17). The effect of a poison, however, may vary greatly among the species of animals. A poison that is virulent for one species may fail to affect another species. The red squirrel, for instance, seems to feed freely on certain mushrooms of the genus *Amanita* which are lethal to human beings (Tiffany and Tiffany, 1944). Many birds likewise, without apparent harm, eat such fruits as those of poison ivy, pokeweed, and nightshade, all of which are poisonous to man (Judd, 1902: 62).

PREFERENCE RATINGS. Attempts to develop preference ratings for the several foods eaten in nature by a particular kind of animal have been made by a number of investigators (J. S. Dixon, 1934; Stegeman, 1937; Glading, Biswell, and Smith, 1940; Bellrose and Anderson, 1943; Hill, 1946). Each preference rating should be based upon the proportions of the several kinds of food present in the habitat compared with the proportions of each kind of food actually consumed by the animals. Inasmuch, however, as the best methods now in use for measuring the quantities of foods available in natural ecosystems are far from satisfactory and because our measures of the proportional amounts of each kind of food consumed are only approximately accurate, any preference rating calculated from such data must leave much to be desired in the way of precision.

The preference rating for each food species necessarily varies more or less with the season and with the ages of the consumer individuals. Furthermore, any measure of the food preferences of a given kind of animal actually applies only to the particular area and to the particular conditions for which it is calculated (Cowan, 1945). Preference ratings as precise as possible will, of course, be desirable in critical studies, but for many ecologic investigations a simple classification will suffice. It is suggested that a classification of food preferences that includes only the 4 categories of highly preferred, moderately eaten, slightly eaten, and refused will often be adequate.

Availability

Any measure of the food preferences of a given species of animal based on digestive-tract, regurgitated-pellet, or feces analysis must necessarily take into account the kinds and quantities of the various foods available to the animal. A kind of food that is very abundant may be taken by an animal in greater quantity than another more preferred food that is rare in the habitat. If all kinds of suitable food are scarce, an animal may eat food that usually would be refused. Also, some foods that are present in the habitat may be relatively inaccessible to a particular individual because they are outside his home range, are located in a position exposed to attack from predators, or are in a place which the animal finds difficult to reach.

The foods eaten by a given animal, therefore, are actually an indication of the kinds of food available to him, as well as a measure of his food preferences. Most kinds of animals have at least a small degree of adaptability in their food habits, as has already been pointed out. If their preferred food is not at hand, they are able to subsist on other less desirable food types. The relative availability (McAtee, 1932: 135) in the ecosystem of the various possible kinds of food consequently has much to do with the quantities of each kind of food consumed by a given species of animal.

Availability may be defined as the relative ease with which a particular food item can be secured at a given time in a given ecosystem by the species of animal under consideration. No simple measure of availability, however, has come into general use. Perhaps the simplest rating would be an index in which 1.0 would indicate that the food item could be secured to satiation regularly by the species without undue exertion. Inasmuch as a good quantitative method for constructing estimates of availability is lacking, such ratings will for the present have to be based on the judgment of the observer.

Availability to a carnivore depends on many factors, among which may be mentioned seasonal and daily periods of activity both of the carnivore concerned and of his prey species, the degree of hunger and of vigor of the individual animal which is searching for the meal, the relative abundance of the several possible kinds of food, their relative degree of palatability at various ages or stages of growth, and the relative ability of the several possible food species to escape detection or to avoid capture.

Availability to a herbivore is a simpler matter and presumably involves chiefly the ability to discover the location of the food.

Quantity of Food Required per Individual

The amount of food required per day by each individual animal necessarily varies from time to time. The food requirements of an individual are affected by its size, rate of metabolism, stage in the sexual cycle, weather, and other factors. The food needs of an individual accordingly vary at successive ages and at successive stages in its life history.

Not all foods are equally nutritious, as has already been pointed out. In calculating food requirements due allowance must, therefore, be made for the proportions of the various necessary food elements, including vitamins and essential minerals, that are present in the food. Plants grown on diverse kinds of soil may vary greatly in their content of the several food elements. Foods vary also in nutritive value depending on the conditions in their habitat during the growing season. Forage species grown under adverse conditions may be almost valueless as food (Einarsen, 1946). The quantities of natural food required by a given kind of animal living in nature, therefore, are difficult to estimate.

In studies of nutrition the food requirements of an individual animal often are calculated on the basis of his body weight. The amount of food needed, however, does not increase in exact proportion to body weight. In warm-blooded animals the total metabolism is believed to increase more nearly in proportion to body surface than to body bulk. It is not certain, however, that these relationships are directly applicable to wild animals. In a study of the food requirements of jack rabbits, Arnold (1942: 64) was unable to demonstrate that heavy individuals ate proportionally more than lighter ones. Small lightweight individuals will usually be young, and young animals usually have a higher metabolic rate than do old individuals. It might happen, therefore, that a small animal would eat as much or even more than a larger and older individual.

The ease with which food may be obtained by a species has an important relation to the quantity that each individual consumes. Nearly all animals eat more when food is plentiful than when it is scarce. The number of muskrats eaten by a mink, for example, has been reported by Errington (1943: 822) to vary from 2 adult-sized muskrats per day to 1 in 9 days. The minimum rate of muskrat consumption mentioned is believed by Errington to be sufficient to maintain a mink in a satisfactory state of health. Furthermore, all kinds of animals seem able to exist for long periods of time on a diet considerably below that required to maintain the best degree of health and vigor. Under conditions of malnutrition man, for example, is able to subsist for long periods on a level of metabolism considerably below normal. Other animals undoubtedly have a similar ability. Although breeding and the rearing of young will often be impossible on a deficient diet, the individual animal may be able to survive over a long period of low food availability. This variation in food consumption by animals makes very difficult any calculation of the food requirements of particular species and of the carrying capacity of a given area.

The rate of food consumption of warm-blooded animals is greater at low temperatures than at high. This is true because at low temperatures a warm-blooded animal needs more fuel to keep warm. Its food requirements consequently are greater in winter than in summer. The rate of food consumption is also greater if the animal must climb over rough terrain to secure its food or if it must travel long distances for food or water than if no great muscular exertions are required (Schwan and Swift, 1941). Pregnant or nursing females, of course, require a greater amount of food than other females.

Cold-blooded animals, on the other hand, require less food at low than at high temperatures. They do not utilize energy for the sole purpose of keeping their bodies warm. Active animals, whether warm-blooded or cold-blooded, require more food than inactive or dormant individuals.

The food requirements of wild animals have been ascertained for only a few species. For example, the average air-dry weight of forage consumed by various Alaskan game animals studied by L. J. Palmer (1944) varied from 5 pounds per day for a 150-pound Sitka deer to 35 pounds per day for a 1,200-pound moose. These estimates of food consumption have of necessity been made on captive animals and may not exactly represent the requirements of wild individuals.

Observations by Fitch (1948a: 594) and others indicate that adult California ground squirrels (*Citellus beecheyi*) kept in captivity eat an average of about 22 grams of concentrated dry food per day. When fed upon natural green forage of preferred food species, the amounts consumed ranged from 10 to 100 grams daily, representing a dry weight of 6 to 25 grams.

The number of prey insects destroyed by a predaceous insect during the course of its life may be considerable (Sweetman, 1936: 229). For instance, each larva of *Coccinella californica* consumes an average of 475 aphids during its larval period of approximately 24 days (Clausen, 1916: 257). A single individual of another ladybird beetle, *Hyperaspis binotata,* may destroy during its larval life as many as 90 adults and 3,000 larvae of the terrapin scale (Simanton, 1916: 201).

EFFECTS OF INADEQUATE FOOD. Should the food supply for a given species on a particular area be inadequate either in quantity or in quality, the individuals of that species may be seriously injured (Shelford, 1929: 101-22). A lack of sufficient food during the period of growth of young organisms usually results in stunting. Even though food later becomes abundant, the stunted individuals often fail to grow properly. Food shortages that are of long duration often result in the starvation of many individuals.

Sometimes the food is sufficient in quantity but may lack certain essential elements. This lack may affect the individual animals as seriously as a shortage of food. For example, the lack of some essential vitamin may seriously affect the growth and behavior of the individuals concerned. Animals that have a food ration that is inadequate either in quantity or quality often exhibit abnormal types of behavior. They are especially inclined to wander extensively. Many of the mass emigrations of animals are probably based in considerable part on food shortage.

Plants suffer no less than animals from shortages in their food elements. Because most terrestrial plants are dependent upon the soil solution for their supply of water as well as of food, plants are especially susceptible to droughts. Individual plants that secure only an inadequate supply of water or of any essential plant food cannot grow properly, and if the deficiency is very severe they may die.

Improper or insufficient food may bring other ills than direct death through starvation. Emaciated and weakened animals become easy prey for carnivores. They also are likely to be carried off by disease or to be killed by adverse weather conditions. Starvation can be expected to reduce the rate of maturity and also the rate of reproduction. The utilization of emergency foods, therefore, does not necessarily mean that these foods are adequate for the continued existence of the individuals driven to use them.

PRODUCTIVITY OF THE ECOSYSTEM

Numerous attempts have been made to measure the total productivity of particular communities. It is evident that a measure, or, failing that, an index of the actual or potential productivity of a given community would often be of great practical value. Aquatic biologists in particular have long sought to derive such an index (Welch, 1935: 321). It is doubtful, however, if any single index of community productivity can be found.

Measurement of Primary Productivity

QUANTITY OF CHLOROPHYLL. One possible measure of the primary productiveness of an ecosystem is the amount of chlorophyll present per unit area (Harvey, 1933; Fleisher, 1935). The amount of chlorophyll present at any given situation, however, may not always be a good index of the amount of plant food produced by the community. Chlorophyll is found in the lower levels of lakes, where the light intensity is far below the level required for photosynthesis (Kosmunski, 1938). This is due undoubtedly to the rain of chlorophyll-bearing organisms from the upper levels. A more serious objection to this index is that the production of food materials by plants is not necessarily correlated with the amount of chlorophyll present. The organisms in a community may contain a large amount of chlorophyll, but if the light is intermittent or weak, the productiveness will be far less than the maximum possible. Another difficulty is that the kinds of chlorophyll presumably differ in their efficiency. The measurement of the quantity of chlorophyll present in an ecosystem, therefore, is not a practical measure of its productiveness.

BIOMASS AS A MEASURE OF PRODUCTIVITY. Certain authors have attempted to use the total biomass of a community as an index of its productivity. That the total biomass does not indicate the productivity of the community was, however, recognized by Demoll, who first proposed the concept. The inappropriateness of total biomass as a measure of productivity has been further demonstrated by the studies of Birge and Juday (1922: 151-57) on the plankton of Wisconsin lakes. This by no means implies that the concept of biomass has no value. On the contrary, estimates of the biomass of a particular species or of a group of species which serves a common ecologic function in a community may be of considerable value in indicating the amount of energy available to a particular link of a food chain.

Included within the total biomass are organisms which are consumers of various ranks as well as those which are primary producers. A certain amount of the energy existing within any biological system is dissipated by each link in the food chain through which it passes. The relationship of the biomass to the primary productiveness of the ecosystem, therefore, will vary with the proportion of primary producers to consumers, a proportion which constantly fluctuates in every community.

Total biomass has the further defect as a measure of productivity that, as usually calculated, it comprises the total mass of the organisms in the community, including their skeletons, integuments, and other parts that contain little or no energy. These inert materials make up a considerable part of the weight of certain organisms, but they are of only slight value as food.

Trophic Levels

In analyzing the productivity of a community it is helpful to distinguish the more important levels of food production and utilization. There are first of all the primary producers, which nearly always are green plants, then the primary consumers, secondary consumers, and so on (Thienemann, 1926), depending upon the number of links in the food chain under consideration. Each of the more important steps in the food productivity of the community may be called a trophic level (Lindeman, 1942).

The most important trophic level is that of the primary producers, which must be represented in every community. It is possible for a community to exist without any other trophic level, the several associated species being related only through their competition or co-operation with one another. In most communities, however, consumer trophic levels will also be present, and their number may vary from one to many. Furthermore, a given species may at the same time or successively be represented in 2 or more trophic levels. The differences among the several trophic levels are most evident in the lowest levels and become progressively more confused as the number of links in any given food chain becomes greater.

A clear distinction needs to be made here between the material (potential energy) present at any given trophic level in a community and the actual energy utilized at that level (Macfadyen, 1948). Materials present in an ecosystem circulate and may be used in part at several successive trophic levels or they may in part again enter into the chemical composition of the organisms of the primary-producer level. Technics which are used for estimating the quantity of potential energy present at each level must differ from those used for estimating the quantity of energy actually utilized at that level.

CROP. The actual crop of a given species produced over a stated period of time by a particular ecosystem can be estimated by various methods. The simplest method is to harvest the crop on sample areas of specified size and then to compute the productivity of the whole area concerned. The yield is the amount of the crop of a particular species actually removed over a specified interval of time (Krumholz, 1948).

Mathematical formulas for the estimate of the biologic productivity of particular species have been presented by Clarke, Edmondson, and Ricker (1946). These formulas are general in character and are based on the rate of assimilation per unit of population, rather than on the amount of energy received by the ecosystem.

Accurate prediction of the annual productivity of a given species in a particular ecosystem from a knowledge alone of the food or energy available and of the physical conditions of the environment, however, is rarely possible. Too little is known about the complex ecologic interrelations of the organisms that make up any community to enable such a prediction to be made with any degree of reliability. Furthermore, it is not possible to evaluate fully the effects on productivity of the frequent fluctuations in the physical factors of the habitat. With the present meager knowledge of the factors that control productivity, therefore, the best basis for the prediction of the crop of any given species is an empirical calculation based on its yield in past years, duly weighted by the physical and biotic conditions currently existing in the ecosystem at the time the prediction is made. Predictions of anticipated productivity for various kinds of crops are periodically issued by the United States Department of Agriculture.

Degree of Food Utilization

No species of animal is ever able to utilize all the suitable food present in its habitat. Some of the food may grow in inaccessible places; some may be covered by other materials or be tramped into the soil; some may deteriorate before it is eaten; or there may not be enough animals to consume all the food during the period when it is suitable for use. Precise measurement of the actual proportion of the available food consumed is often desirable. Such measurements are of particular importance in range and pasture management.

MEASURES OF UTILIZATION. In range-management practice the term utilization means the degree to which animals have consumed the total current herbage production of a range area; it is expressed in percentage by weight (Stoddard and Smith, 1943: 185). Complete utilization is taken to be 100 per cent.

A reliable measure of the degree of utilization of the food in a given ecosystem, however, is not easy to secure. One of the best methods for estimating the degree of utilization of range grasses, according to Pechanec and Pickford (1937a: 754), is to measure the quantity of forage on 2 sets of plots, each composed of an equal number of standardized and of randomized plots, one set being completely protected from grazing, the other set being grazed by the species of animal under study. At the season of best development of the plants and after the grazing has been completed, the forage on both sets of plots is clipped at a height of 1 inch above the ground (the assumed lower limit of grazing height), air dried, and weighed. The total weight of air-dry forage from the ungrazed plots (A) minus that from the grazed plots (B) gives a measure of the amount of utilization of the pasture under the conditions of grazing employed. An index of utilization may then be obtained by the following formula:

$$\text{Index of utilization} = \frac{(A - B)}{A}.$$

A somewhat similar procedure could be used to estimate the proportional utilization of seeds, fruits, and other classes of food materials by nongrazing animals. This method unfortunately requires that 1 set of plots be protected against utilization. It can be applied only in special situations.

Numerous other methods for estimating the degree of range utilization have been proposed, but in the opinion of Stoddard and Smith (1943) none of them is fully satisfactory.

THE USE FACTOR. The relative forage value of a given forage species on a particular range is by range managers called its use factor. In order to obtain an estimate of the use factor it is necessary to establish a type of range management under which all the more valuable forage species will thrive indefinitely. Then the percentage of consumption by weight of the forage available to animals of the forage species under consideration in comparison to all the forage produced on the area during the current year constitutes the use factor. The very misleading term "palatability" found in the older literature is a synonym for use factor.

FOOD WASTAGE. A part of the food produced in a given community may fail of immediate utilization, though much or all of this wasted material may later be consumed by saprophytes of various kinds. Trampling by large and small animals destroys many parts of shrubs and of tender herbs. Many seeds and fruits fall to the ground and fail to be utilized as food, though some of the seeds may later germinate and thus fulfill another function. Some food materials grow in places where they cannot be readily reached by animals. For example, terrestrial animals that are nonarboreal cannot reach above a certain height, and therefore plant foods growing above this critical height are beyond their reach. Some plants may be protected from animals because they grow on cliffs or in other inaccessible places, such as among stiff branches or thorns.

Many animals are wasteful in their eating habits and do not utilize all the food materials they collect or cut down. For example, the beaver often cuts down more trees for food than he can eat before the bark dries and becomes inedible. Some pieces of wood still covered by bark also are used by the beaver for constructing his lodges and dams. A few of the trees that are cut off fall against other trees and cannot be reached by the beavers (Bradt, 1938: 155). As much as 64 per cent of the food on aspen trees cut down by beavers may thus be wasted (S. E. Aldous, 1938: 219).

Jack rabbits frequently cut off parts from forage plants which they make no effort to eat, thereby wasting these food materials. Frequently also jack rabbits consume only the succulent leaves and basal internodes of the culms they have cut off and leave the coarse parts of the stem uneaten. The food wasted by the Arizona and antelope jack rabbits in southern Arizona has been estimated to amount to 1 per cent or more for numerous species of plants, and to range as high as 14 per cent for certain food plants (Arnold, 1942: 77, Tables VIII and X).

From a study of the effects of the California ground squirrel on range vegetation, Fitch (1948a: 594) concluded that the reduction in the productivity of the experimental plot studied was 10 times as great as the amount of food which the squirrels might have eaten. Much of this loss must have been due to the stunting of plants partly eaten during the early stages of their growth and to the trampling and cutting of plants not actually eaten.

When prey are abundant and easily secured, many kinds of predators kill more than they are able to consume. Man, too, is often wasteful of food. The Indians of interior Alaska, for example, told me that they consider white men very extravagant because they fail to eat the excellent meat on the heads of rabbits, fish, and other animals. Errington (1943: 822) has stated that the mink is a ready killer of many kinds of prey when conditions are favorable for easy predation. Many predators kill and store prey, which, if fresher or more desirable food is at hand, may never be eaten. Adolph Murie (1936) noted that in southern Michigan in winter the red foxes kill more cottontails, mice, and other animals than they are able to eat. These surplus animals are usually stored and some are later used for food by the foxes or by other animals. Shrews and moles are killed by the foxes, but are seldom either eaten or stored.

In the process of collecting its food one kind of animal often destroys food that could be utilized by another species. For instance, the ground squirrel in California discards and wastes many filaree fruits after eating the fine seeds (Horn and Fitch, 1942: 128).

Carrying Capacity

The carrying capacity of a given ecosystem for a particular species of animal will usually be limited primarily by the quantity of food required by each individual animal in relation to the quantity of food produced by that ecosystem. The availability of shelter and of breeding sites also is a factor which controls the carrying capacity of a given ecosystem for a particular species. In this chapter, however, only the limitations imposed by the available food are under consideration.

Many of the smaller herbivores increase rapidly in numbers during their annual breeding season. This increase usually coincides with or immediately precedes the season of maximum plant food, at which time there may actually be a great excess of food. In certain years, however, the seasonal increase in animal numbers may produce such a large population that the food supply becomes exhausted, with resulting starvation or forced emigration for the animals. The calculation of carrying capacity for a species that fluctuates greatly in numbers from season to season or from year to year, therefore, is especially difficult.

MEASUREMENT OF CARRYING CAPACITY. The measurement of carrying capacity as regards food is by no means simple. It has already been pointed out that the food requirements of individual animals vary from time to time in accordance with their age, sex, life-history stage, breeding season, amount of activity, and other factors. Food requirements also are influenced by numerous factors of the environment, such as temperature and wind movement. The kinds and amounts of food produced by a given ecosystem likewise vary from time to time, depending upon seasonal changes and upon longer climatic fluctuations. The amount of food produced may sometimes be curtailed because of previous overutilization. Part of the food that is produced may deteriorate before it is used or for one reason or another may fail to be utilized by the animals. Furthermore, the amount of food available to a given species is often greatly affected by competition with other species. The exact carrying capacity of a given area with regard to food, therefore, is extremely difficult to calculate.

As an example of the estimation of the carrying capacity of a particular kind of community for one kind of animal may be cited a study of the beaver by Bradt (1938: 157). From counts in southern Michigan of the average number of poplar trees cut by a beaver colony and of the average number of poplar trees growing on an acre, Bradt estimated that 1 acre of poplar would support a beaver colony of 5 individuals from 1 to 2.5 years. Bradt admitted, however, that this was a very rough estimate and that the conditions at any particular location might considerably modify its carrying capacity.

VARIATION IN CARRYING CAPACITY. In estimating carrying capacity due attention must be given to the fact that the available food varies from season to season and from year to year. In winter in northern climates, for example, there are no lush annuals, the leaves are off the deciduous trees, and snow may cover other suitable food.

Animals often vary considerably in their food preferences at the several seasons. Accordingly, it is necessary to calculate the carrying capacity separately for each season. In the north the winter is usually the most critical period. The food available in the winter, therefore, often determines the carrying capacity of the area for the several resident species.

During the growing season it often happens that food of numerous kinds is present in abundance. Much of the food produced in a given ecosystem may, in fact, never be utilized. The consuming organisms are unable to keep pace with the productivity of the community, in spite of the influx of seasonal migrants and in spite of seasonal increases in numbers by almost all the species. On the other hand, during seasons when little or no food is being produced, there may be a great scarcity of certain food items, with resulting privation and perhaps with the starvation of certain individuals. It is particularly important, therefore, to measure carrying capacity at each season of the year and during poor years as well as during very productive years.

ASCERTAINMENT OF DEGREE OF STOCKING. Although it is in general very difficult to measure accurately either the available food or the food requirements of individual animals per unit of time, it usually is possible to determine whether the food present in a given stand is being fully utilized and also whether the range is being damaged by overutilization. This information provides a basis for deciding whether the stock of the particular kind of animal under consideration can be safely increased on the area, or whether, on the contrary, that form is already too abundant. Thus, S. E. Aldous (1944) has used a percentage sample survey of the utilization of deer browse as an indication of whether a given area is overstocked, properly stocked, or understocked with white-tailed deer.

One method for measuring the safe limit of stocking is to place a given number of individuals of the species being studied on fenced sample plots located in situations typical of the habitat (Davenport, Shapton, and Gower, 1944). Periodic measures of the condition of the vegetation on each plot will then show the degree to which the forage is being utilized. Should the forage deteriorate rapidly on a given plot, it would be evidence that the plot is overstocked. On the other hand, if all the forage available is not utilized, it may be assumed that the plot can carry a somewhat larger population than has been placed there. This method, of course, is expensive in regard to time and effort and cannot be applied to ordinary field situations.

Effect on the Ecosystem of Overutilization of Food

Too great utilization of any plant species may result in temporary or permanent damage to the individual plants, with a consequent reduction in the productivity of the community. Overutilization may be defined as that condition in which the annual use of any particular food exceeds its annual production. Continued overutilization may result in a reduction in the ability of the plants to produce food at all.

In a study of the vegetation on fairly arid prairies near Manhattan, Kansas, A. E. Aldous (1930), for example, ascertained that the greatest amount of forage was produced on sample plots that were clipped only once a year at the maturity of the vegetation. The density of the vegetation on plots clipped at 2-week intervals for 3 seasons decreased about 60 per cent, and on plots clipped at 3-week intervals about 13 per cent. On plots clipped at 2-week intervals the composition of the vegetation deteriorated so much that in 3 years annuals which were practically worthless for feed composed about 50 per cent of the vegetation on these plots. Pastures in Nebraska and Montana also have been shown to deteriorate rapidly when subjected to frequent clipping (Weaver and Hougen, 1939; Holscher, 1945).

Both the amount of available moisture and the richness of the soil, however, affect the degree of damage caused by grazing and browsing. In rich, moist meadows continuous grazing may produce a closed sod of certain species, while eliminating other species. But in a dry and poor situation the same amount of grazing may greatly damage all the vegetation. An amount of clipping which would seriously damage the pasture grasses in Kansas and in other western states, as cited above, may have no serious effect on the grasses in a Michigan or Ohio meadow or lawn.

Certain kinds of plants are better able than others to endure continuous grazing or browsing. Perennial plants that are able to reproduce by vegetative means, such as many kinds of grasses, may not be permanently injured if the flowering stalks are removed, but annuals treated in that fashion would quickly become greatly reduced in the community.

The decrease in food plants caused by overutilization by animals results ultimately in a decrease in the animal population responsible for the overutilization. If the animal species concerned is long-lived, however, the overpopulation may continue for a considerable time, resulting in great damage to the habitat. Because of the shortage of food, few young animals will be produced and those that are born will probably not survive. If predators are absent or few, however, the older animals may live on in a semi-starving and emaciated condition for a number of years, but ultimately the animal population will become reduced. This actually happened to the mule deer of the Kaibab Plateau in Arizona (Rasmussen, 1941: 269) and to the white-tailed deer in many parts of the northeastern United States (Aldo Leopold, 1943). The damage to the habitat is often severe and the restoration of its productivity may take years.

Ultimate Limit of Productivity

The ultimate limit of productivity of a given ecosystem is governed by the total effective solar energy falling annually on the area, by the efficiency with which the plants in the ecosystem are able to transform this energy into organic compounds, and by those physical factors of the environment which affect the rate of photosynthesis. The amount of energy available to organisms from radioactive minerals in the earth itself is so small as to be negligible and the same is true for energy derived from other sources, such as from the stars, from meteorites, or from the tides.

The food relations in each community may, therefore, best be considered in terms of energy. From the standpoint of the dynamics of the community, food is mostly energy. Every individual organism is enabled to exist by transforming energy that exists in one form into energy in some other form. Green plants utilize the energy from the sun for producing stored energy in the form of carbohydrates, proteins, and fats. At each stage in the circulation of matter, which begins with the green plants and passes through the various herbivores, predators, parasites, and saprophytes, the stored energy in the food is changed in form and made available to the next stage in the cycle. At each stage also a part of the energy in the food is dissipated, mostly in the form of heat. The cycle is completed ultimately when all the available energy in the food has been utilized.

The activities of all the organisms that now live on the earth are based, therefore, on the production and utilization of food materials. Yet organ-

isms are never producers of either energy or matter. They are solely transformers (Adams, 1915a: 4). Practically all the energy that organisms utilize
is derived directly or indirectly from the sun. This is true no less of man
than of other animals and of plants (O. P. Pearson, 1948).

The organisms that exist on the earth today are probably by no means
the most efficient transformers that could be devised for capturing solar
energy, for changing the form of chemical substances, or for altering states
of energy. Nevertheless, all organisms perform operations of great chemical
intricacy in the production of food materials and in the various transmu-
tations that these food materials undergo until they return again to simple
chemicals.

Only a part of the solar energy that falls on a given area is actually used
for photosynthesis. Plants are lacking on many surfaces, such as bare rock,
sand, and snow. Even the light and heat that fall upon green plants may be
ineffective because the surrounding air or water temperatures are so low or
the supply of water or of plant food so inadequate that photosynthesis proceeds only slowly, if at all. The high seas, for example, are much less productive of plankton than the waters near land (W. E. Allen, 1934: 175),
presumably because of a lesser supply of plant nutriments in the open
ocean. It is probable also that diverse kinds of plants vary in their efficiency
in performing photosynthesis. Furthermore, in many climates the majority
of the plants become more or less dormant during certain seasons, with the
result that at such times they are unable to utilize fully the energy from the
sun. Measurement of the solar energy received by a given ecosystem, therefore, may not give a good indication of the actual productivity of the
community.

Of the energy that reaches the earth from the sun, Lotka (1925: 332)
estimated that 35 per cent is reflected into space, much of it from clouds.
According to a summary by G. A. Riley (1944), the efficiency of green plants
over the earth as a whole in utilizing the energy of sunlight is 0.18 ± 0.12 per
cent. The mean efficiency of plants on land is only 0.09 per cent, though in
the best forests this may rise to 0.25 per cent. In an Illinois cornfield producing 100 bushels of corn per acre during the summer, however, the efficiency for gross plant production may rise as high as 1.6 per cent (Transeau,
1926) and for net corn grain it may reach 1.2 per cent (G. L. Clarke, 1946:
333-34). In the water over Georges Bank, off the coast of Massachusetts,
the diatoms have a maximum efficiency of production of about 0.3 per cent
(Clarke, loc. cit.)

Any given animal is able to utilize only a part of the energy stored in
the plant or animal foods that it eats (Lindeman, 1942). Much energy still
remains in its feces and in its nitrogenous wastes. Many plants, moreover,
die without having been eaten by any herbivore. Such materials, however,
are not wasted. Organisms of various kinds, saprophytes, molds, bacteria,
and various kinds of animals work over these animal and plant materials

again and again and ultimately extract a very considerable proportion of the contained chemical (not atomic) energy.

The process of the extraction of energy from the food materials elaborated by green plants is almost never accomplished at a single step by a single plant or animal, but nearly always involves a whole chain of organisms, including producers, primary consumers, secondary consumers, and so on. Food chains build the food materials up into complex kinds of chemical compounds in highly organized plants and animals, and decomposition chains break the food materials down again into simple compounds.

Every individual animal living on the earth today is able to exist because of his position in some food chain. This is also true of those plants that are unable to manufacture their own food through photosynthesis. All of the life of the earth is based on energy derived from the sun and transformed, principally through the activity of chlorophyll, into other forms of energy, such as food. The food relationships between the several organisms that make up any community, therefore, are basic to the organization of the community.

AVAILABLE FOOD DETERMINES THE CHARACTER OF THE COMMUNITY

The kinds of food available in each habitat determine the kinds of plants and of animals able to exist there. As has been previously pointed out, each kind of animal is more or less specialized in regard to the kinds of food that it is able to utilize. Consequently, in ecosystems furnishing only a few types of food the number of animal species also is limited, whereas in ecosystems having a wide variety of food a greater diversity of kinds of animals can be supported.

Green plants seem in general to be less specialized for particular kinds of food materials than are animals. Because they are able to synthesize their own food, these plants require only relatively simple food elements. Nevertheless, the presence or absence of such essential plant foods as the nitrogen compounds determines to a considerable extent the types of plants that can grow in a given habitat.

Those plants that are not provided with chlorophyll are completely dependent upon the kinds of foods available to them, just as are animals. The varieties of fungi and similar plants that can grow in a particular ecosystem, therefore, are completely controlled by the types of elaborated food available there.

The amount of food available in a given ecosystem likewise limits the numbers of individual organisms that can find sustenance there, except insofar as food from outside the ecosystem may be utilized. In general, if there is scanty food production in a particular ecosystem, the biota there will be scanty, both in species and in individuals, whereas abundant food tends to produce a rich biota, represented by many individuals and numerous species. For example, a coniferous forest usually supplies little food and has a scanty flora and fauna, whereas a hardwood forest is often rich both in species and in numbers. Food plays a most important role, therefore, in determining the characters of every community.

SELECTED REFERENCES

Elton, Charles. 1927. Animal ecology. New York: Macmillan Co. Chap. 5.

Lotka, Alfred J. 1925. Elements of physical biology. Baltimore: Williams and Wilkins Co. Chaps. 16 to 20.

Sverdrup, H. U., Martin W. Johnson, and Richard H. Fleming. 1942. The oceans: their physics, chemistry, and general biology. New York: Prentice-Hall. Chap. 18.

Welch, Paul S. 1935. Limnology. New York: McGraw-Hill Book Co. Chap. 14.

VIII

FLUCTUATIONS IN POPULATIONS

All the individuals of a given species that live at a given time in a particular area constitute a population. A population, therefore, is composed only of the members of a single species. An aggregation of individuals belonging to 2 or more species of ecologically related organisms constitutes a community rather than a population, according to my usage of these terms (see T. Park, 1939: 237, and Godsil, 1948: 5, for different usages).

The area occupied by a population may be either small or large. Thus, all the individuals of a certain species that live at a given moment in a particular stand or in any other continuous area constitute a concrete local population. From a broader point of view, all the individual members of a given species which are living at one time anywhere in the whole world constitute a species population.

Local populations of the same species often are more or less completely isolated from one another. Where such local isolation occurs the over-all species population becomes an abstraction.

The number of individuals that together make up a species population on any given area is subject to constant fluctuation. Some of these fluctuations may have a large amplitude. Thus, the numbers of the chinch bug have been calculated by Shelford and Flint (1943: 441) to vary at a certain place in Illinois from a low of 16,000 per acre in one year to a maximum of as many as 70,000,000 per acre in another year. Estimates by Shelford (1943: 477), based on counts made by Twomey, indicate that the collared lemming (*Dicrostonyx rubricatus richardsoni*) of northern Canada can increase in a period of only 2 years from a minimum of 6 to 7 to a maximum of 4000 per 100 hectares (250 acres). Not all species, fortunately, have such violent fluctuations as these in numbers, but practically all species fluctuate more or less in abundance from time to time. These fluctuations in population have a profound effect on the composition and organization of ecologic communities.

The population of any species in existence at a given time and place depends upon (1) the rate of reproduction of the species and (2) its rate of mortality. When reproduction exceeds mortality, the species will increase in abundance. When, on the contrary, mortality exceeds reproduction, the

154

population density will decrease. Immigration and emigration by mobile animals also affect local abundance in particular communities, but do not change the total population of the species concerned. This chapter deals with the factors that cause changes in populations as a whole; a discussion of the effects of migratory movements is reserved for a later chapter.

REPRODUCTION

The multiplication that occurs in any given population is affected by the type of reproduction employed by the species, by the proportion of reproducing individuals making up the population, by the fertility of the individuals, and by periodicities in reproduction.

Types of Reproduction

SEXUAL REPRODUCTION. Sexual reproduction at some stage of their life history is the general rule for nearly all kinds of plants and animals. During sexual reproduction a male and a female gamete unite to form the zygote from which the individual of the next generation develops. In most animals and in some plants the male and female gametes are produced by separate individuals. In a few kinds of animals, however, both sexes may be represented in the same individual, either at the same time or consecutively. If both sexes are present at the same time, the individual animal is called a hermaphrodite.

Many individual plants, also, produce both male and female gametes, either in the same or in different flowers. In some species, such as the beans and the dandelions, self-fertilization is the rule, but devices to prevent it have been developed in many kinds of plants. Where self-fertilization occurs, a single individual is able to perpetuate the species. With most kinds of plants and animals at least 2 individuals of opposite sex must be present in the community if reproduction is to be achieved.

PARTHENOGENESIS. Parthenogenesis is a modified type of sexual reproduction that does not require the male sex. In most kinds of animals, parthenogenesis, where it occurs, is a temporary method of reproduction that is interrupted from time to time, usually once each year, by sexual reproduction. In a few forms of rotifers and other animals, however, parthenogenesis is the only known method of reproduction, and no males have ever been discovered.

ASEXUAL REPRODUCTION. Asexual reproduction is practiced by many kinds of plants and animals. In those species where it occurs, however, asexual reproduction usually alternates with sexual reproduction at some stage of the life history. For instance, many plants, such as the grasses, multiply asexually by rhizomes, but during the summer they also flower and produce seeds by sexual reproduction. Asexual reproduction also is common among the invertebrates, but it is not practiced by any of the vertebrate animals.

COMPARISON OF TYPES OF REPRODUCTION. Each of these types of reproduction has its advantages and disadvantages for the species concerned and
also has important effects on every community. Sexual reproduction allows
for the dispersal of hereditary factors within a population and for the formation of new combinations of these factors. This type of reproduction is
of particular value for species which have a complex morphology, physiology, or psychology, based on a large number of hereditary factors. Sexual
reproduction has made possible the evolution of the great diversity of life
now present on the earth. Parthenogenesis allows for the rapid multiplication, during favorable seasons, of a well-adapted form (Banta, 1939: 353),
but limits the amount of variability within the species. Asexual reproduction allows extremely rapid multiplication of a successful species, but also
restricts variability and thereby hinders further evolution.

Proportion of Reproducing Individuals in the Population

Not all the individuals in a population are of equal value for reproduction.
Sterile, immature, or dormant individuals are not capable of reproduction.
Males and females perform different reproductive functions. When a species reproduces by the sexual method, both males and females must be
present in proper proportion to ensure the production of fertile eggs or
seeds.

SEX RATIO. In animals that reproduce by the usual sexual method it is
the general rule to find males and females in approximately equal numbers
in the population (Aldo Leopold, 1939: 105). Any deviation from 1:1 in the
sex ratio is usually the result of differential mortality. In certain animals,
however, notably some of the insects, fewer males are produced than females
(Whiting, 1947).

In a monogamous species in which a single male mates with a single
female, any inequality between the numbers of males and of females in a
population will decrease the average rate of reproduction per individual
because not all the individuals will be able to breed. In a polyandrous
species in which 1 female mates with more than 1 male, reproduction will
be inefficient when equal numbers of the 2 sexes are produced. Polyandry
is said to be of regular occurrence among certain human tribes. Among
animals polyandry seems to be rare, but does sometimes occur. Evidence is
presented by Laskey (1947) that throughout all of 1 season a single female
bluebird was mated with 2 males, and that 3 young fledged from the first
nesting, 4 from the second, and none from the third.

In polygynous species, in which one male mates with 2 or more females,
a reduction in the number of males will not decrease the rate of reproduction so long as enough males are present to fertilize all the females. Actually,
in such a polygynous population the rate of reproduction per individual
in the population will be greatest when the males are in a considerable
minority.

Fecundity and Fertility

The terms fecundity and fertility are often used interchangeably, but it seems desirable to follow Pearl and Surface (1909) in making a distinction between them. Fecundity may be defined as the rate at which an individual organism produces reproductive units. These reproductive units may be spermatozoa, ova, or units which are produced asexually. Fertility is the rate of reproductive capacity of pairs of male and female organisms as exhibited by their ability to produce living offspring. It is evident that fecundity is a factor in fertility, but that the actual production of young through the sexual process involves many additional factors.

VARIATION AMONG SPECIES IN FECUNDITY AND FERTILITY. Species of plants and animals vary tremendously in their fecundity and fertility. A single plant may produce thousands or even millions of spores or of seeds per year (Salisbury, 1942). A fish or mollusk may liberate millions of sperm and ova during a single reproductive season (Sverdrup, Johnson, and Fleming, 1942: 316). Depending on her size and condition a single oyster, for example, may contain 16,000,000 to 60,000,000 ova (T. C. Nelson, 1921). Many of the larger mammals and a few birds produce only 1 young per year, and in a few species of mammals the young are brought forth only at intervals of several years. Even closely related kinds of animals may differ greatly in their fertility. Certain species of British mosquitoes, for example, produce successive generations throughout the summer, while other species produce only a single generation per year (Marshall, 1938: 18-19).

AGE AT REPRODUCTIVE MATURITY. The age at which reproductive maturity is attained varies greatly among the plants and animals that live on the earth. Organisms that reproduce asexually often begin to multiply at a very early age. Parthenogenetic reproduction also may take place very early in life. Many kinds of flies, butterflies, and other insects likewise reach sexual maturity in a very few days. Complete generations, therefore, may succeed each other at very short intervals of time. Some of the smaller rodents also reach sexual maturity very rapidly and thus are able to produce several generations per year. On the other hand, many kinds of plants and animals do not reach reproductive maturity until they are 2 or more years of age. Man, for example, is an animal with a prolonged childhood.

INDIVIDUAL VARIATIONS IN FERTILITY. The individuals which make up every population vary in their fertility, both because of the random assortment of hereditary factors and because of variations in the physiologic condition of individuals. Some sexually mature individuals may fail to reproduce to their full capacity during a given breeding season or perhaps during their whole lifetime (Aldo Leopold, 1939: 114). More seeds, for example, are produced by some individual plants than by others of the same age. Also, very young or very old female birds and mammals often produce smaller sets of eggs or litters of young than vigorous females in middle life.

Certain individuals may be sterile and unable to produce offspring. Hunters, for example, report that each year in the deer herds some "dry" does have failed to breed. Sterility, however, is often only temporary, as is true of immature individuals. Other individuals may fail to reproduce during a certain period for such causes as temporary malnutrition, infection, or injury, but later may again be fertile. A few individuals may be permanently sterile; for example, among the social hymenoptera and termites the worker and soldier castes rarely produce offspring.

As specific examples of individual variations in fertility the following are cited: several adult female Beechey ground squirrels in a California population studied by Evans and Holdenried (1943: 241) showed no evidence of pregnancy or lactation at any time during the breeding season. In the U.S.S.R. the proportion of fertile females of the little ground squirrel (*Citellus pygmaeus*) was determined by Varshavski (1938) to vary from place to place and from year to year between extremes of 12 and 98 per cent. Certain individuals of the house wren breed during the first breeding period of the summer but fail to breed during the second period. Other individual wrens undoubtedly skip more than 1 successive breeding period. The proportion of young wrens which breed when less than 1 year old is smaller than that of older wrens (Kendeigh and Baldwin, 1937: 105). Young female fox squirrels that are born late in the year fail to breed early in the spring of the following year but may produce young in the late spring or summer (D. L. Allen, 1943: 111). Breder (1936: 2) has noted that certain female sunfishes may fail to produce eggs during a certain year.

RELATION OF FERTILITY TO BODY SIZE. Body size has an important relation to fertility, as has been pointed out by MacArthur (1942). Within any given species the number of young per litter tends to be correlated with body size. Thus, in the laboratory house mouse those strains having large body size produce larger litters than strains that are smaller in body size. A similar correlation between body size and number of young per litter is exhibited by large and small breeds of domestic animals and also by the large and small races of certain species of wild mammals. This correlation, however, does not hold when species of widely diverse habits are compared. Large ungulates and large carnivores, in comparison with rodents, generally have smaller rather than larger families.

EFFECT OF PSYCHOLOGIC FACTORS ON FERTILITY. Psychologic factors may have an important effect on the fertility of certain kinds of animals. The stimulus produced in the proper season by the presence of a member of the opposite sex often operates to initiate the reproductive process. Also the loss, through adverse environmental conditions, of part or all of a set of eggs or of a litter of young may stimulate further reproduction by the parents concerned. It is well known that the removal of 1 or more eggs from the nest of a bird often results in the production of additional eggs. Many female flickers can thus be induced to lay 25 or more consecutive eggs (Burns, 1900). The ring-necked pheasant, which normally produces only a single brood per season, may make 3 or 4 or even a greater number of attempts at nesting if the first attempts are unsuccessful (Errington, 1942). Changes in fertility due to psychologic stimuli, however, are undoubtedly of greater importance among the birds and mammals than among the lower animals.

EFFECT OF ENVIRONMENTAL FACTORS ON FERTILITY. Environmental conditions that affect the well-being of the individuals of any species affect also to a greater or lesser degree their fertility. Unfavorable weather may reduce the flowering and fruiting of plants. A deficiency in food may prevent certain individual animals from breeding or may cause a decrease in the size or number of litters of young or in the clutches of eggs produced (Aldo Leopold, 1939: 28; D. L. Allen, 1943: 107). In a *Drosophila* culture the number of eggs produced is affected by both the quality and quantity of food, by the temperature, by the humidity, by oviposition stimuli, and by the presence of other individuals (Robertson and Sang, 1945).

Infection by parasites is another factor that is known to reduce fertility (Kalabukhov, 1937: 512; Varshavski, 1938). Overcrowding likewise results in lowered fertility in at least certain kinds of animals (Pearl, 1925: 131) and plants.

Many organisms give off waste products which, when they are too greatly concentrated in the habitat, may affect the health of the organisms themselves or their associates. In experimental populations of flour beetles, for example, it has been shown (Crombie, 1944) that there is a reduction of fertility unless the old "conditioned" medium is removed frequently and is replaced with fresh "unconditioned" flour.

Among laboratory rodents those females that become pregnant when they are suckling young produce smaller litters than females that are not suckling. Thus, female albino rats from which the young are removed at birth produce larger litters than do those females that are allowed to suckle their young. The age of the female rat, the age at which she first became pregnant, the interval since her last pregnancy, and the amount of her experience in breeding all affect her fertility (Asdell, Bogart, and Sperling, 1941).

An increase of temperature within their limits of toleration causes some species, both of plants and of animals, to reproduce more vigorously. Species that are adapted for reproduction at a low temperature may, on the contrary, suffer a decrease in fertility when the temperature rises above their optimum. The slackening of breeding in the wood mouse (*Peromyscus leucopus noveboracensis*) of southern Michigan during the hot summer months (Burt, 1940, Fig. 7) may be assumed to be correlated with the adverse environmental conditions of that season.

ANNUAL VARIATION IN FERTILITY. Year-to-year variation in fertility is exhibited in nature by many kinds of organisms. In plants the crops of fruits or of seeds may vary greatly in successive years (Salisbury, 1942: 3).

In animals the length of the reproductive period, the percentage of individuals breeding, and the number of broods produced per season all vary in accordance with the conditions of the habitat during the year concerned. For example, the number of eggs laid by birds of prey and the number of broods they produce vary from year to year, particularly in accordance with the abundance of the mouselike rodents which serve them for food (Kalabukhov, 1937: 511).

During at least one winter the prairie deermice (*Peromyscus maniculatus bairdii*) that were living in field-shocked corn (maize) in southern Michigan bred vigorously (Linduska, 1942: 358), while in natural situations where the food supply is presumably not so abundant the animals usually do not breed between November and March (Blair, 1940*b*). Furthermore, in those corn shocks the average number of embryos carried by the pregnant females was greater than would be expected in the natural grassy-field habitat of the species. In certain British rodents, likewise, breeding was absent in one winter, took place slightly in another, and continued unabated through a third winter. The variation in the breeding periodicity of these British rodents was not correlated with the severity of the winters and its controlling factors are unknown (Baker, 1930). The actual environmental factors that are responsible for this kind of annuation are only in part known or suspected, but there can be no doubt that there are such fluctuations in the rate of reproduction of organisms in nature.

The number of generations produced by a species also varies from year to year, depending on the local weather and on other environmental factors. Most plants and many kinds of animals, however, are adjusted to produce only a single generation per year. As a rule neither an increase in the length of the growing season nor an improvement in environmental conditions will cause an increase in the number of generations produced per year by such forms.

Environmental conditions that are not precisely suitable at the time the males or females are ready for breeding may operate to prevent an individual or even a whole population from reproducing during a given year. Heavy rain or low temperatures during flowering time may, for instance, keep insects from being active and thereby prevent the fertilization of certain kinds of flowers, with a resulting failure of the fruit crop. Reproduction is for most kinds of organisms a highly complex process that for successful completion requires the co-ordination of numerous internal and external stimuli. The failure of a few individuals to complete the reproductive process in any given season, therefore, should occasion no surprise.

GEOGRAPHIC VARIATION IN FERTILITY. Geographic variation in reproductive rate within the range of a species frequently occurs. Such variations are especially evident among plants but also occur among animals. For example, the number of young produced per litter or per clutch of eggs and the number of litters or of generations produced per season by a given species of animal often vary in accordance with the local climate. This effect has been reported for many kinds of insects (Bodenheimer, 1938: 30-48).

As a particular example of geographic variation in reproductive rate I may cite the white-tailed deer, which in southern New York has a higher fertility than in the northern part of the state. The percentage of does that are pregnant is higher, the proportion of female fawns of the year that become pregnant is much greater, and the number of embryos per adult doe and per fawn is higher in the south than in the north (Morton and Cheatum, 1946). This difference in fertility of deer in the 2 parts of New York State is probably due in part to the difference in the length of the growing season for plants, with a resulting effect on the essential nutrients available to the deer. Climatic factors may also have some direct effect on the reproductive cycle of the deer.

In regions with a short growing season many kinds of insects, birds, mammals, and other animals produce only a single generation per year. In regions with long and favorable growing seasons, on the contrary, these same species may produce 2, 3, or even 4 generations (Fal'kenshtein, 1939).

Geographic gradients of temperature may be directly responsible for differences between the north and the south in the fertility of certain marine fishes along the coast of Norway. The number of years required for individual fish to reach breeding age is longer in the northern parts of their ranges. The number of eggs produced by the females also is generally smaller in the cold northern waters, where the limit of the range of the species is approached, than in the warmer waters of the south (Johnsen, 1945).

RACIAL VARIATION IN FECUNDITY AND FERTILITY. The geographic variations in the fecundity and fertility of many species may be based, at least in part, on variations in racial heredity rather than on environmental factors. The strains or races that make up a species may vary considerably in their fertility. Thus, Gowen and Johnson (1946), in a study of 9 inbred laboratory strains of *Drosophila melanogaster* descended from stocks taken in diverse parts of North America, estimated that the average number of eggs produced during the whole lifetime of a female varied in the several strains from 263 to 1,701. These are presumably hereditary differences, for in the laboratory the animals were all exposed to the same environmental conditions.

Periodicities in Reproduction

Very few kinds of organisms reproduce constantly at a uniform rate. On the contrary, most plants and animals produce their offspring in batches, clutches, or litters and this produces fluctuations in their populations.

SEASONAL PERIODICITIES IN REPRODUCTION. All the individuals making up a population of plants or animals are usually more or less synchronized in their period of reproduction. They produce their seeds or young at ap-

proximately the same season each year in a cycle which is adjusted to the
seasonal cycle of the environmental factors. Even in a tropical rain forest,
where there are only slight seasonal changes in the physical factors, all the
individual plants of a particular species over a fairly large area may burst
into bloom on the same day (H. H. Bartlett, personal communication).

In the Temperate and Frigid zones most kinds of organisms bring forth
their young or produce their spores or seeds in spring or in summer. In
these same zones, however, a few species, by reason of special adaptations,
reproduce in autumn and a very few forms bring forth their young in
winter. For instance, the young of the black and the grizzly bears of North
America are born in a very immature condition in January or February at
a time when the mother is in hibernation. The rule is that the young of all
kinds of organisms are produced at the season when they can best survive
(Westermarck, 1891: 26).

The season of reproduction in the tropics and in some parts of the
temperate zones may be correlated with the wet or dry seasons rather than
with spring or summer. The coming of the rains in an arid region, for example, initiates reproduction in many kinds of plants and animals (Went,
1949). Certain species, indeed, may be stimulated to reproduction by a single heavy rain. Thus, the spadefoot toads of southwestern North America
may lie dormant burrowed in the soil throughout long dry periods. Following a heavy rain in warm weather the toads immediately emerge and lay
their eggs in the temporary pools (Bragg, 1945: 53-54). The young tadpoles
mature so rapidly that they have become transformed into young toads and
have gone away by the time the pools have dried up, perhaps only a few
weeks later.

Asexual reproduction or parthenogenesis, in those species in which it
occurs, often takes place at a somewhat different season from sexual reproduction. In most of the perennial grasses asexual reproduction by rhizomes
is very vigorous, at least in the temperate parts of North America, during
the cool weather of spring and fall, while seeds are produced mostly during
the summer. In the plant aphids parthenogenesis is the usual method of reproduction during the spring and summer, and sexual reproduction is most
apt to occur as winter approaches. Nevertheless, certain kinds of plants and
animals multiply by sexual and by nonsexual types of reproduction at practically the same season.

A few kinds of plants, especially in the tropics, seem not to have any
regular season of reproduction but to produce their seeds and fruits at irregular times. Thus, in a tropical forest an individual tree of a given species
may be in flower or fruit at the time when other members of its tribe show
no evidence of reproduction (H. H. Bartlett, personal communication).
Likewise, certain tropical animals, notably many primates including man,
produce their young with little respect for the seasons. The general rule for
most species, nevertheless, is that reproduction occurs at a particular season
and that at other times of the year no offspring are produced.

ANNUAL PERIODICITIES IN REPRODUCTION. Annual periodicities in reproduction are exhibited by numerous kinds of long-lived plants. Thus, many forest trees set a good seed crop only at intervals of several years. The failure of the seed crop in a given year may be due to unfavorable weather at the flowering season, to the attacks of insects, or to other environmental factors. In an area where a species is living near the limits of its geographic range, reproduction may occur only in especially favorable years.

Numerous kinds of animals also exhibit annual periodicities in reproduction that are controlled at least in part by environmental conditions. In addition, a few kinds of animals show periodicities that are due to the maturation of the whole or almost the whole population in the same year. The most notable of these animals are the periodic cicadas. One strain of cicada requires as long as 17 years to complete its life cycle and practically the whole population emerges as adults in the same summer (Marlatt, 1907).

A few species of animals have annual periodicities in reproduction which are related to the habits of the species. Thus, a female grizzly or brown bear breeds in alternate years or at longer intervals (Adolph Murie, 1944: 201). This breeding cycle is presumably related to the fact that the bear cubs are very small and defenseless. During the first summer after they are born the mother bear fiercely protects her cubs against all other animals. She will not tolerate even a male bear near her cubs and accordingly she has no opportunity to mate.

Reproductive Potential

The potential rate at which any species tends to reproduce itself at a given time and under a particular set of environmental conditions may be called its reproductive potential. Aldo Leopold (1939: 22) called this the "breeding potential." The term "biotic potential" was used by Chapman (1928: 114) for much this same concept, but in my opinion Chapman's term is too inclusive. S. A. Graham (1939: 37) assumed that a definite numerical value may represent the "biotic potential" of each species. In other words, he assumed that in the absence of "environmental resistance" each species has a constant "biotic potential."

No species or individual, however, can exist apart from its environment, and therefore there is no possible way of measuring any physiologic process except in relation to the environment of the concerned organisms. It was recognized by R. N. Chapman (1931: 186) that the number of reproductive units produced per individual varies from time to time and is affected by the environmental conditions. Individual differences in heredity may also produce differences in fertility. The reproductive potential of every species is consequently variable both from time to time and from place to place.

The reproductive potential of a species must be carefully distinguished from its actual rate of reproduction under a given set of environmental conditions. For the practical ecologist the actual rate of reproduction is a much more valuable measure than is the reproductive potential. As a matter of fact, the calculation of what the rate of reproduction would have been under theoretically optimal conditions is usually impractical, and the reproductive potential, therefore, is in most cases of only theoretic interest.

MORTALITY

From the foregoing discussion it will be evident that many factors affect the rate of reproduction of every kind of organism. An important factor is the mortality that eliminates many individuals before they have completed the process of reproduction. Before a mathematical treatment of the rate of reproduction is given, therefore, the factors that affect the rate of mortality will be considered.

Every individual organism sooner or later must die. The rate at which the individuals die is as important to the species as the rate at which they are produced. Death begins to take its toll of a species from the moment that fertilization of the ovum or ovule has occurred, or, if reproduction is parthenogenetic or asexual, from the moment the reproductive unit has become differentiated from the parent. A very few individuals, because of excellent constitutions and good luck, may live to a ripe old age. Many individual organisms, however, perish early in life, and in most species only a moderate number live to reproduce their kind.

Causes of Mortality

Mortality is caused by many kinds of physical and biotic factors. Only a few of the more important of these factors will be considered here.

DEFICIENCIES IN HEREDITY. Every species carries in its heredity at least a few unfortunate genes or combinations of genes that act as lethals or semilethals. A zygote that receives an unfavorable combination of hereditary factors may not be able to develop into an embryo, or, if development begins, the embryo may die and then be resorbed or aborted. Thus, in many species there is known to be a high rate of prenatal mortality which is due at least in part to poor heredity. Deficiencies in heredity may handicap individuals at any age and may even cause mortality late in life. A seedling plant that has a hereditary lack of chlorophyll can survive only so long as it is supported by the food contained in the seed from which it has sprouted. Albino animals, on the other hand, sometimes survive for a number of months or years, but they always are at a disadvantage in the struggle for existence.

UNFAVORABLE PHYSICAL ENVIRONMENT. Adverse physical conditions in the environment are another important cause of death for all kinds of organisms. If the environment becomes too hot or too cold, too dry or too wet, or passes any limit of toleration for the species, the individuals suffer or die. The natural catastrophes of flood, storm, and fire may be considered only extreme examples of unfavorable environment. Accidents of various kinds also are a constant hazard to every individual. Arboreal animals, for example, fall out of trees; terrestrial animals fall in the water and are drowned; aquatic forms are stranded on land. Trees or other plants may be blown down by the wind, washed out by water, or dried out by drought. Organisms that are not killed outright by adverse physical conditions may be weakened so much that they are more than usually susceptible to other causes of mortality.

The time of germination is an especially critical period for most plants. Young seedlings may be killed by improper soil, by unfavorable light intensity, by unsuitable temperature, and by other harmful physical factors. A drought at the time of seed germination, for instance, may result in the survival of few or no seedlings of certain of the more delicate plants. Unfavorable weather occurring during the period of immaturity of plants or animals is also likely to produce heavy mortality because young organisms are usually less resistant to unfavorable physical conditions than are adults.

UNFAVORABLE BIOTIC ENVIRONMENT. Unfavorable biotic environment is another mortality factor which may be of special importance for the early life stages of certain kinds of organisms. The viability of seeds and of eggs, for example, is controlled indirectly by numerous factors that affect the parents. Robertson and Sang (1945) have shown that in *Drosophila* the viability of the eggs is affected by the age of the mother and by her frequency of copulation. The viability of both the eggs and larvae of this insect are affected by the quantity and quality of food eaten by both the parents (Reynolds, 1945).

The health of the mother is particularly important to the survival of the young in all those kinds of plants and animals in which the mother nourishes the developing young within her body. This includes especially the viviparous animals. There is evidence that a considerable number of the mammalian embryos that are implanted in the uterus fail to survive to the age of birth. Some of this prenatal mortality undoubtedly is due to defective heredity, but part of it is probably due to unfavorable uterine environment. Among conditions unfavorable to the mother that might affect her embryonic young are scanty food, the nursing of too many young, the ravages of disease, severe weather, or extreme exertion.

FOOD INADEQUACY. Inadequacy of food is a very frequent cause of death for many kinds of organisms. Starvation may not immediately kill the individual, but may so weaken it that it succumbs to the attacks of predators or disease or to adverse environmental conditions (Adolph Murie, 1944: 87). The deficiency of any essential food item, such as a vitamin, may be as disastrous as the complete absence of food. Furthermore, an animal that is highly specialized in its food requirements may starve amidst an abundance of food of improper kinds.

PREDATORS AND HERBIVORES. Many individual animals die because of the attacks of predators and many plants because of the ravages of herbivores. To be eaten sooner or later in life is the fate of the great majority of organisms. Numerous animals that are attacked by predators manage to escape, but a few of these may be so injured that they die later. Many of the plants that are attacked by herbivores are only partly eaten, but often the plants are weakened and made more susceptible to other causes of mortality.

In certain situations herbivores may destroy all the seeds or seedlings of their preferred food plants. Thus, on certain experimental plots in England all the acorns and young oak seedlings were destroyed by birds, rabbits, and other animals (Watt, 1919). Only when the herbivores were excluded by a tight screen fence did a growth of young oaks become established.

PARASITES AND DISEASES. The attacks of parasites and of various kinds of infectious diseases frequently cause the death of many kinds of organisms. Almost all plants and animals suffer from these attacks during some part of their lives. An individual may be attacked at the same time by a number of different viruses, bacteria, fungi, spirochaetes, or other parasitic organisms. Even if these attacks do not cause the immediate death of the individual organism concerned, they often weaken it so much that it succumbs more easily to adverse environmental conditions. Unfortunately, few data are available on the mortality produced by infections and by parasites in natural plant and animal populations. Some good work in this field has been done by the Soviet ecologists (Kalabukhov, 1937), a little by the Bureau of Animal Population at Oxford, England, and a few random studies have been made in the United States (Green, Larson, and Bell, 1939).

COMPETITION AND STRIFE. Competition for light is an important cause of mortality among plants. Such competition may be especially fatal to the young seedlings. Competition among the plant roots for soil moisture also results in the death of many individuals (Shirley, 1945). Other kinds of competition must also at times be important for the survival of practically all kinds of plants.

Among animals competition for space, for food, or for mates often results in intraspecific strife, and this sometimes has fatal results for certain individuals. Among muskrats it has been noted by Errington (1943: 822-25; 840-41) that intraspecific strife is most severe when the populations are crowded or occupy unfavorable habitats. Under these conditions certain individuals, particularly those that are immature, may be killed outright and others may be so injured that they become more vulnerable to predators and more likely to succumb to an unfavorable environment. Intraspecific competition for food among fish often results in the stunting of the competing individuals (Lagler, 1944).

OVERPOPULATION. Population density often has a close relationship to mortality rate. Under crowded conditions the competition among individuals for food, shelter, and mates is likely to be severe. In crowded populations predators can more easily find their prey. Likewise, a dense population may attract predators from adjacent communities. Under crowded conditions, moreover, parasites and diseases multiply because the transfer of the infection from host to host is facilitated. Overpopulation, therefore, usually results in a high mortality rate.

UNDERPOPULATION. Sparse populations may under certain circumstances be subject to greater mortality than more dense populations. This is particularly true of highly social species. Thus, individual bobwhites studied experimentally by Gerstell (1939) were able, when in tightly huddled coveys, to withstand low environmental temperatures that were fatal to single birds.

INTERRELATIONS OF THE MORTALITY FACTORS. The several kinds of factors that serve to produce mortality in any given species are frequently more or less interrelated. A factor that is not in itself lethal may so weaken certain individuals that they succumb to some other cause of death more readily than is usual. For instance, bobwhites in Iowa that were suffering from a lack of food succumbed to a winter storm that caused no serious difficulty to better fed birds (Errington, 1941). It has also been pointed out earlier that disease or parasitic infection may render individuals more susceptible to predation or to other mortality factors.

Differential Mortality

Certain classes in a population often suffer a higher mortality rate than other classes. In times of severe food shortage, for instance, a higher proportion of the young individuals than of the older animals may die. The young animals often are unable to reach food supplies available to the larger adults. Thus, the fawns of deer may perish in numbers when the browse has been eaten by the older deer to a height above which the fawns can reach. The larger adults of various kinds of animals also are able by their strength to drive the younger individuals away from local food supplies. Very small young may not be well taken care of by starving parents and the young individuals are especially subject to accidental injury in overcrowded situations. Furthermore, the young are less able to defend themselves from predators and they may not be so successful in finding food as the adults.

DIFFERENCE BETWEEN THE SEXES IN MORTALITY. One sex may at certain ages or seasons have a higher mortality rate than the other sex. In human populations, for example, males seem to have a higher mortality rate than females at all ages, although the sex ratio at birth is in favor of the males. The exact proportions of boys and girls born seem to vary somewhat with different races and perhaps also at different places and different times, but at least in the Caucasian races more male than female babies are born (Pearl, 1924: 107). In old age, as a result of the higher male mortality, females outnumber males in practically all human populations. Among the bees, to cite an extreme example of unequal sex ratio, the wintering colony contains no males at all. All the males are eliminated from the hive on the approach of cold weather.

PRENATAL MORTALITY. Estimates of the rate of reproduction of viviparous animals usually are based on counts of the number of living offspring born. In every species, however, there seems to be a considerable amount of prenatal mortality, so that in calculations of reproductive rate based on counts of the number of embryos carried per female a correction must be made for the age of each set of embryos used in the computations.

The rate of prenatal mortality has been determined for only a few species of animals. A British vole (*Microtus agrestis*) under laboratory conditions showed a prenatal mortality of at least 21 per cent. Further, more than 14 per cent of those·born alive died under laboratory conditions during the 14 days between birth and weaning (Ransom, 1941). A peculiarity of *Microtus agrestis,* at least under laboratory conditions, is that certain females and males, called "rogues" by Ransom, have a greater tendency than others to eat or to lose their young before the weaning age. The "rogue" females also have a greater tendency than normal females to resorb their embryos.

From a study by Brambell (1944) based on counts of *corpora lutea* it is estimated that 60 per cent of the litters of the English wild rabbit (*Oryctolagus cuniculus*) that are conceived are lost because of the death and resorption of all the embryos. The loss in litters that survive to birth is between 9 and 10 per cent. In pocket gophers (*Thomomys bottae*) it was estimated by M. A. Miller (1946) that about 8 per cent of the embryos counted in the earliest stages die before birth and are resorbed. It is evident, therefore, that at least in mammals prenatal mortality is a very important factor affecting rate of reproduction.

INFANT MORTALITY. Infant mortality is another important factor in keeping down the numbers of most species of animals. The same thing is, of course, true of plants, the seedlings of which die in great numbers. Those species of animals that are given special protection by their parents may be assumed in general to have relatively low mortality rates in early life, while those that are early abandoned to the mercy of the environment have relatively high mortality rates at that period of life.

The degree of development of the young at birth undoubtedly has much to do with their chance of survival. Among the birds the young of certain species are born in a very undeveloped and helpless state, while the young of other forms are born in a much more self-sufficient condition. Every species, however, has special habits for the protection or concealment of its young. It may consequently happen that those young birds that are born in a very weak and helpless condition may, by reason of the protected location of the nest and/or the care provided by their parents, have a better chance of survival to maturity than the young of another species that are born in a well-developed state, but which receive less parental care.

Mortality Rate

The rate of mortality in a wild population of plants or animals never is uniform throughout the year, from year to year, or from place to place. On the contrary, the death rate is likely to be highest at certain ages, in certain seasons, in some years, and in certain areas. As has been pointed out, the young of many species die at a higher rate than the older individuals. Also, the death rate in winter is likely to be higher than in summer because of the more rigorous environmental conditions in the cold season. Furthermore, there are differences in rate of mortality from year to year due to variations in weather conditions, in the abundance of predators, in the prevalence of infectious disease, and in other factors. The rate of mortality, therefore, never is a constant for any species, but on the contrary it fluctuates from time to time and from place to place.

ENVIRONMENTAL RESISTANCE. R. N. Chapman (1928: 114) has suggested that the failure of realization of the "biotic potential" of a species must be due to "environmental resistance." Environmental resistance may perhaps be considered the sum of all the mortality factors that affect the individuals of a given species. No satisfactory methods are available, however, for measuring the whole environmental resistance. This is, in my opinion, an abstract term of little direct application and of ambiguous implications.

POPULATION DYNAMICS

The quantitative features of the variations that occur from time to time within a population are called population dynamics. A mathematical statement of the dynamics of every population would evidently be very useful to the ecologist if it could be obtained. If migration is negligible and if the rates of reproduction and of mortality in a given population are constant, a fairly simple formula will specify the balance between them. The resulting structure of the population may then be calculated. Unfortunately for the biometrician, the rates of reproduction and of mortality in nature are never constant for any species; on the contrary, there are frequent and sometimes violent fluctuations in both. Furthermore, migration is often an important factor in the dynamics of local populations. As a result, the mathematics of population dynamics is extremely complicated.

Measures of Reproductive Rate

The actual rate of reproduction of a given species will usually be measured in terms of the average number of offspring produced over a given interval of time by the individual organisms that make up the population. Due attention will need to be given to the method of reproduction and to the composition of the population according to sex and age class. Sterile and immature individuals will not be concerned in reproduction, but they must be considered in calculating the average rate of reproduction per individual in the population. Also it will be necessary to secure estimates of the variability in the rate of reproduction of the species from time to time and from place to place.

In sexual reproduction a new individual originates at the moment when the spermatozoon unites with the ovum. It is practically impossible, however, to observe the actual fertilization of the ovum. In measures of rate of reproduction, therefore, the offspring usually are counted at some stage in the life history later than fertilization. A new individual is generally assumed to have arisen as soon as it has become free from the parent and is capable of continuing to exist independently. In other words, fertility rather than fecundity is usually measured.

With many aquatic organisms no pairing of the sexes occurs, but both the ova and the sperm are discharged directly into the water, where fertilization occurs. In these aquatic forms the newly produced individuals can often best be counted as larvae. The rate of reproduction of many kinds of insects and other invertebrates may be estimated from counts of the number of eggs produced. Estimates of the reproductive rate of most fishes, amphibians, reptiles, and birds may also be based on counts of the number of eggs.

In any calculation of the rate of reproduction it is essential to specify a particular stage in the life history of the species as the time at which the next generation has originated. For practical considerations the stage of origin specified may vary somewhat from species to species depending upon the method of reproduction. Where fertilization occurs outside the body of the female, for example, the number of ova or of larvae may often be counted directly. Where fertilization is internal, on the contrary, counts of the number of offspring cannot usually be made until they have become free from the mother, as seeds, eggs, or living young.

The potential annual reproduction of a sexually reproducing species of animal is sometimes roughly calculated by multiplying the average number of breeding females per unit area by the average number of eggs or young which each female produces per litter or per clutch, and this by the average number of litters or clutches per breeding season. If more than one generation is produced by the species per year the calculations become more involved.

This potential annual rate of reproduction, however, is never realized owing to (1) the death of some females before all their litters or clutches of eggs have been produced, (2) the failure of some females to breed, and (3) variations in fertility caused by local environmental influences. The number of males in a population usually is sufficiently great to ensure the fertilization of all the females, but in those situations where there is a deficiency of males the potential rate of reproduction may be thereby decreased. In small populations the number of young actually produced may also deviate from expectation on account of chance variations from the averages used in the calculations.

In any calculation of the rate of reproduction special consideration should be given to the fact that mortality and the attainment of sexual maturity may cause the numbers and proportions of reproducing individuals in a population to change considerably during the course of each breeding season.

For many kinds of plants the reproductive rate may be calculated in terms of the number, volume, or weight of seeds, fruits, or spores produced per unit area of habitat. The measurement of reproductive rate consequently is much simpler with most kinds of plants than with animals. The fertility of seed-bearing plants also may be calculated from the average number of mature seeds produced per individual plant. Salisbury (1942: 43) defined average seed output as the mean number of seeds per fruit times the mean number of fruits per plant. He likewise defined average reproductive capacity as the average seed output multiplied by the proportion of germination, modified when necessary by an estimate of the rate of vegetative reproduction.

MEASURES OF REPRODUCTIVE SUCCESS. The degree of success achieved in rearing their young can be determined for certain kinds of animals, even though the precise mortality factors cannot always be distinguished. In a study made near Cleveland, Ohio, for example, Kendeigh (1942) noted that the several species of birds varied considerably in the degree of their success in rearing young to maturity. Some nests are destroyed or abandoned before any eggs are laid, but this may only delay rather than reduce the number of eggs ultimately laid. A small proportion of the eggs fails to hatch by reason of infertility or because development is arrested. Included among the causes of arrested development are hereditary and embryologic defects and failure of proper incubation at some stage. The proportion of infertile and of addled eggs is appreciably greater at high and at low than at medial air temperatures (Kendeigh, 1941a: 245-46). The eggs or the young birds in the nest may be destroyed by accident or by predators in any stage of their development.

In a general tabulation of the proportion of nests of birds that are successful in reaching the hatching stage, Kalmbach (1939) gave an average of 43 per cent for upland species nesting on or near the ground, 52 per cent for species nesting above ground level, 73 per cent for hole-nesting species, and 60 per cent for waterfowl. From a study of the California quail, Emlen (1940) concluded that each adult living in May has a 50 per cent chance of surviving a full year to the following May, but that the chance of an egg hatching and the young bird surviving to the age of 1 year is only 8.5 per cent.

TENDENCY TOWARD OVERPOPULATION. The reproductive potential of every species, if it were not checked by mortality, in theory would ultimately produce an enormous population. Even such a slow breeding species as the elephant, if it were not held in check by various mortality factors, would in time become excessively abundant, as was pointed out many years ago by Charles Darwin (1859) in his book on the origin of species.

To express reproductive potential in very simple mathematical terms, let B represent the average number of young reared to reproductive maturity in each generation per individual in a given population, let y be the number of generations the population continues under observation, and let P be the initial number of reproducing individuals in the population. Then the number of individuals expected in any given future generation may be computed from the following formula:

$$\text{Size of subsequent generation} = B^y P.$$

In this formula the number of generations is the exponent of the rate of reproduction B. Should the value of B be 1.0 the population will be main-

TABLE XIII

RELATION BETWEEN RATE OF REPRODUCTION AND INCREASE IN POPULATION

Theoretical increase in total population with various rates of reproduction.
Parents assumed to produce only 1 set of offspring and then to die.

Filial Generation	Number of Young Which Survive to Reproduce, per Parent per Generation						
	1.1	1.2	1.5	2.0	3.0	5.0	10.0
1.........	1.1	1.2	1.5	2	3	5	10
2.........	1.2	1.4	2.3	4	9	25	100
3.........	1.3	1.7	3.4	8	27	125	1,000
4.........	1.5	2.1	5.1	16	81	625	10,000
5.........	1.6	2.5	7.6	32	243	3,125	100,000
6.........	1.8	3.0	11.4	64	729	15,625	1,000,000
7.........	1.9	3.6	17.1	128	2,187	78,125	10,000,000
8.........	2.1	4.3	25.6	256	6,561	390,625	100,000,000
9.........	2.4	5.2	38.4	512	19,683	1,953,125	1,000,000,000
10.........	2.6	6.2	57.7	1,024	59,049	9,765,625	10,000,000,000

tained without change; if B is less than 1.0, the population will decrease in density; while if B has any value greater than 1.0 the population will tend to increase, according to a geometrical progression (Table XIII).

This formula greatly oversimplifies the process of reproduction in nature. It takes no account of the different responsibilities of the 2 sexes in reproduction nor of the effects of any inequality of the sex ratio on reproduction in the population concerned. No account is taken of the variations in fecundity between individuals nor of possible variations in rate of reproduction between generations. The differential effects of mortality are ignored. So also is the possibility that some individuals may reproduce during several successive breeding seasons and thereby produce an overlapping of generations. Possible changes from time to time in the proportion of immature, overage, or sterile individuals in the population are not considered. The formula is presented simply to show how great is the tendency for expansion in numbers by every species, no matter how slow its rate of reproduction.

More complex formulas can be developed which take account of certain of the variable factors that affect the rate of reproduction of particular species in nature (Aldo Leopold, 1939, appendix C; Kelker, 1947). A detailed mathematical treatment of the rate of increase in a particular population has been presented by Birch (1948). Special formulas will be needed for varying situations because the factors that control population growth differ for each species and for each kind of environment (Hammond, 1938-39). It is difficult, however, to devise formulas that make adequate allowance for all the variable factors that may affect the rate of reproduction. One thing is certain: whatever formula is used to describe the natural rate of increase of a species, the tendency is always for the population to increase.

A graphic demonstration of a geometric rate of increase may easily be given by plotting the time intervals against the logarithms of the population densities. If the rate of increase of the population is according to a geometric progression, the resulting curve will form a straight line (Severtzov, 1934).

Certain natural populations seem, in fact, to increase for a time in a geometric progression, such as would be expected if there were no check on their multiplication. Thus in Gatchino, near Leningrad, U.S.S.R., the partridge (*Perdix cinerea*), in periods after the population has been greatly reduced by a plague, sometimes increases for several years in a geometric progression (Severtzov, 1934: Fig. 3). That the multiplication of this bird is not entirely free from restriction is suggested, however, by the fact that its rate of increase differed in successive periods of years.

No population, however, can continue to increase in size indefinitely. There is an ultimate limit to the amount of food and space available in any habitat. As a species approaches the limits of its resources, we say that its habitat has become overcrowded. Through the attacks of predators, the ravages of parasites and infections, the competition of its fellows, and all the other causes of mortality the rate of increase of the population becomes retarded. Ultimately, if the conditions in the ecosystem remain uniform, the population will become more or less stationary at a density where reproduction and mortality balance each other. Thus, under laboratory conditions, with the temperature held constant and with a uniform amount of food added each day, small colonies of *Drosophila melanogaster* were found by L'Héritier and Teissier (1933) to reach an equilibrium of population at about the fortieth day following the origin of the colony.

Measures of Mortality Rate

Actual measurement of the mortality rate in nature is very difficult. Dead individuals are seldom found. The carcasses of most kinds of animals quickly disappear, even if they are not eaten by a predator. Many animals crawl into holes or crevices to die and consequently their bodies are easily overlooked. Dead plants, especially the smaller forms, usually vanish rapidly and often leave no trace. Even when a dead organism is found, it rarely is possible to determine the cause of its death.

The difficulty of measuring mortality rate directly is undoubtedly the reason why certain ecologists have attempted to secure such a measure indirectly by comparing the density of population at a given time with the theoretical density that should have resulted from a given rate of reproduction in the absence of mortality. Such calculations must necessarily be very inaccurate because of the numerous variables involved.

For small closed areas, such as ponds or lakes, it is possible to calculate the mortality rate of certain species of animals from counts of previously marked individuals of known age retaken in samples of the population collected at stated intervals (Jackson, 1939; Ricker, 1945). These calculations are subject to the limitations and errors involved in the estimate of population density according to the proportional method (see Chap. IV) and, as at present developed, are not widely applicable to natural populations. A major objection to the method in areas which do not have closed boundaries is the difficulty in distinguishing between mortality and emigration.

For those species in which the age of the individuals can be reliably determined, the mortality rate can be calculated from the differences in the proportions of the several age classes in the population. This method is especially applicable to those teleost fishes whose age can be ascertained from their scales (Ricker, 1945: 112; Silliman, 1945) and to those trees whose age is shown by their tree rings. For example, if it is calculated from samples of a given population that there are three-fifths as many individuals of a given age class as of the next younger age class, this indicates a survival rate of 0.60 and conversely, a mortality rate of 0.40 for the time interval between these age classes. This method assumes that the rates of reproduction were the same at the times when the 2 age classes compared were produced, that there has been no differential mortality between the 2 age classes, that any immigration into or emigration from the area of study has affected both age classes equally and that the sampling methods are adequate.

RELATION OF MORTALITY RATE TO POPULATION DENSITY. Mortality rate increases as population density increases. The relationship seems in at least some situations to form a geometric progression. At high densities, accordingly, the mortality rate may become so high that it equals or perhaps even exceeds the rate of reproduction of the species concerned. When this happens the population density must either remain stationary or begin to decline.

Fluctuations in Abundance

Recurrent cycles or irregular alternations of population growth and decline are exhibited by practically every species living in nature. Only very rarely does any species maintain itself at a stable density over a considerable period of time. Although man probably has more nearly stable population densities than any other organism, even human populations are subject to considerable fluctuations in density from time to time.

When we consider the fluctuations that occur both in the reproductive rates and in the mortality rates of practically every species that lives in a natural community, it is not surprising that fluctuations occur in the resulting population densities. The amazing thing is that any population is able to maintain even a semblance of stability.

SEASONAL CYCLES OF ABUNDANCE. In those species that have an annual reproductive season the total population will usually reach an annual maximum at the time the last reproductive units of the season have been produced. From that time until the next reproductive season has begun mortality will cause a decline of the number of individuals in the population. Most plants and animals of the Temperate and Frigid zones and many of the inhabitants of the tropics have well-defined breeding seasons, and all these accordingly pass through such a seasonal cycle of population.

The amplitude of the annual population cycle will usually be small in those species that are long-lived and have a low rate of reproduction. Species that are short-lived and have a high rate of reproduction, on the other hand, may have very violent seasonal fluctuations in numbers. This is true of many kinds of annual plants and of numerous kinds of insects and other invertebrates and of some vertebrates, such as the rodents. Seasonal fluctuations in numbers are likely to be especially large in those forms that produce several generations during each breeding season.

Seasonal cycles in the populations of many species of animals and plants are shown not only by fluctuations in numbers but also by changes in the proportions represented by the several life-history stages and age classes. Annual plants thus are represented in a community at certain seasons only by their seeds or other reproductive units. Likewise many kinds of perennial plants which die back to their roots in winter are not represented above ground in the community except during the growing season. Similarly, many kinds of animals pass the winter, or more rarely the summer, in a dormant condition. Many kinds of invertebrates become encysted and thus survive an unfavorable season. In other kinds of invertebrates some one stage in the life history is the one that survives the winter and is then ready in spring to perpetuate the species. In the wasps, for example, it is the fertilized queens that survive the winter and establish new wasp colonies in the spring (Duncan, 1939: 98). Other kinds of insects, however, may pass the winter as eggs, larvae, or pupae.

Most species of plants and animals have a single annual peak of abundance which coincides with the time of maximum production of their offspring. A number of species, however, have 2 or more peaks of abundance during a single year. Numerous species of marine organisms, for example, have more than a single annual peak of numbers. Such multiple seasonal peaks of numbers may be produced by those species that have more than 1 breeding season during the year and also by those that produce their young in more than 1 successive brood or litter during the breeding season.

PERIODIC FLUCTUATIONS IN ABUNDANCE. In addition to the changes from season to season in the numbers of most kinds of organisms, many species also fluctuate in abundance from year to year. Such periodic fluctuations have been described for many kinds of plants and animals. Aldo Leopold (1939: 51) has classified the annual population curves as flat, when little change in the population occurs from year to year; cyclic, when there is a somewhat gradual change in numbers which recurs at more or less regular intervals; and irruptive, when the population suddenly and at irregular intervals greatly increases for a brief period.

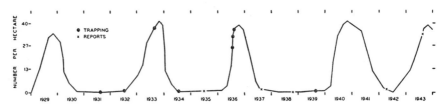

FIG. 26. Cyclic fluctuations from 1929 to 1943 in the estimated abundance per hectare (2.5 acres) of the varying lemming (*Dicrostonyx groenlandicus richardsoni*) in the Churchill area, Canada. (Redrawn from Shelford, 1943.)

The periodic fluctuations in abundance of certain species fall into a more or less regular cycle, with a fairly uniform number of years between successive periods of maximum or minimum numbers (Chap. VI). The snowshoe hare, muskrat, and lynx of Canada, and the New Brunswick salmon, for example, are said (Elton and Nicholson, 1942a, 1942b) to have an average periodicity of about 10 years between peaks of abundance. Many kinds of small rodents also exhibit periodic oscillations in numbers of a somewhat cyclic type (Fig. 26). Some of these fluctuations are said to have a periodicity of about 4 years (Hamilton, 1937: 788; Elton, 1942: 55, 219). In birds, Spiers (1939) reported that in the Toronto region of Canada the American rough-leg hawk, the snowy owl, and the northern shrike have a 3- to 5-year cycle of abundance, the pine grosbeak a 5- to 6-year cycle, and the goshawk and horned owl a 9- to 11-year cycle. For the ruffed grouse, C. H. D. Clarke (1936: 106) and King (1937) report an approximately 10-year cycle.

Diverse kinds of organisms exhibit varying amplitudes of fluctuations in their abundance. Certain species have a barely perceptible cycle of abundance, detectable by statistical methods, or perhaps no cycle at all. For example, Rall (1938) found an annual constancy in the numbers of a Middle Asiatic gerbille (*Pallasiomys meridianus*) over a period of 6 years. Certain species, however, have very violent year-to-year fluctuations in numbers, as is true of the snowshoe hare (*Lepus americanus*) of northern North America. In years of scarcity one may travel for miles and find little evidence of the presence of the species. During years of peak abundance, on the contrary, the animals often are exceptionally numerous and their tracks and droppings are almost everywhere (Seton, 1912: 95). Long-continued studies of populations have, unfortunately, been made of only a few kinds of organisms. Little information is at hand, therefore, concerning the amplitude of the fluctuations exhibited by the populations of most kinds of plants or animals.

The cycles of abundance of certain species undoubtedly are correlated with cycles in the physical factors of their environments, notably with temperature and with precipitation, but very likely also with many other physical factors. Many animal cycles evidently are directly related to food availability, which in its turn perhaps is controlled by climatic cycles. The

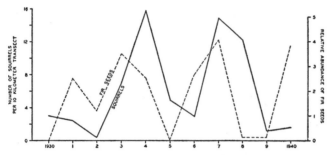

FIG. 27. Relation between the numbers of squirrels in the Gorkovsk District, U.S.S.R., and the abundance of fir seeds. (Redrawn from Formozov, 1942, after a figure published in the *Zoologitsheskij Journal*.)

principal factor causing the periodic fluctuations in the population density of snowshoe hares in a part of northern Wisconsin was determined by Green and Evans (1940) to be a variation in the mortality of the young hares, while there was no important variation in the rate of reproduction. Formozov (1942) has presented evidence to show that the numbers of the tree squirrel in a part of northern U.S.S.R. are related to the quantity of fir seeds available to the animals for food (Fig. 27). Other animal cycles may be caused by the attacks of predators on their prey and by the infection of their hosts by parasites.

Periodic fluctuations in the abundance of a given species are not always synchronous over all parts of its geographic range. Thus, the numbers of snowshoe hares and other animals may be increasing in one region of North America and at the same time decreasing in some other part of the range of the species (Chitty and Elton, 1940, Fig. 2; Chitty and Chitty, 1941, Figs. 3-4). This evidence suggests that fluctuations in the abundance of species are probably not entirely dependent upon a general climatic factor, such as sunspots, but are in considerable part controlled by local agencies.

Periodic fluctuations in the abundance of organisms, as already pointed out, will be more violent in species that have a short life span than in those in which each individual persists over a number of years. Annual plants accordingly are likely to fluctuate in numbers more than perennials, and short-lived animals more than those which are long-lived. Some of the most violent fluctuations in numbers are exhibited by certain insect pests, most of which live only for a brief season.

NONCYCLIC FLUCTUATIONS IN NUMBERS. Although the year-to-year fluctuations in the abundance of certain kinds of organisms seem to fall into more or less well-defined recurrent cycles, this is not by any means true of all plants or animals. Many species exhibit pronounced fluctuations in numbers which do not fall into any detectable cycle. For example, about 1931 and in the immediately following years eelgrass (*Zostera*), a seaweed, almost completely died out along the Atlantic coasts of Europe and North America. This plant is an important food for a number of kinds of waterfowl and it also serves directly or indirectly as a source of food for many marine animals (C. Cottam, 1934). Its disappearance produced serious alterations in many littoral and off-shore communities.

In the western yellow pine of northern Arizona, to cite another example, successful reproduction occurs only irregularly and often only at those long intervals when 2 or more years of climatic conditions favorable for the generation and growth of seedlings immediately follow a year of good seed crop (G. A. Pearson, 1923). During those periods of years in which reproduction is not successful, the yellow pine population will, of course, slowly decrease as a result of mortality.

Cyclic and noncyclic types of fluctuations in abundance are often combined in the same species. For example, a species of mosquito, *Anopheles rangeli,* was determined by Bates (1945: 24) to be about 10 times as abundant in eastern Colombia during its yearly maximum as at its yearly minimum in both the years 1942 and 1943. In 1942, the species was about 10 times as abundant as in 1943. Here then there was an annual cyclic fluctuation in abundance combined with a fluctuation from year to year which presumably was noncyclic.

ANIMAL PLAGUES. Certain kinds of animals may at times grow extraordinarily abundant and by their numbers and destructiveness may become plagues. Furthermore, there is a tendency for these animals, once they have exhausted the food resources of the areas in which they have reproduced, to spread to surrounding areas; there also they may constitute a plague. Such plagues of grasshoppers (locusts), army worms, chinch bugs, and other insects are well known. Plagues of many other kinds of animals have also been described, including the plague of frogs in Egypt described in the Bible.

Plagues of rodents have been reported in many regions (Elton, 1942). These plagues are of particular interest to man because of the damage often caused to growing crops and to stored foods. The lemming of Scandinavia, for example, in certain years becomes extraordinarily numerous and descends from its usual mountain habitat to invade the lowlands. There is some evidence of a 4-year periodicity in the lemming migrations (Elton, 1942: 219).

A nonperiodic type of rodent plague is illustrated by the house-mouse outbreak of 1926 in Kern County, California (Hall, 1927). In this area most of the native mammalian predators had been previously removed. Because of a temporarily favorable food supply in the local area the mice greatly increased in numbers. Then, when their food was exhausted they were forced to emigrate. In the path of their migration so many animals were crushed on a highway that in places the pavement became slippery and dangerous for automobiles.

Mathematical Treatment of Population Dynamics

Precise mathematical treatment of the balance between reproductive rate and mortality rate in any given species is very difficult because of the many variables and because of the complex interrelationships of the numerous factors. For example, in the formula (B^yP) for the increase in a theoretical population previously given the conditions were assumed to be much more simple than would ever be the case in nature. Any deviation of the number of offspring in a particular generation from the average number expected would result in a deviation from expectation in subsequent generations. Variations actually do occur in every generation in sex ratio, in population structure, in individual fertility, and in other factors that affect reproductive rate. Plus and minus variations in rate of reproduction, however, will not balance each other in succeeding generations because of the geometric nature of population increase. For this reason, also, it seems impractical to calculate the variance of the rate of increase.

In many species the parents continue to reproduce after their offspring have reached sexual maturity. This, of course, results in an overlapping of generations and still further complicates the calculation of rate of reproduction. Crombie (1945: 365) has pointed out that the logistic equation cannot be a universal law of population growth. The factors, such as seasonal reproduction, that affect the multiplication of individuals prevent a regular rate of increase of density. Only under greatly simplified laboratory conditions and only for species that reproduce constantly and regularly can the growth of a population be described by simple mathematical formulas.

General mathematical treatment of population problems has been attempted by several entomologists (Sweetman, 1936: 18), and by a number of other biometricians (Lotka, 1925; R. A. Fisher, 1930; Volterra, 1928; A. J. Nicholson, 1933; Gause, 1934a; Bodenheimer, 1938). Many of these computations are based mostly or wholly upon theoretical considerations. Where observational data are employed as a basis for the calculations, these data have been derived mostly from laboratory studies in which the environmental conditions are intentionally made much more simple than those in a natural community. A few attempts, however, have been made to describe the dynamics of natural populations in mathematical terms. Edmondson (1945), for example, has presented information about the population dynamics of a rotifer (*Floscularia conifera*) growing in nature in Connecticut.

In spite of the enormous complexity of the interrelations of the factors affecting the rates of reproduction and of survival of individual organisms living in nature, mathematical treatment of various phases of the subject is possible. As the numerous controlling factors become identified and measured, mathematics will without question become an increasingly valuable tool in the analysis of the dynamics of populations. At the present time thorough and long-continued quantitative studies of the rates of increase, rates of mortality, and fluctuations of populations living under natural conditions are very much needed.

LOGISTIC CURVE OF POPULATION GROWTH. Mathematically the expansion of a population living in a sparsely occupied habitat and its ultimate stabilization at some definite level of density may be represented by a logistic curve (Pearl, 1925: 1-24; Gause, 1934a: 34). In the beginning such a population, if there is no competition with other species and if there is an absence of enemies, may grow at almost the theoretical rate of potential increase and the curve, therefore, turns steeply upward. As the population increases, however, the competition becomes keener and all the mortality factors operate at a higher rate. The slope of the curve then reverses its direction and ultimately approaches the horizontal.

Such curves of population growth actually are obtained from certain experiments in the laboratory. Thus, if a very small number of protozoa, fruit flies, flour beetles, or other small organisms is placed in a container with an abundance of food, the population will grow at approximately the calculated rate until an equilibrium ultimately is reached at a certain level of population density, beyond which the population does not grow further.

With vertebrates, however, population growth under laboratory conditions is not so regular as with the smaller organisms. Thus, in a laboratory study of the effects of crowding on albino house mice, Crew and Mirskaia (1931) found that the death rate, reproductive rate, and fecundity were affected by the population density, but that the degree of response varied greatly from cage to cage because of the inability of certain individuals to adjust to the crowded conditions. Because of individual variations among vertebrates in combativeness and in other aspects of their social relations, detailed studies of the effects of overcrowding in vertebrate populations are difficult to evaluate.

The tendency of every population is to attain a level of numbers at which it comes into adjustment with the resources of its habitat. In a uniform laboratory habitat, in which none of the physical or biotic factors essential for the life of the species concerned is subject to variation, the growth of the population often follows a reasonably smooth curve. Furthermore, the maximum possible population density which is reached tends to be maintained. If, on the contrary, certain important factors of the habitat vary from time to time, or if competitors, predators, parasites, or diseases are present in the community, then the growth of the population is not likely to follow a uniform pattern, nor is the population likely to remain constant at any given density.

It is interesting to note that the rate of growth of the human populations of the United States and of certain other countries has in the past followed logistic curves (Pearl, 1925). The interpretation of this correspondence in the growth of a human population to that of a population of fruit flies in a milk bottle, however, is not easy. The curve at least suggests that there must be an upper limit to the density of human population that is capable of being supported in any given ecosystem, just as there is a maximum density possible for each kind of organism in each natural ecosystem.

INDIVIDUAL LONGEVITY. The individuals of every species vary in their longevity. Should one, for example, take 1,000 newly emerged flour beetles and keep them under uniform laboratory conditions, certain individuals would probably die within their first day of life; while others might survive for 100, 200, or 300 days, and a few might even live more than 400 days (Pearl, Park, and Miner, 1941). These variations in longevity are due in part to variations in heredity and in part to variations in the environmental conditions to which the individuals are exposed.

LIFE TABLES. Human populations exhibit the most constant rates of reproduction and of mortality of any known species. For the regions of the world where birth and death rates are known it has been possible for statisticians to prepare life tables showing the number of years a person of any stated age may be expected to live. Likewise, the proportional numbers of persons who are expected to die at any given age may be estimated. The size of the total population and its age structure, therefore, may be predicted for a number of years.

Methods for preparing life tables and also for calculating the reproductive values of a species have been described by R. A. Fisher (1930: 22-30) and by others. Life tables have been constructed not only for man but also for several kinds of animals grown under laboratory conditions. Thus, for example, life tables have been published by Pearl and Parker (1924) for the fruit fly (*Drosophila melanogaster*) and by Pearl and Miner (1935) for several strains of the fruit fly, for a slug (*Agriolimax agrestis*), and for a rotifer (*Proales decipens*). Greenwood (1928) has published life tables for the house mouse (*Mus musculus*) and Leslie and Ranson (1940) for an English vole (*Microtus agrestis*). Life tables for one species of flour beetle (*Tribolium confusum*) have been calculated by Pearl, Park, and Miner (1941) and for another species (*Tribolium madens*) by T. Park (1945).

It is difficult, however, to prepare life tables for any species of wild organism because precise information about the birth rates and death rates of wild species is lacking and particularly because the rates of reproduction and mortality of organisms living in nature fluctuate from season to season and from year to year. Nevertheless, tentative life tables have been prepared for a few wild populations. In a review of this subject Deevey (1947) gave life tables for certain populations of the bighorn sheep, of the herring gull, American robin, and several other birds, of a rotifer, and of a barnacle. A life table for the herring gull has also been presented by Paynter (1949).

POPULATION TURNOVER. The movement of individual organisms into and out of a concrete population constitutes population turnover. Turnover is produced by the birth of new individuals, by death, by immigration, and by emigration. The populations of numerous species exhibit a very rapid turnover, especially at certain seasons, while in other species it is slower and more regular. The type of population turnover exhibited by any given species depends upon its type and rate of reproduction, upon the frequency with which generations succeed one another, upon the potential length of life of the individuals, upon the habits of the species in regard to dispersal and migration, upon the type and rate of mortality to which it is subject, and upon all other factors that may affect its existence.

The simplest type of population turnover is exhibited by those species in which there is only a single generation per year and in which all the individuals die after they have produced the next generation. In a population of such a species all the individuals are of approximately the same age and there is a complete turnover of the population each year, as is true of annual plants. Many insects and other invertebrates and a few vertebrates also live only 1 year and produce only a single brood of young. These forms also have a complete and rapid turnover in population. A still more rapid turnover may take place in those species that produce more than 1 generation per year.

The individuals of many species, however, live longer than a single generation. Individuals of several age classes, therefore, may exist in a population at the same time. This is true of the perennial plants and of many kinds of animals. The oldest individual organisms now living are the big trees (*Sequoia gigantea*) of California, certain ones of which are reported to be over 3,000 years old (Sudworth, 1908: 141-42). In these groves occur many younger trees of the same species. In such a potentially long-lived species the rate of turnover in population must be extremely slow.

A study of population turnover in the introduced ring-necked pheasant on a particular area in Wisconsin, ascertained through banding, showed that no individual survived to the fifth winter, and that survival in the 4 age classes was represented by the series 100-30-9-1.80. In this species the shrinkage or turnover rate between winters is about 70 per cent, and the data suggest that when once a bird has reached its first winter its chances of survival do not increase with age (Leopold *et al.*, 1943).

The northern race of the American robin (*Turdus migratorius migratorius*) was estimated by Farner (1945) to have a mortality rate of probably 70 per cent between the time the birds are hatched and November 1 of the same year. The annual mortality rate from November 1 to the same date in the following year is slightly more than 50 per cent for each age class, except for that age class which is less than 1 year of age. The average natural longevity in nature is 1.7 years. This is only a fraction of the potential longevity of at least 9 years, ascertained from banded birds, or a total potential longevity of 13 years or more, shown by birds in captivity.

The character of the turnover in the snowshoe-hare population in one part of Minnesota has been shown by Green and Evans (1940) to vary somewhat from year to year because of annual variations in birth rate and in mortality. During the spring census period the proportion of yearling hares making up the population varied in different years from 44 to 85 per cent. Some of the hares lived to be more than 5 years old and in 1 year for which there are data concerning this age class the proportion of these older hares in the population was 2 per cent.

In calculating annual population turnover, zoologists have used various months of the year as the basis for the calculations. Certain authors have assumed each year to start on August 1, others have begun the year on November 1, and still others have used different dates. After a careful study of the turnover of population of several British birds it was recommended by Lack (1946*b*) that in the northern hemisphere all calculations of survival rate should use January 1 of each year as a starting date. In the southern hemisphere, because of the difference in the breeding season, it will be necessary, of course, to start the year on July 1 instead of on January 1.

POPULATION STRUCTURE. The structure of every population varies from time to time because of changes in the proportions of the several classes of individuals that make it up. Periodicities in reproduction and in mortality result of necessity in frequent changes in population structure. Seasonal and annual changes in the composition of populations are especially conspicuous in annual plants and in short-lived animals, but practically all populations vary from time to time in their structure. Some attention has been given by ecologists to the mathematical statement of population structure (Bodenheimer, 1938: 21-28). In most populations, however, the variables are too numerous for simple analysis. A graphic illustration of the changes that are continually in progress in the structure of a population of California ground squirrels is given in Figure 28.

The proportional length of the reproductive life of the individuals affects in a very important way the composition of every population. With a species that lives for either a few or for many years and produces a single set of reproductive units, the population will be composed mostly of immature, nonreproducing individuals. Examples are the century plant and other members of the agave group, the periodic cicadas, and many kinds of aquatic insects.

At the opposite extreme are the annual plants and animals, which flourish during a single growing season, reproduce, and then die. During the reproductive season populations of these annuals will be composed almost exclusively of breeding individuals. Biennial plants die in their second year

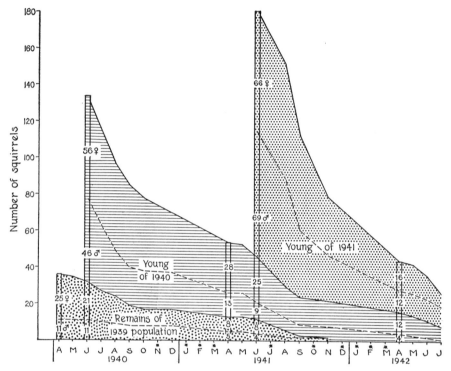

FIG. 28. Seasonal and annual fluctuations in the structure of a population of California ground squirrels. (After Evans and Holdenried, 1943.)

of life, after they have produced a single set of seeds. A population of biennials, therefore, is composed during the growing season of 2 classes, the immature plants of the year and the 2-year old plants that are now capable of reproduction.

A still more complex sort of population is produced by those perennial plants and animals that continue to produce offspring for a number of years after they have reached reproductive maturity. Such a population will be made up of young, immature organisms of various ages, of reproducing individuals which also represent various ages, of perhaps a few individuals which have passed the reproductive age or have at least begun to decline in their reproductive capacity, and of individuals sterile for other reasons.

Separated populations of the same species often differ from one another in their structure. Human populations, for example, usually are made up of immature individuals of both sexes, of sexually mature females and males, of females that have passed the reproductive age, and of old and more or less decrepit males. In a frontier community, however, the human population may for a time be composed almost exclusively of mature and vigorous males.

Individuals living in nature rarely attain the age to which they would potentially be able to live if not exposed to the hazards of predators, disease, and other natural mortality factors. Their ranks are constantly depleted by death. Old age is almost never attained. The result is that in those natural populations which include several age classes most of the individuals are relatively young.

The population structures of natural populations, therefore, differ greatly from those of modern human populations, in which a considerable proportion of the individuals are relatively advanced in age. Lack (1943), for example, has shown that in the British blackbird (*Turdus merula*) individuals which are near the end of their potential life span are exceedingly rare.

Among primitive peoples the population structure presumably approaches that of the natural populations of other animals. Old individuals are rare in primitive societies. Burial records from ancient Rome and Hispania, for example, indicate that the population structure at that time was nearly like that of a natural population and differed greatly from the population structure of modern man (Macdonell, 1913).

SATURATION POINT. The maximum size of population possible for any species on a given area is not fixed solely by the carrying capacity of the area in terms of food and shelter. Increase of the amount of available food above a certain point may not result in any increase of a desired species. The density above which a given population fails to increase has been termed its saturation point by Leopold (1939: 50).

The saturation point of each species is fixed by the interactions of a complex of factors, among which the social habits of the form may be considered important. In a species, for instance, that sets up fixed breeding territories, each inhabited as a rule by a single pair, the total population per unit area will depend upon the size of the breeding territories. When the territories have been compressed to the minimum size tolerated by the species, there will be constant fighting among the animals and no more breeding pairs will be able to occupy the area. The stags of the European red deer, for instance, frequently fight, both during the breeding season and at other times of the year. The young often are wantonly killed. This species, therefore, will not tolerate any overcrowding (Darling, 1937: 35).

The flour beetle (*Trilobium confusum*) likewise cannot endure crowding. Under crowded conditions the larvae and adults eat many of the eggs which are laid. This factor helps to prevent a population of this species from increasing above a certain maximum level, even though flour for food may be present in abundance (Chapman and Whang, 1934). This cannibalistic habit of the beetles, however, is not the most important factor in limiting the density of population that flour beetles can attain under a favorable laboratory environment. Under crowded conditions fewer eggs are produced because the fecundity of the females is affected. This decrease in fecundity seems to be one of the most important factors fixing the saturation point of these beetles (Boyce, 1946).

The distinction between saturation point and carrying capacity should be clearly understood. Certain species fail to increase beyond a certain population density, no matter how much the conditions in their habitats may be improved. When the population densities of a species do not increase beyond a certain level in stands of varying quality, it may be assumed that some factor in the habits or in the physiology of the species itself imposes this limit of density. The limit to population density thus imposed by the species itself is its saturation point. Carrying capacity, on the contrary, refers to the number of individuals which an ecosystem could support in the absence of biotic controls.

OPTIMUM POPULATION DENSITY. The level of population density at which a given species reaches its maximum of productiveness may be called its optimum population density (Elton, 1930: 25). This is a term borrowed from human biology (Carr-Saunders, 1922: 201). The optimum population density is a point of great interest to wildlife managers, foresters, agriculturalists, and human ecologists.

The optimum density for a population will seldom be at its saturation point because with overcrowded conditions the fertility of the breeding individuals will probably be reduced. At the saturation point also there will likely be heavy mortality among the young individuals and those which survive may be more or less stunted in their growth. Neither will the productiveness of a species be at its maximum when the population density is low, for under such conditions the number of breeding individuals will be insufficient to produce enough offspring to utilize fully the resources of the habitat. In the haddock (*Melanogrammus aeglefinus*) of the New England banks, for example, it has been shown by Herrington (1944) that there is an intermediate density of population at which the productiveness of the haddock fishery in terms of weight of fish produced is greatest. When the population density is low, the productiveness of the haddock fishery is low because of the limited spawning stock. When the population density is too high, the productivity also is reduced, presumably because of the competition of the young fish with the overabundant adults for food and because many of the young are devoured by the larger fish.

MINIMUM SIZE OF POPULATION FOR SURVIVAL. When the numbers of a species fall very low in a given area, the species often completely disappears.

A new stock for the area usually is soon provided by immigration from adjacent populations. If, however, the numbers of the species have everywhere been reduced to very low levels, then there may be no reserve for repopulation and the whole species may rather suddenly become extinct. This seems actually to have happened to several forms that have become extinct in recent years, such as the passenger pigeon and the heath hen.

The exact reasons why a small population is not able to maintain itself are not fully known. Aldo Leopold (1939: 86) has pointed out that any local misfortune, such as an epidemic disease, a violent storm, or the concentrated attack by a number of predators, may by chance destroy a local population. He has also suggested that for those species which travel in herds or flocks, a small group will not be as well able to survive as a larger band.

Social species often fail to thrive unless the individuals are able to form social aggregations of proper size. Many kinds of animals facilitate reproduction and survival by living in a social group (Allee, 1938). Large colonies of certain gulls are believed by Darling (1938), for example, to be more successful in reproduction than smaller colonies of the same species. A careful study of redwing blackbird colonies by H. M. Smith (1943), however, failed to reveal any correlation in that species between colony size and reproductive success. Many kinds of plants also succeed better when several are growing in a group than they do as solitary individuals. For many, but not by any means for all kinds of organisms, therefore, too low a density of population may be a handicap to survival.

It may also be pointed out that when the individuals of a sexually reproducing species are thinly scattered over a considerable area, they may have difficulty in finding mates. I have often wondered whether or not the large ears of desert mammals are not specially adapted to the finding of mates in this arid environment, rather than to helping them escape enemies, which is the more usual explanation of the large ears.

Another possible explanation of the failure of small isolated populations to survive is the decrease of fertility that is frequently the accompaniment of inbreeding. In the laboratory it is seldom possible to carry a strain of *Peromyscus* inbred by brother-sister matings for more than about 4 generations. The sterility factors, presumably recessive in nature, that are brought out in such inbred strains must be widespread in wild populations, where they are of little consequence so long as there is a sufficiently large population to avoid close inbreeding.

RELATION BETWEEN REPRODUCTIVE RATE AND MORTALITY RATE

The reproductive rate and mortality rate of every kind of organism must evidently be related. This was pointed out long ago by Herbert Spencer and has been referred to by many more recent authors, for example, by Severtzov (1940) and by Moreau (1944).

Herbivorous animals have higher rates of reproduction than do carnivores. Because a carnivore during its life may consume many herbivores, it is evident that herbivores must as a rule have a relatively high rate of reproduction. The herbivorous rodents, for example, have in general much larger litters and more litters per year than do the snakes, hawks, owls, foxes, and other predators that prey upon them.

Some of the larger herbivores, however, such as the horses and cattle, have a relatively low rate of reproduction. Notwithstanding this fact, large mammals of every type usually are successful in maintaining themselves because of their relatively low rate of mortality. On the contrary, parasites, no matter what their size, usually have exceptionally high reproductive rates, which are obviously correlated with the hazard of any individual parasite reaching a suitable host.

The statement sometimes is made that reproductive rate is adjusted to mortality rate. A more correct statement is that mortality rate is adjusted to reproductive rate. But neither of these statements tells the whole truth.

The chance of success of a given reproductive unit is related not only to its ability to find a suitable habitat but also to its ability to survive there in competition with the other organisms already occupying the site. Salisbury (1942) has forcefully pointed out that a plant which is to begin life in the shade of a forest or in a community where competition with other individuals is severe must generally have a larger reserve of food (and therefore have larger seeds) than a plant which begins life on bare soil. In a thick sod, for example, a considerable supply of reserve food is required for a young plant to grow tall enough to reach the sunlight and thus to begin to make its own food by photosynthesis. Those saprophytic plants of which the young seedlings are parasitic, or which are able to establish symbiotic relations with mycorrhiza, however, may succeed with very small seeds.

The amount of its substance which any individual organism can afford to utilize for the purpose of reproduction is obviously limited. The number of reproductive units produced must accordingly have a direct relationship to their size. If a large number of reproductive units are produced per individual parent, the size of the units must be small. Not as many acorns, for example, can be produced by a plant of a given size as can wind-blown seeds or spores. Nor can a small mammal produce as many offspring as an oyster of similar bulk.

Every species accordingly must establish a compromise between the numbers of reproductive units which it produces and the store of energy with which they are provided or the stage of development at which they are released. Those species for which suitable niches exist only temporarily on widely dispersed sites (such as the hosts available to a parasite) must of necessity produce a great number of reproductive units and these consequently must be small. On the contrary, those species of which the offspring usually occupy the same stand or microstand as the parent will usually find it desirable to give their offspring as good a start in life as possible, either by providing them with a good reserve of stored food (Salisbury, 1942: 232) or by producing them, like certain viviparous animals, in an advanced state of development.

The size and kind of reproductive units produced by any species, then, are adaptive characters which must be adjusted to the conditions of existence of the young individuals. Natural selection tends to establish as an inherited character the rate of reproduction which is most favorable to the continuing success of each species (Lack, 1948).

The most significant feature of reproductive rate in all kinds of plants and animals is that the rate in every species is on the average greater and often is very much greater than is necessary for the maintenance of the current population density. The advantages of producing a surplus of population over that needed for maintaining the average density are numerous. Such a surplus forms a reserve against temporary adversity; it enables the species to spread out into neighboring suitable habitats; and it provides for progressive evolution. Nevertheless, the individuals which are surplus must sooner or later be removed by mortality.

SELECTED REFERENCES

Bodenheimer, F. S. 1938. Problems of animal ecology. London: Oxford Univ. Press. Chaps. 1, 2, and 3.

Chapman, Royal N. 1931. Animal ecology. New York and London: McGraw-Hill Book Co. Chap. 8.

Elton, Charles. 1927. Animal ecology. New York: Macmillan Co. Chaps. 8 and 9.

———. 1942. Voles, mice, and lemmings; problems in population dynamics. Oxford: Clarendon Press.

Graham, Samuel A. 1939. Principles of forest entomology. 2d ed.; New York: McGraw-Hill Book Co. Chaps. 3 and 4.

Leopold, Aldo. 1939. Game management. New York and London: Charles Scribner's Sons. Chaps. 3 and 7.

Salisbury, E. J. 1942. The reproductive capacity of plants. London: George Bell and Sons.

IX

FLUCTUATIONS IN COMMUNITY COMPOSITION

The composition of every ecologic community undergoes constant changes, due to germination of new plants, birth of new animals, growth of the individuals, transformation of the individuals from one life-history stage to another, deaths, local movements, and migrations. Some individual plants and animals may at times become inactive or dormant. In certain seasons a species may be represented in a community only by seeds, spores, or cysts. Each member species exhibits frequent fluctuations of greater or lesser amplitude in its population density and in the activity of its individuals. The several species composing a community vary also from time to time in the proportional representation of their several age classes, life-history stages, and sexes.

Although the several species that make up a community have many interdependencies with one another and although the rise and fall of the population densities of numerous member species may be directly or indirectly controlled by the same cyclic factors in the environment, nevertheless every species differs to some extent from every other species in its life history, in its behavior, and in its responses to the various environmental factors. In particular, species differ from one another in their periods of reproduction, in their seasons of greatest mortality, and in their times of activity. Animal species differ also from one another in the distances that the individuals cover in their daily wanderings and seasonal travels.

As a result of the differences among the several member species in their times of activity, in the patterns of their fluctuations, and in population density, the composition of every community varies from hour to hour, from day to day, from season to season, and from year to year. Some of these changes in community composition are minor fluctuations in the relative abundance of certain member species; others are shifts in the presence or absence of certain species that result in important changes in community structure. Changes in community organization often are caused by the more violent variations in community composition. In this discussion, however, no attempt will be made to distinguish the variations which affect only community structure from those variations which also affect community organization.

190

NONSYNCHRONOUS FLUCTUATIONS IN POPULATION DENSITIES

The fluctuations in population densities of the associated species in any particular community often fail to coincide in time. This lack of synchrony
in the variations of the densities of the member species often results in
striking fluctuations in community composition. The several species of fruit
flies of the genus *Drosophila* living at Austin, Texas, for example, vary in
their seasonal abundance independently of one another. Certain of these
species reach their greatest abundance in the summer, others in the winter,
spring, or fall. Certain species of the flies are abundant in both spring and
fall, but are scarce or absent in summer and in winter (Patterson, 1943, Fig.
66).

DIVERSITY IN SEASON OF REPRODUCTION. Lack of synchrony among the
several member species in their time of reproduction is one of the more important causes of fluctuations in the composition of communities. Only a
few kinds of plants or animals have a constant rate of reproduction, as was
pointed out in Chapter VIII. Most species reproduce periodically; some of
them several times per year, others only once annually, and still others only
at intervals of several years. The season of reproductive activity also varies
for each species. The reproductive units produced at a given season may not
immediately begin to grow into mature organisms. Among the plants, particularly, the seeds or spores may remain dormant in the ground for many
months or even for years before germinating.

The annual reproductive period of most kinds of plants and animals is
limited to a particular season of the year. With many species the season
during which new individuals appear is very brief. Periodicity in reproduction results in an increase of the population density of the species concerned
during its breeding season. For the remainder of the year, when no reproduction is occurring, the incidence of mortality will cause a gradual decrease in the population density. The populations of those species of animals that produce several broods or litters during a single breeding season
will show additional fluctuations in abundance, due to the increase in density at the time of birth of each brood and to the decline in density between
these periods.

In certain communities the reproductive seasons of a considerable number of the member species may closely coincide, and thus these associated
species may annually increase in abundance at the same season. In frigid
and temperate climates, for example, the young plants and young animals
of most species appear during the short summer. Under such conditions a
more or less synchronous increase in the population densities of numerous
member species would be expected during the breeding season, with a corresponding synchronous decrease in population densities during the remainder of the year. In other words, while there may be considerable fluctuation in population densities, the proportional composition of the community may be expected to remain about the same throughout the year.

Actually, in spite of numerous correspondences of reproductive rhythm among the members of the same community, no community ever maintains uniformity in its composition for any length of time. Even though several associated species may have the same breeding season, certain of these forms will multiply much more rapidly than others; consequently, there will be seasonal changes in their proportional representation. Species vary also in the age at which their members attain reproductive maturity and in the time required for the growth of their offspring.

Progression of Life-history Stages. Almost all organisms in the course of their individual development pass through several life-history stages. The successive life-history stages of a single species may differ greatly from one another in their ecologic relations. Thus, a tree is a very different type of organism from the seed or even from the seedling from which it grew. Likewise, young plants and young animals in their early life-history stages may occupy very different niches in the community from those occupied by the mature individuals. The larvae of many kinds of insects, for example, are members of aquatic communities, while the adults are free flying and are members of adjacent terrestrial communities. The larvae of terrestrial insects often are much more restricted in their habitats than are the adults and utilize foods differing from those consumed by the adults. Among parasitic species the several life-history stages frequently utilize several successive hosts. Among the social insects a number of castes may be produced, each having special adaptive characters.

The changes from one life-history stage to another seldom are synchronous among the several member species of a given community. Consequently, the changes in life-history stage which succeed one another in the member species produce important fluctuations in the composition of the community.

Dissimilarities in Mortality Pattern. Dissimilarity among the species in mortality pattern is another factor that produces fluctuations in community composition. The incidence of mortality differs for each member species of a community. The mortality rate is greater for certain species than for others. The season of heaviest mortality for each species also differs more or less from that of every other species. A certain species, for example, may suffer so severely from winter mortality that it may be almost or completely eliminated from the community. On the contrary, other species may suffer their greatest mortality during seasons of heat or of drought. These dissimilarities among the several associated species in mortality rates and patterns result in constant fluctuations in their relative abundance in the community.

Length of Life Span. Certain of the species that make up a community have much longer spans of life than others. Thus, the individuals of some species of organisms live only a few days or have even a shorter life span. On the other hand, certain kinds of animals may live for a score or more of years and certain kinds of forest trees may live for a number of centuries.

Those species that are long-lived cannot have rapid fluctuations in their abundance, while the shorter-lived species may fluctuate violently in numbers within a short period of time. These dissimilarities in life span among the several member species of a community, therefore, are related in an important way to fluctuations in community composition.

DIFFERENTIAL RESPONSE TO THE PHYSICAL HABITAT. The several associated species that compose any given community often respond differently to the fluctuations in the physical factors of the habitat. A decrease in temperature, for instance, may be fatal to many individuals belonging to a warmth-loving species, but may produce an increase in the populations of those species that reproduce at low temperatures. In summers following severe winters in the Woods Hole region of Massachusetts, for example, certain species of the local marine invertebrates decrease in number, but certain species of northern affinities increase in abundance (Allee, 1919, 1923). During a drought the mesic species may be eliminated or greatly reduced in numbers in certain terrestrial habitats at the same time that the xeric species increase in abundance. This effect is well illustrated by changes in the composition of certain grassland communities on the Great Plains which took place during the great drought of the 1930's (J. E. Weaver, 1943).

INTERNAL PHYSIOLOGIC RHYTHMS. Numerous kinds of organisms possess physiologic rhythms which are more or less independent of the external conditions of their habitats. Such an internal rhythm, for example, is present in every species which requires more than a single year to complete its life cycle. The internal rhythm of each species usually differs from that of every other species. Consequently, the times of reproduction and of activity differ from species to species, and this also produces fluctuations in community composition.

DEPENDENCE ON ASSOCIATED SPECIES. The fluctuations in the population densities of certain species follow the cycles of abundance of one or more of their associated species. For instance, the cycle of numbers of the Canada lynx follows and lags a little behind the cycle of abundance of its principal prey species, the snowshoe hare (Seton, 1912: 98). An increase in abundance of one species may, on the other hand, cause a decrease in the numbers of a competing species.

FLUCTUATIONS IN ACTIVITY

Lack of synchrony in the periods of activity of the numerous associated species of plants and animals that make up a community is another factor that produces many fluctuations in community structure. Many species either exhibit periodicities in their activity during each 24-hour period (O. Park, 1940) or have fluctuations in their activity which are correlated with the seasons. Many species, too, have periodicities of both types. The periodicities in activity of the several species making up a community, moreover, frequently do not parallel one another.

DIEL VARIATIONS IN ACTIVITY. During their daily inactive periods most plants continue to maintain the same positions that they occupy when they are active. Their function in the community, however, may vary in the several diel phases. For example, when the sun shines, green plants perform photosynthesis. In darkness they consume part of their stored food.

The diel rhythm of dormancy, which in animals is called sleep, affects the composition of the community in much the same manner as the more prolonged seasonal dormancy induced in many species by such environmental factors as cold, drought, or scarcity of food.

During the part of the day that an animal is inactive he has a different relation to the community from that which he bears when he is active. An animal also may occupy a somewhat different microhabitat at the times when he is active from that which he occupies when he is resting. Animals that burrow into the soil or into the plant debris on the surface of the ground, for example, often retire to their burrows during their resting periods. When they are active, they may occupy other strata in the community.

Individual animals whose periods of daily activity do not come at the same hour may never meet, though they may live in the same local ecosystem. The nocturnal community made up of species of animals active at night and including both herbivores and carnivores, accordingly, is often very different in composition from the diurnal community which lives at the same site.

SEASONAL VARIATIONS IN ACTIVITY. Seasonal variations in the activity of the associated species of plants produce many fluctuations in community composition. During winter many kinds of plants become dormant and the above-ground parts of numerous species die. Certain species may have only a brief period of growth during spring or summer, after which they again become dormant. In arid regions there may be similar alternations in the activity of certain species of plants between wet and dry seasons.

Many kinds of animals likewise have seasonal periodicities in their activity. In the colder climatic zones certain species become dormant (hibernate) during winter, while in xeric areas numerous species become dormant (estivate) during the summer. The degree of torpidity reached varies greatly among the species that become dormant. Thus, the hibernating woodchuck becomes completely torpid, but the hibernating bear is always able to defend itself. Seasonal dormancy may be induced by various internal and external stimuli (Shelford, 1929, Chap. 6).

The seasonal dropping of their leaves by deciduous plants has an especially profound effect on the character of the communities in which such plants are conspicuous members. We are all familiar with the great difference between summer and winter in the character of a deciduous forest. Almost equally great differences between summer and winter are exhibited by cold-temperate prairies and by arctic tundras. In warm-temperate and tropical areas important seasonal changes in the character of the vegetation may be correlated with the wet and dry seasons, rather than with summer and winter.

When the individuals of 1 or more species of plants or animals become seasonally inactive or dormant, the composition of the community is to that extent altered (Storer, Evans, and Palmer, 1944: 174). Although the inactive individuals are still members of the community, their relationship to the community and the ecologic functions that they serve there have been to some degree changed. Dormant individuals often are found and devoured by predators. A dormant individual also may serve as the host of 1 or more active parasites. On the other hand, the fully dormant animal is not itself engaged in feeding nor does the dormant plant perform photosynthesis.

LOCAL MOVEMENTS BY INDIVIDUALS

The local movements of individual organisms often produce considerable fluctuation from moment to moment in the composition of communities. Animals are generally more mobile than plants, and consequently their movements affect community composition more than do those of plants. In terrestrial communities the movements of plants are for the most part confined to the dispersal of their seeds, spores, and other disseminules. In aquatic communities, however, many of the simpler plants float about in the water and a few of them have limited powers of locomotion.

The local movements performed by an individual animal often are confined within the limits of a single stand or microstand. Here its travels may cover a small horizontal area or may include vertical shifts of position that carry the individual up or down from one stratum to another. Some of the horizontal movements of individual animals and of individual plant disseminules may carry them into or across one or more of the adjacent communities. Movements within a given stand or microstand may not alter the organization of the community concerned though it may change the community structure somewhat. Movements that carry member organisms outside a community or introduce others from outside may, on the contrary, produce considerable alteration in community organizations.

DIEL VERTICAL MOVEMENTS. Periodicities in their local movements correlated with the daily cycles of the physical or biotic factors of the ecosystem are characteristic of many kinds of animals. Many plankton animals, for example, both fresh-water and marine, perform daily vertical movements that in considerable part are correlated with the regular daily variations in light intensity, but which also are affected by water temperature and by other factors (Dice, 1914; Welch, 1935: 226).

Vertical movements with a daily periodicity also are performed by many terrestrial insects (Sanders and Shelford, 1922: 319). The physical factors that control these diel vertical movements in terrestrial communities are not fully known, but it is certain that they are not the same for all kinds of organisms. Certain cockroaches living in the forests of southern Michigan, for example, seem to distribute themselves in accordance with the relative humidity of the air. During the daylight hours these animals are characteristic of the "terrestrial-hypogeic" stratum, but at night, when the air humidity is high, they spread into the "shrub-terrestrial" or even into the "deciduous-arboreal" stratum (Cantrall, 1943: 23-24). The daily vertical movements of certain desert reptiles are controlled in considerable part by air and soil temperatures. When the above-ground temperature increases to an unfavorable level, the animals retreat beneath rocks or into burrows or sometimes they burrow into the sand (Cowles and Bogert, 1944).

SEASONAL VERTICAL MOVEMENTS. Many kinds of animals perform seasonal movements that carry them from one stratum to another in the same

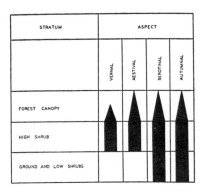

FIG. 29. Seasonal changes in the strata occupied by the wood pewee in Trelease Woods, Urbana, Illinois. The width of the black area indicates the time spent by the species in each stratum. The bird is absent from the area during the hiemal and prevernal aspects. (Redrawn from Twomey, 1945.)

stand. Thus, in the North Temperate Zone many insects and other invertebrates hibernate in the leaf litter on the forest floor or burrow into the soil, but in the warm part of the year they move upward into the herb, shrub, or tree stratum (Weese, 1924: 12). Certain birds likewise exhibit seasonal variations in the strata they occupy (Fig. 29). Toads that are active summer inhabitants of the ground stratum may burrow into the soil for hibernation. Soil invertebrates move deeper into the soil during fall and winter and return closer to the surface of the ground in the spring (Dowdy, 1944). Annual plants and many perennials by the growth of their vegetative parts move from the ground stratum, where the seeds or living parts pass the dormant period, upward into the herb or shrub stratum. Many of the freshwater and marine plankton organisms also perform vertical movements from one stratum to another in accordance with the seasons.

MOVEMENTS WITHIN HOME RANGES. During their periods of daily activity practically all mobile animals move about more or less within the limits of their home ranges if, indeed, they are limited to individual ranges. These movements are necessary for such purposes as securing food, courtship and mating, obtaining nest materials, rearing young, and escaping enemies.

OTHER LOCAL MOVEMENTS. Local movements by certain kinds of animals are frequently produced by temporary variations in the location of their available food. Bees and other insects may be attracted in great numbers to a particular tree or other plant that is in flower. Plants with ripe fruits or seeds may attract birds, mammals, insects, or other animals. For instance, Beebe (1916) noted 76 species of birds in one wild cinnamon tree near Pará, Brazil, many of which were attracted to the tree by its scarlet fruits. Farmers well know the devastating raids made at times by wild birds and mammals on ripening crops of fruit and of grains. At the times when these special foods are available, animals of numerous species may be attracted from considerable distances.

Various factors besides food may influence the local movements of certain animals. Among such other factors may be mentioned the attacks of insect pests, changes of weather, a fall of snow, presence of predators, competition with other animals, seasonal changes in the vegetation, and fires. Changes in the weather are particularly likely to produce local movements by certain animals. Johnston (1942), for instance, has observed that strong winds cause certain birds to seek sheltered areas and that changes in the direction of the wind may result in local movements of these animals from exposed positions to others more sheltered. She also noted that low temperatures cause birds to feed almost constantly and to sing little, while a rise in temperature decreases the amount of feeding and increases that of singing. Darling (1937) has noted the effects of weather conditions and of insect pests, as well as of seasonal changes in the food supply, on the local movements of the Scottish red deer.

Constant adjustments in the area included by any individual in its home range are undoubtedly due to the population pressure exerted by adjacent individuals, to changes in the habitat which in part are associated with the weather and with the season, and to physiologic changes within the individual concerned. Such changes in a home range may involve only a slight modification of the home-range boundaries or they may result in the complete abandonment of a previously occupied range and the establishment by the individual of a new home range either close at hand or at some distance. For example, the cardinal in Illinois is almost entirely confined during its breeding season to territories that extend along the elm-maple forest border. As soon as the nesting period is over, however, the birds move deeper into the forest (Twomey, 1945: 188).

Those herbivores that have very small home ranges are likely to deplete the vegetation in the vicinity of their homes, with the result that they then are forced to move to a new home range. The steppe lemming (*Lagurus lagurus*) of West Kazakhstan, U.S.S.R., for example, completely denudes the grass from an area of 5 to 6 square meters, after which it moves to a new situation 3 to 4 meters distant (Formozov and Voronov, 1939: 115). Some types of primitive agriculture require a similar exploitation of a limited plot for a few years, after which the individual farmer or tribe moves to a new site.

In their regular daily movements certain animals move across associational boundaries and thus become at successive times of the day members of 2 or more associations. This is well illustrated by those birds, such as the mourning dove (*Zenaidura macroura*), that nest and roost in forests or brush, but feed in open fields. Many of the ducks and geese also rest on the open water but feed along the shore or in fields. Many ducks and other water birds secure much of their food from the water but nest on land. So also do the osprey and the kingfisher. Bats feed in the air, but roost in terrestrial habitats. The movements of these and other mobile animals produce, during the course of each day, fluctuations of considerable significance in the composition of the communities affected.

SEASONAL MOVEMENTS BETWEEN COMMUNITIES. Seasonal movements between communities are performed by many animals. Many kinds of terrestrial invertebrates, for example, hibernate in the forest, but spend the warmer part of the year in the forest edge or in the adjacent meadows (Weese, 1924: 53). The cottontail rabbit (*Sylvilagus floridanus*) in Michigan has been noted by Haugen (1943: 117) to move in winter from certain exposed upland types of forest, where food is then deficient, to the more protected valley forest, where food presumably is more abundant. The seasonal migrations of the American elk (*Cervus canadensis*) take it in winter out of areas of deep snow into areas where its food is more easily obtained (Olaus Murie, 1935a: 47).

For still another example of a seasonal movement between communities the bobwhite quail (*Colinus virginianus*) of northwestern Oklahoma may be cited. In this area the coveys that breed on the sagebrush uplands move in winter to the bottom lands and to dune areas, where they set up new home ranges. The movement is not gradual, but each covey abruptly changes its home range (Duck, 1943).

Although many of the species of organisms in a given community may perform seasonal local movements of greater or lesser extent, certain of the species may move very little or not at all. For example, certain species of Orthoptera living in southern Michigan have been noted by Cantrall (1943: 176-77) to change their habitats in accordance with the progression of the seasons, while other species do not.

Progression from one life-history stage to another in certain insects may involve a change in habitat which produces considerable change in the composition of certain communities (Sanders and Shelford, 1922: 319). Thus, numerous terrestrial insects, such as the mosquitoes, have aquatic larvae. The adults and the larvae consequently are members of wholly different communities.

The movement of toads to their breeding pools in spring denudes for a time the other communities of the region of their toad populations. When the young toads have completed their metamorphosis they disperse from the aquatic community in which they have spent their larval period. At that time there is a sudden reduction in the toad population in the aquatic community, but a sudden great increase of the toad population in the communities into which the young toads move.

The several species of animals that are associated in a given community seldom perform their local movements at the same times of the day or at the same seasons of the year. The result is that the composition of a given community may be relatively uniform for a brief period of time, but may then suddenly be changed by the influx or the egress of a few or of many individuals of a particular species.

DISPERSAL OF YOUNG. The dispersal movements of young organisms from their places of origin often have a considerable effect on community composition. Some dispersal movements are merely a change in the position of the individual within the same stand in which it originated. Such movements involve a change in the relation of the individual to its associates, but produce no alteration in the composition of its community. Should the individual move to a different stand of the same kind of community, it will produce a slight change in the number of individuals living in each of the stands affected, but probably will cause no change in the species composition of either community. Should the individual, however, in its travels invade a neighboring community, then it may alter the species composition of that community. In their dispersal movements individual animals often travel across and become for a time members of communities in which they do not become permanent residents, but which they nevertheless temporarily alter in composition.

Many plants are dispersed by their seeds or spores. Many kinds of plants have, in fact, developed seeds that are especially adapted for dispersal by the wind, by currents of water, or by animals (Daubenmire, 1947: 295-96). Many kinds of plants are, in addition, able to spread to adjacent areas by means of rootstocks or other vegetative means of reproduction.

The dispersal of many kinds of aquatic organisms is carried out by free-swimming or floating larvae or reproductive units. Many kinds of algae, sponges, corals, barnacles, mollusks, polyzoans, and other attached organisms are thus distributed in the early stages of their life history. Among the insects, it is the winged, adult stage in the life history that usually is especially adapted for dispersal.

The dispersal of many kinds of young birds occurs very shortly after they have been abandoned by their parents. Those kinds of birds that live in social flocks, however, may have special seasons when dispersal takes place. The season of dispersal for the bobwhite quail, for example, is said to be in the autumn (Aldo Leopold, 1931: 49-50). The turkey also has a fall dispersal period (A. S. Leopold, 1944: 153).

Many migratory birds join in flocks soon after the young are sufficiently grown to be able to fly. The dispersal of the young of such migratory species seems to occur mostly in spring, at the time when they are arriving on their breeding grounds.

Among mammals the dispersal movements often are performed by the young animals shortly after they are weaned. The young of the fox squirrel disperse from their places of birth shortly after they become able to take care of themselves (D. L. Allen, 1943: 152). In the raccoon, both the young males and young females move away from their home sites during the autumn following their birth, though a few wait until the following spring (Stuewer, 1943: 230).

It is the 2-year old beavers that disperse from their place of birth, while the parents, the kits of the year, and the 1-year olds remain together in the parental lodge. In Michigan these dispersal movements are usually carried out in spring at about the time when a new set of kits is born. At this time the old beavers become very hostile to their 2-year old young. The 2-year old animals, however, may remain for a time on the pond where their parental lodge is located and their actual dispersal to a new home site may not occur until summer or perhaps later (Bradt, 1938: 159-60).

From the point of view of the community, dispersal is a stabilizing influence that keeps the several stands of each community type uniform in composition. Any unoccupied habitat suitable for a given species will quickly be reached by the individuals of that species in their dispersal movements. The result is that every part of each given type of habitat will be inhabited by essentially the same aggregation of species of plants and of animals.

GEOGRAPHIC MIGRATIONS

Travels extending beyond the geographic area occupied are called migrations to distinguish them from the local movements previously described. A migration may be defined as a more or less permanent change of geographic location, while a local movement involves only a temporary change of location within the same geographic area. The distinction will usually be clear, but not always, for it depends in part upon the concept of the term "geographic." For instance, certain mammals, such as wolves, travel over home ranges that are many miles across (Adolph Murie, 1944). The movement of an insect over as great a distance would be considered a migration. The degree of permanence of the change in location is an essential part of the distinction in terms. A change in location enduring for only a few hours or a few days is generally called a local movement, while a movement that carries the organism to a new location that he occupies for weeks or months is a migration.

EMIGRATION AND IMMIGRATION. Many of the movements by animals and plants that produce fluctuations in communities do not recur in a regular cycle. A species may emigrate from a given community more or less permanently. Conversely, a species may immigrate into a community where previously it was not present. The terms emigrant and immigrant may be applied to individuals as well as to species.

IRREGULAR MIGRATIONS. A period of unfavorable conditions may temporarily drive some of the more mobile species completely out of a particular region. Such an irregular migration is performed by the snowy owl. During the winter of 1941-42 considerable numbers of these owls migrated southward over parts of southeastern Canada and northeastern United States, far beyond their usual winter range (Snyder, 1943). This migration is presumed to have been caused by a decrease over parts of northern Canada of the populations of the small rodents that are the usual winter food of the owl. Irregular changes of range of a somewhat similar sort have been reported for the purple finch (R. L. Weaver, 1940) and for many other kinds of birds and mammals. The migratory movements that often accompany animal plagues are of this irregular type.

Seasonal Migrations

The migrations of many kinds of animals are of an annually recurrent type related to the seasons. During the spring and summer breeding season, for example, a northern community will be composed not only of the year-round resident birds but also of numerous migratory species. During the breeding season this community consequently will contain a greater number of species and a much greater number of individuals than in winter. Conversely, the southern communities which are the winter home of these migratory birds will contain a more diversified bird fauna in winter than in summer.

As a result of seasonal migration a single individual animal may be a member alternately for longer or shorter periods of 2 or more geographically separated communities. The summer breeding community may be hundreds or even thousands of miles distant from the wintering community. Furthermore, during its travels between wintering and breeding grounds, the migrating individual often becomes a temporary member of a number of communities along its route. In general, it may be said that each species, in whatever region it finds itself, chooses habitats of a generally similar type. A shore bird, for example, will haunt the shores in each region through which it passes, a field animal will select open types of habitat, and a forest species will select forests.

BIRD MIGRATIONS. The best known seasonal migrations are those of the numerous species of birds which breed in the North Temperate or North Frigid zones, but which spend the winter in warmer climates. Less well known are the flights of certain birds which live in the Northern Hemisphere to the plains of the temperate parts of southern South America. Here these species do not breed, though the period of their residence is during the South American summer, when numerous local birds are rearing their young. Many kinds of birds that breed in the tropics also perform migratory movements in various directions (Wetmore, 1943: 227), though the ecologic factors involved are still obscure.

In many species of birds the sexes migrate at slightly different times. Most frequently the males arrive on the breeding grounds a few days in advance of the females and stake out their territories before their mates appear. In at least 1 species of bird, the English robin, the males are resident, while some of the females leave the breeding region during the winter (Lack, 1940a: 306).

Most birds in their seasonal migrations seem to move more or less directly between their summer and winter homes. The migratory movements of some individuals, on the contrary, are not at all direct, but may be highly erratic (A. L. Thomson, 1926). At the close of the breeding season, for example, certain individuals that have been reared in the north may fly short distances to the east or west or even to the north before beginning their southern migration. It seems to be mostly the young birds that make these erratic flights (Lincoln, 1939: 101).

MIGRATIONS BY MAMMALS. Many kinds of mammals also perform seasonal migrations, though the details of these movements are known for only a few species. Many bats, for instance, are known to carry out extensive seasonal movements, though the distances they travel have not as yet been fully ascertained (G. M. Allen, 1939, Chap. 16). Likewise, the fur seals that breed on the Pribilof Islands of Alaska migrate during the nonbreeding season for varying distances to the southward in the Pacific Ocean (Osgood, Preble, and Parker, 1915). These seals, according to present knowledge of their migrations, do not all winter in the same area, but on the contrary they spread out widely over the parts of the ocean favorable to their existence.

The seasonal migrations of certain terrestrial mammals are merely local movements from one life belt to another up and down a mountain side. Such seasonal movements by the mule deer (*Odocoileus hemionus*), for example, have been well described by Russell (1932). The seasonal migrations of certain mammals are still more restricted and consist only in the dispersal of the animals into summer range that is inaccessible to them in winter because of the presence of snow. Thus, the bighorn sheep (*Ovis dalli*) of Alaska in summer spread into those high areas where in winter the snow lies deep, but they continue to occupy also their winter range on the lower hills and flats (Adolph Murie, 1944: 68-75).

MIGRATIONS BY REPTILES. Certain marine turtles are known to perform seasonal migrations. These animals must visit the land in order to deposit their eggs, though during the remainder of the year they are fully aquatic. As soon as they are hatched the young turtles move toward the sea (Thomson and Geddes, 1931: 79). The travels of other kinds of reptiles and of all the amphibians probably should be called local movements rather than migrations.

MIGRATIONS BY FISHES. Many kinds of fishes migrate to and from their breeding grounds. With certain species the migration takes place wholly within the waters of 1 stream system or within a single lake. Other forms, such as the salmon, breed in fresh water but spend most of their lives in the sea (Moulton, 1939). The eels, on the contrary, live mostly in fresh water, but breed in the ocean. The extent of the migrations of certain kinds of fishes, notably the eels, rivals that of the birds (Coker, 1947: 287). For instance, the species of eel that lives in the fresh-water streams and lakes of northern Europe migrates almost entirely across the Atlantic and breeds in the ocean to the northeast and north of the West Indies. The larvae then make their way back across the ocean, metamorphose into elvers, and enter again the fresh water streams of Europe (Schmidt, 1925).

The homing instincts possessed by such fish as the salmon have been extensively debated. It has been proved, however, that most of the salmon which are reared in a particular stream return to it for breeding after their sojourn in the ocean. Pink salmon have been known to return to their natal stream from a considerable distance away in the ocean and in their journey to pass near the mouths of other streams that seemed equally suitable for their breeding activities (Pritchard, 1944). This movement of the salmon is not a hereditary impulse, but is a response to the impress of the environmental conditions to which the young are exposed (Rich and Holmes, 1929).

MIGRATIONS BY INSECTS. Some insects are known to perform migrations, though the precise process is imperfectly known. Certain kinds of butterflies perform seasonal flights that in some ways resemble those of birds (C. B. Williams, 1930). In Florida the southern cabbage butterfly (*Pieris monuste*), however, sometimes migrates southward in the spring of the year toward an unknown destination (Ball and Stone, 1928). Ladybird beetles often collect in winter in considerable aggregations, but it is not known from how large an area these aggregations are drawn, nor whether the beetles later return to the region of their birth.

MIGRATIONS BY OTHER ANIMALS. Some other kinds of animals are known to perform regular migrations of greater or lesser extent, but detailed information is available for only a few forms. The best known migrations among the marine invertebrates are those of certain kinds of crabs, which carry the adults considerable distances between inshore and offshore habitats or between one part of a bay or estuary and another part (Flattely and Walton, 1922: 174; Newcombe, 1945: 19).

SHORT-RANGE SEASONAL MIGRATIONS. The seasonal migrations of birds, mammals, and other animals do not always involve long journeys. Many species travel actually only short distances between their summer and winter homes (Lincoln, 1939: 84-87). For example, certain species move in accordance with the seasons only up and down between belts on the same mountain side. Grinnell (1908: 22-24), for example, has pointed out that many southern California birds migrate out of the lowlands after their breeding season is over and move to higher life belts in the mountains where summer food is more abundant. This vertical migration to escape the summer drought and food shortage of the lowlands is distinct from and in addition to the regular north and south migrations performed by many of the same species.

Mass Migrations

Mass migrations including the majority of those members of a particular species which live in a given region may occur at rare intervals. The mass migrations of the Norwegian lemming mentioned in the previous chapter are a classic example. Somewhat similar migrations, but far less frequent and much more irregular in their occurrence, have been reported for the gray squirrel of eastern North America (Seton, 1929, Vol. 4).

Care must be taken not to confuse these mass migrations with the seasonal migrations performed every year by certain birds and other kinds of animals. The distinction is that there is no general return movement following a mass migration, while a seasonal migration includes a later return to the ancestral home by the majority of the migrants.

Any factor or combination of factors that produces unfavorable conditions for a given species in its usual habitat may force it to emigrate in numbers and thus a mass migration occurs. Shortage of food is probably the factor most often responsible for such an emigration. For example, in Norway in 1921 the crop of cranberries, cowberries, blueberries, and other kinds of berries was a complete failure because of a severe and protracted drought and a cold spring which included hard frosts in June. It was estimated by one observer that in parts of Norway there was produced only 1 per cent of the usual berry crop. The waxwings (*Bombycilla garrulus*), which depend on berries for their staple food supply, were forced to emigrate and they invaded Denmark and Great Britain in considerable numbers (Ritchie, 1940: 301-2). The mass migrations of the snowy owl, the gray squirrel, the Siberian nutcracker (Formozov, 1933), the sharp-tailed grouse in Canada (L. L. Snyder, 1935), the lemmings and other rodents (Elton, 1942), and numerous other kinds of animals seem likewise to be based at least in considerable part on shortages of food.

PERMANENCY OF MEMBER SPECIES IN THE COMMUNITY

The permanency of any given species in a particular community depends upon the extent of its fluctuations in numbers in that situation and upon whether or not it performs local movements or geographic migrations. Species that perform local movements may be absent from the community during certain hours of the day; those that perform geographic migrations may be absent during certain seasons; and those that are erratic in their wanderings may be absent during certain years. If the species is one that is subject to considerable fluctuation in numbers, it may at times be entirely eliminated from a community, which it may then subsequently reinvade from more permanently occupied communities in the same or in an adjoining region.

To classify the degree of permanency of a species in a given community the following terms may be employed: Permanent occupancy indicates the continual occurrence of the species in some phase or other of its life history in the community under consideration. Periodic occupancy indicates a recurring appearance in the community broken by more or less regular periods of complete absence of the species. Erratic or sporadic occupancy is the occasional occurrence of scattered individuals of a species, or even of a considerable population, in a community where the species is unable to survive for even 1 full generation (Cantrall, 1943: 21-22).

Special names have been applied by ornithologists to the seasonal permanence of the several bird species in a given area. A resident species remains all year in the locality under consideration, though a part of its individuals may migrate. A summer visitant or migratory breeder is a species that breeds in the area under consideration, but migrates elsewhere for the nonbreeding season. A winter visitant is one that spends the winter at the locality, but does not breed there. A transient species migrates through the area, but neither breeds nor passes the winter there. Intergradations, of course, exist between these categories. It may happen occasionally that a few individuals of a summer breeding species winter in the area in which they have bred, though usually all of the population migrates southward; or owing to a mild season or other causes, a species may winter in an area in which it usually is only transient.

When the permanency of residence of individuals rather than of species is considered, somewhat different terms must be used. An individual that spends its whole life within a single community may be called sedentary, while one that moves from one place to another in a regular manner is migratory.

These various terms obviously fail to distinguish between those forms that present much the same characteristics during the whole period of their lives and those forms that change their characters greatly from season to season or from one life-history stage to another. Neither an evergreen tree nor a mammal, for example, changes very much in character from time to time, but an annual herb, a deciduous tree, or an insect often does. When a species is represented only by spores, seeds, or eggs, it obviously occupies a much different position in the community than when it is in fully active condition. The great range of variation in the life histories of plants and of animals, however, makes it impracticable to attempt to include a consideration of their activity in classifying their permanency as members of a given community.

NOMADISM. A few kinds of animals never at any time have a fixed home, but instead constantly move about. An animal that frequently moves its place of residence, never remaining long in 1 place, is a nomad. A good ex-ample of a nomadic species is the caribou (*Rangifer*) of northern North America. The caribou lives during most of the year in herds that wander more or less sporadically across the tundra. Although the herd may perform rather extensive geographic migrations, it does not follow a regular route. The irregular movements of the caribou herds are undoubtedly in part a racial habit correlated with the very slow growth of the lichens and other arctic plants which are their principal winter food and which need long intervals of freedom from pasturage in order to thrive (Olaus Murie, 1935*a:* 48).

PERIODIC CHANGES IN COMMUNITY COMPOSITION

Certain of the changes that occur in community composition recur in more or less regular cycles. Thus, there are cycles which are repeated every day; others are correlated with the seasons and are repeated annually; still others cover a period of several years.

Not all fluctuations in communities, however, are cyclic in their occur-rence. On the contrary, many fluctuations occur in a highly irregular manner and are impossible of prediction. In general, it may be said that those fluc-tuations are regularly cyclic which are closely dependent upon the alterna-tions in the physical habitat produced by the daily rotation of the earth and by the travels of the earth in its orbit around the sun. On the other hand, those fluctuations in community composition which are mostly dependent upon the vagaries of weather or upon the activities of other kinds of organ-isms are usually less regular in their occurrence.

DIEL CYCLES. Cycles with a 24-hour periodicity in the composition of communities are produced by variations in the times of day at which the several member species are active and by variations in the times of their local movements. The effect of diel vertical movements, for example, either by terrestrial or by aquatic invertebrates, is to produce fluctuations in the composition of the several strata of the community concerned.

SEASONAL CYCLES. Seasonal variations in community composition which are correlated with seasonal changes in the conditions of the habitat are evident in many regions. For an example see Table XIV. The combined effects of seasonal cycles in the reproduction of many kinds of organisms, of seasonal variations in mortality, of seasonal migration, and of seasonal dormancy often result in profound seasonal fluctuations in the composition of communities. These fluctuations are often so great that the community type is completely changed at certain seasons of the year. Seasonal aspects are very conspicuous in the frigid and cold-temperate zones and in certain of the xeric communities of the tropical and warm-temperate zones. An especially pronounced seasonal variation in community composition occurs in those temporary ponds that dry up during a part of the year and are followed by a terrestrial aspect (Welch, 1935: 341).

ANNUATION. The year-to-year variation in composition which many communities exhibit may be called annuation (Clements, Weaver, and Hanson, 1929: 328). Annuation may sometimes fall into a more or less regular cycle, covering recurrent groups of years. More frequently, however, the year-to-year fluctuations in communities are irregular in their occurrence, not forming any detectable recurrent pattern.

Cycles of climate that cover periods of several years have been described in Chapter VI. Cycles of alternation of climate from dry to wet or from

TABLE XIV

SEASONAL VARIATION IN A REGIONAL COMMUNITY

Occurrence of migratory and nomadic species of birds at Fazenda Boa Fé, Brazil (data from D. E. Davis, 1945). Winter visitors (W); summer breeders (S); residents not listed.

Species	June	July	August	September	October	November	December	January	February	March	April	May
Columba plumbea	..	..	..	..	..	..	..	..	..	W	W	W
Claravis geoffroyi	..	..	..	..	..	..	..	..	?	?	..	..
Forous passerinus	..	..	..	..	..	..	S	S	S	..	..	..
Melanotrochilus fuscus	..	..	..	..	..	..	..	S	..	..	..	..
Attila rufus	..	..	..	..	S	S	S	S	S	..	..	..
Pachyramphus polychropterus	..	..	..	..	..	S	S	S	S	S	..	..
Phibalura flavirostris	W	W	W	W	..	..	..	..	..	..	W	W
Sirystes sibilator	W	W	W	W	W	W	..	..	W	W	W	W
Myriarchus ferox	..	..	..	..	S	S	S	S	..	..	..	..
Empidonax euleri	..	..	..	..	S	S	S	S	S	..	..	..
Myiodynastes solitarius	..	..	..	S	S	S	S	S	..	..	..	..
Leptopogon amaurocephalus	W	W	W	W	..	..	..	..	..	..	..	..
Pipromorpha rufiventris	..	..	..	S	S	S	S	S	S	..	..	..
Xanthornus decumanus	..	..	S	S	S	S	S	S	..	..	..	..
Sporophila frontalis	..	..	..	..	..	..	S	S	S	..	..	..
Haplospiza unicolor	..	..	..	..	..	S	S	S	S	S	S	S

warm to cool, of course, produce corresponding cycles of vegetation and of animal abundance. Moisture-loving species of herbivorous animals usually increase in abundance in wet years when the vegetation is lush, while the same species are likely to decrease in abundance in dry years when the vegetation is sparse (Elton, 1942: 87, 145). Conversely, xeric species tend to decrease in wet periods and to increase in dry periods. Predators tend to increase and to decrease in accordance with the numbers of their prey species. Likewise, the abundance of parasites is related to the abundance of their hosts. The annuation of a given community, therefore, usually follows, at least in part, cycles which are related to the climatic cycles of the region.

Plankton communities, both fresh-water and marine, often have an extreme degree of annuation in composition (Birge and Juday, 1922, Figs. 22-23). In fact, the fluctuations of community composition in open-water ecosystems are so great that many limnologists and oceanographers refuse to attempt the classification of plankton communities. The great fluctuations that occur from year to year in the abundance of many species of crustacea in the fresh-water lakes of Wisconsin have been described by Birge (1897: 317): Certain species, such as *Daphnia retrocurva* and *Diaphanosoma*, which may either be absent or present in very small numbers in a given lake in 1 year, may appear in great abundance during a succeeding year. Furthermore, there is no regular seasonal sequence of algae and of other organisms in these lakes, corresponding to the sequence of aspects in terrestrial communities. Somewhat similar irregular fluctuations, often of great amplitude, have been described by Wesenberg-Lund (1930: 57) for the communities which inhabit Danish ponds.

An example of irregular fluctuations in the composition of a terrestrial community has been described by Saunders (1936: 139). The ruby-throated hummingbird in Allegany State Park, New York, is usually closely associated with patches of the bee balm (*Monarda didyma*). The bee balm, though it is a perennial, does not flourish in the same places every year. The distribution of hummingbirds in that area consequently fluctuates irregularly from year to year. Another example was given by S. E. Jones (1946), who stated that many of the invertebrates living in a deciduous-forest community near Urbana, Illinois, fluctuate irregularly in their abundance.

Animals that breed in social groups frequently select differing sites for their colonies in successive years, leading to variations in the community composition at the sites affected. Breeding aggregations of grouse locusts are stated by Cantrall (1943: 75-76) thus to vary their local site from year to year. On the other hand, suitable breeding sites for many kinds of marine birds are limited, and accordingly a colony of these birds may remain for many years in exactly the same place.

Very severe changes are sometimes produced in certain communities by an extraordinary increase in the members of 1 particular species. Such a plague or "outbreak," whether of a blight, a locust, an army worm, a lemming, or any other kind of organism, may produce severe alterations in the composition of the communities affected.

Lack of Quantitative Data on Community Fluctuations

Very few quantitative details have been published concerning the changes that occur from time to time in the composition of communities. It is known, however, that some of these changes are very profound, often completely altering the characters of particular communities. It has been observed, further, that some of the fluctuations in community composition are cyclic and that some, but not all, of them are correlated with periodic changes in the physical environment, such as are produced by alternation from day to night, from season to season, and from wet to dry years. Some information is available about the interrelations of a few organisms in certain communities. The precise causes of many of the changes in composition that communities undergo from time to time, however, are still largely unknown.

Progress in the discovery of the factors that produce fluctuations in particular communities is almost impossible without more quantitative information than is now possessed. When quantitative data about a community have been collected, usually only a particular species has been measured and few reliable records have been obtained of the fluctuations in abundance of its predators, parasites, competitors, and other associates. Here is an important field for study, which so far has received much too little attention.

SELECTED REFERENCES

Calhoun, John B. 1944-46. Twenty-four hour periodicities in the animal kingdom. Journ. Tenn. Acad. Sci., Vols. 19, 20, and 21.

Elton, Charles. 1942. Voles, mice, and lemmings; problems in population dynamics. Oxford: Clarendon Press.

Park, Orlando. 1940. Nocturnalism—the development of a problem. Ecol. Monog., 10: 485-536.

Shelford, Victor E. 1929. Laboratory and field ecology; the responses of animals as indicators of correct working methods. Baltimore: Williams & Wilkins Co. Chap. 6.

Thomson, A. L. 1926. Problems of bird-migration. London: H. F. and G. Witherby.

X

RELATIONS OF ORGANISMS TO THEIR ECOSYSTEMS

The degree of success that any given type of organism achieves in a particular community is determined by the way in which its structure and habits fit the conditions present in that ecosystem. Limiting factors in the ecosystem may prevent a species from thriving in a given community or may condemn it to play but an inferior role. The existence of a mobile species in any community is further dependent upon its possession of reactions that lead it to reach and to remain in that particular location.

REQUIREMENTS FOR EXISTENCE

The essential requirements for the continued existence of any species of plant or animal may be listed as follows: physical conditions tolerable for the species, sufficient sunlight for green plants to perform photosynthesis (not required by plants that lack chlorophyll nor by most animals), an adequate amount of suitable and available food, adequate shelter to protect the individuals from undue destruction by their enemies or by temporarily unfavorable physical conditions, and conditions suitable for successful reproduction.

The greatest hazard to the existence of a particular species may fall in any one of its requirements for existence. For a sea bird feeding on fish, for instance, there may be no lack of food, but suitable breeding places may be scarce. A desert plant may be limited in its distribution by lack of water, though there may be an abundance of sunlight. In a heavy forest, on the contrary, where there is an abundance of water and of plant food, the individual plants may be in severe competition with one another for sunlight.

TOLERABLE PHYSICAL CONDITIONS. Each species of plant or animal is adapted for life under a particular combination of physical conditions. A local climate, for example, that would enable one form to thrive may quickly be fatal to another. Certain kinds of organisms are adapted for life in sea water, while others cannot endure contact with even a slight concentration of salt.

SUNLIGHT. Only plants that are provided with chlorophyll are able to perform photosynthesis. Green plants, therefore, require sunlight in order to live. Most animals and those plant parasites and saprophytes that lack chlorophyll do not have this requirement. Many animals, nevertheless, are stimulated to activity by sunlight, and certain species are dependent upon sunlight for the synthesis of some of their essential vitamins.

ADEQUATE FOOD. The food requirements of organisms vary greatly from species to species. Carbon dioxide, which is the most essential food material for green plants, is present in sufficient amounts in the air almost everywhere. The other essential food materials for terrestrial plants, including water, are mostly obtained from the soil. Aquatic plants must usually obtain their carbon dioxide, as well as their other food materials, from the surrounding water. Most animals and also plant parasites obtain their food from plants or from other animals. Saprophytes derive their nourishment from decaying organic material. No organism can long exist in any community unless it can secure there the kinds of food which it requires.

SHELTER. Under the requirements for shelter are included temporary resting and hiding places for animals as well as their more permanent homes (Elton, 1939). By game managers this requirement is often called "cover." Many animals have psychologic reactions that cause them to seek shelter whenever they are in danger of attack by predators. Proper shelter is also of value to many kinds of animals in enabling them to survive storms and other temporary kinds of unfavorable physical conditions. The local distribution of flatworms (planarians) in fresh water, for example, is largely dependent upon the presence of suitable places away from light where the animals may come to rest during the day (Kenk, 1944). Large plants may protect smaller ones by providing shade or protection against damage by wind. Thorny shrubs or those with stiff branches may protect certain delicate herbs from being injured by large herbivorous animals. Certain kinds of organisms are able to manufacture their own shelter, but most terrestrial animals and many land plants are dependent upon the shelter furnished by other organisms.

CONDITIONS SUITABLE FOR REPRODUCTION. The period of reproduction is a critical one for most species of plants and animals. There must be freedom from undue disturbance during courtship and mating; suitable food for the young must be at hand if the young require a different kind of food from that of the adults; and all other features for successful reproduction must be provided. Furthermore, the conditions essential for the reproduction of each kind of plant and animal must recur at sufficiently frequent intervals to ensure the continuation of each species in the community.

Many species are able to exist in a greater variety of ecosystems than is suitable for their reproduction. Conditions in the ecosystem suitable for successful reproduction are, of course, essential only during the reproductive season of the species concerned. In other parts of the year it may not matter if very different conditions prevail.

CLASSIFICATION OF ECOLOGIC REQUIREMENTS. Theoretically it should be

possible to catalogue the ecologic requirements of those organisms that
together compose a single community or group of communities. Such terms
as "saxicolous" or "calcifugous," for example, are attempts to classify organisms according to their ecologic requirements and restrictions. The
attempts that have been made in the past to classify any large group of
organisms in this way, however, have not been fully successful.

CONTROLLING FACTORS

Many diverse physical and biotic factors are involved in controlling the
activities and also the survival of each of the numerous species of plants
and animals that compose a community.

Variations in Controlling Factors

The intensities of many of the environmental factors operating within any
given ecosystem fluctuate from time to time. The physiologic state of each

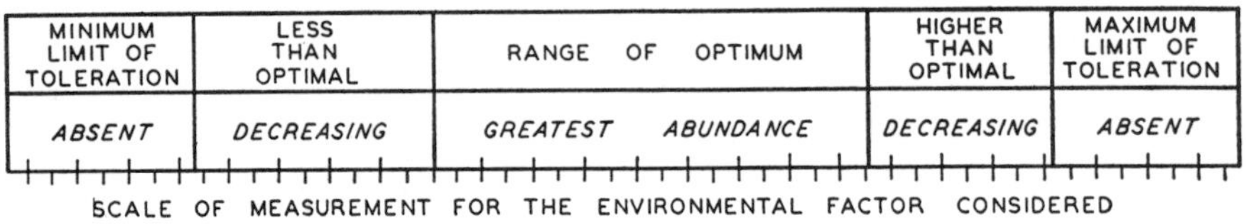

MINIMUM LIMIT OF TOLERATION	LESS THAN OPTIMAL	RANGE OF OPTIMUM		HIGHER THAN OPTIMAL	MAXIMUM LIMIT OF TOLERATION
ABSENT	DECREASING	GREATEST	ABUNDANCE	DECREASING	ABSENT

SCALE OF MEASUREMENT FOR THE ENVIRONMENTAL FACTOR CONSIDERED

Fig. 30. Operation of the law of toleration.

individual organism also varies from hour to hour. In consequence, the
relation of every organism to its physical and biotic environment is constantly changing. In particular, the effectiveness of each controlling factor
tends constantly to fluctuate.

OPTIMUM AND LIMITS OF TOLERATION. The range of a particular environmental factor within which a given kind of organism thrives best may be
called the optimum for that factor (Fig. 30). The maximum and minimum
values of this particular factor which the species is able to endure are its
limits of toleration. In temperature, for instance, there may be for any given
species a maximum limit of toleration, which, if exceeded, will produce heat
stroke, and a minimum limit of toleration, below which the organism will
perish from cold. Somewhere between the upper and lower limits of toleration for high and for low temperature, respectively, will be the optimal
values of temperature for the species concerned (Shelford, 1911: 598; 1913:
302-4; 1931: 462-63). The range of a given environmental factor which is
above and below the optimum for the species concerned, but still within
its limits of toleration, is sometimes called the pessimum. Presumably, each
species thrives best in the geographic area where all its essential environmental factors are optimal.

VARIATIONS IN HEREDITY. The individuals of which every population
is composed vary more or less in their heredity. The particular combi

nation of hereditary factors which any individual receives undoubtedly controls his physiology as well as his morphology (R. J. Williams, 1946). This variability in heredity probably explains why individual plants and animals often react in ways that are not usual for their species. Individuality of response is exhibited especially by the more complex types of organisms, in which presumably the number of hereditary factors is greatest.

VARIATIONS WITH SEASON. The limiting factors of most kinds of organisms vary at the several seasons of the year. Thus, in their dormant condition many organisms are able to endure extremes of temperature or of humidity that would be fatal during their growing seasons. The winter buds of many plants, for instance, will withstand without injury temperatures that are below zero Fahrenheit, but the growing vegetation of these same plants may be injured by even a light frost (Livingston and Shreve, 1921: 100).

VARIATIONS WITH AGE. Young plants and young animals often have much narrower limits of toleration for certain of the environmental factors of their habitats than do older individuals of the same species. The young of many species actually live in a very different type of environment from that of the adults. This is particularly true of those species that undergo a metamorphosis. Many insects, for instance, have aquatic larvae, though the flying adults are mostly terrestrial in habit. A small seedling may occupy a very different local environment from that occupied by the mature tree. Numerous birds perform annual migrations, with the result that they may breed in a particular association in one biotic province, but spend the winter in an entirely different province, perhaps even on a different continent.

EFFECT OF PREVIOUS EXPOSURE. Certain stages in the growth or maturation of numerous kinds of organisms are known to be controlled in part by the environmental conditions to which the individuals have been exposed at some earlier time or in some previous life-history stage. For example, the seeds and resting reproductive units of certain plants and animals that live in the cold-temperate or frigid zones will not grow properly until they have been exposed for a time during winter to chilling temperatures (Daubenmire, 1947: 198).

ACCLIMATION. The limits of toleration of a particular individual organism to a specified environmental factor are determined to a considerable extent by its hereditary constitution. By continued exposure to an extreme degree of a certain factor, however, individual organisms often are able to extend their limit of toleration in a particular direction. This physiologic change in the individual organism may be called acclimation. Individual terrestrial plants and animals may thus become more resistant to cold, heat, humidity, or other environmental factors. Through exposure to gradually increasing concentrations of various chemicals, such as salts, certain organisms may likewise become acclimated to concentrations far beyond their usual limit of toleration.

Man is an outstanding example of ability to become acclimated to extremes of temperature and of altitude. Thus, white persons exposed in experimental chambers to an artificial tropical climate are within a few days definitely acclimated, as shown by an improvement in their ability to work, by an increase in the amount of sweat produced, and by a decrease in the loss of salt in the perspiration (Weiner, 1946).

Certain species are better able to become acclimated to extreme environmental conditions than are others. For nearly all species there are, however, very decided limits to individual acclimation. Certain species are able to extend any particular limit of toleration only slightly, and such forms consequently have only slight powers of acclimation.

A certain period of time is required for any individual organism to adjust itself to a change in its environment. The rapidity with which acclimation can be accomplished varies with the species, with the age and life-history stage of the organism, and with its previous experience. An important result of acclimation is that the exposure of an organism to a particular combination of environmental factors may continue to affect the physiologic condition of the organism long after it has been transferred to a different type of environment (Hutchinson, 1944: 19).

ACCLIMATIZATION. The process of adaptation of the individual organism is not to be confused with acclimatization, which is an adaptive change in the heredity of a section of a species tending to fit it for a particular set of environmental conditions. Such a change is presumed to result mostly from the selection of favorable hereditary variations already present in the population. The tendency of cultivated plants to become acclimatized to the short growing season of northern climates, for example, is often made use of by horticulturalists, who plant northern-grown seed in southern regions in order to secure rapid growth and early maturity.

That part of a species which becomes acclimatized through a change in its heredity constitutes an ecotype. The process of acclimatization of necessity requires at least several generations to accomplish the required changes in the heredity of the population. Acclimation, on the other hand, affects only the individual or individuals concerned, and there is no good evidence that such a change in the individual affects its heredity in any way.

INTERDEPENDENCE OF THE SEVERAL FACTORS. The several physical and biotic factors that make up any given environment are not independent of one another, but are interrelated, often in a complex manner. The rate of evaporation, for instance, is affected by temperature, relative humidity, barometric pressure, and rate of wind movement. Furthermore, any variation in the intensity or duration of one environmental factor may alter the physiologic effectiveness of its associated factors (F. F. Blackman, 1905). Thus, a man is able to endure for a considerable time in dry air a high temperature that would be quickly fatal in moist air. Also many organisms can endure a brief exposure to a low temperature or to other unfavorable conditions which, if long continued, would kill them. Any statement of the optimum or of the limits of toleration for any given environmental factor, therefore, has litle meaning unless the values and periods of duration of all the other associated factors in the environment also are specified.

OPTIMUM A RELATIVE TERM. The optimum for any species is then not a fixed set of conditions, but is only relative and may change from time to time (Adams, 1915a: 8). The same thing is true of the limits of toleration, though these are quantitatively fixed for certain environmental factors. Thus, the occurrence of temperatures below zero Centigrade may injure or kill certain kinds of plants when they are in active growth. Many species of plants, indeed, are unable to endure frost at any season. Even the damage caused by frost, however, may be affected by the duration of the exposure, by the previous exposure of the plant to cold, and by its stage in growth.

In view of the many variable factors that affect the optimum and the limits of toleration of any given organism, it seems best to use these terms mostly in a very general sense. The interrelations of the several environmental factors and the physiologic condition of the individual organism are usually much too complex to allow any simple statement either of its optimum or of its lower or upper limits of toleration for any factor. The concept of optimum, especially, must always remain vague and difficult or impossible of exact specification (Blackman and Smith, 1911).

Threshold of Activity

Most kinds of organisms have definite thresholds of activity for certain environmental factors. Below a certain intensity of a given factor, for instance, the organism may be inactive. The degree of the factor at which the organism first exhibits activity is then called its activity threshold. At a degree of cold slightly below its activity threshold for temperature, for example, the organism concerned would probably be dormant. The activity threshold of a given organism often is well above its minimum limit of toleration for the factor concerned. Species which are members of the same community may differ greatly from one another in their activity thresholds for each of the several environmental factors.

Rate of Growth

The rate of growth of an organism is usually very slow when the intensity of any important controlling factor is just above the activity threshold for the species. As the intensity of the factor increases, the growth rate also increases over at least the optimal range of the factor. The rate of growth of the individuals of every species varies, therefore, with variations in the intensities of the several controlling factors in the environment. Environmental temperatures, for instance, that are below the threshold for growth for a given species will evidently not add anything to the mass of protoplasm of that species. Only those temperatures that are above the threshold need to be considered.

SUM OF EFFECTIVE DAILY TEMPERATURES. A single method of securing an index of effective temperatures is to add together the amounts by which the mean temperature of each day of the growing season of a given species exceeds the threshold temperature of the species. Merriam (1894), for example, used this method for computing the temperatures effective in controlling the northward distribution of plants and animals in each of the several North American life zones.

LAW OF VAN'T HOFF AND ARRHENIUS. The rate of growth and the rate of other physiologic processes of an organism, however, are not directly proportional to the summation of any given environmental factor, even when the factor is above its threshold for that species. Most organisms, with the exception of the warm-blooded vertebrates, respond to an increase of temperature by an increase in the rate of their activities that is much more than proportional to the increase in temperature. Organisms, in fact, usually follow, within certain limits and with some modification, the Van't Hoff and Arrhenius law. This law states that there is an approximate doubling of chemical and physiologic activity for each rise of 10° C. (Livingston and Shreve, 1921: 211). When exposed to a fairly high temperature, therefore, an organism may grow many times faster than it does when just above its temperature threshold. The law, however, is not followed exactly and a correction factor must be used (Shelford, 1918: 131). As the upper limit of toleration of any species is approached the efficiency of temperature in promoting growth declines, and at a temperature somewhat below its upper limit of toleration growth may cease altogether.

Growth is affected also by many environmental factors other than temperature. Among the factors which affect the growth of terrestrial plants may be mentioned especially air humidity, available soil moisture, available sunshine, wind velocity, and length of the daily period of daylight.

INDEX OF PRODUCTIVITY. Attempts to secure an index of the productivity of a species by the calculation of the efficiency of the various levels of temperature and of other environmental factors in promoting its growth have been made by a number of investigators (Shelford, 1929).

The several environmental factors that control the rate of growth of terrestrial plants, however, are very complexly interrelated, and no simple index of productiveness for a given set of environmental factors can be obtained. The same thing is certainly true of terrestrial animals and of aquatic organisms of all kinds. Nevertheless, attempts to secure indexes of organic productiveness based on measures of the environmental conditions are distinctly valuable. With increase of knowledge about the interaction of the several environmental factors on particular species it may be expected that ultimately predictions of the yields of domestic crops and of other important species for a given year may become considerably more accurate than they are at present.

Threshold for Reproduction

The season of reproduction of many kinds of organisms is controlled at least in part by environmental factors. In certain species of plants and of cold-blooded animals, for example, temperature is an important factor in controlling the breeding season. In certain desert species, it may be the coming of rain that initiates reproduction. In still other forms of plants and of animals the length of the daily period of sunlight has a controlling effect on the reproductive activities. For many kinds of animals the amount of available food seems to exercise considerable control over breeding.

The factors that control reproduction may, to a greater or lesser degree, be the same as those which control activity and growth. Reproduction is not likely to occur unless the organism concerned is active. The threshold of a given factor necessary to induce reproduction, however, may be considerably higher than the activity threshold. Reproduction seems in general to be a highly complex process, which may be affected by numerous factors. For most kinds of plants and animals the precise factors in the habitat that control reproduction are still largely unknown.

Limiting Factors

Any environmental factor that at any time acts to eliminate a given species from a particular community or to prevent its immigration and establishment there may be called a limiting factor.

Certain biotic factors in the ecosystem may be no less important in limiting the success of a species than are the physical factors. The lack of some one biotic item essential for the life of a species may completely prevent its occurrence in a habitat otherwise fully suitable. Thus, in England the wheatear, according to Lack (1933: 246), nests exclusively in rabbit burrows and consequently does not occur in situations where rabbits are absent. In the northeastern United States and adjacent Canada the maximum population of white-tailed deer that any region can support is largely dependent upon the distribution, number, and size of the cedar swamps, where the most satisfactory winter food grows (Gabrielson, 1941: 118).

LAW OF THE LIMITING FACTOR. If any one of the several environmental factors that control the existence of a given kind of organism should at any time reach a level which is near or beyond the limit of toleration, either upward or downward, that species will be severely affected and may be eliminated from the situation. This will be true even though all the other environmental factors may be present at optimal values for the species. One may call this the law of the limiting factor, a law which was first formulated by Liebig (1862, Vol. 2: 225), as the "law of the minimum" and which has been emphasized by several later authors (Blackman and Smith, 1911; Hooker, 1917; G. E. Nichols, 1924; W. P. Taylor, 1934; H. L. Mason, 1936). The law of the limiting factor may be restated as follows: As any environmental factor approaches either the upper or lower limit of toleration for a given species, that factor becomes of increasing importance in controlling the functioning, the growth, and even the existence of the individual members of the species.

Critical Periods

Any particular time during which a species is in danger of local destruction constitutes for it a critical period. Such a period may occur at a certain hour of the day, during a certain season of the year, during a certain year of a climatic cycle, or at any other time when the conditions become severe (W. P. Taylor, 1934: 378). A species may experience during each generation numerous critical periods, each caused by an extreme variation either in the same or in diverse environmental factors.

A critical period is produced every time either the upper or lower limit of toleration for any environmental factor or life requirement of a given species is closely approached. During such a critical period there may be heavy mortality of the individuals, and the species may even become locally extirpated. Thus, much of the desert vegetation in southwestern Utah was destroyed during a short period of exceptionally low temperatures from January 21 to 27, 1937. The creosote bushes and mesquites, which are the most important desert plants in that locality, were killed to the ground; thus the character of the community was completely altered (W. P. Cottam, 1937). In subsequent years, however, these plants regained their position of dominance (Hardy, 1945). Snow and ice often are lethal for many kinds of birds and mammals, and when either is present a critical period may exist.

Special hazards to the survival of a given local population may occur at a particular hour, season, age, or life-history stage, or may be produced by a special combination of environmental factors. For a northern herbivore, for instance, the long winter may be the most difficult season of the year.

Should the limit of toleration for any factor be passed at any time, all the individuals of the species affected will be eliminated. That species, consequently, no longer will form a part of the community, even though a tolerable level for the factor is immediately restored.

Food that is present on an area but which is not available to the individuals concerned will, of course, have no bearing on their survival through a period of critical food shortage. It has been pointed out by Fitch and Twining (1946: 69), for example, that in the San Joaquin Valley of California mice and lizards of a suitable size to form the prey of very young Pacific rattlesnakes are relatively few in number. The lack of prey suitable for the young snakes constitutes, therefore, a factor limiting the numbers of this species, even though there is an abundance of rat-sized and squirrel-sized rodents to serve as prey for the older and larger snakes.

The severity of a given critical period for a particular species often is affected by the local conditions. Thus, the ruffed grouse in Minnesota suffers severely during ice storms in winter when a thick crust forms on the snow, but the presence of heavy conifer trees in which shelter can be found may enable some of the birds to survive (King, 1937).

CRITICAL SEASON. One particular season of the year may be a critical period during which the heaviest mortality of a given species occurs. Thus, Grinnell (1908: 27) has noted that in their winter range in southern California many Audubon warblers die during periods of cold weather in January and February. The birds that die are invariably emaciated, a condition which shows a lack of their proper insect food during this winter season. Other species that are sensitive to heat or to drought may, on the contrary, find the summer their most critical season. According to Grinnell (1924a: 842) it is the amount of food available when the supply is least plentiful that limits the numbers of resident species of animals. The time of migration is often a critical season for migratory birds. Storms that occur during their migrations may destroy many thousands of individuals of certain species (Lincoln, 1939, Chap. 5).

CRITICAL AGE. Many kinds of organisms are especially subject to mortality at a certain critical age. Various species of birds and mammals, for instance, suffer their greatest mortality just after they have left the nest. Likewise, many plants are especially sensitive at the seedling age. A drought that occurs when they are very small may kill great numbers of such plants.

Individual Adaptability

Most individual organisms have considerable ability to adapt themselves to unfavorable conditions. Many species, indeed, are able to exist and even to live moderately well under conditions that are far from their optimum. This individual adaptability is especially demonstrated each time an organism becomes acclimated to a strange set of environmental conditions.

The ability of individual organisms to adjust themselves to adverse situations, however, varies greatly among the species of plants and animals. The individuals of certain species have very little adaptability. Many of the marine algae, for example, are restricted to temperature zones within which the mean maxima of the surface waters of the ocean for the hottest months of the year do not vary more than 5° C. (Setchell, 1920). Likewise, the larvae of many species of insects are able to succeed only on a particular kind of food plant or on a few closely related forms (Brues, 1946).

The individuals of many other kinds of organisms, however, are highly adaptable in their habits and are able within wide limits to adjust themselves to the needs of the occasion. Thus, the sugar maple (*Acer saccharum*) of northeastern North America is able to germinate and to grow in the dense shade of a heavy deciduous forest. When it has attained sufficient stature to reach the forest crown, it is able to flourish also in full sunlight.

Many kinds of animals, too, are more or less adaptable in regard to food. If their preferred kind of food is not at hand, they will turn to other available food of similar kind. The white-tailed deer of eastern North America in summer feeds mostly on leaves of deciduous trees. In winter when leaves are unobtainable the deer eats the twigs and buds of deciduous trees and the leaves and small twigs of conifers. This deer will even eat grass, if necessary, to survive the critical winter period.

As a temporary expedient numerous organisms are able to exist for a time during an unfavorable period by using the reserves of food and of water stored within their bodies. Every organism has at least a slight amount of such reserves, and certain species have special devices for storing large quantities of fat, starch, water, or other necessities of life. A few kinds of animals make stores of food outside the body. Most of these stores, however, whether internal or external, are temporary in character and may become exhausted during a prolonged period of unfavorable conditions.

The amount of adjustment that the individual can make to the conditions of the immediate environment is always limited. Although species vary in the amount of their possible adjustment, even the most adaptable species has its limitations, fixed by its heredity. Any differences in adaptability among the members of a species must be based mostly on intraspecific variability in heredity, though the previous experiences of the individual also play a part here.

ADAPTABILITY MAY BE AN ADAPTATION. The amount of adaptability that the individuals of a species possess may itself be considered an adaptation (Gause, 1942). A species that is able to live under a considerable variety of environmental conditions is usually a member of a large number of different types of communities. Such a species will often be able to survive temporarily adverse conditions better than a more highly specialized species. On the other hand, the specialized species, through its more perfect adaptation to a particular niche, will succeed better in its own special niche than the more generalized and more adaptable form.

Barriers to Distribution

A habitat that is fully suited for the existence of a particular species of plant or animal may still lack that species if a barrier prevents it from reaching the area. That many habitats actually are well suited for species which naturally do not occupy them is proved by the success which certain species have achieved when introduced by accident or by design into the strange ecosystems of foreign continents. Many successfully introduced species have in fact become obnoxious pests in their new habitats. Consequently, the absence of a species from a particular community does not necessarily indicate that the species cannot exist in that ecosystem.

HABITAT SELECTION

Even if a species is present in a given region, its individual members must be able to reach those stands or microstands which are favorable for their existence and to remain in them. The individuals of certain species are mobile throughout their lifetime, and must select and remain in their proper habitats through reactions of some kind. The individuals of other species are fixed in position during most or all of their lives and, therefore, their selection of a suitable habitat usually occurs at a mobile stage in their life history.

Selection of the Individual Habitat

Land plants do not in general select their individual habitats through their own actions. Their seeds or other reproductive units arrive mostly by chance at the place where the plant is to grow. If this situation is unsuitable, the plant has no possibility of moving to another location. It can only grow or die. Many kinds of seed-producing and spore-producing plants, nevertheless, are able to secure a wide distribution and to reach habitats suitable for their germination and growth. This they are able to do by the production and distribution of many more reproductive units than can possibly survive. Even though many of their seeds or spores fall on sites where the resulting plants cannot thrive, at least a few will probably be more fortunate.

Those aquatic animals that are sessile in the adult stage follow much the same plan as the seed plants, producing many reproductive units in the chance that some of them will survive and reach a habitat tolerable for the species. Most terrestrial and many aquatic animals are mobile during the greater part of their lives and are able to select, at least to some extent, their own habitats. Such mobile animals, therefore, do not need to produce a large number of reproductive units per individual.

The selection of its habitat by a mobile animal must be based primarily on reactions to the stimuli present in that situation. If 2 species respond differently to a given stimulus, they may select very dissimilar types of habitats. Relatively little is known about the reactions that enable animals to select their habitats. Presumably, however, these reactions are in general adaptive, leading the individual to choose a situation favorable to itself.

TRIAL AND ERROR. The selection of a suitable habitat by an individual animal does not necessarily require any conscious action on the part of the animal. A simple avoidance reaction when the individual finds itself in an unfavorable situation results in habitat selection in certain of the lower animals. Thus, paramecium, a member of the Protozoa, when it approaches water having an unfavorable temperature, will usually stop its forward motion, back up, rotate on its axis, and go forward in a new direction. The same sort of reaction is given when the animal meets a physical obstruction. This trial-and-error method of behavior will frequently result in the animal reaching a favorable or at least a tolerable situation (Jennings, 1904).

MORE COMPLEX REACTIONS. The movements of many of the simpler invertebrates are based to some extent on tropisms to chemicals, light, sound, touch, gravity, and other environmental factors which in a more or less mechanical way are presumed to lead the organism concerned to a suitable type of habitat. The behavior of the higher invertebrates and of many vertebrates is based largely on instincts that involve the operation of chains of reflexes or tropisms, which appear at the proper stages in their life histories. Certain of these instincts, notably in the insects and birds, are very complex. Although largely mechanical, the behavior at least of a few insects and of many birds may be somewhat modified as the result of experience (Holmes, 1911; Maier and Schneirla, 1935).

EFFECT OF EXPERIENCE. The higher vertebrates utilize instincts and re-actions of various kinds in selecting their habitats, just as do the simpler kinds of animals. In addition, many of the higher animals are able to use also the results of experience in improving the character of their habitat selection (A. H. Miller, 1942; Emerson, 1943: 104). In a few animals which are most advanced mentally, such as man, reason also may play a part in habitat selection.

As an example of the role that the previous experience of the individual may play in the selection of its habitat, the ichneumonid (*Nemeritis canescens*) may be cited. This insect is normally a parasite of the meal moth (*Ephestia kühniella*), but if reared on the small wax moth (*Achroia grisella*) it will, in the absence of its normal host, oviposit on the larvae of the wax moth on which it was reared, but to which otherwise it would pay no attention (W. H. Thorpe, 1940: 354-55). There is good evidence that migratory birds and fishes usually return to breed in the general region in which they themselves were bred. There is, furthermore, an indication that after an individual bird has once established itself in a territory it returns year after year to that same territory.

HOST SELECTION BY PARASITES. The selection by animal parasites of their host species is a good example of habitat selection, even though very little is known about the precise reactions employed. Many kinds of animal para-sites are restricted to particular host species. The parasites undoubtedly se-lect their hosts by reactions to various kinds of stimuli, some of which are probably chemical in nature and involve particularly the senses of smell and taste, although sight, hearing, and the tactile sense may also be utilized. In those species of insects whose larvae are parasitic it is the adult which must select the host, and the reactions of this adult in finding a host on which its larvae can feed must often be very different from the reactions of the nonparasitic adult in finding food and shelter for itself. The instincts and reactions by which adults of some parasitic species find hosts to parasitize are often highly complex and very efficient. Many species of parasitic insects, however, appear to be very inefficient in locating their hosts (Sweetman, 1936: 275).

Factors in the Habitat That Are Selected

The adults of those insects the larvae of which feed on particular kinds of plants must select the proper plant by reactions that cause the eggs to be deposited. It has been shown that odor is the most important property through which certain adult insects recognize a plant as being suitable food for its offspring. Thus, various kinds of butterflies under laboratory conditions made searching movements when passing near leaves of their host plants, but flew in straight paths when passing over other kinds of leaves. The attractive feature of numerous kinds of plants for butterflies of the genus *Papilio* consists of certain essential oils (Dethier, 1941).

The precise factors that guide the individual animal in selecting its habitat, however, have been little studied, nor is much known about the mode of operation of the reactions. That each species of bird recognizes its habitat by the conspicuous, but not necessarily the essential, features is believed by Lack (1933), who also stated that in general each species selects its ancestral habitat and that only rarely does an individual modify this habit.

Inasmuch as the vegetation forms a very significant part of most terrestrial habitats, it may be assumed that vegetation type is one of the most important factors in habitat selection by animals (Dice, 1931b; Brecher, 1943). This is illustrated by the fact that those animals whose ranges cover 2 or more biotic provinces select vegetation types which are generally similar in each province. For example, the North American horned lark is a bird whose habitat is principally broad expanses of short grass. It lives in grassy areas in several biomes and ranges through at least 5 life zones. With the clearing of the eastern deciduous forests and their replacement in some spots by grassy fields, the horned lark has extended its range and may now be found nesting as far east as the sandy barrier beaches of Long Island, New York (Peterson, 1942).

A species often will thrive in an artificial environment that in certain respects resembles its natural habitat. Thus, in eastern Texas it was noted by Taylor and Lay (1944) that the jack rabbit is mostly a prairie form, and that when the pine timber is cut the jack rabbits move into the cleared lands. As these clearings grow up to oaks and other shrubs, however, the rabbits again disappear.

The conditions in the habitat selected by the members of a species must in general be those required for the successful life of the individuals. Animals are often able to live and sometimes to breed successfully, however, in types of habitat not normally selected by the species. For example, on a small island in Grand Traverse Bay, an arm of Lake Michigan, I found the meadow vole (*Microtus pennsylvanicus*) living and breeding in heavy deciduous forest, a habitat that it usually avoids (Dice, 1925a).

In the laboratory many kinds of animals will live and thrive under conditions they would never select in nature. Numerous races of prairie, deciduous-forest, coniferous-forest, and desert deermice (*Peromyscus maniculatus*), for example, will all live and breed in the same laboratory. It is very likely, therefore, that the reactions involved in habitat selection are in part only inherited preferences or prejudices (Diver, 1944: 45).

SINGING PERCHES OF BIRDS. Certain animals, in fact, have psychologic reactions that prevent them from utilizing habitats otherwise suitable. Thus, the willow warbler of England is reported by Lack (1933: 248) to be absent from most heaths, but it sometimes occurs where an isolated bush is present. In such a situation the bird nests on the heath, from which it also secures most or all of its food. The bush is used mainly as a singing post, and as such it evidently is essential for the presence of this species. Could the reactions of this species become modified in evolution so that it would no longer require the presence of an elevated singing post, extensive areas of heath not now occupied by this species would become available to it as a breeding habitat.

The difference in habitat between the tree pipit and the meadow pipit of England likewise is based on whether or not trees are present in the open fields that are the breeding places of the 2 species. Both species nest on the ground and their feeding habits are similar (Lack, 1933: 247). The selection by certain species of North American birds of shrubby-field habitats, rather than grassland, is similarly correlated with their use of elevated positions for song posts, for nesting sites, or for feeding (Kendeigh, 1945a: 434).

INDICATORS

The fact that a particular species of plant or animal often recurs again and again in widely separated ecosystems of similar type has led to the suggestion that the presence of such a species is an indicator of the characters of the environment. Clements (1920) presented this concept with vigor. He considered that every plant is an index to the soil and to the climate of the place where it grows and that animals likewise may to some extent serve as indicators of the physical conditions of their habitats.

Indicator Species for Communities

Ecologists commonly make use of indicator species for assistance in the recognition of a particular type of community in its various manifestations. The species most useful as indicators are those that are abundant and widespread in the community concerned, but are rare or absent in other community types. For instance, the beech and the maple may be considered indicator species of the beech-maple association of northeastern United States and adjacent Canada.

Care must be used, however, not to rely too heavily on the presence of such indicator species. Situations may be found where only 1 of these species is present, yet the community is obviously characteristic otherwise of the beech-maple community. In other places one or another of these indicator species may be found thriving in a community which is not at all typical for beech-maple.

VARIATION IN DEGREE OF ECOLOGIC RESTRICTION. The several species of organisms that exist on the earth vary greatly in the degree to which they are restricted to particular communities. This results from variability in their requirements for existence, in their tolerances, and in their adaptability. Certain species have very narrow habitat limitations and live only under 1 special combination of environmental conditions. Other species are more tolerant and are able to thrive in a considerable variety of communities of the same general type. Every species, nevertheless, is more or less limited in its possible environments, and no kind of organism lives in more than a small fraction of the diverse types of ecosystems found on the earth.

All the requirements for the lives of certain kinds of organisms may be found, at least for a time, within very narrow space limits. For example, an insect larva living within the tissues of a plant leaf finds both food and shelter in that situation. In the adult stage, however, this insect must leave its sheltered situation in order to reproduce its kind. Many young birds and mammals live for a time during their early lives in especially constructed nests where they are given solicitous care by their parents. When they have reached the fledgling age, however, these young animals must leave the nest and thereafter they have a much wider range of movement.

Numerous kinds of animals are not restricted in their movements to the limits of a single community, but on the contrary, may operate in several diverse community types (Grinnell, 1914a: 95). Thus, some species of birds may nest or roost at night in the forest, but feed during the daylight hours in open fields (Kendeigh, 1941b: 167). In its daily wanderings a large bird or mammal may travel across 2 or more types of communities and for short periods become a member of them.

Those species which are sharply limited in their ecologic requirements will evidently be the best indicators of their ecosystems. On the contrary, a species which is widely adaptable and which is a member of many diverse types of communities will not be of much value as an indicator of any one ecosystem. Actually, only a very few species are completely limited in their occurrence to a single type of ecosystem. Furthermore, it is only rarely that a species which is closely limited to a single type of community will occur throughout the whole geographic range of that community.

Much too great dependence has been placed by certain field ecologists on indicator species. In the western United States, for instance, the yellow pine is often considered an indicator of the Transition life zone, and certain investigators have gone so far as to mark as Transition every area in which a yellow-pine grove occurs. The yellow pine, however, is a fairly adaptable tree and the result is that many diverse types of communities have been classed as Transition. Many communities that lack yellow pines, but which obviously belong in the same life belt as the yellow-pine forests, have been excluded from the Transition. While indicator species are definitely useful, the ecologist should always consider them to be only an indication of the community concerned rather than a certain diagnosis of its presence or absence.

Indicators of Community History

During the course of succession the environmental conditions within an ecosystem may gradually become unfavorable for certain of the member species of the community. Those species, however, that have a wide range of toleration may linger on in the community for a considerable period of time. The presence of such a relict species may indicate, therefore, what the immediately preceding stage of the community has been. The lone white pines that are present in many hardwood forests in northern Michigan may thus indicate a preceding pine-forest stage. Certain member species of a given stand may accordingly be indicators of the past history of that situation.

Indicator Communities

The whole community is a much better indicator of the conditions of its habitat than any 1 species can be (Sampson, 1939: 199). Individual species vary in their limits of toleration for the several factors of the environment. One species in a community may, for instance, be unable to tolerate a greater amount of soil moisture than is usually present in that type of habitat, while another species may be unable to grow under more arid conditions. In a community where both of these species grow together the soil moisture, therefore, is indicated to be intermediate in amount. Although nearly every species can thrive in more than 1 community type, the combination of species that together form a community can exist only in 1 particular type of environment. The whole community, therefore, is the best indicator of its habitat.

The natural communities that grow on particular plots of ground are frequently used by farmers as indicators of the kinds of crops that will best succeed there. For this purpose the vegetation, because of the ease with which it may be observed and its relative permanence, is usually a much more useful index than the animal members of the community. A determination of the natural plant communities of a region and their distribution, therefore, is often of very practical service to the agriculturalist, forester, and wildlife manager (Shantz, 1911; Kearney and others, 1914; Diver, 1938*b;* E. H. Graham, 1944: 46).

It should not be overlooked, however, that many communities are able to modify considerably the physical factors of their habitats. Through convergent succession, for example, the same type of climax community may ultimately be produced on many diverse types of soils, and the community may not be a good indicator of the underlying soil type. In the process of succession each successive community will usually have altered the upper soil layers so that the situation is adapted to its needs. Although due caution, therefore, must be used in accepting any particular community as a complete indicator of the habitat, nevertheless the community as a whole is usually a very reliable indicator of at least the climate and of the existing surface soil.

ECOLOGIC NICHE

The term "niche" has been widely used by ecologists, but unfortunately not always with exactly the same meaning (Clements and Shelford, 1939: 242). Grinnell (1917) first proposed the term to designate the place in a specified association occupied by a single species of animal and to include a consideration of the adaptations of structure and of habit that fit the individuals of the species to the local environment. Grinnell (1924b: 227) later called the ecologic niche the ultimate unit of habitat, and still later (1928a: 435) he defined it as the "ultimate distributional unit, within which each species is held by its structural and instinctive limitations." Elton (1927: 63-68) in using the term emphasized the habits of the animal in relation to food and mentioned other activities of the animal in the community. Gause (1935a: 6) mentioned the food, habits, and mode of life of a species as the features which define its ecologic niche. Hutchinson (1944: 20, footnote) defined niche as the sum of all the environmental factors acting on the organism.

In their concept of niche most ecologists have included a consideration of the use which the species concerned makes of particular physical and biotic features of the ecosystem and of the dependence of the species on these features. This concept was certainly present in the mind of Grinnell in his use of the term. On the other hand, no special term, other than micro-habitat, seems necessary to designate a minor space division of a habitat. Accordingly, I define niche as the ecologic position that a species occupies in a particular ecosystem. The term "niche" includes, therefore, a consideration of the habitat that the species concerned occupies for shelter, for breeding sites, and for other activities, the food that it eats, and all the other features of the ecosystem that it utilizes. The term does not include, except indirectly, any consideration of the functions that the species serves in the community. As thus defined niche is a rather loose and broad term that often proves useful in ecologic description.

BIOTOPE. Certain ecologists have used the term "biotope" as though it were synonymous with niche (Hesse, Allee, and Schmidt, 1937: 135). Hesse (1924: 141, 143) in his original use of the term, however, specifically stated that the biotope is a geographic unit of habitat and that it does not apply to minor habitats. In its original usage, therefore, biotope is not at all the same concept as niche.

DEGREE OF RESTRICTION OF NICHES TO COMMUNITY BOUNDARIES. Certain kinds of organisms occupy niches that are highly specialized and very local. For instance, a nematode that is parasitic within the tissues of a particular plant may occupy a very simple and very restricted niche, whereas a species that is highly adaptable in its life requirements may occupy a very complex and widely diversified niche. This is especially true of the niches of those species which simultaneously are members of several communities. For example, the common kingfisher of North America secures most of its food in the water, but it perches on the branches of trees that form part of adjacent terrestrial communities, and it nests in burrows in steep dirt banks. Because the niches of many species thus extend beyond the boundaries of a single community, it is impossible to treat the niche as a subdivision of the community or of the ecosystem.

SUBDIVISIONS OF NICHES. The niche of each species may be divided into several more or less distinct parts. One may accordingly speak of the food niche, the shelter niche, the mating niche, the nesting niche, and so on, of each species. There is considerable question, however, about the usefulness of such subdivisions of the niche. The several phases of the activity of any individual are usually closely related to one another. It is only rarely, for example, that the feeding niche and the shelter niche of a species are completely distinct from each other.

CLASSIFICATION OF NICHES. Attempts have been made by a few ecologists to classify the organisms in a community or region according to their ecologic niches (Judd, 1902; W. P. Taylor, 1941). These attempts have been only partly successful. Because of the numerous relations that every species has to its ecosystem there is an almost infinite number of possible niches. The niche of any given species differs more or less from that of every other species. Furthermore, the niches of the several species in a community often overlap broadly. Any attempt to classify species according to their niches seems, therefore, at least at present, to be impractical.

OCCURRENCE OF TWO SPECIES IN THE SAME NICHE. Two member species of a community rarely occupy exactly the same ecologic niche. If 2 kinds of plants grow in the same situations, for example, they will practically always differ in their requirements for sunlight, in the depth to which their roots penetrate the soil, or in their season of activity, or they will have some other important difference in their life histories. Consequently, 2 such associated plants are usually not in direct competition in every respect. Should 2 kinds of animals which live in the same habitat be alike in food habits, they will probably differ in their time or place of breeding. Should they breed at the same sites, they will probably differ in breeding behavior, in food preferences, or in some other way.

Any 2 forms that occupy exactly the same ecologic niche will be under intense competition all along the line and one or the other of them will be almost certain to succumb. This deduction, made long ago by Charles Darwin (1859, Chap. 3) in his book on the origin of species, is supported by many diverse types of evidence.

Wherever 2 species under controlled experimental conditions come into direct competition for any essential item, such as food, one of the species nearly always drives the other out completely (Gause, 1934a: 113; Crombie, 1947). In nature, however, the interrelations of species are usually very complex, and it will seldom happen that 2 species competing for a given life essential will have exactly the same requirements for all the other essentials and also will have identical tolerances to the various factors making up the environment. Under 1 set of environmental conditions one of the competing species may have the advantage, but under a different set of conditions the other species may succeed better. In the constant fluctuation of environmental conditions characteristic of most habitats, first one and then the other competing species may have the advantage, with the result that neither may ever attain complete mastery over the situation.

If 2 species are in competition for only part of their requirements, then both may be able to exist and even to thrive in the same community. Such survival will, of course, depend in considerable part on the availability of the necessary resources at the points where the 2 species come into competition. If there is an abundance of food and of other essentials for both forms, competition may not be disastrous for either. For example, 2 or more species that utilize a certain type of food which temporarily is very abundant may have very different habits in regard to their other foods. Theoretically, therefore, they may never come into acute competition. When a certain prey species such as a lemming is very abundant, numerous predators will utilize it. Because there is a superabundance of lemmings the predators are not in competition for this food. When the lemming becomes scarce, then the several predators may each turn to its own special kind of prey; here, too, they may not be in competition. The gathering of predators to feed on a superabundant item of food, therefore, does not necessarily demonstrate any competition among them (Lack, 1946a).

Species that are closely related taxonomically tend to compete with one another in more ways than forms which are more distantly related. This is true because closely related forms are likely to be similar to one another in many details of their structure and of their habits. A rule formulated by Grinnell (1924b: 227) states that a given ecologic niche is occupied by only a single species or subspecies. If 2 closely related forms do occur in the same region, they usually occupy different communities (Cabrera, 1932). If they actually live in the same community, they usually utilize different kinds of food (Lack, 1944) or otherwise occupy different niches. On certain of the Galapagos Islands, for example, 2 or more of the resident species of finches may differ from one another in size of bill, with which is correlated a difference in the size of food utilized, although they all eat the same general kinds of food (Lack, 1947: 161).

There are, however, a number of known instances of pairs of closely related species that live together and that, so far as our present information goes, have much the same habits. As an example may be cited the pinyon mouse (*Peromyscus truei*) and the juniper mouse (*Peromyscus nasutus*), which over a considerable geographic area in Colorado, New Mexico, and Arizona may be found together in the same communities. In certain situations in this area, however, the pinyon mouse, and in other situations the juniper mouse, may be found alone (Dice, 1942). In these cases present information is inadequate to offer an explanation for the apparent flouting of the usual rule that 2 related species do not live together. A good review of this subject is given by Mayr (1948: 212-16).

The apparent success of 2 related species in the same community, occasionally observed, may be due to some important difference in their habits, which prevents them from coming into destructive competition with each other for any essential of life (Diver, 1940). From a study of the cormorant (*Phalacrocorax carbo*) and shag (*P. aristotelis*) in England, for instance, Lack (1945) concluded that the food of the 2 species differs considerably and that they occupy different types of nesting sites. These 2 forms, although they often live in the same habitats, do not seriously compete with each other.

Theoretically, there is only 1 kind of ecologic situation in which 2 species having the same requirements can exist together. Such a situation is one in which the abundance of each species is maintained, by factors other than population density itself, at a level so low that no competition occurs between the 2 forms for any essential for the life of either (Crombie, 1945: 393; 1947). It is possible that the occurrence of such situations in nature may explain those instances where 2 species apparently nearly identical in habits live in the same communities. The factors that control natural populations, however, are so little known that at present it may be said that such a relationship is theoretically possible, but has not been demonstrated. In general, 2 species having identical or nearly identical habits do not occur in the same community.

SELECTED REFERENCES

Blackman, F. F. 1905. Optima and limiting factors. Ann. Bot., 19: 281-95.

Chapman, Royal N. 1931. Animal ecology. New York and London: McGraw-Hill Book Co. Chaps. 2 to 6.

Clements, Frederic E. 1920. Plant indicators: the relation of plant communities to process and practice. Publ. Carnegie Inst. Wash., 290: 35-36, 72-104.

Elton, Charles. 1927. Animal ecology. New York: Macmillan Co. Chaps. 4 and 5.

Grinnell, Joseph. 1914b. Barriers to distribution as regards birds and mammals. Amer. Nat., 48: 248-54.

Lack, David. 1933. Habitat selection in birds; with special reference to the effects of afforestation on the Breckland avifauna. Journ. Animal Ecol., 2: 239-62.

Livingston, Burton E., and Forrest Shreve. 1921. The distribution of vegetation in the United States, as related to climatic conditions. Publ. Carnegie Inst. Wash., 284: 97-148.

Shelford, Victor E. 1913. Animal communities in temperate North America as illustrated in the Chicago region. A study in animal ecology. Chicago: Univ. Chicago Press. Pp. 299-308 (law of toleration).

——— 1929. Laboratory and field ecology; the responses of animals as indicators of correct working methods. Baltimore: Williams and Wilkins Co. Chaps. 3, 7, 11, 12, 15.

XI

HOME RANGES AND TERRITORIES

The precise place in the ecosystem at which each individual plant and animal is situated in relation to its neighbors is of considerable significance in the organization of the community. Those individual plants and animals which are permanently attached to the substratum occupy a fixed position in the community, but most animals have at least some degree of mobility and for that reason their position in the community varies from time to time.

Notwithstanding their freedom of movement individual animals do not as a rule wander about at random, but the great majority spend their lives within closely limited areas. Even though an animal may have the ability to travel over a wide area, unless he is forced out of his home range he usually confines his movements to only a small part of the habitats that are fully suited for his existence and over which he is potentially free to roam.

HOME RANGES

The area over which an individual animal habitually travels while engaged in his usual daily activities may be called his home range. His nest, bed, or roosting place must be situated at some place inside this home range. The home range also includes all the feeding sites, breeding sites, and places of refuge habitually used by the individual, and all the other areas regularly traversed by him. The term "cruising range" has essentially the same meaning as home range.

Most knowledge about the home ranges of animals pertains to the terrestrial vertebrates, particularly the birds and mammals. Many reptiles, amphibians, and fishes are also known to restrict their activities to more or less fixed home ranges. Less is known about the habits of the lower invertebrates, but at least some of them also live in home ranges. This is true certainly of some of the termites, ants, bees, and wasps. Any mobile animal that has a home must of necessity have a home range within which his home is located. For this reason the web-weaving spiders and many of the other invertebrates that live in burrows or in fixed abodes of any kind also must have home ranges.

A few kinds of animals apparently never establish home ranges at any season. The nomadic habit of the caribou has been described in Chapter IX. It is possible also that many kinds of insects and of marine organisms do not live in fixed home ranges, but information on this point is very limited.

The home range of a given individual animal may lie wholly within 1 particular kind of ecosystem. Numerous kinds of animals, especially some of the larger and more mobile forms, however, may have home ranges that overlap several habitat types. In particular, a large mammal, such as the wolf, that regularly travels over a considerable area may have a home range that includes many diverse types of ecosystems.

METHODS FOR ASCERTAINING HOME-RANGE LIMITS. The areas ranged over by fairly large animals which are active only in daylight, such as many birds and certain mammals, may be ascertained with considerable accuracy by direct observation. The movements of small or of secretive forms, such as many insects, on the contrary, may be impossible to follow by sight. The travels of nocturnal animals are especially difficult to trace. The tracks of certain of the larger mammals can, it is true, be followed in sand, mud, or snow. Unfortunately, the substratum usually does not retain tracks well. Consequently, it is usually expedient to trap the individuals, mark and release them, and retrap them in other parts of their home ranges. By setting a sufficient number of traps in a grid pattern, the movements of each animal may be deduced from the location of the traps in which he is from time to time recaught (Blair, 1941).

Several methods have been proposed for calculating from trapping records the areas of the home ranges of mammals (Mohr, 1947; Hayne, 1949). Of these methods that of Blair (1942) is perhaps the most useful. According to this method the influence of each trap is presumed to extend in every direction on the average one-half the distance to the next adjacent trap. The area under study, therefore, is assumed to be divided into quadrats which have dimensions equal to the distances between the traps and with 1 trap in the middle of each quadrat. It is assumed also that the home range of each individual animal occupies the area connecting the outside corners of all the quadrats in which he is at any time captured (Fig. 31).

Each animal, however, is almost certain to have a home range considerably different in shape and in area from that estimated by any such conventionalized method. The average area per home range calculated from trapping records is probably in most cases smaller than the areas actually wandered over regularly by the individuals because of imperfections in the trapping. Furthermore, the calculations are affected by the distance between traps, by fluctuations in the daily and seasonal activities of the animals, by irregularities in the character of the habitat, and by numerous other factors.

A single capture of an individual obviously gives only a small bit of information about the area covered by his home range. Even 2 or 3 recaptures of the same marked individual may give only incomplete information about the area over which he regularly travels.

From a study of cottontail rabbits in southern Michigan, Haugen (1942*a*) concluded that the home-range areas of the adult females during the breeding season were reasonably well defined by 9 recaptures of each individual and that little additional information was secured by further retrapping. The males, on the contrary, were not so restricted in their activities, and estimates of their home-range areas continued to increase for each additional recapture of a given individual (Table XIII). Many other kinds of

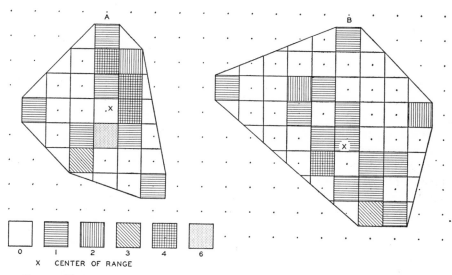

Fig. 31. Home ranges of breeding females (A) and (B) of woodland deermouse (*Peromyscus maniculatus gracilis*) in northern Michigan, with home-range boundaries outlined according to the method of Blair. The large dots indicate traps, spaced 45 feet apart. Each trap is assumed to control a quadrat which extends half the distance to each next adjacent trap. The number of times the animal was caught in each trap is indicated by the shading of that quadrat. The total number of quadrats included within the boundaries of any given home range is the number of quadrats wholly within those boundaries plus one-half the number of quadrats which are only partly within the boundaries. (Redrawn from Blair, 1942.)

animals seem to be like the male cottontails in giving an increased estimate of home-range area with increase in the numbers of recaptures of each animal. Calculations of home-range area based on trapping records, accordingly, must take into consideration the number of recaptures on which the area has been estimated.

Another difficulty with the trapping method for ascertaining home ranges is that an animal may change the position of his home range during the trapping period and thereby cause an erroneous estimate to be made. Individual animals that are wandering irregularly or are in migration cannot be considered to have home ranges, even though they may remain for a few days in one area. Some arbitrary decision, consequently, may be required on the number of days an individual must occupy a given area before he is considered to have a home range there.

A month was selected by Evans and Holdenried (1943: 249) as the minimum time requirement for the recognition of a home range of the Beechey ground squirrel of California. For other species of animals perhaps other minimum time limits might be desirable. Such time limits are in part required because of the slowness with which trapping records accumulate, rather than necessarily being due to the time required for the animal to settle himself in a new home range. It is possible that one or a very few days may suffice for an individual animal to make himself familiar with all the landmarks of a new situation and for him to feel entirely at home.

Because of the numerous inaccuracies involved in the trapping and marking method for ascertaining the home ranges of animals, it is evident that only a rough estimate is given of the limits of any individual home range or of the differential use made of the various parts of the area. The information obtained is nevertheless of value for comparing the average home-range areas of one species in various types of ecosystems and for comparing the home range areas of dissimilar species. A measure of average home-range diameter is also needed for calculating the average distance beyond a setting of traps from which the animals come to the traps.

CENTER OF HOME RANGE. Each animal will usually visit certain parts of his home range more frequently than other parts. The center of range ("center of activity" of Hayne, 1949) of a given individual animal may be considered the geographic center of all the trap locations at which he is captured during a given interval of time. The center of range may be calculated by the following method: On a chart of the trap grid numerical values are assigned to both the horizontal rows and to the vertical columns of traps. Next, the average of the numerical values of all the vertical columns in which the animal was trapped is determined. If the animal was taken more than once in a particular column, the value of each capture should be included. Next, an average is secured of the values of the horizontal rows in which the animal was trapped. Finally, the point at which the average values for the columns and for the rows intersect is marked on the chart. This point will be the center of range for the animal (Fig. 31).

In general each animal will probably be caught more frequently in traps near his home than in more distant traps, but this will not always be true. The center of range is accordingly not to be taken as an indication of the home site. In fact it may happen (as in Fig. 31A) that the animal is never taken in the trap which is nearest the center of his range.

Territories

Although the individuals of many species of animals seem to have no objection to the proximity of other individuals of the same species and although certain species prefer to live in social groups, the individuals of a number of kinds of animals appear more or less antagonistic to other members of their own species, especially during the breeding season. The result of this antagonism is that the individual animals may defend their home ranges against trespass by other members of the same species. A home range or part of a home range that is thus defended is called a territory. A territory may best be defined as any defended area (Nice, 1941: 441). The first clear description of the defense of territories by birds and other animals was given by H. E. Howard (1920), though Bernard Altum and others had earlier noted this type of bird behavior (Mayr, 1935).

DIFFERENCE BETWEEN HOME RANGE AND TERRITORY. It is not always easy to determine whether the members of a particular species defend their home ranges, which then would be territories, or whether there is no such defense. Sometimes only a part of the home range is defended. The home ranges of the red-tailed hawks illustrated in Figure 32, for example, were rather clearly defined, but the parts of the home ranges that were defended fluctuated from time to time. Also, certain species may at one season defend their home ranges, but at a different season defense may be lacking.

If all the individuals of one sex of a given species which live within a particular area occupy individual home ranges that do not overlap one another or which overlap only slightly, then a tendency toward the defense of individual territories is commonly assumed. The actual existence of territorial behavior, however, can only be considered proved when it has been shown that the presumed holder of a territory actually defends its boundaries against trespassers.

TYPES OF HOME RANGES AND TERRITORIES

The relation of the home range or territory of a particular individual animal to the organization of the community varies according to the habits of the species concerned. The diversity of types of home ranges and territories represented by the various species and classes of animals is very great. It seems desirable, therefore, to describe some of these types.

Birds

SONG BIRDS. Territorial behavior is best known among the song birds. When a brilliantly colored male bird sings loudly from a tree one is apt to think that he is expressing his joy in living and perhaps also is impressing his mate. Possibly he is, but his performance has a far more important ecologic significance. By his conspicuous colors and behavior and by his loud and characteristic song he is advertising to all the members of his species that here a vigorous male has pre-empted a territory. Should other males attempt to enter the territory they will be attacked and likely driven away, unless one of them should be so much stronger or more aggressive than the owner of the territory that he can successfully challenge and dispossess him. The

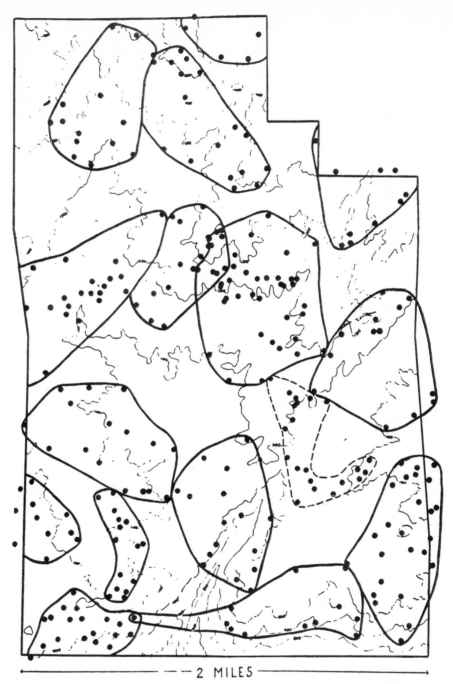

←— ——— 2 MILES ———————→

FIG. 32. Locations of some of the principal perches of 16 pairs of red-tailed hawks in 1939 on the San Joaquin Experimental Range, California. The heavy lines enclose the perching area of each pair, but do not represent territorial boundaries. The broken line encloses the range of a pair which disappeared early in the season. The actual area defended by each pair fluctuates. (After Fitch, Swenson, and Tillotson, 1946.)

song, bright plumage, and display behavior are warnings to weak males to keep away from an occupied territory. At the same time the male is advertising to the females of his species that here is an attractive male waiting for a mate.

Among the migratory species of song birds the males often arrive on the breeding grounds several days before the females. By the time the females arrive the males already have established their territories and are in full song. The females then go to the territories of the males and become mated to them. According to Friedmann (1928: 558), it is the female which usually chooses the exact site for the nest, somewhere within the territory of the male. After a female has become mated to a male she may join him in the defense of the territory, but this is true only of certain species. Often the male alone continues to defend his holdings. When the breeding season is past, the males often abandon their territories, and in the nonbreeding season they may join with other males, with females, and with young individuals to form social flocks.

The method of selecting the territory, however, varies with the species, and it is not always the male alone who makes the selection. The males and females of numerous migratory species of birds arrive on the breeding ground at approximately the same time, and in at least a few of these species the individuals are already mated when they arrive. Certain resident birds also may become paired before the territories are selected.

HORNED OWL. Many kinds of birds other than song birds also defend territories. Thus, the male great horned owl of North America is said by Baumgartner (1939) to patrol his territory during the nesting season and to defend it against the trespass of any other large owls except his mate and young. Not only are other owls of the same species driven away, but large owls of every species are excluded. Both adults of the horned-owl pair hunt for food only within the limits of the defended territory. This limits the depredations of a given pair of horned owls to a relatively small area.

PHALAROPE. The role of the sexes in territorial behavior is reversed in the phalaropes from the pattern usual for birds. This reversal of sexual behavior is correlated with the fact that the female phalaropes are more brightly colored than the males. The females of the red-necked phalarope (*Phalaropus lobatus*) of East Greenland, for example, arrive on the breeding grounds before the males and soon establish territories which they defend, though somewhat weakly, against other females. The females sing and display on their territories and the males come there for mating. Often, however, a female will allow other females on her defended area and she sometimes fights and sings outside the usual boundaries of her territory. The collection of food is not confined to the territory. Both sexes of the phalarope collaborate in the construction of the nest, but the male alone seems to incubate the eggs and to care for the young (N. Tinbergen, 1935).

HUMMINGBIRD. Hummingbirds of both sexes establish and defend separate territories during the breeding season (Saunders, 1936: 161). The territory of the male seems for the most part to include a source of food supply. The female defends at least the immediate surroundings of her nest. The male defends his territory against other males and also against females. There is consequently no co-operation at any time between the members of a mated pair of hummingbirds for the defense of a territory or for the rearing of the young. It is possible that the males may be polygynous (Pitelka, 1942).

NESTING TERRITORY ONLY. A modified form of territory which covers the nesting site only and does not include the feeding area is exhibited by some species of birds. Those marine birds which obtain their food from the water often show this type of behavior. In these forms competition for food usually is not severe, and furthermore it would be impossible to set up and defend a territory located on open water. No attempt then is made by these aquatic birds to defend their feeding grounds against other individuals. Nesting sites suitable for the species, however, are often scarce, and there is accordingly severe competition for nesting space. Each breeding pair commonly sets up on land a very small territory, which often is barely large enough to contain the nest, and the pair vigorously defends this breeding site against all intruders. For example, any alien gull, even an immature chick, that may trespass upon a territory of the herring gull is immediately attacked and perhaps killed by the adult owners (Herrick, 1912).

MATING TERRITORY ONLY. The American woodcock (*Philohela minor*) is peculiar in its territorial relations because the male maintains an open-country singing and mating territory separate from his feeding area, which usually is in a near-by woods (Fig. 33). The male defends his mating area but not his feeding area (Pettingill, 1936; Mendall and Aldous, 1943: 66). The nesting activities are carried out solely by the female. Neither the area around the nest nor the female's feeding area is believed to be defended. Mating occurs on the display area of the male. Display territories and their adjacent feeding areas are sometimes established for a time by migrant males in regions where the species does not breed (Pitelka, 1943).

Display or singing stations, to which the females come for mating, also are established by the males of numerous other kinds of birds. The male usually defends his individual display station against other males. Thus, it constitutes a territory, even though there is no defense of the females, of the nest, or of the feeding area. As an example of a bird that establishes such a male display territory may be mentioned the ruffed grouse (*Bonasa umbellus*) of North America (King, 1937).

COMMUNAL MATING GROUNDS. The males of certain kinds of birds concentrate their display stations in the vicinity of one another. These grouped display stations thus form a collective breeding area, which is called their "booming," "dancing," or "gabbling" grounds. North American prairie chickens (Lehmann, 1941), sage grouse (Simon, 1940), and sharp-tailed grouse (Hamerstrom, 1939), among others, have this habit. On the collective display grounds each male may, at least in certain species, maintain a particular station or territory which he defends against the other males congregated there (Davison, 1940a: 57).

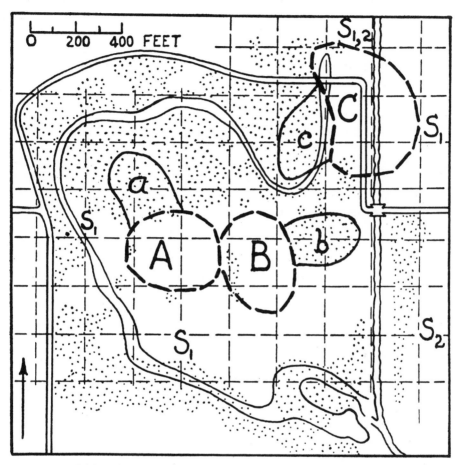

FIG. 33. Division of the home range of the woodcock into distinct breeding and feeding parts. Open-country display areas (A, B, C) and adjoining feeding areas (a, b, c) of 3 male woodcocks in Illinois. S_1 and S_2 are additional singing males. The stippled areas are woodland or thickets; the unstippled areas are open, with herbs, scattered shrubs, and a few small trees. Each space in the grid covers 1 acre. (After Pitelka, 1943.)

WINTER TERRITORIES. During the nonbreeding season certain kinds of birds continue to maintain territories. California mockingbirds of both sexes maintain and defend winter territories, whether or not they are paired, and thus they defend their food supply. The winter territory of the mockingbird may or may not coincide with the area included in the summer breeding territory, which usually is defended by the male alone (Michener and

Michener, 1935). The California wren tit also remains paired during the
winter, and both sexes defend their territory throughout the year. Their
defense of the territory in winter, however, is not so vigorous as it is during
the breeding season (Erickson, 1938: 318-19). Many of the Ohio song
sparrows studied by Nice (1937: 211) also remained in the same home ranges
throughout the year, but they defended them only during the breeding
season. The male English robins, which are resident, maintain winter as
well as summer territories; the females, some of which migrate, do not maintain winter territories (Lack, 1940a: 306).

PARASITIC BIRDS. The male European cuckoo is said (Alverdes, 1927: 19)
to establish a territory, although this species is parasitic on other species of
birds and does not build its own nests. The females are promiscuous and
roam from one male to another, often pairing with as many as 6 males.

COLONIAL BIRDS. Certain species of nonparasitic American cuckoos live
in colonies which maintain and defend colonial territories. The territory is
divided into 2 parts, one part for sleeping and the other part for feeding.
Certain pairs may establish their own territories within the territory of the
colony. These, then, are territories within territories. The territories of the
pairs, however, are weakly defended and possibly indicate the manner of
origin of the colonial territory (D. E. Davis, 1942: 121).

Birds that nest in colonies often defend the colony as a whole at the
same time that each nesting bird has an individual territory surrounding
its nest. The black-headed gull of England, for instance, nests in large
colonies in which each nesting bird controls an area having a radius of
about 1.5 feet from the center of its nest. There is no fighting so long as
the neighboring birds remain outside the defended territory. The defense
of the nesting territory results in an even spacing of the nests and a consequent effective use of the limited nesting space.

Immature black-crowned night herons when confined in small quarters
under experimental conditions may establish and defend small group territories (Noble, Wurm, and Schmidt, 1938). The number of these nonbreeding immature birds in a group varies from 2 to 7. Occasionally, a
single bird also defends a small territory. Whether such territories are established by juvenile herons in nature is not known.

SOCIAL BANDS OF BIRDS. Several individuals of the same species may have
home ranges that overlap, at least in part. The tendency for the overlapping
of home ranges reaches an extreme in those social animals that travel in
bands. All the members of one social band may have identical home ranges.
Thus, in a part of Mariposa County, California, studied by McLean (1930),
the members of each covey of mountain quail generally had a common
home range, which included a spring of water. Furthermore, the home
ranges of separate coveys overlapped at some places. Winter coveys of bobwhite quail in the eastern United States also usually occupy fairly well-fixed
home ranges (Errington and Hamerstrom, 1936: 312-16).

Many social bands, on the contrary, are only loosely bound together, and the individual members accordingly may have home ranges that coincide only in part. Numerous kinds of birds and of bats, for instance, roost in large groups, at least in certain seasons, but the group separates for feeding. The common crow of northeastern North America gathers in winter in large roosts in which the night is spent, but in the daytime the birds separate into smaller flocks for foraging.

Moving Territory. A few kinds of social birds defend the flock itself, but not the home range. Thus, the winter coveys of the California quail live in well-defined home ranges, though a given covey may visit only a small part of its home range on any particular day. The members of the covey attack other coveys or other individuals that approach too closely, thus establishing a defense of the covey. There is no evidence that they defend any part of the flock home range or that they establish during the winter a geographical territory of any kind (Emlen, 1939; Howard and Emlen, 1942).

A somewhat similar moving territory surrounding a family of blue geese has been reported by Allee (1942: 291). The moving territory around the blue-goose family is defended not only by both parents, but also sometimes by the young (Jenkins, 1944). During the breeding season, after the young of the previous year have been driven away, the gander defends the vicinity of his mate, who then forms the center of a territory. Later, when a nest has been constructed, this becomes the center of another kind of territory. Jenkins observed that certain other places, such as feeding or roosting areas, were also defended as territories by this species of goose. A single species, therefore, may establish several dissimilar kinds of territories, and any given territory may be a combination of several of these types.

Mammals

Small Mammals. All the species of small mammals that have been carefully studied live in more or less well-defined individual home ranges, but it has not been proved that many of them defend territories. Females of certain species when in breeding condition are said to occupy exclusive territories (woodmice, Burt, 1940; cottontail, Haugen, 1942a; vole, Blair, 1940d), but it has not been demonstrated for any of these species that the territory actually is defended. On the other hand, Blair (1940a, 1940b, 1940c, 1942) concluded that neither sex of the jumping mouse (Zapus), prairie deermouse (Peromyscus maniculatus bairdii), shrew (Blarina), woodland deermouse (Peromyscus m. gracilis), and eastern chipmunk (Tamias) defends home ranges. The home ranges of breeding females of these forms often overlap broadly, and 2 wild females of the prairie deermouse may even keep their young in the same nest. In many of these small mammals the males have individual ranges that overlap those of the females. Usually the male range is relatively large in area and 1 male may travel over the ranges of several females.

Among the Sciuridae there is some evidence of territorial behavior. The individual ranges of the males of the Beechey ground squirrel (*Citellus beecheyi*) of California are said by Evans and Holdenried (1943: 252, 257-58) to overlap only slightly or not at all, while those of the females overlap broadly. The males of this species are aggressive and chase away other adults of both sexes, though their ranges overlap those of the females. They tolerate the presence of very young squirrels, but become increasingly combative as the youngsters grow older. The females are only slightly aggressive. Linsdale (1946), however, presented evidence that it is mainly the burrows of these ground squirrels that are defended as territories and that elsewhere in their home ranges there may be considerable common use by different individuals of the same observation posts and of the same shelters.

Certain chipmunks and squirrels were said by Gordon (1936) to defend territories, though the sexes were not clearly ascertained. Hatt (1943) also believed that the Colorado pine squirrel (*Tamiasciurus fremonti*) maintains territories. Burt (1943) observed that a female eastern chipmunk (*Tamias*) drove other individuals of the species away from the vicinity of her nest, and he concluded that in this species there is good evidence of territorial behavior. D. L. Allen (1943: 147) has evidence that when a fox squirrel (*Sciurus niger rufiventer*) is occupying a nest it will defend the immediate vicinity of this nest, but that it does not attempt to drive squirrels away from other parts of its home range.

LARGE MAMMALS. Few studies have been made of the home ranges of individual large mammals, but the published observations seem to indicate that most large animals have, at least temporarily, a more or less fixed cruising range. Of white-tailed deer tagged in Minnesota when they were fawns all the does that were later recovered had traveled less than 5 miles from their place of marking. The bucks traveled farther, their average distance of capture from the place of marking being 5 miles, and the greatest distance 13 miles (Olson, 1938: 282). During winters of heavy snowfall in northeastern North America a number of white-tailed deer may congregate in a place where food is available and there form a "deer yard" (Hamerstrom and Blake, 1939; Trippensee, 1948: 192). The caribou, on the contrary, does not have a home range, but is always roving (Olaus Murie 1935a: 48).

The bands of stags of the Scottish red deer occupy home ranges that in winter are separate from those of the bands composed of the hinds and young. In summer, however, the ranges of the 2 sexes overlap somewhat. The home ranges of both the stag bands and the hind bands are subject to alteration from time to time. There is no evidence of any defense of a territory by either sex. During the rutting season the stags invade the ranges of the hind bands and there establish their harems. Each stag vigorously defends his harem against encroachment by other males. The stag, however, seems not to defend any particular plot of ground, but only his group of females. The harem, in fact, moves about more or less on the home range of the hinds (Darling, 1937: 31-60).

The individuals of certain kinds of carnivores are believed by trappers to have home ranges many miles in diameter which they cover every week or so in the course of their travels. For example, a family of timber wolves studied by Stebler (1944) in northern Michigan in winter was estimated to range over an area of 260 square miles. A social group of wolves studied in Alaska by Adolph Murie (1944: xvi) traveled over a home range known to be at least 50 miles in diameter. When the young are in the nest, however, the mother must have a considerably more restricted range than at other seasons.

Raccoons have home ranges but not territories. The ranges of the adult males may have a diameter of as much as 2 miles. The mean diameter of 19 male ranges measured by Stuewer (1943) in southern Michigan was 1 mile. The home ranges of the females and of the immature mates are somewhat smaller. The home ranges of all sexes overlap and there is no evidence of defense of a territory.

Although raccoons and numerous other kinds of animals do not defend spatial territories, there is evidence that certain individuals resent the close approach of another member of the same species. Old males are especially likely to be unsociable. Observations by Tevis (1947) in California, for example, showed that a male raccoon expresses his displeasure at the approach of a stranger by bluffing and if necessary by fighting. A local abundance of food may attract a considerable concentration of raccoons, but the individuals are present only singly, in pairs, or in small family groups, never in large aggregations. The unsocial behavior of the individuals results in their generally even distribution over the habitat, with a consequent maximum efficiency in utilization of the resources of the ecosystem. The unsocial behavior of such species thus achieves a result similar to that obtained in other species by the defense of spatial territories.

BATS. The red and hoary bats studied by McClure (1942) in summer in Iowa have definite roosting places during the daytime, but little is known about the area of the flight range over which they feed in the air at night.

PRIMATE BANDS. Each band of howler monkeys has, according to C. R. Carpenter (1934), a definite home range over which it wanders. The home range of one group which was intensively studied on Barro Colorado Island covered about 300 acres. It overlapped only slightly the ranges of the adjacent bands. There is accordingly some suggestion of territorial defense by this species. Social groups of red spider monkeys studied by C. R. Carpenter (1935) in Panama also have fairly definite home ranges at any given season, but these ranges probably vary from time to time, perhaps in accordance with the fruiting of diverse kinds of food trees.

SEALS AND SEA LIONS. Male fur seals and male sea lions establish territories on shore during the breeding season. The males arrive first on the breeding grounds and set up territories on the beach. When the females arrive the males compete for them and drive them into harems. The stronger males are able to maintain territories in the situations most suitable for securing females, while the younger and weaker males are forced into areas where they secure few or no mates. The territories of these pinnipeds are used for parturition and for the nursing of the young, as well as for mating. Localities suitable for the landing of the females and for the rearing of the pups are scarce, and consequently there is much competition among the males for territories and for females. The males of the fur seal do not eat during the whole breeding period, but the females go fishing daily in the adjacent water. After the breeding season is over the harems break up, and the animals no longer maintain territories (Osgood, Preble, and Parker, 1915: 18-20).

Reptiles and Amphibians

Relatively little is known about the home ranges or territories of amphibians and reptiles. It is known, however, that certain individual toads, frogs, and lizards remain in more or less fixed localities. It may be presumed, therefore, that some or all of these forms have rather definite home ranges.

LIZARDS. The fence lizard (*Sceloporus occidentalis*) in Oregon lives in rather small home ranges, and an individual may spend its entire life within a radius of a few hundred feet. During the breeding season the males weakly defend territories which frequently shift their position (Fitch, 1940: 171).

The mountain swift (*Sceloporus graciosus gracilis*) in the Lassen Volcanic National Park, California, also lives in a definite home range. Certain individuals inhabited the same home ranges over a period of at least 3 years. No clear evidence of territorial defense by this species, however, has been obtained (R. C. Stebbins, 1944; Stebbins and Robinson, 1946).

Both the males and the females of the Cuban lizard (*Anolis sagrei*) defend territories which average approximately 400 square feet in area. Each territory contains a lookout post in the form of a tree, stump, or fence post. A family is composed of a male and 1 to 4 females. If a strange female approaches a territory occupied by a pair, the resident male prevents the resident female from attacking and he courts the stranger (L. T. Evans, 1938).

SNAKES. Evidence that a considerable number of kinds of snakes have home ranges has been presented by Stickel and Cope (1947). So far as is now known, no snakes have territories.

TURTLES. The box turtle (*Terrapene carolina*) has a home range with a diameter of about 220 yards. One exceptional individual wandered as far as one-half mile. There is some evidence that during the passage of years an individual turtle may shift the position of his home range (J. T. Nichols, 1939).

The desert tortoise (*Gopherus agassizii*) of southwestern North America is said to have a home range covering an area of from 10 to 100 acres (Woodbury and Hardy, 1948). Some of the aquatic turtles also have home ranges, but there is no evidence that these home ranges are defended (Pearse, 1923; Cagle, 1944).

Fishes

Many kinds of fishes live within definite home ranges and numerous forms also defend breeding territories. I shall be able to present examples of only a few of the known types of piscine spatial behavior.

That at least some fresh-water fishes have home ranges is indicated by the observations of Rodeheffer (1941) and Schumacher and Eschmeyer (1943). Studies of the fish populations of Foots Pond, Indiana, showed that the fishes marked at 1 end of the pond were much more likely to be found again in the same place than at the other end of the pond (Lagler and Ricker, 1943: 63-65). Many anglers are convinced that a particular big trout may live for weeks in a certain pool.

During the breeding season the males of numerous species of fishes establish home ranges around their nests, but do not defend the nest sites. For instance, the male river chub (*Nocomis micropogon*) in southern Michigan builds a nest of stones, but he rarely drives off males of the same or of alien species (Reighard, 1943: 413). The male river chub, therefore, has a breeding site around which his home range is situated for a time, but he does not defend a territory.

The males of many other kinds of fishes, however, do defend territories. For example, many North American sunfishes of the family Centrarchidae defend territories during the breeding season, though at other times of the year they are not territorial in behavior. The males alone construct the nests and each male defends a small territory surrounding his nest against the encroachment of other males. The males of certain species continue to defend the nest until the young are able to take care of themselves (Breder, 1936).

The male of the stickleback (*Gasterosteus aculeatus*) defends a territory surrounding his nest, which he digs in the soil. N. Tinbergen (1939: 215) has noted that early in the breeding season the males defend and dig over rather large territories, each perhaps 20 by 40 inches in area, but that as the actual time of breeding approaches they confine their fighting and digging activities to smaller and smaller parts of their areas, until each nest ultimately is confined to a space of about 2 by 3 inches.

The paired male and female of the aquarium jewel fish (*Hemichromus bimaculatus*) join in defending a territory, for which the most important qualification is a place suitable for the attachment of the eggs (Noble and Curtis, 1939).

A shifting territory surrounding the female is defended during the breeding season by the male of the cyprinid fish *Notropis longirostris* (Hubbs and Walker, 1942: 103).

Insects

Certain social insects are known to defend territories. Elton (1932), for instance, has observed that each of 7 nests of wood ants (*Formica rufa*) in 1 area in England had independent food territories, trees, and tracks. Furthermore, there were no connections between the trackways of neighboring nests. The ants of each colony of *Pronolepis imparis,* as observed by Talbot (1943), in the Mississippi Valley, have a well-marked foraging range. The foraging ranges of 2 adjacent colonies may overlap, and individuals of 2 separate colonies, therefore, may feed successively on the same fruit, but never at the same time. One instance of fighting between colonies was noted.

The home range of the male African tsetse fly has been ascertained by Jackson (1940) to have a mean diameter of about 1 mile but the home ranges of numerous males may overlap. Many other kinds of insects probably also have home ranges, but little information about this phase of insect ecology is at hand.

Other Invertebrates

CRUSTACEANS. Information about the home ranges of invertebrates other than insects is scanty. The fiddler crabs that abound on the sandy shores of many oceans, however, are said by Pearse (1914) to have well-defined home ranges. One of these crabs seldom wanders more than 1 or 2 meters from his burrow. The home ranges actually are territories also, for they are defended against intruders. The males are particularly vigorous in the defense of their territories against other males, but males also sometimes fight with females, and females may fight with other females.

MOLLUSKS. A few kinds of mollusks live in fairly well-defined home ranges. The small, naked, pulmonate mollusk (*Onchidium*), of Bermuda, is said by Arey and Crozier (1921) to live in small colonies of about a dozen individuals each, which together occupy a "nest." Once a day the members of the colony leave the nest to feed, but they all return to the same situation within about an hour. None of the individuals of one nest will enter a foreign nest. The individuals of a species of California limpet (*Acmaea scabra*) also have home ranges (Hewatt, 1940), but certain other species of limpets do not have this habit (Test, 1945).

Classification of the Types of Home Ranges and Territories

The examples given above demonstrate the diversity of the types of home ranges and territories among animals. In the class of birds alone almost all gradations of territorial defense may be found, ranging from a weak defense of a small area for a brief time to the strong defense of a whole home range throughout the year. There are innumerable variations in the part of the home range that is defended and in the number of individuals associated in the joint defense of the territory. As the studies of animal behavior in nature are expanded, new varieties of territorial defense are continually being discovered.

Among the features within home ranges that may be defended by various kinds of animals may be mentioned: (1) the nest, homesite, or roosting place, (2) the feeding area, (3) the food itself, (4) the mating site, (5) the mate or mates, (6) the eggs or young, (7) the area around the individual himself, and (8) the area around the mate or around the social group. This list, however, cannot be considered complete. To add to the complexity, any given territory is likely to contain more than one of the features listed. Furthermore, the features that are defended in a territory, and even the tendency to defend a territory at all, may vary with the season and with the physiologic state of the individual.

A satisfactory classification for the types of territories established by animals, therefore, has proved difficult to construct, a fact which is not surprising in view of the wide diversity of types of territories that animals maintain.

VARIATION IN HOME RANGES AND TERRITORIES

The marked difference between species in the types of home ranges and of territories which they establish is well appreciated by most ecologists. It is not so generally recognized that there may be considerable variability in the home ranges and territories of the individual members of the same species.

VARIATION IN SHAPE. The shape of the home range or territory may vary widely from individual to individual and from species to species. A given home range may cover a compact and continuous area or it may be broken into 2 or more disconnected parts. If the individual feeds and makes his home in a uniform type of habitat of wide extent, his home range will be expected to tend toward a circular shape. If, on the contrary, food and shelter are irregularly distributed in the habitat, then the home range may be irregular in shape. For example, those individuals that inhabit the shores of a stream must have long and relatively narrow home ranges.

Not every part of an individual's home range is necessarily visited every day. Many animals travel over their home ranges on more or less regular routes. In fact, they often beat down paths, which sometimes become very well marked. Some paths of red deer in Scotland were said by Darling (1937: 61) to be almost certainly of immense age. Those parts of the home range that are easily accessible to the animal, by path or otherwise, will be visited more frequently than less accessible parts. The Tulare kangaroo rat (*Dipodomys heermanni*), for example, feeds along the edges of its runways and it does not cover uniformly the whole area of its home range (Fitch, 1948*b*: 31-32).

A certain part of a home range may, at a given time, be more attractive to the owner than the other parts because of such factors as the presence of a particular kind of food, an attractive resting place, shelter from enemies, or a homesite. Variations in the physical conditions of the habitat, such as the flooding of a part of the home range, or circumstances which make an unusual amount of shelter desirable, may also result in variations in the use which is made of the several sections of the home range. The attacks of insect pests and other unfavorable biotic factors likewise may deprive an individual for a time of the use of a certain part of his home range.

Certain types of home ranges are composed of several separate parts, in each of which a different activity is carried out. Discontinuous home ranges are especially characteristic of those highly mobile animals, such as certain bats and many birds whose homesites are situated at a distance from their feeding areas. An individual which has a relatively fixed roosting range may vary its feeding range considerably from day to day. The woodcock (Mendall and Aldous, 1943) and a few other birds have discontinuous home ranges because their mating sites are separated from their feeding and nesting sites. The several isolated parts of a given discontinuous home range must be connected by paths or flight ways that merely serve the function of transportation.

VARIATION IN AREA. The size of the home range or territory occupied by an individual animal is probably correlated not only with the needs of the individual for food, but also with its needs for shelter and for homesites. It might be expected, therefore, that in poor habitats the home ranges would be larger than in more adequate habitats. In accordance with this expectation Blair (1943b: 35) has ascertained that in the xeric mesquite association of southern New Mexico the deermouse (*Peromyscus maniculatus*) and the woodmouse (*Peromyscus leucopus*) both have larger home ranges on the average than do their related subspecies living in the blue-grass, beech-maple, and oak-hickory associations of southern Michigan. Likewise, in one part of California a certain subspecies of loggerhead shrike (*Lanius ludovicianus nevadensis*) has larger territories than a related subspecies (*gambeli*) which lives in another part of the same state. This difference between the 2 subspecies of shrikes in their average territorial area is apparently correlated with corresponding differences in the characters of their habitats (A. H. Miller, 1931: 156).

Seasonal variations in food supply are especially likely to produce fluctuations in the size of home ranges. At seasons when food is abundant and easily secured an animal usually can find nourishment within a short distance of his nest or roosting place. On the other hand, when food is scarce the animal may have to search widely to secure enough food. For example, D. L. Allen (1943: 141) stated that at seasons when food supplies in southern Michigan are at a minimum certain fox squirrels may travel a mile or more from their nests, while when food is abundant their movements are usually much less extensive.

The age and vigor of each individual affects the size of his home range, as might be expected. In the Beechey ground squirrel of California, for example, it has been noted by Evans and Holdenried (1943) that at first the young range only a few yards from the burrow in which they were weaned. When they are somewhat older, however, certain of the young individuals of both sexes may for a time have ranges greater in size than the average range of the adults.

Males of species that do not defend territories often have home ranges that are somewhat larger than those of the females. This is true of many kinds of small mammals and perhaps is correlated with the greater amount of activity shown by males in general. The range of 1 male accordingly may overlap the ranges of several females. Furthermore, the boundaries of the home ranges of the males of small mammals seem often to be less firmly fixed in position than those of the females.

Breeding activities often affect the size of the home range. Many birds and other kinds of animals that have a restricted home range during the breeding season may be much less limited in their movements during other parts of the year. Certain oceanic birds, for instance, wander over very extensive parts of the marine world during their nonbreeding season. An albatross or a petrel can hardly be said to have a home range except during the short breeding season when it is attached to a nest on land.

All the habits, activities, and social relations which influence the movements of an animal species may also affect the size of the area over which each individual regularly travels. It is important, therefore, in specifying the area of the home range of any species to indicate the age, sex, and season of the year considered, and also any other factors that might influence the size of the area over which the individuals habitually range.

POSITION OF THE HOMESITE. The position of the nest or roosting place of an individual within his home range or territory is a matter of considerable ecologic interest. The position of the regularly used nest or resting place may be considered to constitute the homesite of the individual concerned. The homesites of many kinds of animals are located near the middle of their home ranges, but other kinds of animals place their homes toward 1 side of their ranges.

Many of the song birds usually have their homesites situated near the middle of their home ranges or territories. Various kinds of mammals and other animals also seem as a rule to place their homes near the middle of their home ranges. Thus, the den of a band of wolves is usually near the middle of the hunting range of the band. At any given time, however, the band may hunt most frequently in those parts of the home range where food is most easily secured (Adolph Murie, 1944: 42).

It is not necessary to assume that because the homesite of an animal may be near the middle of his home range or territory, the position of the home was first determined and that the home range was then established around this site through habit. Undoubtedly this is the method of establishment of some home ranges and territories, as for instance those of the bay-winged cowbird (Friedmann, 1929, 12), but many species establish the home range or territory first and only later do they select a homesite.

An individual may, in fact, move from one homesite to another and still keep the same boundaries to his home range or territory. The wood-mouse (*Peromyscus leucopus*) of southern Michigan, for example, frequently moves from one homesite to another within its home range. Nursing females of this species regularly move their young from one nest to another, perhaps because an occupied nest soon becomes unsanitary (Arnold J. Nicholson, 1941). Litters of young mink also are moved at intervals to new dens (Errington, 1943: 814). Many other mammals are known to move their young to a new home, presumably within the same home range, when the old site has been disturbed. The successive nests built during a season by a pair of California wren tits (*Chamaea fasciata*), for instance, may occupy various positions but all are placed within the limits of the same territory (Fig. 34). The boundaries of the territory remain practically constant, irrespective of the position of the nest (Erickson, 1938, Fig. 4). It is evident, therefore, that the home ranges and territories of many species of animals are more firmly fixed in position than are their homesites.

The homesites of numerous kinds of animals are not situated near the middle of their home ranges, but instead are regularly placed near 1 border. This is true, for instance, of those birds and other animals that roost and nest at the edge of the forest but feed in the adjacent open fields. It is true also of those aquatic birds that roost or nest on shore, but feed in the near-by waters. The home ranges of all these forms are very lopsided in respect to the location of the nest or roosting place. With many of these species, indeed, the homesite may be placed on the very edge of the home range.

The part of the home range nearest the homesite presumably will be more frequented by the owner than the outlying parts of his range and accordingly will constitute a "headquarters" area. The "singing tree" of a song bird (Mousley, 1919) will usually be in the headquarters area. Many birds and other animals, however, may have subsidiary roosts or shelters in parts of their territory remote from the homesite, in which case no clearly defined headquarters may be established. Thus, A. H. Miller (1931: 158) has noted that a single loggerhead shrike used several roosting places within its territory.

DEGREE OF RESTRICTION TO HOME-RANGE BOUNDARIES. The extent to which any given individual is restricted in his movements within fixed home-range boundaries varies greatly with such factors as season, sex, and species. During the season when an individual is caring for eggs or young in a nest its movements must necessarily be restricted to the distance from which it can return at frequent intervals to the nest. The occupied nest is then a fixed point in the home range. The roosting or resting place usually is less firmly fixed in position. The individuals of certain species have within their home ranges several resting places, as has been pointed out. Mating sites are fixed in position for a few species, but for many species mating can occur in any part of the home range. The food of some species is widely distributed and abundant, but other species find their food only in very limited spots.

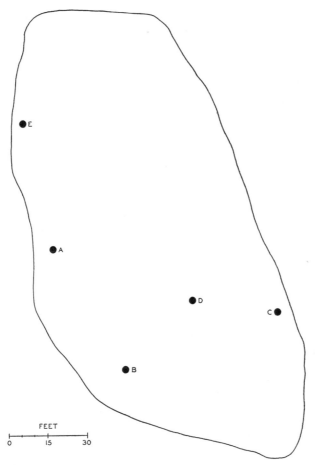

Fɪɢ. 34. Successive nest sites of a pair of wren tits (*Chamaea fasciata*) during the breeding season of 1932, near Berkeley, California. All the nests were built within the limits of the same territorial boundaries. At none of the sites did the birds succeed in rearing a set of young. (Redrawn from M. M. Erickson, 1938, by permission of the Univ. of Calif. Press.)

It is possible, for example, for the home range of an individual at a given time to be closely restricted in regard to homesite, but to have almost no limits in regard to possible feeding sites. During at least part of the year, moreover, certain species are not restricted to any particular area either for feeding or for resting but wander about as nomads.

Even when a territory surrounding a nest may be defended, the parent birds often feed outside this territory. The American robin, for example, has been observed by J. C. Howell (1942) to feed regularly outside its defended territory, sometimes at a considerable distance from its nest. It is well known that an unusually abundant supply of food will often attract individual birds and mammals from a wide surrounding area. Even if an individual has established a territory in the area which includes the food supply, he will seldom be able to repel all the invaders.

The boundaries of any particular home range or territory can seldom be defined precisely. Only occasionally are the boundaries defined by natural features of the habitat. Some areas lying well within an individual's home range may theoretically never or only rarely be visited by him, while certain outlying areas may be visited frequently. The parts of the home range that are most regularly used often change with the age, season, and stage in the reproductive cycle of the individual animal, with fluctuations in the populations of associated organisms, and with changes in the physical habitat. An animal may actually at one season inhabit a different part of its home range from that inhabited at another season.

Individual animals at times appear at a considerable distance beyond the usual limits of their home ranges. These individuals may have been temporarily driven from their homes by some disturbance. More likely they are merely exploring or visiting.

Although as a rule it is impracticable to draw precise boundaries for the home range of any given individual, nevertheless it usually is possible, with a proper amount of observation or of trapping, to ascertain the parts of his range which he most frequently uses at any given season. The chart of the home range drawn from such data, however, must always be interpreted as representing a minimum area and not the whole area with which the animal is acquainted and over which he may range.

CHANGES OF LOCATION. An individual animal sometimes gives up an established home range and moves to a new location, where he establishes an entirely new home. Such changes of location are especially characteristic of young animals at the time when they are dispersing from their place of birth.

The manner in which young animals disperse from the place where they were born and later establish home ranges or territories of their own is imperfectly known. Many kinds of young vertebrates, however, are known to leave their birth places very soon after they become independent of their parents. In the woodmouse (*Peromyscus leucopus*) it was noted by Arnold J. Nicholson (1941) that a litter of young may remain together for a time after they have been deserted by their mother. In this species the mother presumably leaves the young in possession of their home nest, while she takes up residence in another nest within her home range. As the young mice mature they move away and establish home ranges of their own. Young house wrens (*Troglodytes aedon*) disperse within a few days after they are fledged (Kendeigh, 1941*c*: 18).

During the period when they are dispersing from their places of birth, immature animals often appear in habitats entirely unsuited for their existence. Thus, I have sometimes observed young muskrats in a residential section of a city, a long distance from any suitable semiaquatic habitat.

Those animals that perform seasonal migrations must of necessity change their home range whenever they migrate. This is true whether the distance of migration is long or short. Very little information is available about the winter home ranges that may be set up by migratory animals. Observations on migrant white-throated sparrows, however, indicate that certain individuals establish temporary home ranges in those places where they stop for a few days while passing between their summer and winter homes (Borror, 1948). It seems likely, also, that at least some kinds of birds live in more or less well-marked home ranges while they are in their winter quarters.

The individual migratory bird that has once established a territory in a particular place during a breeding season usually returns to that same territory or to an adjacent one in each subsequent breeding season. This habit has been shown to be characteristic of the house wren (Kendeigh, 1941*c*), bank swallow (Stoner, 1942*a* and 1942*b*), song sparrow (Nice, 1937), and many other birds. Young birds usually return from their first migration to the general region in which they were born, but they seldom return to the exact parental home locality or home territory.

An adult animal sometimes suddenly abandons his home range and moves elsewhere. He may later return and be found again in the original place. In some instances it is impossible to discover why he moved away or why he returned. In other instances there may have been some obvious change in the habitat that gives a clue to the cause of his movements.

In situations where the habitat is not optimum for their existence individual animals may not have as permanent home ranges as in more suitable areas. In the mesquite association of southern New Mexico, for example, most of the kinds of small mammals except the woodmice had fairly stationary home ranges during a period of study extending from March to May, 1940. Each individual woodmouse (*Peromyscus leucopus*), on the contrary, usually occupied a home range for only a brief period and then moved off the area (Blair, 1943*b*: 36). It is likely that the woodmice, which usually live in deciduous forest, are not so well adapted to this xeric habitat as are the small mammals that are more often found in deserts. This, therefore, may explain why the woodmice set up only temporary residences there.

The territories available at any particular locality undoubtedly are subject to frequent fluctuations in their suitability for a given species, due to such causes as the growth of vegetation, variations in the local food supply, and changes in the physical factors of the habitat. The growth of vegetation during the course of a single breeding season, for instance, considerably restricted the area suitable for the horned lark near Ithaca, New York, with a consequent alteration in the size of the individual territories (Pickwell, 1931: 52-53). A flood during 1 year in late May, also near Ithaca, caused many changes in the long-billed marsh wren territories (Welter, 1935: 10).

The number of territories in a given area and their relation to one another often vary from week to week during the breeding season and may fluctuate considerably in successive years. The maps of the territories of

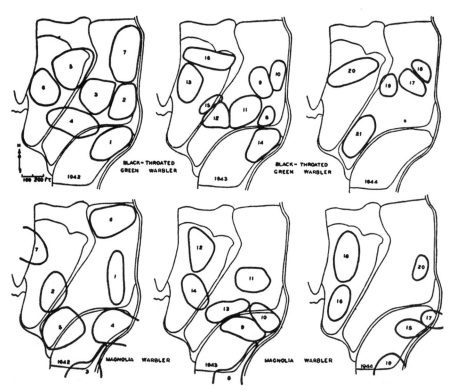

FIG. 35. Changes in the locations of the territories of 2 species of warblers in a beech-maple community on the Huyck Preserve, Rennsselaerville, New York, during 3 successive years. (After Kendeigh, 1945b.)

various warblers on the Huyck Preserve in New York, given by Kendeigh (1945b), for example, show a considerable amount of variation from year to year (Fig. 35). Certain territories, nevertheless, remain relatively constant over long periods of time, as Lack (1940a: 309) has noted for the English robin.

POPULATION PRESSURE

Animals that defend their territories exert pressure on the adjacent territories. This pressure will be especially heavy when the population is so dense that all the more desirable sites in a given habitat are filled with territories. Plants also exert pressure on adjacent plants through competition for sunlight, for soil moisture, or for other essentials for existence. Population pressure may be defined as the tendency of individual organisms to expand their holdings at the expense of their neighbors.

Population pressure may be assumed to result in relatively large territories when the population density of a given species is low and in more restricted territories when the population density in a particular area is high. For instance, Lack (1940a: 306) has noted that the average size of the breeding territories of the English robin varies somewhat from year to year, apparently because of changes in population pressure. Kendeigh (1941c: 36-37) likewise has noted that a male house wren which arrives early on its breeding grounds and establishes a large territory may later be restricted to a much smaller area after the other males have arrived. The territories of the American robin also have been noted by J. C. Howell (1942: 531) to be smaller in area when the population is dense than when the population is sparse.

Population pressure seems also to exist to at least some degree in species that do not defend territories. Thus, Blair (1940b: 304) found no evidence of territorial defense among the prairie deermice (*Peromyscus maniculatus bairdii*) of southern Michigan, but nevertheless when the local population was removed from a small area in the midst of a large expanse of prairie the denuded area was repopulated from the surrounding prairie. Conversely, when surplus deermice were liberated in a small area, they usually moved away from the overpopulated situation.

The best evidence as to the source of the animals that invade an unoccupied home range or territory was presented by Stickel (1946) from studies in Maryland. Woodmice (*Peromyscus leucopus*) living in an undisturbed habitat usually confine their activities to restricted home ranges. If the individuals are removed from a part of the area, however, those individuals which occupy the adjacent habitats move into the vacant sites. It is not known whether this movement is due to an expansion of the home ranges of the adjacent individuals, or whether there is an adjustment of all the home ranges in the vicinity.

The common tern (*Sterna hirundo*) of New England lives in colonies in which the nests usually are spaced about 6 feet apart. Each territory is less strongly defended near its borders than near its center. The aggressiveness of the birds, consequently, increases when, as a result of population pressure, the nesting territories become crowded. Under greatly crowded conditions many of the birds desert their nests, and there is heavy mortality among the young. R. S. Palmer (1941: 53) noted that in certain colonies the nests were spaced only 17 inches apart, and he believes that this is near the lower limit of tolerance for the species.

Actually, very little is known about the operation of population pressure in nature, and conclusions must be based mostly upon laboratory observations. If only 1 pair of domestic pigeons is confined within a small area, it will occupy the whole space, but as more and more pairs are added the territorial limits of each pair become contracted. If a pair be taken away, the adjacent territories expand to occupy the vacancy. The size of the territory occupied by each pair, however, is in considerable part dependent upon the vigor of the animals concerned. There is also more toleration between the members of adjacent pairs than between birds that are total strangers (W. S. Taylor, 1932).

Species vary in their ability to withstand the compression of their territories through population pressure. A good example of such variation is shown by the 2 species of bishop birds studied by Moreau and Moreau (1938) in Tanganyika. The males of both species vigorously defend territories during the breeding season. *Euplectes nigroventris* has territories of varying size, depending upon the pressure of population. A fully functional territory of this species can include an area as small as 9 or as large as 1,000 square yards. On the contrary, the related species *Euplectes hordeacea,* which lives in a somewhat dissimilar habitat in the same region, occupies territories which average 900 square yards in area. Only 5 out of 50 territories of this species studied covered less than 600 or more than 1,200 square yards. In this species only slight compression in size of the territory by increase of population pressure seems possible. Both species are polygamous, and a single male mates with up to 3 females in *hordeacea* and up to 5 females in *nigroventris*. The individuals of neither species are fully dependent for food or for nesting materials on the resources contained within their territories.

Although population pressure has been shown to compress the individual territories of certain species of wild animals and thereby to make the area defended smaller, there is probably a minimum area to which any territory can be reduced. Many wild species will stand only a limited amount of crowding. When the size of the territory has been reduced to some minimum area, the defense becomes so vigorous as to defy any attempt at further intrusion; otherwise the whole territory may be abandoned. Huxley (1934), for example, has pointed out that the territories of coots are compressible, but only to a certain minimum area. Erickson (1938: 281) thinks that if a territory of the California wren tit (*Chamaea fasciata*) were greatly compressed, any normally vigorous pair would defend the minimum area so forcefully that it could never be forced to vacate the holding.

RESERVOIR OF UNLOCATED INDIVIDUALS. That the demand for territories sometimes exceeds the number of territorial spaces available in a region is shown when a territory which becomes vacant for any reason is immediately filled by another individual or pair. For example, A. A. Allen (1924), in a study in New York State of the small birds preyed upon by screech owls, found that if both members of a breeding pair of song birds are taken by owls in the same night, that pair of birds ceases to be represented in the community. Such a vacant territory may be taken over by an entirely new pair of birds, or the adjacent territories may expand to fill the space. If only 1 member of a breeding pair be taken in 1 night, however, the survivor often secures a new mate almost immediately and the territory remains occupied. The birds studied by Allen were able to secure new mates rapidly because of the reservoir of unmated birds present in the locality. Some of the unmated birds which move into a vacant territory are perhaps young individuals who migrated late or whose reproductive organs were slow in maturing. Others may be the less vigorous individuals which for one reason or another previously have failed to secure or to hold a territory or to find a mate.

Not all situations, however, seem to have a reserve of unlocated individuals. In a study of song sparrows in Ohio, Nice (1937: 86) found little evidence of any surplus birds. After nesting was under way a male that lost a mate often failed to secure a replacement. In 2 instances, reserve males served as mates for females that had lost their previous mates.

UNOCCUPIED SPACE BETWEEN TERRITORIES. The individuals of a given species are not always numerous enough to fill with territories all the available space in a particular stand. In such a case there may be open spaces between the territories and some areas that would make good territories may not be utilized by the species. The estimates made by Twomey (1945, Table 2), for example, of the populations and territories of certain species of birds in an elm-maple forest in Illinois indicate that a considerable proportion of the area each year fails to be occupied to its full capacity. Under such conditions there will, of course, be very little population pressure on these species.

For a few species of animals it has been noted that defense is most vigorous near the middle of the territory or near the nest or headquarters, and that the vigor of defense falls off rapidly toward the edges of the territory. There is in these cases a neutral zone between adjacent territories (Gordon, 1943: 62). Sometimes this neutral zone is rather wide. An individual, therefore, may wander over and feed on a much larger area than that which it defends as a territory. Burt (1943: 349), for example, noted that a certain female chipmunk (*Tamias*) vigorously defended an area covering a radius of about 50 yards around her nesting site, but she foraged over a considerably greater undefended area, which sometimes extended as much as 100 yards from her nest. Kendeigh (1945b: 163) likewise has noted that certain of the wood warblers of New York State wander over a wider area of home range than they attempt to defend as a territory. The extension of the home range beyond the limits of the territory most commonly takes place after incubation has been begun by the female. Few critical studies, however, have been made of the behavior of animals in defense of their territories.

It may be surmised that the presence of a neutral zone between adjacent territories of a given species indicates that the population density is below the level required for complete saturation of the habitat. Should the population density increase, the neutral areas between the territories would be expected to disappear. Many communities in nature undoubtedly are unsaturated with particular species, which, therefore, have vacant spaces or neutral areas between their territories.

SIGNIFICANCE OF HOME RANGES AND TERRITORIES

The habit of living within home ranges and also the habit of defending territories may be presumed under certain conditions to be profitable to the individuals and species concerned. Furthermore, such habits may have significant effects on community organization.

No awareness of the adaptive value of a home range or territory need be assumed to exist in the mind of the individual animal concerned. Animals, of course, possess consciousness, but the animal who establishes a home range or who defends a territory is probably no more aware of the ultimate biological importance of his behavior than man himself is aware of the underlying biologic significance of many of his actions.

Significance of Home Ranges

Each animal may be assumed to be well acquainted with all the features of the terrain within his home range. Here he is familiar with the paths best suited for his use, with the best homesites, with possible refuges, with sources of food, of water, and of other necessities for his life, and with the situations where danger usually lurks. Each individual accordingly is able to move rapidly and efficiently about in his home range to secure the food and other materials essential to his existence and to escape the ever-present dangers to his life. If such an animal is attacked at any time by a predator, he can retreat directly to a refuge, the position of which is well known to him. The possession of a home range, therefore, is evidently of great value for most mobile animals.

When he is driven outside his home range an animal is no longer acquainted with the available paths and places of refuge. He then is handicapped in his search for food, he is vulnerable to the attacks of predators, and in other ways he operates inefficiently.

So far as possible each animal tries to keep within an area that is familiar to him. Hunters make good use of the knowledge that it is difficult to drive a rabbit, fox, or other mammal outside his home range. When chased by dogs the hunted animal usually circles about, keeping within his home range. If the hunter remains quiet, the animal will in time probably pass within range of his gun.

IMPROVEMENT OF THE HOME RANGE. The individual animal often is able to modify the environment within his home range at least slightly and to make it more suited to his own use. The routes which he uses become trails, over which he can travel more readily than over the unmodified terrain. Sometimes he may even remove obstacles to his movements. In certain places or along certain paths he may leave his scent, which then serves as a guide to him or to his associates. He often digs special burrows or constructs edifices which serve as refuges, shelters, or homes. In these and in many other ways an animal may improve his home range and make it a more suitable place for his existence.

EVOLUTION OF THE HOME-RANGE HABIT. Any animal who possesses associative memory may be expected to form the habit of staying within a particular area in which he can operate efficiently. Only those animals that possess associative memory can establish home ranges. It is probable, moreover, that the ability to establish a home range varies with individuals, and consequently is subject to natural selection. The habit of living within home ranges, which many species of animals exhibit as part of their inherited behavior pattern, accordingly, may be assumed to have developed through evolution.

Significance of Territories

The defense of territories ensures first of all that certain individuals in the population or that certain breeding pairs and their young shall have an adequate supply of the essentials for life. The habit of defending territories operates to limit the number of individuals of a given sex that can live on a given area, that is, it limits the number of pairs that can breed and successfully rear their families in a particular stand.

TERRITORIAL BEHAVIOR A REGULATORY MECHANISM. The territorial habit, therefore, is a regulating mechanism in the community, which helps to ensure the survival of a part of the population and which aids the successful reproduction of certain individuals, while it handicaps the survival and reproduction of the remainder of the population (Erickson, 1938: 315). It prevents the overutilization and depletion of food and of other resources in the ecosystem, thereby lessening for the species concerned the danger of recurrent crises caused by the lack of one or more items essential for its existence.

TENDENCY TOWARD MINIMUM OF FIGHTING. An animal that lives in an established territory will ordinarily meet only his immediate neighbors. The social-dominance relations of any given individual accordingly need be established only for a few other members of the population. The habit of living in territories results, therefore, in a minimum amount of fighting among the members of a species compared to what might take place if each individual roamed about widely over the habitat.

Among those species in which individual territories are vigorously defended there are, nevertheless, sometimes very bloody contests between the individuals. This very often happens when the habitat is overcrowded. In intraspecific encounters between muskrats Errington (1943: 822-25, 840), for example, has noted that many individuals are injured and some are killed. Young animals which have not yet succeeded in finding an unoccupied space in which they may establish a territory of their own often wander across established territories of older animals and thereby cause conflicts. The dispersing young, because they are not yet mature and therefore are weaker than most of the individuals that have established territories and also because they are strangers and not well able to defend themselves, often suffer severely.

THE DEFENDED AREA. That part of the home range which is most vital to the continued existence of the species or which is most in danger of depletion seems to be the part which is defended most vigorously. For instance, where the food of the species is abundant but possible nesting sites are limited, as is true for many marine birds, it is the nesting site rather than the feeding area that is defended. When the young birds are fed a special insect food which must be secured within the immediate vicinity of the nest, as is true of many song birds, then the feeding area around the nest is most strongly defended. Resident winter birds whose winter food supply is limited often defend their store of food. In general, it may be assumed, though it has not yet been proved, that the size and resources of the area defended are adjusted more or less closely to the requirements of each individual or of each family.

Certain special types of territorial defense are related to the habits of the species concerned. For example, those birds that nest on open ground where their eggs and young are exposed to the attacks of predators often form nesting colonies which are defended by the whole group of associated individuals. Likewise, in those species of birds in which the males defend only their mating stations, it is possible that the female and her young may be able to survive without any special defense by the males.

VALUE OF DISPLAY CHARACTERS. The songs, bright colors, and display behavior of many male birds when they are on their territories may be assumed to be in part adaptations that reduce the amount of fighting among the males. The characters displayed by the male who is in possession of a territory give some indication of his vigor. It is consequently not necessary for each male to fight every other male in an area in order to determine their order of social dominance (Hingston, 1933).

A reduction to the lowest possible level in the amount of fighting between individuals during the breeding season is evidently of advantage to the species concerned. Fighting often endangers the female, the eggs, and the young. A peaceful environment, on the contrary, enables the members of a mated pair to devote most of their energies to securing food, to building their nest, and to caring for their young. Freedom from disturbance actually benefits all the members of the community. For this reason display characters which indicate the relative vigor and strength of the males may operate to promote tranquillity in the community.

The songs, colors, and display of the males of certain species, however, may serve other biological ends besides intimidating rivals. These secondary sexual characters of the male may serve as a physiologic stimulus to the female, preparing her for mating; they may serve as a warning to enemies of other species informing them of presence of danger, or they may serve still other functions (Huxley, 1938a: 418).

ABSENCE OF DEFENSE AGAINST ALIEN SPECIES. It is usually against individuals of the same species that the defense of the territory is wholly directed (Collias, 1944: 98). Individuals of alien species are nearly always permitted without molestation to enter a territory that would be vigorously defended against another member of the owner's species. Consequently, it may happen that part of the benefits of a territorial defense are lost through the appropriation of food or of other essentials by an associated species which is not attacked. The most severe competition is always between members of the same species; 2 species rarely have the same habits or compete for exactly the same essentials for life. The territorial habit, therefore, should in general be beneficial to those species which practice it even though it may fail to defend the area completely against all possible competitors.

EVOLUTION OF THE TERRITORIAL HABIT. Territorial defense has probably arisen mostly through the natural selection of purely instinctive behavior (H. E. Howard, 1920). In a species in which the territorial habit contributes to the success of the individuals or pairs, those individuals which have instincts leading them to be vigorous in territorial defense will be expected to have a better chance of survival and of reproduction than individuals with less well-developed instincts of this kind. In a dense nesting colony of gulls, for example, it is harmful to the eggs and young to be tramped over and perhaps attacked and eaten by the numerous members of the colony. Those pairs of parents which best possess the instincts to defend their nests and young will accordingly have the best chance of rearing offspring successfully. Instincts to defend the nest and young will consequently be favored by natural selection, and the habit will tend to become fixed in the behavior pattern of the species.

The habit of the males of certain species to defend their territories or their mates presumably operates to select the more vigorous and stronger males to be the parents of the next generation. This is of obvious advantage to the species concerned, if it is not overdone. There is, however, the possibility that through selection the evolution of pugnacity and of the special weapons used only in fighting between the males has in some species been carried further than is for the best interests of the species as a whole (Haldane, 1932: 120). For example, the growth each year by the males of the moose, stag, caribou, and other Cervidae of an enormous set of antlers, used almost entirely for fighting other males, must be a great drain on the strength of the individual males without being of any value to the females or to the young of the species.

TERRITORIAL DEFENSE VERSUS SOCIAL BEHAVIOR. In the process of evolution the tendency to develop habits of territorial defense must often oppose the tendency to form social groups. In defending a territory the individual concerned acts in an antisocial manner toward others of his kind, except perhaps toward his mate and offspring. In the evolution of the territorial habit, consequently, many of the advantages of social co-operation must be sacrificed.

Many species combine a certain amount of territorial behavior with some degree of social behavior. This is seen in the song birds, as a single family, which is a small social group, usually occupies each territory. Fairly large social groups, such as the bands of certain monkeys, may likewise defend a band territory. Certain birds which live in family territories during the breeding season may join to form large social flocks during the winter. In these and other ways the habit of defending territories may be combined with the habit of living in social groups, thereby securing some of the benefits of both adaptations. Nevertheless, in the process of evolution there must often be a conflict between these tendencies, which in their most extreme manifestations lead on one hand toward solitary existence and on the other hand toward social life.

VALUE OF TERRITORIAL HABIT LARGELY HYPOTHETICAL. While there are apparently certain advantages to the species concerned in the habit of defending territories, it is also true that the actual value of the territorial habit to any species has not been very accurately measured. The conclusion that the habit is advantageous for any given species is usually based mostly on assumption rather than on proof (Lack and Lack, 1933). Such evidence as exists supports the general conclusion that the territorial habits of many species of animals are of advantage to the species concerned and that they have arisen through natural selection. Yet it may well be true that the territorial habits of certain species are not wholly beneficial either to themselves or to their associates.

Relation of Home Ranges and Territories to Community Organization

The home range habit enables individual animals to operate efficiently and to succeed in habitats where otherwise the species concerned might not be able to exist permanently. Stability in community organization is further promoted by the home-range habit through a reduction in the amount of turmoil that would be produced if all the individuals were constantly moving about. The individuals of the same and of dissimilar species that live in a small circumscribed area undoubtedly in time become known to one another and make mutual adjustments. If all the individual animals of a given community were continually wandering about rather than being restricted to definite home ranges, the difficulty of making mutual adjustments among all the individuals of the numerous associated species would be very great.

The defense of territories by many kinds of animals restricts the population density and consequently preserves the carrying capacity of the ecosystem. The number of territories that can be maintained by a particular species in a stand of given area is limited. By population pressure territories can be compressed to a certain degree, but there is a limit beyond which the population density cannot be further increased. The limitation of population density resulting from the incompressibility of the territories acts to prevent serious damage to the habitat through overpopulation and the consequent reduction of the carrying capacity of the ecosystem.

Territorial behavior may be assumed to promote the conservation of food and of other essentials for the existence of the individuals of the species concerned and for the successful rearing of their offspring. The setting up of territories, therefore, is a regulatory mechanism that prevents excessive fluctuations in population densities. This habit accordingly helps to maintain stability in the community.

Changes frequently occur in the locations of the individual territories within each ecosystem, as has been described. For those species that defend territories every new individual added to the community and every existing individual subtracted likewise necessitates a new adjustment in the territorial boundaries of all the neighboring individuals. Nevertheless, in spite of the dynamic state of the territorial relations between the associated individuals, the community remains reasonably stable. The added individual finds his place, perhaps by a rearrangement of the existing territories, or he is forced out of the community. The place of the subtracted individual may be occupied by a newcomer or may be absorbed through the expansion of neighboring territories.

It may be concluded, therefore, that the habit of many kinds of animals of living in more or less sharply defined home ranges is not only of great value to the species concerned but promotes community stability. The defense by many kinds of animals of individual territories likewise seems in general to be of benefit to the species, although with the loss of some of the advantages that might be obtained by social co-operation. Territorial behavior has especial significance for community stability because of its tendency to limit the population density of each species to the carrying capacity of the ecosystem.

SELECTED REFERENCES

Darling, F. Fraser. 1937. A herd of red deer; a study in animal behavior. London: Oxford Univ. Press. Chaps. 3 to 5.

Howard, H. Eliot. 1920. Territory in bird life. London: John Murray.

Leopold, Aldo. 1939. Game management. New York and London: Charles Scribner's Sons. Chap. 4.

Nice, Margaret M. 1937. Studies in the life history of the song sparrow. I. Trans. Linn. Soc. N. Y., 4: i-vi, 1-247.

XII

EFFECTS OF SOCIAL BEHAVIOR ON THE COMMUNITY

The individuals of many species of plants and animals are not distributed at random over the communities of which they form a part, but are in clumps or groups. The tendency of some organisms to form aggregations, which often are social groups, has an important effect on the composition and organization of every ecologic community and therefore merits special attention.

The term "social" is here used only for the relationship between members of the same species. Relationships between members of different species are considered to be symbiotic in nature and are treated in another chapter.

SOCIAL GROUPS

AGGREGATION. An aggregation is a group of individual organisms, either of the same or of different sexes and age classes and either of 1 or of more than 1 species. This general term carries no implication of social attraction between the individuals making up the aggregation, nor does it deny the possibility of social relations. Aggregation, therefore, is a wholly noncommittal term (Allee, 1935: 919). Every aggregation, whether or not it is a social group, affects the organization of the community in which it occurs.

SOCIETY. A society or social group is an aggregation of 2 or more individuals of the same species which are co-operating to win the means of subsistence, to produce conditions in the habitat favorable for themselves, or to perpetuate the species (Sumner and Keller, 1927, I: 6-7; Allee, 1940: 155). Either term applies to a mated pair, to a harem, to a family consisting of one or both parents together with their offspring, or to any other social combination of individuals of the same species. Some social groups exist for only a short time. The pairing attachment between the male and female of certain kinds of insects, for instance, may be of very brief duration. On the other hand, certain social attachments are more lasting. An individual man, for instance, may spend his whole life within a very limited local society.

The term "society," unfortunately, has been used (improperly in my opinion) by the plant ecologists for various types of minor communities, each of which is composed of several species. The zoologist, on the contrary, thinks of a society as a co-operating group of individuals of the same species.

264

The ecologist, therefore, must be careful in his use of the term "society" in order to avoid ambiguity. It is suggested that in any case where confusion might occur the term "social group" be used rather than "society."

Many organisms exhibit no social behavior whatever during any part of their lives. It can hardly be said, for example, that most plants have social habits. In many marine and fresh-water animals the sexual products are discharged into the open water, where fertilization takes place. In these forms there is accordingly no pairing of the sexes and in many of them there is no evidence of co-operative social life. Although certain of these organisms may form aggregations, very few of them seem to form societies.

Traces of social behavior, nevertheless, are present in certain very simple organisms. For example, some kinds of infusoria, including various species of Paramecium, produce a faintly acid secretion which tends to hold a group of these organisms together. Individuals that happen to come into the area where the water has been turned slightly acid by the presence of this secretion usually remain. The greater the number of individuals that come to make up such a social group, the more acid is produced and the greater the volume of habitat that is conditioned to the needs of the species (Jennings, 1942: 109). The individual infusorians co-operate, therefore, but presumably wholly without intent, to produce a condition more favorable for themselves. Thereby they perhaps may qualify as social organisms. Many infusorians also include in their reproductive cycle a stage in which conjugation occurs and this must definitely be classed as social behavior.

Certain kinds of plants by growing in a group may improve the local conditions for their existence. Tall trees, such as certain pines, that grow singly or in a scattered stand are in danger of being blown over by the wind. A dense grove of these trees, on the contrary, is much less subject to wind damage. Although such an aggregation of plants or trees may derive mutual aid through their association, yet there is no suggestion of any social attraction, and it is doubtful whether biologists would consider them a social group.

A strong social attraction between individuals is a conspicuous feature of behavior in those species which have highly developed social habits. Thus, the individuals that make up the social bands of many kinds of birds, mammals, and other animals usually remain associated when feeding, when resting, and when carrying out their other activities. The permanence of any society composed of mobile animals is dependent upon this social attraction between the individual members of the group.

Consciousness is not a necessary part of social behavior, either in the infusorians mentioned above or in more complex forms of animals. Although consciousness undoubtedly plays an important role in the social behavior of the higher vertebrates, it is not certain at what level of evolution it first appears. Much of the social behavior of all kinds of animals and especially of the social insects seems to be based on more or less mechanical instincts.

NONSOCIAL AGGREGATION. The aggregations of individuals of certain species of animals that occur in nature are not societies because the individuals not only do not co-operate, but may be in strong competition with one another. Mobile animals, for example, tend to become concentrated in situations where the habitat is favorable and where food is abundant. Certain reptiles form winter aggregations (Noble and Clausen, 1936) which are possibly only the result of their concentration in places favorable for hibernation. The formation of aggregations in favorable situations does not necessarily indicate any social attraction or co-operation between individuals, though it does, of course, indicate the absence of any strong antagonism.

A distinction, therefore, must be made between those aggregations of individuals of the same species that are formed through the operation of environmental factors alone and the societies that result from co-operation among the individuals. Nonsocial aggregations of animals frequently are formed in places where there is a particularly abundant food supply or, in an arid region, near a supply of water.

It is, nevertheless, not always easy to decide whether or not a particular aggregation is a society. In case of doubt that the individuals of a group are co-operating with one another to their mutual advantage, it is better to call the group by the noncommittal term "aggregation."

BAND. There is need for a general term which may be applied to a concrete social group of mobile animals of any kind, composed of 2 or more individuals. The term "society" is not entirely satisfactory for this purpose because of its occasional use with other meanings. Among the various species of animals many diverse terms have been used for social groups. Terms that are in common use include flock, covey, wisp, flight, band, herd, pack, army, tribe, horde, school, swarm. From this list of names I choose band as being probably the best to designate a social group of indefinite composition. A band, therefore, may be defined as any social group composed of 2 or more mobile individuals of the same species. The term indicates a mated pair, a family, or any other combination of sexes and of age classes.

COLONY. A colony is an aggregation composed of individuals of 1 species which has a more or less permanent location in the community. Certain plants and certain attached marine invertebrates, for example, form colonies by asexual reproduction. The offspring in such colonies often remain, at least for a time, attached to the parent or to one another.

Colonies also are formed by many kinds of animals of which the individuals are not fixed in position. Thus the prairie dog (*Cynomys*) of North America forms "towns" that are fixed in position, though the animals themselves move about both inside and for a short distance outside the colony. The European rabbit (*Oryctolagus cuniculus*) likewise lives in colonies that are called "warrens." The Beechey ground squirrel of California lives in colonies consisting of from 5 to 50 individuals (Evans and Holdenried, 1943: 249). The colonies of bees and of other kinds of social insects also are fixed in position, but the individual members may forage for a considerable distance outside the colony.

In large nesting colonies of birds the nests are sometimes arranged in series of small subgroups. Thus Kirkman (1937: 33-37) described a large colony of black-headed gulls in Lincolnshire, England, in which the nests were placed in 60 subgroups, each containing from 4 to 15 nests. These gulls defend their territories more vigorously against intruders coming from other subgroups of nests ("outsiders") than against birds who are members of the same subgroup ("insiders"). In this colony there was evidence of 3 levels of social organization: (1) the mated pair, (2) the nesting subgroup, and (3) the whole colony. With the arrival of young in the nests the social organization becomes still more complicated.

From the above-mentioned examples it is evident that some colonies are societies, based on co-operation of the associated members, but that other colonies are aggregations that may have no social significance. The main distinction between a colony and any other kind of aggregation is that the colony is composed of individuals of 1 species and that it occupies a fixed location in the community.

SOLITARY INDIVIDUALS. In contrast to those species which by mutual attraction between their members form societies or which by passive toleration of one another are able to live together in aggregations, the individuals of certain other species are actively antagonistic to one another during a large part of their lives. Individuals that usually live singly are said to be solitary in habit.

Many kinds of animals never gather in social groups except for the brief time when they live as pairs or families during the breeding season. Among birds, for example, neither the song sparrow (Nice, 1937) nor the mockingbird (Michener and Michener, 1935) ever seems to form flocks. Carnivorous species among all classes of animals are more likely to be solitary in habit than are herbivorous forms. The large cats, such as the cougar and the tiger, are solitary in habit. Wolves and certain other kinds of canids, however, live in small bands that may in part be family groups.

Social intolerance for others of their kind is not only exhibited by most large carnivores, but at certain seasons is characteristic of many animals of much smaller size. All those birds and other animals that defend breeding territories, for example, are socially intolerant during the breeding season. This intolerance may be directed only against other members of the same sex and same species or it may extend more widely to include the members of the opposite sex except, temporarily, the mate and may even extend to species similar in appearance. Furthermore, the social intolerance may be confined to the breeding season only or it may continue throughout most of the year. The degree of social intolerance varies between individuals of a species as well as between species.

Even among those mammals that usually live in social groups certain

males and, more rarely, certain females may lead a more or less solitary existence. Such solitary males among the elephants are called "rogues." Among
the bighorn sheep the solitary individuals, which usually are rams, are
known to hunters as "hermits" (Honess and Frost, 1942: 5).

Many species of birds and other animals exhibit social co-operation at
1 season and social intolerance at a succeeding season. Young birds and
young mammals must exhibit social behavior while they are living in a
family, but after they are mature the individuals may live alone. It may be
assumed then that social attraction and social intolerance are delicately
balanced in the individuals of these forms and that their social behavior at
a given time is controlled at least in part by changes in their physiology
correlated with the stage of activity of the sex glands. Information concerning these matters, however, is still very scanty.

TYPES OF SOCIETIES

Societies may be organized on various levels (Wheeler, 1923; Allee, 1932:
145). The individuals of certain species, as has been said, are usually solitary
and associate with other members of the same species only briefly during
the mating period. In other species there is a more or less prolonged pairing
of the sexes and perhaps also a period of care for the offspring. Still other
species live at times in large social groups. In those species which are most
advanced socially the individuals live at practically all times as members of
societies. In certain societies there is more or less division of labor among
the several classes of individuals. This division of labor leads in some insect
societies to the development of castes which are distinguished by morphologic type as well as by behavior.

No comprehensive classification of the types of societies that are to be
found in the animal world will here be attempted. I shall merely call attention to a few of the more conspicuous types of social groups.

Mating Societies

Mating societies are of special importance to the community because they
may be presumed to be the kind of social group most frequently formed by
animals. Mating societies have another important relation to the community, inasmuch as mating is necessary for the reproduction of most species
of animals, and consequently the persistence of each member species as a
member of the community depends upon the formation of at least temporary mating pairs.

The smallest possible mating society consists of a single male and a single
female. In numerous species the association between the female and the
male is so brief, and the mating society formed by them is consequently so
temporary that it can have little effect on the community beyond that of 2 independent individuals. On the other hand, some of the large and relatively

persistent mating societies, such as those of certain marine birds, have considerable effect on the local communities concerned.

The mating societies of animals may be classed as monogamous, when a single male pairs with a single female; polygynous, when 1 male pairs with more than 1 female; polyandrous, when 1 female pairs with more than 1 male; and promiscuous, when there is no definite pairing between the sexes and the individuals of both sexes may mate with more than 1 individual of the opposite sex. The term "polygamous" refers to matings of either the polygynous or the polyandrous type.

PAIR. Monogamous mating societies are formed at least temporarily by many species of mammals and birds and by certain other vertebrates and invertebrates. The duration of the pairing attachment between the males and females, however, varies greatly from species to species (Aldo Leopold, 1939: 102-5). In a few kinds of mammals, notably the wolf and the beaver, the pair seems to remain permanently associated in the nonbreeding season as well as in the breeding season. A few kinds of birds also remain mated for life or until the death of 1 member of the pair. Geese, swans, parrots, pigeons, and certain other birds, when held in captivity, pair for life. It is believed that these forms also pair for life in the wild.

The great majority of mammals, a great many birds, and almost all the lower vertebrates and invertebrates, on the contrary, do not pair for life, but if mating occurs, it is for only a relatively short time during the breeding season. The length of the time of pairing varies, moreover, from a few moments to a number of days or months. In many kinds of birds and certain mammals the mated pair remains together only during the period when the young are being reared. If more than a single brood of young is reared in a single breeding season, the adults often choose different mates for each brood (Lack, 1940b). Many male mammals, however, do not assist in any way with the care of the young. The males of certain species will, in fact, kill or injure their own young if they can find them. Thus, the males of many kinds of cats will kill and eat any young cat they may find unprotected by its mother.

HAREM. Harems, consisting of 1 breeding male and several breeding females, are formed by numerous species of birds and mammals. Our domestic chicken is a good example. The cock, acting as harem master, will vigorously attack and drive off any rival male, and he alone copulates with the hens composing his harem. He will, however, tolerate the presence of young chicks, including immature males. Similar harems are organized during the mating season by the fur seal, European red deer (Darling, 1937), and numerous other kinds of birds and mammals. The females of the harem seem not to have any permanent attachment to the harem master except through capture, and they presumably have no objection to capture by another male.

MATING AGGREGATION. Aggregations of mature males and females are formed by many kinds of animals for the purpose of mating. Thus, mating swarms are formed by numerous kinds of protozoans, worms, crustaceans, midges and other insects, fishes, frogs, snakes, and more rarely by birds and by mammals (Allee, 1938: 33). Among the marine birds, many species gather into groups within which communal courtship takes place (Darling, 1938: 79-102). Some of the grouse locusts also form breeding assemblies which remain together from the end of May until early summer (Cantrall, 1943: 75-76). The biological importance of the mating swarm probably lies in the fact that all or most of the sexually mature individuals of the species concerned in a particular area are brought together, with the result that they are more certain to find mates than if the search for a mate must be made by an individual alone.

The breeding aggregations of certain species are made up almost entirely of males, the females coming only briefly to the group for mating. Thus, the males of the yellow-thighed manakin (*Pipra mentalis*) (Skutch, 1949) and a number of other kinds of birds establish communal display grounds to which the females come for mating. The males of the boat-tailed grackle (*Cassidix mexicanus*), however, gather in a flock that does not have a fixed location, and the females visit the flock of males (Lack, 1940b). In many kinds of insects, such as May flies and midges, the males form breeding swarms, to which it is believed that the females come for fertilization (Alverdes, 1927: 20).

Other types of breeding aggregations may include both sexes. Thus, *Crotophaga ani,* a nonparasitic species of American cuckoo, builds communal nests in which all the females of a colony lay their eggs. The marital relations in the colony are very flexible. In certain colonies, however, there is strict monogamy and a single pair may even build an independent nest (D. E. Davis, 1942: 121).

Families

The family is a very important type of society which not only serves to ensure the successful growth of the offspring, but which also plays a significant role in the organization of communities. In its ecologic sense I define a family as a society consisting of 1 or more offspring together with 1 or both parents, or of 2 or more full or half brothers and sisters unaccompanied by either parent.

The social relationship of the young to the parents varies greatly in the various animal species. Among many kinds of animals neither of the parents ever sees the young. This is particularly true of those insects and other animals which lay winter eggs that hatch in the spring long after the parents have died. In a very few species, notably in the more highly organized insect societies, special castes or age classes care for the young. Many of the invertebrates pay no attention to their young, though they may live in the same community. Even forms that guard their eggs may fail to offer any care to the young after they have hatched.

The young of many birds and mammals, on the other hand, are given protection and care over a considerable period of their youth. In these species the life of the family group is of necessity extended. The mammal mother must remain with her young in their early life to supply milk and to provide care and protection. The young of the red deer, for example, usually remain with their mothers until they are 3 years old (Darling, 1937: 68). The young of the chimpanzee are dependent upon their mothers until the age of 2 years (Yerkes, 1943: 55). The beaver family group includes the 2 parents, the kits of the year, and often the yearlings (Bradt, 1938: 149).

TWO-PARENT FAMILY. In those species in which the sexes remain paired during the growth of the young, the male often assists the female with the family duties. There is, however, much variation among animals in the manner in which the male assists in the rearing of the family. He may assist by defending the home territory, by building the nest, by bringing food to the mother or to the young, or by defending the female and young against aggressors. Among the birds the male also may assist in incubating the eggs and in brooding the young. No good term seems to be in use for this complete type of family. The term "two-parent family" is here proposed for that social group which is composed of a mated male and female together with their offspring.

Two-parent families are the rule among many species of birds and of mammals. A good example is afforded by the roe deer, in which the family consists of the buck, the doe, and a fawn. The fawn remains with its parents for 1 year, until the birth of the next fawn (Darling, 1937: 93). The social group in this species, therefore, always remains small. In certain fishes also both parents care for the young, as is true of the jewel fish (Noble and Curtis, 1939).

MOTHER FAMILY. When the mother alone is associated with the young, the group is called a mother family (Espinas, 1924: 265; Alverdes, 1927: 67). Many mammal and bird families are of this type. In the reptiles, amphibians, and fishes there are a few forms in which the mother for at least a short time associates with her young. The females of a number of kinds of insects guard their eggs or carry them about, but only a few kinds, and these mostly the social insects, give their young any care. A few other arthropods and a few of the lower invertebrates, including some of the spiders, scorpions, and leeches also live for a brief period in mother families.

FATHER FAMILY. A family in which the male and not the female assumes most or all the responsibility for the care of the young may be called a father family (Espinas, 1924: 317; Alverdes, 1927: 66). This is true, for instance, in the phalarope, one of the shore birds, in which the males incubate the eggs and care for the nestlings, while the females may gather in "bachelor" flocks. Father families would seem to be impossible among the mammals because only the female can nourish the young. In certain kinds of fishes, however, the father builds the nest, remains with the eggs and protects them, and sometimes also protects the young until they are able to fend for themselves. This is true of the stickleback, of some of the sunfishes (Breder, 1936), of the dogfish (*Amia*), and of several other kinds of fishes (Flattely and Walton, 1922: 252). In certain kinds of amphibians and of insects the males carry the eggs until they hatch.

CHILD FAMILY. When the offspring are abandoned or are driven out of the nest by the parents, the young sometimes remain together for a time and they then constitute a child family (Alverdes, 1927: 69). Such child families are formed for a brief period by certain kinds of mammals, such as *Peromyscus* (Arnold J. Nicholson, 1941), by some birds, and by a few kinds of fishes. Young pythons are said to keep together at first in a child family, though they later become solitary. Child families also are formed by a few kinds of insects, such as the processionary caterpillars (*Thaumatopaea*).

COMPLEX FAMILY. Among certain kinds of animals an interesting addition to the family is what in birds has been called "helpers at the nest." These helpers are usually members of the same species. Among the birds, according to Skutch (1935), helpers at the nest may be classed as (*a*) juvenile helpers, (*b*) unmated helpers old enough to be sexually mature, or (*c*) mutual helpers. The juvenile helpers often are the young of a previous brood that remain associated with the mother and assist in caring for the young birds of a later brood. Unmated helpers are adults that for some reason have not secured mates of their own, but who associate themselves with a family and assist in its care. Mutual helpers are individuals or pairs who join more or less completely for mutual assistance. The society formed when more than 1 adult of each sex aids in the care of a group of young may best be called a complex family.

As an example of a complex family I may cite the observation of Darling (1938: 80) that several mother eider ducks may combine their broods to form a single society. The Alaskan wolf likewise forms societies which may be composed not only of a mated pair and their pups, but may include 1 or more additional adults of either or of both sexes. On one occasion, for instance, 2 mated pairs of wolves denned near together and reared their young in a common group, which also included an extra adult male (Adolph Murie, 1944).

The ant-eating woodpecker (*Balanosphyra formicivora*) also has been noted, both in California and in Costa Rica, to have a strong tendency toward communal family life (Leach, 1925; Ritter, 1938; Skutch, 1943).

Other Kinds of Societies

In addition to mating societies and families a number of other kinds of social groups are formed by animals. Some of these types of societies are of moderately simple structure, but certain insect states, vertebrate social groups, and human societies may be highly organized.

CLAN. A clan is a society including several families, all members being related more or less closely through descent from a common progenitor. The terms "family" and "clan" should not be applied to aggregations made up of individuals having diverse ancestry and especially not to groups consisting of more than 1 species. A clan of plants, for example, may be formed through vegetative reproduction or through the germination of seeds close to a parent plant (Tansley and Chipp, 1926: 18). If, however, all the members of such a group are not known with certainty to be descended from a common ancestor, it is best to call the group a colony.

CLONE. A group of individuals all of whom have arisen from a common ancestor through asexual reproduction constitutes a clone. The members of a clone sometimes remain associated with one another, but more often they do not. Certain colonies of corals, for example, are clones.

BAND OF ONE SEX. Social groups composed entirely of one sex are at times formed by certain kinds of animals. Herds of bachelor males, composed mostly of immature individuals, for example, are said by Alverdes (1927: 72-73) to be formed by many kinds of mammals, including guanacos, sea lions, and antelopes. Certain kinds of birds also form social aggregations consisting of 1 sex only. Male eider ducks, for instance, were noted by Darling (1938: 80) to form social groups during the late breeding season when the females were nesting.

The red deer of Scotland has 2 types of social groups, which may be called, respectively, stag groups and hind groups. The immature young, both female and male, form part of the hind group. During most of the year the adult stags live together in bands entirely separate from the hind bands. These bands of stags, however, are loose aggregations that frequently break up into smaller groups. Often a single stag will stray off by himself or he may join another band. The bands that contain the hinds, on the contrary, are more closely bound together, though these also break up at times into smaller units. The unit in the hind group is a mature hind and her calves aged 1 to 3 years. The hinds leave the hind band in June or July to have their calves, and at this time the young stags, now 3 years old or rarely only 2, break away from the hind group to form a stag group of their own. During the rutting season the mature stags invade the territories of the hinds, and there set up harems, each composed of as many hinds as 1 stag can keep under his control (Darling, 1937).

WINTER BAND. During winter many kinds of birds and mammals and a few other kinds of animals gather into small or large social bands. The winter bands of ducks, geese, crows, and other birds are well known. Certain kinds of deer and other ungulates also spend the winter in social groups. These winter bands are often most conspicuous during the seasonal migrations. There is some evidence that the social bands of certain species may be formed especially for migration, but this is certainly not true of all winter bands, for the individuals of many kinds of birds remain together in bands after their southern migratory flight has been completed.

Certain winter bands are family groups consisting of the 2 parents and their young. This according to Yeatter (1934) is usually true of the Hungarian partridge where it has been introduced into the Great Lakes region of North America, yet there is some interchange of individuals between the partridge coveys during the winter. Among the mice of the genus *Peromyscus* the last litter born in the fall often remains with the mother over winter, but this family may be joined by other individuals, so that the winter aggregations of these mice often include more than a family group (Arnold J. Nicholson, 1941; W. E. Howard, 1949).

Many winter flocks of birds, however, are not formed on a nucleus of family groups. It has been pointed out by Sherman (1924) that the first brood of young from a species that rears more than 1 brood per season would only by chance join with their parents and brood mates to form a winter flock. Even the last brood of the season may not remain with the parents to form a winter group. Many kinds of birds have a fall dispersal period, which breaks up the family groups. The young of the black-capped chickadee of the northeastern parts of the United States, for example, disperse widely in early fall. The loose winter flocks of these chickadees are made up of a nucleus of older birds returning to a former winter home range, augmented gradually by newcomers from various sources. It is notable that the old birds are often found each winter on the same flock range (G. J. Wallace, 1941).

The species of animals vary considerably in the amount of social cooperation exhibited by the members of a band. With certain species, such as the sandpipers and ducks, the members of the band remain together during all operations of feeding, flying from place to place, and roosting. The members of the bands of other species may roost together, but go their individual ways for feeding and for other activities (Allee, 1932: 110). Among the rodents, for example, the flying squirrel (*Glaucomys sabrinus*) of eastern North America (Sollberger, 1943: 171), certain mice of the genus *Peromyscus* (Arnold J. Nicholson, 1941; W. E. Howard, 1949), and a gerbille (*Pallasiomys meridianus*) of middle Asia (Rall, 1938) are known to nest in winter groups, but these rodents do not seem to travel together in social bands. Many bats, likewise, form communal roosts, but feed singly.

Numerous kinds of animals besides birds and mammals form winter aggregations. This is true, for example, of certain snakes (Paul Anderson, 1947), salamanders (Hamilton, 1943), ladybird beetles and other insects (Brues, 1946:8), desert tortoises (Woodbury and Hardy, 1940), and many other kinds of animals (Allee, 1938: 32). Some of these aggregations, however, may be merely concentrations of individuals in favorable situations, rather than groups based on social behavior.

COMMUNAL ROOST. The communal roosts that are formed in winter by English sparrows and by numerous other birds are true social groups because the members arrive at their roosts and leave them in unison or in subordinate groups of various sizes (Friedmann, 1935: 143). These communal roosts may be very large. Certain winter crow roosts studied by Emlen (1938) in New York State, for example, contained thousands of individuals that dispersed in the daytime over many miles of territory. One such crow roost was estimated to contain 55,000 individuals.

Certain kinds of birds may maintain communal roosts during summer. The martins (*Progne subis*) living near Tucson, Arizona, for instance, were said by Cater (1944) to gather in a communal roost, which immediately after the breeding season may include as many as 13,000 individuals drawn from distances as great as 19 miles. The aggregation at the roost seems to include all the members of the species in the region except those females attending their nests. The males of the American robin are said by J. C. Howell (1942: 535) to spend the night together in a communal roost, even during the season when in daytime they actively defend their individual nesting territories.

MIGRATORY SWARM. Migratory swarms of locusts, army worms, chinch bugs, and other insects are sometimes formed (Allee, 1938: 35-36). In times of overpopulation and consequent emigration animals that otherwise are not particularly social may perform huge mass migrations. Among examples may be mentioned the Scandinavian lemming migrations (Elton, 1942: 209-22), the gray squirrel migrations of the eastern United States (Seton, 1929, Vol. 4), and the mouse migration of Kern County, California (Hall, 1927).

INSECT STATE. The social habit reaches an especially high development among the insects, which form numerous diverse types of societies (Plath, 1935). Certain kinds of ants and termites form complex social "states." Many of the bees, wasps, and their relatives also live in large societies. In general each insect social group is made up of the descendants of 1 or of a few females, who are called "queens," though they have little function other than the production of eggs. Many species among the termites and ants produce special types of individuals, including workers, soldiers, food reservoirs, and sexually functional males and females (Wheeler, 1923). A single colony of these insects may be composed of thousands of individuals, which forage over a wide area surrounding the nest.

PERMANENT VERTEBRATE SOCIETY. Many kinds of primates live throughout the year in societies. The bands of the howler monkey, for instance, on Barro Colorado Island, Panama, are composed of 1 to 7 males, 1 to 10 adult females, many of whom are carrying infants, and 1 to 13 infants and juveniles of varying ages. The total size of the band varies from 4 to 35. In addition, there are complemental males which are not attached to any group, though they may rather suddenly become attached to an already organized band. A female may mate with any adult male in the band and frequently with more than 1 individual in immediate succession (C. R. Carpenter, 1934).

Other kinds of mammals besides the primates also live in societies which do not break up into pairs at the breeding season. Thus, certain of the wild horses, asses, and zebras, and also some kinds of goats, sheep, cattle, bison, and their allies live in societies that seem to be fairly permanent. Knowledge of the organization of the societies of most of these animals, however, is unfortunately very scanty.

In a small society of this kind there may be 1 dominant male who breeds with most of the females as they come into heat, while the subordinate males are either driven from the band or kept away from most opportunities for breeding. The female may retire from the band to bring forth her young, but she soon returns with her offspring to rejoin the band. The feral goats of Scotland, for example, live in small bands consisting of both sexes and of all age classes. In each band there is a leading male, but this male tolerates the presence of other younger males in the group (Darling, 1937: 94).

HUMAN SOCIETY. A human society is so much more complex in its organization and has so much greater control of its habitat than any other society that it deserves special description from the ecologic point of view. Space, however, is insufficient except to point out that a human society differs chiefly in degree rather than in kind from the societies of other mammals. The basis of its social organization is similar to that of the societies of the higher subhuman primates (C. R. Carpenter, 1942).

Open Versus Closed Society

A distinction must be made between "open" and "closed" societies. Into a closed society new members are only rarely admitted and the individual member, once he is admitted, almost never voluntarily withdraws (Alverdes, 1927: 107). Most insect states are examples of completely closed societies.

The bands of vertebrates, on the contrary, are probably never completely closed societies, though in many species strangers are admitted only after a shorter or longer period of partial toleration. Coveys of California quail, for example, are in part family groups, but strangers often join such a flock. Though at first they are attacked by the members of the covey, they eventually are admitted to membership (Emlen, 1939). Individual California Valley quail, when artificially transported into a strange locality, are attracted by any covey of the same species that they encounter. Established members of the covey dominate strangers of their own sex, exclude them from close association with the covey for a period of several weeks, and then finally accept them as members. Partly accepted birds similarly dominate aliens of subsequent introduction (Howard and Emlen, 1942).

A wolf pack is also, to at least a considerable extent, a closed society, as has been shown by the observations of Adolph Murie (1944: 43). According to his statement, a strange wolf that attempted to join an established band of wolves was attacked and driven off.

Open societies are aggregations that freely admit strangers of the same species. It may be assumed that many of the winter bands of vertebrates, especially those that are formed just preceding migration, are open societies. Very little actually is known, however, about the social relations of the individuals making up the bands of most kinds of animals.

SOCIAL DOMINANCE

In every social group of vertebrates certain individuals dominate the others in the band by their strength or aggressiveness (Crawford, 1939). In a flock of domestic hens, for instance, certain individuals are able to peck other individuals lower in the "peck order" and in their turn may be pecked by those individuals which rank higher (Allee, 1932: 155). The inhabitants of interior Alaska, where I spent a winter, believe that in any given village each Malemute dog has a more or less fixed social position. He seems to know which dogs he can get the best of in a fight and which are better fighters than he is. When a new dog is introduced into the group, he must fight every dog in the village until his social position is determined. Thereafter, there is little fighting among the dogs of the village until some new dog is introduced. When a dog grows old or weak from any cause, he is expected to move downward in dominance. Likewise, a young dog as he gains strength and courage is expected to move upward.

$$A \longrightarrow B \longrightarrow C \longrightarrow D \longrightarrow E \longrightarrow F$$

FIG. 36. Dominance relations in a band of 6 animals organized according to peck-right. The most dominant individual (A) in the band dominates all the others; the next dominant individual (B) dominates all except A; and so on to individual F, who is dominated by all the others and is able to dominate no one.

In speaking of chimpanzees, Yerkes (1943: 46) stated: "A dominant individual is one who takes priority of response over its companion and is able to satisfy its needs, desires, or whims to the total or partial exclusion of another's rights." We may best speak of the dominance relations within a social group as social dominance to distinguish it from other kinds of dominance recognized by ecologists.

PECK-RIGHT. In small flocks of birds, such as domestic chickens, the dominance relations are often of a despotic, firmly fixed sort, which is called peck-right. The most dominant hen in the group is able to peck all the other hens, each of which submits to her domineering, with no defense other than attempts to escape from her attacks (Fig. 36). The hen next in order of dominance can peck all the others, except the most dominant, and so on down the line to the least dominant hen of all, who is pecked by all the others but has no one she can peck (Schjelderup-Ebbe, 1935). A similar sort of "hook-order," mostly straight line in sequence, is found in small herds of domestic cows. Here my own observations confirm those of A. M. Woodbury (1941).

PECK-DOMINANCE. Many kinds of birds and other animals, however, have a less rigid order of social relations which is called "peck-dominance"

(Masure and Allee, 1934:314). In species with this type of dominance a sub-ordinate bird that is attacked by a more dominant individual in the flock will sometimes fight back and under certain conditions it may be the victor in the encounter. Triangular relations of dominance also sometimes occur, so that individual A dominates individual B, B in turn dominates C, but C dominates A. Still more complex relationships of dominance, involving more than 3 individuals within a social group also may occur (Fig. 37).

Factors Affecting Social Dominance.

Within a given species social dominance is affected by the sex, age, stage in the sexual cycle, physiologic state, mental ability, inherited pug-nacity, and previous experience of the individual and by the season, size of the group, and numerous other factors (Allee, 1938: 175-208). A given indi-vidual may change his position of relative dominance within a group as a result of growth, age, state of health, experience, stage of sexual rhythm, and changes in the other members of the group.

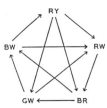

Fig. 37. Dominance relations in a band of 5 female pigeons, showing peck domi-nance. The arrows point to the subordi-nate individuals. (Re-drawn from Masure and Allee, 1934.)

RELATION OF SEX TO SOCIAL DOMINANCE. Sex has an important relation to social dominance because the members of 1 sex often are larger and more powerful than those of the opposite sex, which they consequently can dominate. The males of certain species, such as those of most kinds of ungulates, may also have special weapons for fighting. Nevertheless, the social domi-nance within a band often is organized with respect to 1 sex only. Thus the order of social dominance in a flock of domestic chickens chiefly concerns the hens. This is true also of a herd of domestic cattle. The males of both species are well able to dominate the females, but in general the sequence of social dominance in each band is organized without respect to the male. Should there be more than 1 male in a band, the order of social dominance among the males may be organized sepa-rately from that of the females.

RELATION OF PHYSIOLOGIC STATE TO DOMINANCE. The age, stage in the sexual cycle, and other factors affecting the physiologic state of the indi-vidual have an especially important effect on his social position. The order of social dominance in a litter of dogs has been shown by Berg (1947) to vary with the vitamin B_1 (thiamine) level of the individuals. Game cocks strengthened by a course of vigorous exercise are especially aggressive and are able to overpower cocks that have not been given the special exercises (Fennell, 1945). In the breeding season male animals in general are more aggressive than in the nonbreeding season. As young males grow and become sexually mature they move upward in dominance among the members of their social group. The male sex hormones, at least in certain species, evi-

dently have a direct effect on aggressiveness, and consequently on the dominance relations among the males within a society.

Other things being equal, the stronger individuals will be expected to
be dominant over weaker individuals, middle-aged animals will dominate
those which are very young or very old, and individuals in vigorous health
will be dominant over those which are diseased or in poor health.

EFFECT OF VARIATIONS IN HEREDITY. Although the several individual
members of a species have in general the same kind of social behavior,
nevertheless, there is considerable variation between individuals (Schjelderup-Ebbe, 1935: 947). Among laboratory animals both individuals and
strains are known to differ in their aggressiveness and in the vigor with
which they defend their territories (Ginsburg and Allee, 1942; Collias, 1944).
At least a few of these differences in behavior are known to be inherited
(Keeler and King, 1942; J. P. Scott, 1942; Fennell, 1945). It may be presumed that similar differences in social dominance distinguish the races and
species of animals in nature, though little search has so far been made for
differences in behavior between wild animals from dissimilar stocks. The
degree of pugnacity shown by the members of a population of course determines to a considerable extent the type of social dominance exhibited by
the individuals and the form of social organization which is possible for
the species (J. P. Scott, 1943).

RELATION BETWEEN MENTAL ABILITY AND SOCIAL DOMINANCE. Social
dominance may also be related to mental ability, though this has not been
proved. Gordon (1943: 93) noted that those chipmunks (*Eutamias*) and
golden-mantled ground squirrels (*Citellus lateralis*) which were most competent in solving experimental problems in the field were usually at or
near the top of the social order. He pointed out, however, that individual
animals which were low in the social order were continually harried by
their fellows and were given little opportunity to demonstrate any mental
ability which they may have had.

EFFECT OF EXPERIENCE. The previous experience of the individual also
may have a considerable effect on his dominance relations. Animals that
are accustomed to being bullied by larger and stronger individuals are not
likely to challenge the more dominant members of the group. But if a
subordinate game cock is removed from his group and allowed to become
the dominant member in another group, he will, when returned to the
first group, immediately challenge the flock master (Fennell, 1945). This
may be interpreted as the development of a habit of dominance.

EFFECT OF SIZE OF SOCIAL GROUP. The size of the social group has a
significant effect on the dominance relations of the individual members.
Dominance relationships are much more complex in large groups of animals
than in small ones. It has been noted by Wessel and Leigh (1941), for instance, that peck-right prevails in captive flocks composed of 3, 4, or 5

white-throated sparrows. In flocks composed of 6 individuals, however, several instances of triangular sequences of dominance were observed.

Social Dominance in Nature

Under natural conditions it is not at all certain that social dominance is as important as it is in domestic bands or in confined laboratory quarters. Schneirla (1946: 396) questioned the adequacy of the theory of social dominance for explaining vertebrate social behavior. Some social dominance undoubtedly is exercised by the individuals of most species. The members of a band in the wild, however, can escape combat by retreating when threatened by an aggressive individual.

Very few actual studies of the operation of dominance among wild animals have been made except insofar as dominance is maintained within territories. At stations where baits were placed to attract chipmunks (*Eutamias*) and golden-mantled ground squirrels (*Citellus lateralis*) it was noted by Gordon (1936; 1943: 63) that certain individuals were dominant over others and chased them away. The situation, however, was somewhat unnatural because of the artificial supply of food.

Evidence has been presented by J. W. Scott (1942) to show that on the mating grounds of the sage grouse certain males are dominant and that other males occupy lesser ranks. Scott estimated that in a mating group of sage grouse the master cock mates with 74 per cent of the hens and that all the other cocks together mate only with the remaining 26 per cent of the hens; however, the possible establishment of very small territories on the communal mating grounds of these and other kinds of grouse makes further verification desirable. This whole problem of social dominance in nature needs much more study.

Among the primates the adult males are almost always dominant over the females. There is, however, considerable variability among the species of primates in the amount of dominance that 1 male exercises over the other males of the same band. In the howler monkey, for example, there is nearly complete communism among the males in the utilization of food and in copulation with receptive females. In the baboons and to a lesser degree in the rhesus monkey, on the contrary, one of the males in each band is dominant and the other adult males constitute a descending gradient of dominance (C. R. Carpenter, 1942).

The relative dominance of the males plays an important role in the dominance of one primate band over another. A band containing 1 or more very dominant males may be able to dominate all the neighboring bands. Evidence for this is given by the fact that when the extremely dominant male in 1 band of rhesus monkeys was experimentally removed, that band no longer was able to wander at will over the territories of the adjacent bands (C. R. Carpenter, 1942).

Relation of Social Dominance to Social Organization

The type of social dominance exhibited by animals in nature seems always to be related to the social habits of the species. Those species that commonly live in social bands, such as many of the sparrows, often exhibit only a limited, weak, or temporary type of social dominance. Conversely, those species that are solitary in habit, such as the towhee, have a very vigorous and permanent type of social dominance in which an established individual fights and usually dominates any other individual that may encroach on his territory (Tompkins, 1933).

Social dominance is apparently absent in those species in which social co-operation is most highly advanced. In social flocks of the wood quail (*Odontophorus gujanensis*) of Costa Rica, for instance, there is the most perfect amity among the individuals. No individual raises any objection when food that he has uncovered by scratching is picked up by another member of the band (Skutch, 1947: 218-20). Skutch likewise found no indication of a peck-order of any kind in these bands. He noted that the individuals even helped to preen one another. He further stated that he had observed only slight indication of social dominance among other wild birds and none at all among those species that are most highly social in their habits. In the evolution of social behavior it may be presumed, then, that co-operativeness comes to be substituted for social dominance.

Relation of Social Dominance to Territory

Social dominance obviously has a direct relationship to the defense of a territory (Noble, 1939). Every animal which effectively sets up a territory must be dominant over other individuals of the species within the particular area that he defends. Otherwise, of course, he will be dispossessed. The individual that defends his own territory valiantly may, however, retreat ignominiously when he is attacked beyond his boundaries. Nearly everyone has noted that a domestic dog, for instance, is much braver within his own yard than outside it. Breder (1936: 20) stated that it is well known to aquariists that an individual fish established in an aquarium dominates a stranger that may later be introduced. Colquhoun (1942a) has reported that in the blue tit of England social order is related to territory. A similar effect has been noted in other species of birds (Allee, 1942: 290). Whenever a territory is established by any animal, social dominance thereupon comes to have a geographic relationship, at least insofar as that individual is concerned.

In a group of pigeons held in a limited space each pair controls a certain territory. The size of the territory which a pair is able to control depends in part on the dominance of the 2 individuals making up the pair. In very crowded conditions the size of the territory controlled by each pair is much smaller than it is under less crowded conditions (W. S. Taylor, 1932).

There is, however, considerable doubt whether territories in nature ever become very greatly constricted in size when natural populations grow dense. It seems more likely that in order to relieve the crowded conditions, individuals which are not so vigorous or fortunate will be driven to establish territories in unfavorable types of habitats that under less crowded conditions would not be occupied by the species.

Relation of Social Dominance to Responsibility

In the social bands of certain kinds of birds and mammals a particular individual may assume a considerable responsibility for warning his group of the approach of possible danger. The older individuals usually assume more responsibility than do those that are immature. Sometimes all the members of the flock are equally alert to danger, but often only 1 or a few serve as sentinels while the others feed or rest. Various adult members of the flock may take turns as sentinels, a fact which seems to be true of certain kinds of quail (E. L. Sumner, 1935). In the hind groups of red deer in Scotland, however, the dominant adult female of the group is believed by Darling (1937: 69-70) to take the most responsibility for the safety of the band. In the 2-parent family of the roe deer, on the contrary, it is the male who serves as sentinel and protector of the group (Darling, 1937, p. 92).

The oldest ewe in a band of sheep is the leader of the group. According to the interpretation of J. P. Scott (1945: 26) she achieves this position because the lambs have the instinct to follow their mothers, while the mothers become accustomed to being followed by their lambs. Each year when a ewe raises a lamb she loses part of her instinct to follow and becomes more of a leader. Ultimately, then, the oldest female in the band will be the most independent and most likely to lead the others, while the younger members of the group will be followers. The precise mechanism involved in this assumption of leadership is, however, not known and may be based in part on physiologic changes associated with aging as well as on the formation of habits.

This kind of leadership has no necessary relation to social dominance. The ewes fight very little among themselves, and there is no struggle for the leading position in the band. In the sheep the males are usually larger and stronger than the females and as such they secure first choice of the available food. In spite of the social dominance of the rams an old ewe nearly always leads the band when it is traveling, and the rams follow along farther back in the group.

Leadership in the sense in which it occurs in a human society seems to be almost entirely lacking in subhuman groups, even in those in which dominance relations are clearly established. In coveys of California quail, for instance, E. L. Sumner (1935: 210) pointed out that there is no acknowledged leader. In flocks of domestic fowls the most dominant individual is as likely as any other to dash for cover when danger threatens. Social dominance may often be assumed to be only a form of bullying, and it has no necessary relation whatever to social responsibility.

Nevertheless, in certain species of mammals the more dominant individuals do seem to assume a small amount of responsibility for the safety of the social group of which they are a part. This is true of the red deer and roe deer mentioned above and is true also of certain primates and of numerous other kinds of social mammals. The degree of leadership that the more dominant individuals exercise in these social groups has, however, not been clearly ascertained.

PSYCHOLOGIC BASIS FOR SOCIAL BEHAVIOR

The social behavior of animals, as well as other features of their behavior, must obviously be based on their nervous equipment and instincts. Social co-operation is possible only in those species that possess social reactions (Alverdes, 1927; Allee, 1935). The social reactions, however, vary greatly among the species of animals and are often highly complex.

Animals that have well-developed social habits seem definitely to derive satisfaction from being associated with other individuals of the same kind. Conversely, they are restless and seemingly unhappy when isolated. This is well illustrated by man himself, who has strong social instincts. One of the most severe punishments that can be imposed on a man is to place him in solitary confinement. The importance of companionship to the members of a bird flock has been emphasized by Lorenz (1935) and by Nice (1943).

HEREDITY OF SOCIAL BEHAVIOR. There seems no doubt that social behavior among animals is in considerable part instinctive. No amount of training, for example, will make a cat as tractable as a dog. That social behavior is at least in part inherited also in the laboratory house mouse has been proved by J. P. Scott (1942).

As another example of the strength of inherited instincts in the control of social behavior may be cited the difference in social habits between the blackface sheep of Scotland and the Spanish merino (Darling, 1937: 95). In Scotland it is desired that the sheep scatter for feeding. Consequently, there has been conscious or unconscious selection for this habit, with the result that the sheep do not gather into bands of more than 5 or 6 individuals. They cannot readily be driven by herders and their dogs. In Spain, on the contrary, the sheep must be driven for long distances between winter and summer feeding grounds. Also, it is the custom in that country for each flock to be tended by a shepherd and his dogs. By selection, therefore, these merino sheep have acquired an instinct to flock together in large bands, both when feeding and when traveling.

MODIFIABILITY OF SOCIAL BEHAVIOR. Social behavior, though it is based on heredity, is subject to modification by the experience of the individual concerned. This is illustrated every time a wild animal becomes a pet. Wild adults of most species are difficult to tame, but if an individual be taken captive when young it may become adjusted to a wholly different social environment from that to which the species is accustomed. There are, however, great differences among species in the degree to which their instinctive behavior can be modified by training. Certain species, for example, can never be successfully tamed.

CONFLICT BETWEEN EGOTISM AND ALTRUISM. The frequent conflict between the selfish interests of the individual (egotism) and the social interests of the group of which he is a member (altruism) have been pointed out by many authors (Allee, 1943b). Both interests are important to the life of the individual and also to that of the group. Actually, the most adaptable societies have evolved in those classes of animals that allow the most independence and initiative to the individual, that is, among the vertebrates, rather than among the insects (Simpson, 1941).

Both egotism and altruism are necessary and desirable elements in behavior. The precise mixture of egocentric and of altruistic behavior that the individuals of a given species exhibit, however, must be adjusted to the whole behavior pattern of the species concerned and to the conditions under which the individuals live. The individuals of certain species seem to succeed best when they live alone, while the members of other species are unable to exist except through the aid of the social group of which they form a part. The great majority of animals, however, are neither wholly solitary nor wholly social, but exhibit a combination of these 2 opposing tendencies.

The same individual at successive hours of the day, at successive seasons, or at successive ages frequently changes his type of behavior so that he may at one time be more social, at another time more individualistic. It has been pointed out, for example, that the individual birds or bats which roost together when they are resting may be solitary when they are feeding. Likewise, when they are young the individuals of certain species may live as members of families, and when they are older they may be solitary. Furthermore, at the breeding season many animals live at least temporarily in a mating society of some kind. The type of social behavior which the members of a species exhibit, therefore, often changes from time to time from predominantly egocentric to strongly altruistic or vice versa.

EVOLUTION OF SOCIAL BEHAVIOR. We may assume that social behavior arises in animals in the same way that any other character evolves. Types of behavior that are beneficial to the individuals of a species will theoretically become fixed in the heredity of the form, while unfavorable types of behavior will be eliminated by natural selection. Should the position of any species in a given community change in such a way that its relation to any of its associated species is altered, its type of behavior may become subject to evolutionary modification. It is not necessary to assume that the evolution of social behavior is always progressive along a single line. On the contrary, it is more likely that the course of evolution of social behavior, no less than that of any other kind of character, follows an erratic path with many irregularities and sometimes with temporary retreats alternating with advances.

SIGNIFICANCE OF SOCIAL BEHAVIOR

The social habit enables many weak forms to succeed in habitats that otherwise would be inhospitable for them. A social species, therefore, may thrive in a community in which it could not exist without the aid of the social habit. On the other hand, the aggregation of individuals into social groups produces certain results that may be disadvantageous to the species concerned.

Advantages of the Social Habit

Life in a social group may have several possible advantages for the individuals of a social species (Kropotkin, 1902; Wheeler, 1923; Allee, 1938). Among the factors of survival value which a social group of animals may render to its individual members (Shoemaker, 1939) are (1) more effective securing of food, (2) conservation of body heat during cold weather, (3) conditioning of the habitat to make it more suitable for the species, (4) facilitation of mating, (5) detection of predators, (6) co-operation in defense, (7) decreased mortality of the young, and (8) special services rendered to one another.

MORE EFFECTIVE AID IN SECURING OF FOOD. Many social bands constitute efficient organizations for feeding. A flock of cormorants (Fig. 38) swimming and diving along a more or less well-defined line, for example, is more effective in securing fish for food than are the individual birds working alone (Bartholomew, 1942: 13-21). Domestic turkeys when feeding in a meadow often advance, according to my observations, in a more or less regular line, nearly all the birds facing in the same direction. Any grasshopper or other insect that flies up in front of the flock is run down and captured. A California quail that discovers an unusually good supply of food calls other members of the covey to share it with him. Sentry duty is also performed by certain members of the quail covey, giving the other members a better opportunity to feed without having to be so constantly on the alert against danger (E. L. Sumner, 1935: 206-7).

CONSERVATION OF BODY HEAT. Small warm-blooded vertebrates that roost in social groups are better able to survive periods of cold weather than are solitary individuals. Woodmice (*Peromyscus leucopus*) by congregating in compact groups during periods of cold may be aided in surviving the winter (Arnold J. Nicholson, 1941). The warmth of the combined group of bodies conserves heat and aids the survival of all the members. Gerstell (1939) has demonstrated by experiment that bobwhites in a group have a much better chance of surviving low temperatures than has a solitary bird.

The honey bee is able to survive cold weather through the combined heat production and heat conservation of the social group (Allee, 1927: 380).

It may be assumed that the aggregations of bats, ladybird beetles, reptiles, and certain other animals formed in winter may also be of survival value through heat conservation.

CONDITIONING OF THE HABITAT. The products given off by certain kinds of animals "condition" the habitat to make it more suitable for the life of the individuals. Aquatic animals when living in a group thus are often able to survive unfavorable environmental conditions that would be fatal to a single individual, as has been demonstrated by Allee (1938: 50-89) and others. Similarly, should an injurious substance happen to be present in the

FIG. 38. A social group of cormorants organized for effective feeding. (After Bartholo-mew, 1942.)

water of an aquatic habitat, a group of animals living there may absorb and neutralize a sufficient amount of the poison to enable the group to survive where an isolated individual would succumb.

FACILITATION OF MATING. Mating often is facilitated by social groups through the presence in such groups of members of both sexes. This is of special importance for those species of animals whose population density in a given area is low. If the individuals are very widely spaced over an area, the chances of securing mates may be so low that some individuals fail to breed. When combined into social groups, on the contrary, there is much better opportunity for each individual to secure a mate.

Among certain fishes 2 or more males actually may co-operate to mate with a single female. In the white sucker (*Catostomus commersonii*) and red horse (*Moxostoma aureoleum*), for example, 2 males co-operate to hold a female between them in proper position while the sexual products are extruded into the water. In the hog sucker (*Catostomus nigricans*) the number of co-operating males is not less than 6 nor more than 8. In these suckers there is no defense of territories and instead of antagonism there is co-operation between the males for spawning (Reighard, 1920).

DETECTION OF PREDATORS. The members of a social band also may aid one another in detecting the approach of predators while there still is time to escape attack. The effectiveness of detection of predators by a flock of the bush tit of California has been well described by R. C. Miller (1922). The great number of eyes and ears possessed in the aggregate by the flock and the wide area to which the attention of the flock is directed give the social group great value in notifying its members of danger.

CO-OPERATION IN DEFENSE. The members of a society, furthermore, may actively co-operate in the defense of the group. The musk-ox herd, the baboon pack, and many other similar bands thus operate to give the individual member a much more effective defense than he could provide by himself.

DECREASED MORTALITY OF THE YOUNG. The rate of mortality of social animals may be reduced because of their organization into societies. For example, the adults of certain kinds of penguins co-operate in caring for the young of the flock. Many other kinds of birds aid the survival of the young members of the society by providing protection from enemies and by furnishing aid in finding food (Friedmann, 1935). A good illustration of the aid given to the young by certain social animals is afforded by the ants, which feed, clean, and otherwise care for their larvae (Wheeler, 1923).

SPECIAL SERVICES RENDERED ONE ANOTHER. Among other special services rendered to one another by members of social bands may be mentioned especially mutual preening (Skutch, 1947). The primates, social birds, and ants present many well-known examples of such mutual preening.

DIVISION OF LABOR. The more highly developed insect states often exhibit a conspicuous division of labor. This may go to the extreme of the production of a number of castes, such as sexual females, males, soldiers, and workers of several sizes. Such a division of labor may be assumed to be specialization for the more effective utilization of the energy available to the society.

In vertebrate societies division of labor is confined mostly to those differences in physiology and in behavior which distinguish the 2 sexes and those which distinguish young from mature animals. In the more complex human societies division of labor is highly developed, but does not involve the morphologic specialization of any class of workers.

Disadvantages of the Social Habit

Although the social habit may be in many ways advantageous to those species that practice it, certain unfavorable results may be produced by the close association of individuals of the same species.

COMPETITION WITHIN THE SOCIETY. The individual members of a social group have identical needs, except insofar as they may be differentiated by sex, age class, or stage in life history. The members of each social group may consequently come into severe competition with one another for food or for other necessities of life.

DEPLETION OF RESOURCES. A social group also is likely, because of its concentration in space, to exhaust its local habitat of food or of some other item essential for the life of the individuals. A band of insectivorous birds, for instance, may exhaust the supply of insects in the local area frequented by the group. Such an overuse of any item essential for the existence of the species will intensify the competition among the individuals.

INCREASE IN PARASITISM. Social groups, like other kinds of aggregations, are often heavily parasitized. Because of the close association of the individuals within a society, parasites and disease organisms find it especially easy to infect the members of the group.

ATTRACTION OF PREDATORS. Another disadvantage of the social habit is that aggregations of any kind attract predators, which may be able to find and ravage an assemblage of their food species.

Significance of Societies in Community Organization

The effect of a social group on the community of which it forms a part is not solely the sum of the effects of the individuals of which the group is composed (Allee, 1935). The effects produced by a society may be many times greater than those which would be produced by the members of the group acting individually.

IRREGULAR DISTRIBUTION OF POPULATION. Social behavior produces an irregular distribution of the population of every social species. Wherever a social group is located there will be a greater-than-average population density, while in other parts of the ecosystem the population density will be less than the average for that species. Social behavior, therefore, has an effect on community organization exactly opposite to that of social intolerance, which operates to spread a species evenly over its habitat.

The presence of a concentration of individuals of 1 kind may result in the local exhaustion of certain resources of the habitat, as has been pointed out. A society of herbivores, for example, may by overgrazing seriously damage the food plants on a local area, while if the individuals composing the society had been distributed singly over the habitat no damage of consequence to the plants might have resulted.

An aggregation of social animals necessarily has a more extreme effect on the individual members of its associated species than does a single animal. A social group, for example, requires a comparatively large amount of food for its support, and the members of the group accordingly may engage in severe local competition for food with the members of various associated species.

Because of the local depletion that it produces in some important re-source, or perhaps merely because of the disturbance resulting from its presence, a social group may drive the members of certain associated species away from a particular locality. On the contrary, the presence of a social group may attract those species which derive benefit from that society and which accordingly associate themselves with it.

EFFECTS OF MOBILE SOCIETIES. Many social groups, especially those of the vertebrates, are mobile and from time to time change their position in the ecosystem. A local situation, for instance, may at one moment have a large population of a particular species of social bird, while a moment later, when the flock has flown away, none of that species may be present.

The movements of such a mobile society produce frequent changes in the composition of the community of which it is a part. Each change of lo-cation of a mobile society necessitates adjustments in all those member species of the community which compete with the social species for food, roosts, or homesites and in all those other species which are dependent upon the social species for food or for special services.

RELATION TO COMMUNITY STABILITY. It has been pointed out that the social habit enables certain forms to live in an ecosystem where they would not otherwise be able to succeed. Insofar as the social habit enables species to persist within a community, it promotes community stability. Even the disadvantages of social life for certain species may act in part as regulatory mechanisms in the community, tending to prevent the development of too great a population density of the social form.

Social life in particular promotes stability in communities through aid-ing the survival of a species at a time when its population density in a par-ticular ecosystem may be low. Under such conditions the social group, by facilitating mating and by aiding the survival of the individuals, operates to maintain that species as a member of the community.

The occurrence of social groups may, on the other hand, sometimes oper-ate to produce irregularity and instability within communities. For example, the tendency of a social group to deplete its local habitat of certain items essential for the existence of its members or of their associates often forces a local readjustment in the organization of the community concerned. Mobile societies especially may cause fluctuations in the organization of communities through their frequently changing relationships to the local ecosystems of which they temporarily form a part.

SELECTED REFERENCES

Allee, W. C. 1938. The social life of animals. New York: W. W. Norton and Co.
Carpenter, C. R. 1934. A field study of the behavior and social relations of howling monkeys. Comp. Psychol. Monog., 10: 1-168.
Murie, Adolph. 1944. The wolves of Mount McKinley. Fauna Nat. Parks U. S., 5: i-xix, 1-238.
Wheeler, William M. 1923. Social life among the insects. New York: Harcourt, Brace and Co.

XIII

ECOLOGIC RELATIONS BETWEEN SPECIES

The associated organisms that constitute a community are variously inter-related. Certain species supply food, shelter, or special services to other members of the community; other species exploit these resources. No simple division, however, can be made between producers and exploiters. Every species in order to exist must utilize the resources available to it, but every species also in its turn directly or indirectly supplies essential materials or services to 1 or more of its associates. Even after death the bodies of plants and animals furnish food for scavengers and saprophytes. The organic debris that finally remains serves to increase the fertility of the soil.

One of the species included in certain ecologic relationships may be eaten or injured by the other; consequently, while one profits, the other suffers. Frequently the injury is not inflicted directly by one species upon the other, but results from competition between the 2 for some necessity of life or is produced in some other indirect manner. Not all ecologic rela-tionships, however, result in injury to one or to the other associated species. In many ecologic relationships one species profits from the association with-out injury to the other. In a considerable number of cases, moreover, both species profit from their association.

SYMBIOSIS

Symbiosis is the living together of individual organisms of dissimilar species. Each individual that lives in association with an individual of another spe-cies is a symbiont. A parasite, for example, is one kind of symbiont. Animal ecologists, such as Pearse (1926), use the term "symbiosis" in a more restricted sense to designate those relationships in which both associated species bene-fit to some degree. Here, however, the broader definition used by most plant ecologists has been adopted (Daubenmire, 1947).

Symbiosis may be either conjunctive or disjunctive. Conjunctive sym-biosis is that association where 2 individuals of dissimilar species live in a condition of close bodily contact which cannot be broken without the possibility of damage to one or to both individuals. Examples of conjunctive symbiosis are lianas, epiphytes, lichens, root tubercles, and insect galls. In disjunctive symbiosis, on the other hand, the associated individuals are free to go their separate ways. Most of the plants and animals of a given stand, for example, live in disjunctive symbiosis with one another (McDougal, 1918).

Food Relationship Between Species

The most frequent symbiotic relationship between 2 species which live in the same community involves food. A given species may either utilize another species as food or itself be utilized. A single species of animal may indeed be the eater of certain species of plants or of animals and in its turn be eaten by other kinds of animals. The complexity of the food relationships within communities has already been described in Chapter VII.

An animal that is highly specialized for feeding upon a particular species of plant or animal must necessarily have a continuous and close association with the species upon which it feeds. On the other hand, an animal that is widely adaptable in its food habits will have less rigid ecologic relationships. Those animals that utilize different foods in their successive life-history stages or at successive ages necessarily must change their ecologic relations to at least some degree each time their food habits are changed.

DAMAGE CAUSED BY HERBIVORES. In the process of feeding, herbivores necessarily damage to some extent the plants upon which they feed. The amount of injury to plants that are only lightly grazed or browsed may be slight and the parts eaten may quickly be restored by natural growth. On the other hand, individual plants that are heavily eaten may be unable to survive the injury. Certain insects, for example, may at times seriously damage their food plants by feeding upon the buds or by removing a large proportion of the leaves. Particularly severe damage is sometimes caused to forest trees by girdling. For example, the larvae of certain wood-boring beetles in feeding on the inner bark of a tree may construct burrows completely around the trunk under the bark and thereby girdle and ultimately kill the tree. Deer, bear, or rodents also may damage or more rarely may girdle the trunks of trees by feeding upon the bark or by scratching or tearing it.

The damage to plants caused by the feeding of herbivores may be generally uniform over a considerable region, or it may be confined to small local areas. If widely distributed and not very intensive, the damage may be hardly noticeable. On the other hand, if the herbivores confine their attention to small areas they may produce very extensive local damage to certain kinds of plants. Within a small radius around each nest of the harvester ant on the Great Plains of North America, for example, the vegetation may be completely removed. Certain rodents also confine most of their feeding activities to the vicinity of their homes, with the result that their homesites are surrounded by denuded areas on which only a few inedible plants may exist. This habit of denuding the area around the homesite is characteristic of the Great Plains prairie dog, of the steppe lemming (Formozov and Voronov, 1939: 115), and of numerous other animals.

RELATION OF SEED-EATING ANIMALS TO PLANTS. The seed-eating mammals and birds have a particularly close relationship to the seed-producing plants. These animals, in fact, may in certain years utilize all or nearly all the seed crop of a given plant species. To some degree this thinning of the plants in advance of germination may be advantageous to the species if sufficient seed is left to produce at least a few seedlings. In many years, however, all the seeds are consumed by the seed-eating animals and none are left for germination. For example, Cahalane (1942) in a study during 1 winter in southern Michigan found that practically all the crop of acorns and hickory nuts was eaten by the fox squirrel (*Sciurus niger rufiventer*). Not all these seeds were consumed at once, but those that were buried in the ground in autumn by the animals were later recovered and eaten, leaving almost none for reproduction.

Because of the depredations of seed-eating animals, the reproduction of many plant species may be entirely prevented except during those seasons when the crop is so heavy that the animals are unable to consume all of the seeds and when the conditions for germination the following spring are suitable. Thus, in northern Arizona the yellow pine is able to reproduce effectively only when a generous seed crop in 1 year is followed by favorable rains the following season. In years of ordinary or scanty seed production the rodents and birds not only eat the seeds as they ripen, but they may even dig up and destroy the young seedlings that previously have germinated (Taylor and Gorsuch, 1932). In England the successful generation of the beech is limited to years of full mast because in other years the seeds and young seedlings are all destroyed by the attacks of various kinds of animals and of fungi and by other mortality factors (Watt, 1923).

CARNIVOROUS PLANTS. A few kinds of plants reverse the usual sequence of food relations in the community by feeding upon animals. Among carnivorous plants may be mentioned the Venus flytrap, the sundew, and pitcher plants of several kinds. Many of these plants grow in bogs where plant food is scanty or is difficult to obtain from the soil. The extra food provided by the digestion of small animals, mostly insects, makes it possible for such plants to survive, even though their habitats are poorly provided with the usual kinds of plant foods. The total number of insectivorous plants, however, is small, and they are of importance in only a few communities.

Parasitism

Parasitism may be considered a special type of symbiosis based usually but not always upon food. The parasitic relationship between organisms involves individuals of at least 2 dissimilar species: one the parasite, the other the host. Furthermore, the host is always injured to some extent, but is not immediately killed. Usually the parasite derives its nourishment from the host. Plant parasites, as, for example, the tropical strangling fig, may injure their hosts only by preventing them from securing sunlight. Animal parasites may injure their hosts only by such means as occupying space within their bodies or dwellings, or by giving off poisons (Pearse, 1926: 357). Certain organisms are parasitic during only one stage of their life history and are free-living in their other stages. For example, many of the fresh-water mussels are parasitic on the gills of fish during their larval stage but during most of their lives they are free-living.

The distinction between a parasite and a predator is often difficult to make. In general, an individual animal which attaches itself for a considerable time to another living individual, which it injures, is a parasite, even though it may later abandon this individual host and attach itself to another (Pearse, 1926: 357). A predator never attaches itself to another living individual on which it feeds, though it may feed on a single carcass over a considerable period of time.

The usage of the term "parasite" by biologists, however, is not always entirely consistent. There are many borderline cases which are assigned to the category of parasite or excluded from it according to individual judgment. A mosquito that fills herself with the blood of some vertebrate animal and then flies away would certainly not be called a parasite, but a flea is called a parasite even though it may remain on the body of a particular host for only a brief time. Likewise, the hagfish that attaches itself for only a limited time to the body of another fish is called a parasite; but an animal that lives on a particular plant, even though it spends its whole life on that one individual plant, is not considered a parasite.

PARASITIC PLANTS. Certain plant parasites depend upon their hosts for their supply of elaborated plant food, and they do not themselves perform photosynthesis. Other plant parasites, such as the mistletoe, draw nourishment from their hosts, but do have green leaves and so are able to elaborate at least part of their own food. The place of attachment of the plant parasite also varies. Certain plants are root parasites, while other types of parasites attach themselves to the stems of the host plant. Certain parasites are free-living during at least part of their lifetime. Thus the dodder, a parasite on alfalfa and other herbs, starts life as an independent plant with green leaves, but when it comes into contact with other plants it develops sucking roots which penetrate the tissues of the host. Subsequently the dodder loses its leaves though it retains some chlorophyll in its stems; its connection with the soil is lost; and it becomes entirely dependent upon its host for support and for nourishment (Daubenmire, 1947: 321-22).

PARASITIC ANIMALS. The life histories of some animal parasites are very complex, involving relationships to more than 1 species of host. This is particularly true of certain protozoa, tapeworms, and trematodes. In many of these animals 2 or 3 successive host species are needed to complete the life cycle (Craig and Faust, 1945). Certain trematodes may, in fact, inhabit in succession as many as 4 host species, in only 1 of which does the parasite reproduce sexually (Bosma, 1931). In many of these parasites, and also in certain of the parasitic insects, asexual multiplication may take place during the nonsexual stages.

The requirement of a series of successive hosts causes the parasitic species concerned to have a very involved relationship to its community. If any one of the host species is lacking, that parasite also must be absent from the community, except as it may be brought in by immigrants. Furthermore, the number of proper hosts available at the time when they are capable of being infected by the parasite at each successive stage in its life history has a direct relation to the success of the parasite in the community.

The persistence of a particular species of parasite in a community is dependent upon the reproductive units of the parasite being regularly successful in reaching proper hosts. Inasmuch as the finding of each host individual is in part a matter of chance, many kinds of parasites produce enormous numbers of reproductive units so that a few infective units may find proper hosts and thus continue the species. As has been pointed out in Chapter VIII, reproduction also may occur asexually as well as sexually and sometimes in several of the life-history stages. Those kinds of parasitic insects that are efficient in searching out their hosts, on the contrary, can succeed even though they lay but few eggs compared to the number produced by such a parasite as a tapeworm, which depends on chance for the infection of the host. An effective hymenopterous parasite spends most of its energy in searching for hosts rather than in producing a large number of eggs (Flanders, 1947).

SPECIFICITY OF PARASITES. Many parasites are able in each life-history stage to live successfully on only the one particular species of organism to which they are especially adapted. Such a parasite is an obligate parasite. Other kinds of parasites are more tolerant and are able to live on any of several host species. These are facultative parasites. Of 2 closely related species of parasites one may be very adaptable and able successfully to parasitize several diverse species of hosts, while the other may be closely restricted to a single host species. For example, the cowbird of North America lays its eggs in the nests of a considerable number of other species of birds. The screaming cowbird of South America, on the contrary, is parasitic only on the bay-winged cowbird (Friedmann, 1929: 49, 188).

The several kinds of parasites that infest a particular host individual may occupy various organs and tissues and may, therefore, have dissimilar ecologic and physiologic relations to their host (Sweetman, 1936: 219).

PHYSIOLOGIC RACES OF PARASITES. Physiologic races or strains, which differ from one another in their reactions to the physical conditions of their habitat and to their hosts, occur in many species of parasites. The several strains of the same species of animal parasite may vary in such features as reproductive rate and time of seasonal emergence (Clausen, 1936). In different regions the several strains of a parasitic species must often be adapted to various subspecies or species of their hosts. They often must be adapted also to diverse conditions of the physical habitat, which may exhibit very considerable variations from place to place in the length and severity of the several seasons.

The existence of physiologic races or strains has been especially well demonstrated among the plants. The various strains of wheat rust, for example, differ in their ability to infect particular varieties of wheat. The numerous existing varieties of wheat also vary in their susceptibility to the diverse strains of wheat rust. One variety of wheat may be highly resistant to one strain of rust but very susceptible to another strain. New strains of the rust parasite also seem to arise frequently. Thus, as soon as a variety of wheat resistant to most of the known strains of rust has been artificially produced, some new virulent strain of the parasite is likely to appear (Stakman, 1947). In nature, likewise, there may be presumed to be a constantly fluctuating balance between harmless and virulent strains of parasites and between resistant and susceptible strains of their hosts.

DISEASES. Infectious diseases may be considered a special phase of parasitism. Diseases may be produced either in animals or in plants by the presence of bacteria, spirochaetes, protozoa, molds, rusts, fungi, and other infectious organisms. Certain viruses also are disease-producing agents, though perhaps not all biologists would class them as organisms. Many kinds of disease-producing organisms have complex life histories, involving several hosts; others may have only a simple reproductive cycle.

The reproductive units of certain diseases are transported by the wind; others may be transferred to new hosts by the agency of an animal. The protozoan trypanosome that causes African sleeping sickness, for example, is transferred from host to host by the bite of the tsetse fly. The ecologic relations in this example involve, therefore, 3 kinds of animals: (1) a protozoan parasite, (2) a mammalian host, and (3) an insect agent to transfer the parasite from host to host.

Competition

In addition to the utilization of one another for food or for the parasitic relationship, the several species that together make up any given community may be ecologically related through competition. Plants of the same and of different species compete with one another for sunlight, for soil moisture, and more rarely for space in which to grow. Animals compete for food, for space, and for breeding sites. Certain attached marine animals compete for space with certain of the plants living in the same communities. Animals seldom enter otherwise into direct competition with plants.

Competition arises when the combined needs of all the individuals of all the species occupying a given site exceed the supply of a certain necessity of life (Clements, Weaver, and Hanson, 1929: 317). Competition may arise between individuals of the same or of dissimilar species, but the com-

petition is always between individuals. There may be competition for any
of the necessities of life, and 2 individuals may compete for more than 1
necessity at the same time.

COMPETITION AMONG PLANTS FOR LIGHT. Competition among plants for
sunlight often is very keen. A sun-loving plant which grows taller than
its neighbors will be able to spread its leaves in the sunlight and thereby
can produce food for itself by photosynthesis. At the same time the shade
it produces may prevent its lower neighbors from thriving. In competing
for light, therefore, trees win over shrubs and shrubs over herbs, assuming
that all have the same light requirements.

ROOT COMPETITION. Plants often compete also with one another for soil
moisture and for the chemicals dissolved in the soil solution. The scarcity
of small plants often noted under forests, for example, may be due as much
to competition with the trees for soil moisture as for sunlight (Korstian and
Coile, 1938). In arid regions, particularly, there is in most habitats severe
competition among the roots of plants for the scanty soil moisture. The
almost complete absence of annual plants from the closed sod of climax
prairies is probably in large part due to competition by the roots of the
established perennials and the consequent difficulty for new seedlings to
become established (Clements, Weaver, and Hanson, 1929: 79).

The competition among the roots of plants is in considerable part a competition for water. This is especially true in deserts and in other areas of
scanty soil moisture. Even in soils where there is a sufficient supply of soil
moisture for all the existing plants, however, there may still be strong
competition for the various plant foods dissolved in the soil solution (Vestal,
1931: 233).

The depth to which the roots of plants penetrate the soil varies with the
species (Fig. 39). Certain plants, such as many herbs and grasses, are shallow
rooted and adapted for absorbing the moisture which falls in light rains
and which consequently does not penetrate the soil deeply. Other plants,
such as the oaks, usually have deep roots that utilize the more permanent
moisture deep in the soil. Still other kinds of plants have both shallow and
deep roots, so that they can make use of the moisture at several depths. Such
plants may compete for soil moisture with many of their associates (W. A.
Cannon, 1911; J. E. Weaver, 1919, 1920, 1926).

COMPETITION AMONG ANIMALS FOR FOOD. Several species of animals frequently compete for the same food. In the mountainous parts of Wyoming
the elk, mule deer, and bighorn sheep, for example, may seriously compete
with one another for winter food (Honess and Frost, 1942: 58-59). Likewise,
the American elk (*Cervus canadensis*) and the mule deer (*Odocoileus hemionus*) may compete, especially in winter, for browse. The elk, being the
larger animal, is able to reach higher for food than the deer, which in an
overbrowsed area is at a great disadvantage (Cliff, 1939).

COMPETITION FOR SPACE. Competition for space in which to live is a serious matter for many kinds of organisms. The attached marine organisms, especially, may compete keenly with one another for living space. For example, competition for space may be very active among barnacles, hydroids, mollusks, seaweeds, and other organisms of the ocean littoral (McDougall, 1943: 363). In terrestrial habitats, on the contrary, severe competition between species for space seems to be less frequent, except insofar as this results from competition for light.

COMPETITION FOR HOMESITES. Suitable breeding places and homesites for certain kinds of animals are often limited, with the result that there may be severe competition for these essentials for life. Several species of sea

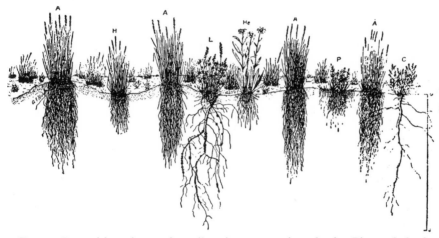

FIG. 39. Competition of roots for soil moisture at various depths. Bisect of slender-wheatgrass community showing differences in the depth of penetration of the roots of the several important species. (After a figure by Sampson, 1919, published in Bull. 791 of the U. S. Dept. Agric.)

birds, for instance, may compete for the limited amount of desirable breeding ground along the ocean shore. House wrens, bluebirds, English sparrows, and other kinds of birds often compete for the use of woodpecker holes or of natural cavities in trees. A few species of insects compete for oviposition sites (Crombie, 1947: 46).

COMPETITION FOR SHELTER. Competition among associated species of animals for shelter seems, on the contrary, to occur only rarely. Such competition for shelter as exists appears to be directed at members of the same species rather than at other species. Neither is there much evidence of competition between species for territories. A few species, such as the kingbird, will attempt to drive off an intruder of nearly any other species, but this habit is rare.

COMPETITION AMONG PARASITES. Competition occurs among parasites as well as among free-living organisms. In fact, competition among the several parasites living on a particular individual host may be especially severe because most kinds of parasites are unable to move from one host to another, and they must succeed where they are or perish.

ABSENCE OF COMPETITION AMONG CERTAIN ASSOCIATED SPECIES. Species that live in the same community sometimes avoid coming into direct competition with one another by being active at different seasons of the year or at different times of the day. Thus, in a deciduous forest many of the plants of the early spring have bloomed and have completed their growth for the year before the leaves of the trees produce sufficient shade to cut off the sunlight from them. Likewise, those species that are strictly nocturnal in habit do not come into direct competition with the strictly diurnal forms. For example, in parts of the San Joaquin Valley of California the giant kangaroo rat and the antelope squirrel live together in the same areas and both feed on the same foods, but the 2 species do not come into direct competition because there is an abundance of food for both and because the antelope squirrel is diurnal and the kangaroo rat is nocturnal in habit (Hawbecker, 1944: 165).

Beneficial Symbiosis

In most of the symbiotic relationships we have considered up to this point, one symbiont profits at the expense of another. Often, indeed, certain individuals are injured or killed as the result of their association. Not every type of symbiosis between the individuals of 2 species, however, results in injury to one or to both of the symbionts. In many symbiotic relationships neither of the associated individuals is injured, while one or both species may profit by the association. This is true both of conjunctive and of disjunctive symbiosis.

BENEFICIAL CONJUNCTIVE SYMBIOSIS. An example of mutually beneficial conjunctive symbiosis in plants is furnished by the bacteria that grow upon the roots of many species of plants, especially of the legumes. These bacteria obtain at least a considerable part of their food from the roots on which they grow, but they in their turn transform nitrogen from the air into a form usable by the plant (Wilson, 1937). Legumes that have these bacteria growing on their roots are thus able to grow in soils that are poorly supplied with available nitrogen. Both the legume and the bacterium profit, therefore, by the symbiosis.

Another example of mutually beneficial conjunctive symbiosis between plants is exhibited by the relation between certain fungi and the roots of many vascular plants and bryophytes. The mycelia of the fungi combine with the roots and sometimes with other underground parts of pines and other plants which are growing in poor soil. Here the fungus aids the plant by supplying it with water and with soil nutrients, while the plant in its turn furnishes food to the fungus. Certain kinds of plants seem unable to thrive on soil of poor quality unless they are aided by these symbiotic fungi (Daubenmire, 1947: 325-28).

Still another outstanding example of mutually beneficial conjunctive symbiosis is given by the whole group of lichens. A lichen is composed of the
cells of a green alga, which manufactures food through photosynthesis, combined with 1 or more kinds of fungi, whose tissues surround the algal
cells and furnish them with mechanical support, with protection from
injury and from drying, and with a medium through which to absorb moisture. The fungi found in lichens are so closely dependent upon their associated algae that they do not exist independently (Daubenmire, 1947: 323).

Among the animals also many conjunctive symbiotic relationships are
advantageous to both associated species. A good example is the relation
between certain cellulose-digesting protozoa and their termite hosts. Termites eat wood but are unable to digest this food. Certain specialized protozoa that live in their digestive tracts, however, ingest the ground-up wood,
digest the cellulose, and supply part of the resulting nutrients to their hosts.
Young termites become infected with the protozoa soon after their birth.
When termites are deprived of their protozoa symbionts by heating or by
other means, they are no longer able to secure nourishment from their
woody food and they soon starve (Cleveland, 1923, 1924). Certain roaches
that eat wood have an intestinal fauna of protozoa related to those found
in termites, which also digest wood for their hosts in the same manner
(Cleveland, and others, 1934).

Not all cases of conjunctive symbiosis, of course, are beneficial to both
associated species. Often one species profits more than the other, and sometimes one species is injured, as in parasitism. As an example of conjunctive
symbiosis in which one species profits, while the other usually is not seriously damaged, may be cited the use that some plant species make of other
plants for physical support. Many mosses and lichens, for instance, grow
upon the trunks of trees and shrubs. Epiphytes, such as Spanish moss, often
are supported by other plants. In many parts of the moist tropics, bromeliads
grow in great numbers as epiphytes on trees. The forest vines or lianas, of
which there are a great many types, support themselves on trees or shrubs,
though they are rooted in the soil and though they bear leaves and carry
out photosynthesis. Common examples in eastern North America are the
grape, Virginia creeper, and poison ivy. The plant which is supported makes
use of the other plant just as it would of a rock or telegraph pole.

BENEFICIAL DISJUNCTIVE SYMBIOSIS. In disjunctive symbiosis, as in conjunctive symbiosis, both species may profit by the relationship, only one of
them may benefit, or one or both may be harmed. As an example of disjunctive symbiosis in which both species benefit may be mentioned the relationship between the leaf-cutting ants of the tropics and the fungus which
grows on the cut leaves and produces food for the ants. Likewise many kinds
of ants establish symbiotic relationships with aphids or other insects with
mutual benefit to both species (Wheeler, 1910: 318, 339). The association
of tick-eating birds with certain large mammals is also of benefit to both
symbionts (Friedmann, 1935: 181).

DOMESTICATION. The domestication of one species by another may be considered a form of symbiosis in which both species benefit to at least some extent while neither is seriously damaged by the association. The domesticated species benefits by being given care and protection, while the master species benefits in various ways. Man is outstanding in the diversity of species that he has domesticated. These include not only many kinds of vertebrates and invertebrates, but also numerous kinds of plants.

POLLINATION OF FLOWERS BY ANIMALS. The pollination of flowers by animals is an important type of service which is rendered by one species to another. For this service the animal often is rewarded by being supplied with nectar or with other food materials. Many kinds of plants are entirely dependent upon the services of animals, mostly insects, for transporting their pollen from a flower where it is produced to the flower, often on a different individual plant, where the pollen is to fertilize the incipient seeds. Even for those plants which are able to produce seeds through self-fertilization, the advantage of at least an occasional cross-fertilization is sufficiently great to have resulted in the production of many elaborate devices to attract insects to the flowers and to use them as agents for cross-pollination.

A classic example of the close interdependence of a plant and the insect that pollinates it is afforded by the yucca and the yucca moth (C. V. Riley, 1892). In various sections of North America diverse species of yucca and of the yucca moth (genus *Pronuba*) are involved in this ecologic relationship, but all the species of yucca affected are closely related taxonomically, and so are all the species of yucca moths. The yucca is believed to be entirely dependent for pollination upon these yucca moths, and the larvae of *Pronuba* seem to be restricted for food to the developing seeds of the yucca. The insect has many special instincts and special types of behavior that lead the female moth to carry the pollen of the yucca flower to the stigma and thereby to initiate the development of the seeds. The moth lays her eggs in the young fruit and the larvae feed on the growing seeds, but since they seldom destroy more than a fraction of the seeds, plenty remain to mature. The yucca and the moth are accordingly completely dependent upon each other for existence. There is even a bogus yucca moth, whose larvae also feed upon the seeds of the yucca. This moth, however, does not pollinate the yucca flowers and is a parasite dependent for its existence upon both the yucca and the yucca moth.

DISPERSAL OF PLANT SEEDS BY ANIMALS. Still another important service that an animal may render a plant is the dispersal of its seeds (Daubenmire, 1947: 312-14). The most common device by which this dispersal is accomplished is the production by the plant of a fleshy fruit that is eaten by the animal. The seeds are often swallowed along with the fruits. Some of the seeds may then pass uninjured through the animal's digestive tract and be voided at a distance from the parent plant (Godwin, 1936: 91-93). The birds, which usually swallow their food whole, are more effective distributors of plant seeds (G. M. Allen, 1925: 165; McAtee, 1947) than are the mammals. Most kinds of herbivorous mammals chew their food fine and thus destroy the seeds; however, many mammals, especially the large herbivores, fail to destroy all the plant seeds in their food. For example, a portion of the seeds of *Amelanchier, Rosa,* and *Gaultheria* are known to germinate after passage through the digestive tract of the black-tailed deer (Cowan, 1945: 138). Seed-eating and fruit-eating animals that are highly mobile, such as the birds and mammals, thus play an important role in the dispersal of many kinds of seed plants. Both the plants whose seeds are dispersed and the animals that eat the fruits and seeds profit by this relationship.

Another method by which plants utilize animals to disperse their seeds is the production of hooks or of sticky surfaces for attachment to the skin or hair of mammals and to the feet or feathers of birds. The seeds of burdock, cocklebur, beggar-ticks, stickseed, and other plants are thus often picked up and transported to a distance by the aid of various animals. In this type of symbiosis only the plant benefits. The animal usually is not injured, though sometimes its fur becomes matted or its skin scratched by the hooks of the seeds.

Rodents and other animals that gather stores of seeds or of fruits often wholly without intention on their part plant some of the seeds they have collected. A part of the stored seeds may fail to be utilized by the animal that stored them and these may later germinate in the storage place, which usually is in the ground (Hofmann, 1920; Godwin, 1936; Grinnell, 1936). Seeds gathered by ants also often sprout either in the storage chambers or in the kitchen middens outside the nests (Wheeler, 1910: 315). Animals thus play an important role in the dispersal of many kinds of plants, but the animals also profit by eating a part of the seeds.

Those plants that produce large and heavy seeds, such as acorns and nuts, could have only a limited distribution if it were not for the services of birds and mammals. Heavy seeds cannot be distributed by the wind. When they are released by the parent plant, they usually fall almost straight down to the ground. On steep slopes acorns and similar seeds will tend to fall or to roll downhill. Water running over the surface of the ground may also transport seeds. If seeds reach a stream, they may be carried for many miles by the water. Nevertheless the spread of an oak forest by these agencies must be almost entirely downhill. The oak forest, it is true, can spread slowly on the level or even slightly uphill by the growth of the individual trees, from the outspread branches of which the acorns will fall a short distance beyond the place where the parent acorn germinated. Many generations, however, will be required for an oak forest to spread by its own efforts as much as a mile or to reach an elevation 100 feet higher up a gentle slope. On the other hand, many kinds of birds and mammals regularly transport acorns and similar heavy seeds over considerable distances, uphill as well as downhill. Such "uphill planters" (Grinnell, 1936), therefore, greatly benefit those plants whose seeds they transport.

A seed that is transported by an animal is very likely to be deposited in a habitat suitable for its germination and growth. This is true because most animals have fairly definite habitat limitations and remain most of the time in the same type of community in which they feed. There is considerable likelihood, accordingly, that the site to which a seed is transported by an animal will be similar in type to the community where the parent plant grew.

In their passage through the digestive tracts of birds, certain kinds of seeds become better able to germinate. The grinding action of the gizzard by thinning the seed coat, aided perhaps by the digestive juices and bacteria, renders the seed able to germinate more promptly than otherwise would be the case (Krefting and Roe, 1949). Most of these seeds, however, would germinate in time anyway, and the more prompt germination that results from digestive action may not always be of benefit to the community.

REMOVAL OF INFECTED INDIVIDUALS. Individual animals that are seriously infected with parasites or infectious disease often are less alert and less active than healthy individuals (O'Roke, 1930: 38). Infected individuals can consequently be taken by predators at a higher rate than noninfected individuals. Infected animals constitute a source of infection for the healthy animals of the population. Their removal by predators is accordingly a service rendered to the prey species by the predators. Little precise evaluation, however, has been made of the effectiveness of this service, and the conclusion that it is important is based mainly on deduction. In support of this deduction, nevertheless, are the observations by Cowan (1947) that the majority of bighorn sheep killed by predators in one part of Canada were old or ailing.

OTHER SPECIAL SERVICES OF ONE SPECIES TO ANOTHER. Numerous examples could be given of other special services which one species renders to an associated form. Thus, Cannon (1913: 78) has noted that the edible betoum (*Pistacia atlantica*) of the Algerian Sahara grows in association with the armed jujube (*Zizyphus lotus*) and is protected by it. The latter is not eaten by animals. In this example the edible plant profits by receiving protection, and the thorny plant is not injured by the association, though it receives no benefit. As another example, Went (1942) presented evidence that on the California deserts certain annual plants succeed best when they grow in association with particular kinds of shrubs.

As an example of the benefit that one species of animal may obtain from symbiosis with another may be cited the relations in Texas between the blue jay and the bobwhite. The blue jay often feeds upon acorns, but it is a careless feeder and drops many fragments of the food, which become available to the bobwhite. The bobwhite is unable by itself to open the tough skin of the acorn, so it profits by association with the blue jay during the season when acorns are available as food (Lay and Siegler, 1937). The blue jay receives no benefit from the association, but neither is it injured in any way.

Many other instances have been recorded in which one animal species benefits another by special services, such as the giving of an alarm on the approach of a predator. These services seem usually to be incidental to the activities of the species that renders the service. It is simplest to assume, for instance, that the alarm note of a jay which heralds the approach of a predator has been evolved to aid in the survival only of the jay species and without any reference to the escape of an associated species of bird or mammal.

The individuals of a species sometimes care for the young of an associated species. Such a symbiosis can readily be induced among many kinds of domestic animals. Several authentic cases also have been reported among wild birds (Ada Antevs, 1947). Hoyt (1948), for example, reported that adults of the red-eyed towhee and the field sparrow whose nests were placed close together fed each other's nestlings. It is assumed that accidental symbiosis of this kind is based on misdirected instinctive behavior. The stories of human infants reared by wolves, however, are undoubtedly all fictitious.

GENERAL RELATIONS AMONG THE MEMBERS OF A COMMUNITY

Many of the ecologic relationships within a community are not limited to symbiosis between 2 member species but are of a more general nature, involving a large number of the associated species.

INTERRELATIONS FOR FOOD. The food relations of any given species usually involve a considerable number of the associated species living in the same community. The majority of animals are not limited to a single source of food, but utilize a great variety of food species. For example, a scavenger may feed upon the carcasses of many diverse kinds of animals. Likewise, a grazing animal usually feeds on a wide variety of grasses and herbs. It is true that a few herbivorous species are each limited to a single kind of food plant, as, for example, the larvae of certain lepidopterous insects. Even these larvae often are able to survive on several related species of plants. Predators nearly always utilize many kinds of prey species and thereby have ecologic relationships with a considerable number of their associated species.

ECOLOGIC RELATIONS OF PARASITES. Parasites in general have relatively few interrelations with other species. Numerous kinds of parasites are, in fact, limited to a single host species. This is true also of many kinds of diseases. Nevertheless, many parasites and many types of disease are able to infect at least a few related species of hosts, and a few of them may attack a wide variety of forms. Furthermore, as has been mentioned, many kinds of parasites during their life cycle utilize more than 1 species of organisms, either as successive hosts, or as agents for transferring the parasite from host to host.

INTERRELATIONS INVOLVING COMPETITION. Every species is likely to find itself competing in various ways with a considerable number of its associates. The competition by plants for light, for example, may involve a considerable proportion of the plant species that make up a given community. The competition among animals for food may likewise involve direct and indirect relations with a large number of the animal members of the community.

INTERRELATIONS FOR SHELTER AND FOR HOMES. The requirements of any given species of plant or animal for shelter are only rarely satisfied through a symbiotic relationship with a single associated species. The existence of those shade-loving plants that live on the floor of a forest, for instance, is dependent upon the quality of the shade cast by the forest trees. The particular kind of plant which produces the shade is of little importance, and accordingly the relationship is between the forest-floor plant and the whole assemblage of trees or other plants which produce the shade.

Those animals which utilize the shelter provided by plants also have in most cases only a general relationship with a whole group of plants growing with them in the same community, rather than with one particular kind of plant. The modification of the local microclimate produced by a growth of vegetation often has profound effects on the local community, but the effects are general, involving direct or indirect relations of practically all plant members of the community.

In choosing their perches, roosts, or nest sites birds and other animals often are able to choose among a wide range of plant species, all of which may offer acceptable facilities of the kind required. Likewise, in constructing their nests, certain animals make use of a wide variety of fibers, including plant fibers of various sorts, feathers, hair, and other materials. The burrows which are dug by burrowing animals are utilized for shelter and for homesites by a considerable variety of other animals, both while the original burrower is still living in the burrow and after he has abandoned it.

INTERRELATIONS INVOLVING THE SOIL. Many kinds of plants do not grow well in raw soil, but thrive only in soil containing humus derived from the decay of the vegetative parts of other plants and to a lesser degree from the excrement of animals and from the remains of their bodies. The organic litter that lies on the surface of the soil in many habitats is an important feature in the lives of the soil-inhabiting animals. This is proved by the fact that when this litter is burned or raked off the abundance of soil animals is greatly reduced (Pearse, 1943). The relations of those plants whose growth is promoted by the humus in the soil to those other plants and animals whose remains produced the humus is necessarily indirect and general. The soil-forming activities of the plants and animals, nevertheless, ultimately affect all the members of the community.

PHYSICAL INJURIES TO PLANTS CAUSED BY ANIMALS. The injuries that an individual plant suffers during its life are likely to be caused by various species of its associates. Large animals, especially the herbivores, frequently damage plants by trampling. Small plants may thus be completely destroyed and larger ones seriously injured. At water holes, salt licks, bedding grounds, on trails, and at other places where large animals congregate the damage to plants may be considerable. Aside from the direct damage inflicted on individual plants by the animals, certain species may be indirectly injured by the exposure of roots, by the initiation of erosion, and in wet situations by the puddling of the soil.

The trampling of large animals, on the other hand, may benefit some plant species. The ripened seeds of certain plants, such as the desirable forage grasses on the western ranges, may be trampled into the soil by large herbivores and their germination thereby promoted. The regeneration of English oakwoods and beechwoods is said to be promoted by the burying of part of their seeds through the activities of swine in feeding (Tansley, 1946: 209). By the grazing and trampling of large herbivores old plant stems are removed or broken down, and thus the tender seedlings are saved from being choked by the dead remains of their own progenitors (Formozov, 1928).

The damage to one species caused by the activities of another sometimes permits the attacks of a third species to be successful. For instance, the damage to plants caused by animals in their feeding or home-making activities may allow the entry of disease organisms. Thus, the burrows in a living tree made by various kinds of beetles may allow the spores of certain kinds of fungi to infect the tree. Likewise, animals injured by the unsuccessful attacks of predators may become infected by bacterial or by other disease-producing organisms.

PRODUCTION OF HARMFUL CHEMICALS. Certain of the chemicals produced by the individuals of a particular species may be harmful to the individuals of associated species. Many parasites, especially the pathogenic bacteria and viruses, thus give off poisons which may harm their hosts. Many kinds of molds and other organisms, for example, give off substances which are toxic to many organisms. These secretions when collected and concentrated in the form of penicillin, streptomycin, and other antibiotics actually are used by man for combating certain disease organisms. The excretions of free-living animals, when present in heavy concentrations, may also be harmful to certain of their associates.

Various large terrestrial plants also are known to produce chemicals that are deleterious to their associates. For example, it has been demonstrated by Went (1942) that few species of plants are able to grow beneath a desert brittlebush (*Encelia farinosa*). From the leaves of this plant Gray and Bonner (1948a, 1948b) have extracted a chemical, 3-acetyl-6-methoxybenz-aldehyde, which in the laboratory inhibits the growth of tomato seedlings. It seems probable that this chemical poisons the ground so that most other kinds of plants are unable to grow under a brittlebush.

COMPLEXITY OF ECOLOGIC RELATIONS WITHIN A COMMUNITY. An almost endless number of other examples of the general relations of the several species within a community could be given (for plants see especially Daubenmire, 1947, Chap. VII). Sufficient evidence has been presented, how-

ever, to show that in addition to the frequent occurrence of direct relationships between 2 members of a community in their quest for food, in competition, in an exchange of services, or in parasitism many of the ecologic relationships in the community are of a more general character, involving a
considerable number of the associated species.

The ecologic relations of the several species that compose a community
are in fact nearly always extremely complex. For example, a species that is
in competition with another form for one or more of the essentials for its
life may in another relationship render that same species some important
service. In northern Russia, for instance, crossbills compete with squirrels
for the seeds of conifers, but the squirrels, and also incidentally certain other
animals, profit by the activities of the birds. The seeds in the fir cones that
are broken off by the crossbills are only partly utilized by the birds. Some
seeds often remain in the cone when it falls to the ground and these may
later be eaten by the squirrels. Furthermore, the cones that fall to the
ground do not open and disperse their seeds in the spring as do those that
hang on the trees. The cones on the ground, being damp, retain their seeds
all summer and into the next winter. These cones with their enclosed seeds
form a food reserve for the squirrels which is of particular importance if the
fir-seed crop is deficient in the following year. On the other hand, the great
spotted woodpecker also feeds on pine and fir seeds, but this bird eats practically all the seeds in the cones that it attacks. Thus it directly competes
with the squirrel without conferring any compensating advantage (Formozov, 1934b).

Let me give another rather simple example of the complexity of ecologic
relations in nature: the transfer of the trypanosome parasite of sleeping
sickness from one host to another by the tsetse fly is a service rendered by
the fly to the parasite, performed only during a brief contact with each of
the 2 individual hosts involved. In this 3-way relationship the parasitic
species benefits, the host species is damaged, and the tsetse fly benefits by
obtaining its meal of blood. Furthermore, the relationship between the
parasite and the host is conjunctive, while the relationship of the fly to both
the other species is disjunctive.

Excellent examples of the simultaneous presence of a number of types
of ecologic relations among species may be found in the nests of ants. Within
the nest of one kind of ant there may live other species of ants, together
with beetles, flies, isopods, and other small animals. Wheeler estimated
(1910: 379) that 1,500 species of such myrmecophiles had been described up
to that time. Certain of these associated species are parasitic on the ants
and may either eat the ant food or parasitize the ants themselves. A few of
the associates may be predators, preying on the larvae, pupae, or adult ants.
Others of the foreign species living in the ant nest do no harm to the ants,
but they themselves profit in various ways, especially by the protection
afforded by the ant nest; sometimes, too, they are defended by the ants

against the attacks of other animals. Still others of the associates that live within the ant nest are beneficial to the ants, inasmuch as they furnish certain services, such as secretions which are relished by their ant associates.

The ecologic relations between species often change from time to time as a result of the growth of the individuals, transformation into other life-history stages, fluctuations in the population densities, progression of the seasons, changes in weather, and other modifications in the habitat. When one considers the many interrelations of the species which make up a community, it is evident that no simple description of these relations is possible.

BEHAVIOR RELATIONS OF ASSOCIATED SPECIES OF ANIMALS

The behavior relations of the individual animals of those species which live together in a stand or microstand have been very incompletely studied. A different reaction will be given by a potential prey individual to an approaching predator from that given to another member of his own social group. The precise reactions involved in most such relationships, however, have been inadequately described, and their psychologic basis is largely unknown. Still less is known about the behavior relations between species in those situations where there is competition for food, for roosting place, or for homesite.

REACTIONS BETWEEN PREDATORS AND THEIR PREY. Predators attack and kill their prey, and the individuals of the prey species often make strenuous efforts to avoid their attackers. When a predator appears, the prey individuals become alert and may make warning signals to others of their kind. They may also take cover or retire to a presumably safe shelter. Such reactions are sometimes called forth by a harmless species that resembles a predatory form. Domestic chickens, for example, often take cover when any large bird resembling a hawk passes overhead. There is, however, little evidence of any great amount of fear of a predator by a prey individual so long as this individual feels itself to be in a secure situation. The bighorn sheep (*Ovis dalli*) of Alaska, for example, was noted by Adolph Murie (1944: 100-110) to make little effort to run away from wolves (*Canis lupus*) so long as the bighorns were in a situation where they could easily escape if attacked. In such a situation the wolves seldom made any effort to attack the bighorns, reserving their efforts for occasions when there was at least some chance of making a capture.

In situations where several species of animals are forced to live together because of the presence of certain essential habitat conditions, most of them probably live in a state of what might be called "armed neutrality." In a muskrat den in South Dakota studied by Errington (1943: 813), for instance, muskrats, mink, garter snakes, cricetid mice, Franklin ground squirrels, striped skunks, and cottontail rabbits all were known to use parts of the same anastomosing system of burrows, which in considerable part were dug by the muskrats. In such a situation each species undoubtedly is aware of the

presence of the others and adjusts its living routine accordingly. When sur-
prised at close quarters by the approach of a member of a potentially dangerous species, the individual animal is likely to put up such a defense that
close contacts will be avoided by all parties, except when predation is an
object.

DEFENSIVE FIGHTING. In self-defense many kinds of animals will fight
or even attack their aggressors with vigor. Many animals also will defend
their homes, their territories, their food stores, and their mates and young
against intruders, not only of their own kind, but also of other species. The
social insects, such as the termites, ants, bees, wasps, and hornets, are especially violent in their attacks on other animals that approach or disturb
their homes. Certain kinds of fish also are said to defend their nests and
young against other species. Many kinds of birds will swoop at or strike
other birds (L. Williams, 1942), snakes, or mammals that come near their
nests or their young. The kingbirds of the genus *Tyrannus* are noted for
being particularly vigorous in attacking and driving off hawks and other
animals that trespass near their nests (Davis, 1941). Wolves attack grizzly
bears that approach their homes or raid their food stores, but the bears are
so powerful that the wolves are unable to prevent the raids. In general,
however, wolves and bears avoid each other (Adolph Murie, 1944: 204).

Several species of animals may at times co-operate for mutual defense.
The "mobbing" of a roosting owl by a mixed group of other birds may be
cited as one example of such co-operation. The "mob" is often led by individuals of a pugnacious species, such as the blue jay, but numerous species
of other birds may combine to augment the commotion. It is not certain
how much defense actually is accomplished by the mobbing of the owl, but
at least it puts the local birds on the alert, and perhaps makes life so un-
comfortable for the owl that he will leave the vicinity.

DEFENSE OF TERRITORY. Birds and other animals that establish territories
defend these areas against individuals of the same species, and sometimes
against those of closely related species. Entirely unrelated species that have
a resemblance to the territorial form may also be attacked. Thus, one of the
American cuckoos (*Crotophaga ani*) is said to expel from its territories not
only foreign birds of the same species, but also the crow (*Corvus nasicus*)
and the black icterid (*Ptiloxena*). On the other hand, *Crotophaga ani* will
sometimes allow a related species, *Crotophaga major*, to remain in its territory and even to sleep within a few feet of its nest (D. E. Davis, 1942: 122).
Breeding male sunfishes not only drive away other males of the same species,
but they also attack fishes of other species that approach their nests (Breder,
1936: 19).

Among the primates it is the rule that one organized primate band will
not tolerate the presence in its territory of another band of the same species.
Primate bands of differing species, on the contrary, often share the same
ranges. C. R. Carpenter (1942: 191) reported that he had seen howler mon-

keys feeding in the same trees with langurs, macaques with langurs, and gibbons with siamangs or with macaques. Intraspecies competition seems here, as among animals in general, to be much more intense than interspecies competition.

AGGREGATIONS OF MIXED SPECIES. Aggregations of birds and of other animals often are composed of members of several species. It must be assumed that some advantage on the part of at least one of the species is derived from the association. In migration several species of birds frequently travel together in such mixed flocks (Friedmann, 1935: 146). Several species of African antelopes often are found in a common herd, in which are also the zebra and sometimes the ostrich (Roosevelt and Heller, 1914: 678). The kulan (*Equus hemionus*) of central Asia may join with various wild sheep, the Tibetan antelope, and the yak in forming a joint aggregation (Hesse, Allee, and Schmidt, 1937: 450).

Mixed flocks of birds are especially likely to be found in tropical areas (Chapin, 1932). In the American tropics, flycatchers, calliopes, tanagers, ant birds, manakins, wood hewers, and woodpeckers often form such mixed flocks (Beebe, 1916: 61). As many as 15 species of birds have been counted by Winterbottom (1943: 438) traveling in 1 mixed flock in Northern Rhodesia, the whole flock including 42 individuals. Within a mixed flock, however, each species forms a smaller subgroup, which behaves somewhat independently of the associated subgroups composed of other species.

Aggregations of mixed species are by no means confined to the tropics, but occur also in temperate and in frigid climates. For example, Hayward (1948: 489) noted that in winter mixed flocks of juncos, pine siskins, robins, Woodhouse jays, and chickadees frequently are found in the mouths and bottoms of canyons in northeastern Utah.

From a statistical study of mixed bird flocks in Brazil, D. E. Davis (1946) calculated the average number of species per flock to range from 3.00 to 9.00 in various months and places, and the average number of individuals per flock to range from 4.50 to 19.00. These figures are not a measure of the tendency of the species concerned to form mixed flocks, but apply only to those mixed flocks that were noted. The individual birds that form these mixed flocks constantly utter a variety of calls, which obviously function to hold the flock together. While the group is forming in the early morning the birds are especially vocal.

It is not entirely clear what advantage the habit of forming mixed bands offers to each of the species concerned. The explanations that have been offered for mixed flocks of birds are that (1) the flock is more readily able to detect and to escape predators through the combined vigilance of its members, (2) the disturbance made by the operations of the flock frightens up food insects that otherwise might escape attention (Neave, 1910: 80), and (3) the flock has a psychological attraction for any individual bird that has social habits (Colquhoun and Morley, 1943: 80).

Evidence has been presented (Nice, 1943: 88) which shows that in mixed flocks of birds the warning cries of 1 species may be recognized by the others. There seems little doubt, therefore, that at least under certain conditions the warnings given by 1 species may aid all the members of a mixed band to escape the attack of a predator. There is also evidence that some of the species that compose the mixed flock benefit by securing insects and other prey dislodged from their hiding places by the other members of the aggregation; however, similar benefits are derived from the operations of a social band composed of a single species, and it is not certain how much additional benefit results from membership in a mixed band.

It has been suggested by Winterbottom (1943: 439) that mixed flocks of birds usually are composed of a "nucleus" species, which is highly social and which occasionally forms unmixed flocks composed of this 1 species alone, and of 1 or more "circumference" species, which are less social in behavior and which almost never form unmixed flocks of their own kind. The gregarious instincts of some of the members of the mixed flock are often very weak, so weak, in fact, that it is difficult to determine whether certain individuals of a particular "circumference" species are actually members of the flock. Winterbottom (p. 441) noted that the drongo (*Dicrurus a. adsimilis*), which is for the most part territorial in its way of life, will join any bird party that passes through its territory, but when the flock passes beyond its territory the drongo turns back.

The mixed flocks of Brazilian birds studied by D. E. Davis (1946), however, were not made up of a "nucleus" species, to which other "circumference" species became attached. On the contrary, each of the Brazilian flocks was made up chiefly of a group of regularly associated species to which individuals of other species more or less accidentally became attached.

NESTING AGGREGATIONS COMPOSED OF SEVERAL SPECIES. Several species of birds often nest together in a combined nesting community. This is particularly true of aquatic birds that nest along the ocean shores. Some of these nesting communities are undoubtedly only aggregations formed because suitable nesting sites are limited. The several associated species may sometimes actually be in competition with one another for suitable nesting places. Frequently, however, the several species aid one another in giving notice of the approach of enemies or in providing mutual aid for community defense. For instance, Formozov (in Gause, 1934a: 19-20) noted that on an island in the Black Sea 4 species of terns were nesting together. The individuals of all the species combined to chase away predators, such as hen harriers, from the nesting community. The several species had diverse feeding habits and there was no competition for food. Formozov (1937: 594) also has noted that around the lakes on the steppes of Kasakstan several species of ducks (*Anas*) nest among breeding colonies of curlews, lapwings, godwits, and various kinds of sandpipers, all of which chase off feathered predators and thus defend the nests of the ducks as well as their own. Likewise a grebe (*Podiceps nigricollis*) often makes its nests in the midst of colonies of the black tern (*Hydrochelidon*).

Roosts of Mixed Species. The same roosting site is sometimes used by 2 or more species of birds (Friedmann, 1935: 143). Thus, Odum and Pitelka (1939) reported that the cowbird, bronzed grackle, redwing, and starling all roosted together in an artificial forest on the University of Illinois campus at Urbana, Illinois. Since there was no evidence of any attachment among the several aggregated species, it is probable that the association of these species was due to the scarcity of suitable roosting sites in this prairie region. Where several species occupy the same roost, each species usually remains apart from the others and occupies a separate section of the roosting area.

Dominance Relations Between Species. When individual animals belonging to 2 dissimilar species meet, one will often dominate the other, even though there is no food relationship nor any defense of a territory. When several species are feeding together, the members of the species that has the largest body size are likely to drive away those of the smaller species, and thus to secure for themselves the best of the food. Among the birds it was said by Bartholomew (1943: 195) that in general an individual of a large species, such as a cormorant, drives smaller birds, such as ducks or shore birds, away from a perching place, and in its turn is driven off by a larger species, such as a swan. Seldom is any active aggression required, but when a large bird appears at a roost, the individuals of the smaller species immediately depart peacefully. Likewise, when a lion comes to a water hole or to an animal carcass, the jackals and other smaller animals draw back and remain in the background until the lion leaves.

A small species, however, will sometimes prove to be more aggressive than a larger one and, therefore, will be dominant over it. Thus in southern Michigan the red squirrel (*Tamiasciurus hudsonicus*) often dominates the much larger fox squirrel (*Sciurus niger*), which retreats precipitously when attacked by its small but more active cousin. The song sparrow (*Melospiza melodia*), when on its nesting territory, drives away a considerable number of other kinds of birds, some of them larger than itself (Nice, 1937: 68). In nuthatch-titmouse flocks in England it is usual for nuthatches to dominate great tits, great tits to dominate blue tits, and blue tits to dominate marsh tits. Individual birds, however, do not always follow exactly this order of dominance. For instance, a blue tit may drive a great tit away from a feeding station, though this is rare. The factor most likely to upset the usual dominance relations between species is the proximity of a nest or roost (Colquhoun, 1942*a*).

In contrast to the pugnacity displayed by certain kinds of animals, especially near their homes or young, many kinds of animals seem to be very tolerant of the presence of other species. The nests of many diverse species of birds often are situated quite close to one another (Mendall and Aldous, 1943: 92). In a study of the small rodents of the mesquite association in southern New Mexico, Blair (1943*b*: 37-38) was unable to discover any antagonism among the several species.

This apparent tolerance between species, however, does not necessarily indicate any friendliness of one to the other, but is almost certainly due only to confidence on the part of each that it is able to take care of itself in any ordinary emergency. As evidence of this self-confidence, it may be pointed out that animals of dissimilar species frequently feed together in open situations, but that in confined quarters it is usual for only 1 species to be present at a time. I have noted, for example, that cardinals and English sparrows often feed together in winter on the lawn of my yard in Ann Arbor, Michigan, but on the window feeding shelf the 2 species seldom are present at the same time.

If 2 species of differing size live in the same community, the smaller form simply avoids the larger form and there is almost never any actual combat between them (Collias, 1944: 98). It seems probable that much of the apparent tolerance between species in nature is based on a confidence of each of the individuals concerned that he is able to escape should he be suddenly attacked. The individuals avoid situations from which escape might not be possible.

INTOLERANCE OF HUMAN DISTURBANCE. A tendency to avoid the vicinity of man is exhibited by a number of kinds of animals, particularly certain birds and mammals. Thus, the wolf and the grizzly bear retire before the advance of civilization and are seldom found near human habitations. In part, this retirement may be due to the destruction by man of their habitats and homesites, but many species actually seem to be shy and to emigrate from areas that are subject to disturbance by man or by his domestic animals. On the contrary, less shy animals, such as the coyote and the fox, often survive and thrive in well-settled areas. The American robin, a species that has little fear of man, thrives especially well in surburban districts.

ADAPTATIONS OF ONE SPECIES FOR ANOTHER

Many diverse adaptations have been developed by particular species of animals and by plants to fit them for their ecologic relations with their associates. Some of these adaptations enable the organism concerned to secure or digest its food; others aid the organism to escape being preyed upon. Adaptations for defense against attack are common, both among plants and among animals. Mention will be made only of the thorns evolved by certain plants for their protection against herbivores and of the mechanisms for rapid running or jumping by which many animals elude their predators. Many kinds of adaptations are concerned with reproduction, as, for example, the special adaptations whereby plants secure the pollination of their flowers by the aid of animals. Every species must of necessity be equipped with numerous adaptations of structure, physiology, and behavior to fit it for existence in its ecosystem.

The instincts and habits of a species often are adaptations which are just as important to it as are its morphologic characters. This is well illustrated by the behavior of the bighorn sheep when under attack by the wolf. The habit of the bighorn of retreating to rocky situations when in danger is as much a factor in its survival as are its structural adaptations (Adolph Murie, 1944: 142).

ADAPTATIONS BETWEEN FLOWERS AND ANIMALS FOR POLLINATION. The close relations between certain plants and the animals that pollinate their flowers have resulted in the production of mutual adaptations between numerous pairs of species. Many plants have special adaptations to attract certain kinds of insects to their flowers and at the same time to exclude undesirable

FIG. 40. Pollination of a flower by the hummingbird, *Lamourouxia exserta*. The tuft of stigmas brushes the flower's own pollen, or pollen brought from another flower, from the bird's forehead. In the flower shown here, the stamen is not fully developed, and only cross-pollination can occur. (After Wagner, 1946.)

species. The plant often provides the animal with nectar and sometimes with pollen to attract it to the flower, and often advertises the presence of the bait by odors and by bright-colored petals of a hue that presumably is conspicuous to the animal (Robertson, 1928; Clements and Long, 1923). Conversely, many insects have adaptive structures that enable them to utilize the nectar available in the flower and to transfer the pollen from antler to stigma. The bumble bee, for example, has an especially long tongue that enables it to suck the nectar from flowers which have long flower tubes. Although many flowers are adapted for pollination by insects, a few kinds have special adaptations for utilizing other animals, such as hummingbirds (Wagner, 1946), for this service (Fig. 40).

ADJUSTMENT BETWEEN PLANTS AND HERBIVORES. The mutual adjustments in their life histories between plants and the herbivores that feed upon them may also be considered adaptations. It is evident that if a plant is so severely fed upon in any stage of its life history that it loses its ability to survive and to reproduce itself, the amount of plant food available in the ecosystem will be reduced. The relations between an insect herbivore and a plant species to which it is restricted for food are worthy of consideration. Should the insect so seriously injure all the plants of this species in a given ecosystem that they fail to produce offspring, then it is obvious that the insect species itself will ultimately suffer. It is to the advantage of the herbivore, therefore, to adjust its life history so that its depredations on the plant come most heavily at a season when the plant is best able to bear them. It is also to the advantage of the plant not to react more violently than necessary to the injuries caused by the insect (Forbes, 1909: 294).

ADJUSTMENT BETWEEN PARASITES AND HOSTS. A still more obvious mutual adaptation is involved in the relationship between a parasite and its host. A few kinds of parasites seriously injure their hosts, by absorbing too great a proportion of their food or tissues, by mechanical injury, by interfering with the activity of the host, or by giving off toxic chemicals. Sometimes also the host reacts so violently to the presence of the parasite that it destroys itself. The destruction of the host results in most cases in the death also of the parasite. Such a result is detrimental to both species. From the standpoint of the host the best kind of parasite is one that does not seriously injure or unduly handicap the host in its struggle for existence.

The most efficient parasite is one that has reduced its virulence and its reproductive capacity to such an extent that it does not overharm its host. Likewise the efficient host is one that has become so tolerant of the parasite that it does not seriously injure itself in trying to be rid of the parasite (Swellengrebel, 1940). These adjustments seem actually to have been made in many parasite-host relationships.

It has, however, been pointed out by Ball (1943) that the destruction of the individual host often does not result in any damage to the parasite. On the contrary, the destruction of the host sometimes is necessary so that the parasite may pass to the next stage in its life history. The degree of adjustment between the host and the parasite, therefore, gives no measure of the length of time that they have been associated. Nevertheless, too widespread destruction of the host individuals by a parasite would ultimately react disadvantageously to the parasite itself, and some mutual adjustment between host and parasite always is essential if both are to survive.

DEFENSE AGAINST ATTACK. All plants and animals have numerous adaptations which serve as a defense against injurious organisms, such as predators or infective diseases. Nevertheless, the success of any individual organism in escaping the attacks of its enemies depends in part on the number and vigor of the attackers. Most plants and animals, for example, have mechanisms for preventing the entrance of disease-producing organisms. They also have mechanisms for disposing of those organisms that are able to penetrate the outer defenses of the body, yet if the infective agents are very numerous the outer and inner defenses of the defender are often inadequate, and the infection may become established. When, for example, a healthy hickory tree is attacked by a small number of boring insects it responds with such a copious flow of sap that it drowns the attackers, and their attempt to gain entrance is usually unsuccessful. If, however, a tree should be attacked at the same time by a large number of bark beetles, as may happen during an insect outbreak, the defenses of the tree may be inadequate to cope with all of its attackers, in which case it will quickly be killed (Blackman and Stage, 1924: 11). Individual plants or animals which are in a weakened condition from any cause are especially vulnerable, for their defenses seem then not to be in perfect working condition.

While many individual organisms succumb to the attacks of enemies in spite of their adaptations for escape or defense, nevertheless, their adaptations are nearly always successful in enabling at least a few individuals of each species to survive in order to perpetuate their kind.

Many organisms have, in fact, been able to evolve very successful means for resisting the attacks of certain types of diseases and of herbivores and predators. A considerable list of plants that are resistant or immune to the attacks of certain disease-producing organisms and of particular kinds of herbivorous insects is given by Sweetman (1936: 38-40). The basis of the resistance to attack is sometimes physical, operating by the production of mechanical devices. Sometimes it is chemical, operating by the production of substances that are unpleasant or harmful to the attacker. The resistance to attack may also sometimes be physiologic, the presence of the invading organism operating to produce antibodies or other substances that tend to destroy the invaders. Frequently the basis of resistance to attack involves a combination of physical and of chemical or physiologic methods. The basis for the immunities of many kinds of organisms against attack by other forms, however, is as yet largely unknown.

GENERAL ADAPTATIONS. Although certain adaptations of a given organism may be directed toward some one associated species, many other adaptations are more general in character. For example, most plants are adapted to survive the attacks of a considerable variety of herbivorous animals. Small herbivorous animals likewise are adapted to exist in spite of the attacks of diverse species of predators. Most of the characters of any given organism, in fact, must adapt it for existence in association with a considerable variety of those other species that live in the same community. Only rarely can a species afford to develop special adaptations for living with a particular associated species.

MEASURES OF ECOLOGIC ASSOCIATION BETWEEN SPECIES

ASSOCIATION INDEX. To measure the amount of association between any one species (A), taken as the basis of comparison, and another species (B), the

association index may be used (Dice, 1945). This index is obtained by dividing the number (*a*) of random samples of a given series in which species A
occurs into the number (*h*) of samples in which species A and B occur together. The name of the species used as the basis of comparison is placed
second in the statement of the index:

$$\text{Association index B/A} = h/a.$$

The formula for the reciprocal index is:

$$\text{Association index A/B} = h/b.$$

For example, let us assume a series of 140 comparable plots, on which
either or both the species *alpha* and *beta* occur. Let us further assume that
alpha alone occurs on 20 plots, *beta* alone on 60 plots, and both species
together on 60 plots. Then the value of *a,* representing the total number
of plots on which the species *alpha* occurs, is 60+20=80. Similarly, the
value of *b* is 60+60=120, and the value of *h* is 60. Substituting in our
formula we find that the association index of *beta* with *alpha* (*beta/alpha*)
is 60/80 or .75. In other words, on three-quarters of the plots on which the
species *alpha* occurs it is associated with *beta*. Similarly the association index
alpha/beta is 60/120=.50, which shows that on half the plots on which *beta*
occurs it is associated with *alpha*.

The possible range of the association index is from 1.0, which indicates
constant association between the 2 species compared in all the samples examined, to 0.0, which shows a complete failure of association. The values
between 1.0 and 0.0 indicate the proportional amount of association between
the 2 species.

The value of the association index between any 2 species is proportional
to the relative frequencies of the 2 forms in the samples examined. The
reciprocal association indexes consequently have the same numerical relationship to each other as the frequencies of the 2 forms. Thus, in the above
example, the reciprocal association indexes, *beta/alpha* and *alpha/beta* are
.75 and .50, respectively, forming a 3:2 ratio. *Beta* occurred in 120 of the
samples and *alpha* in 80 samples, which likewise is a 3:2 ratio. If the 2 species
had occurred in the same frequencies in the samples, their reciprocal association indexes would have been identical.

The percentage of infected hosts sometimes calculated by parasitologists
(Eskey, 1938) is a special application of the association index. The number
of individual hosts in or on which a particular species of parasite is found
divided by the total number of hosts examined gives a parasite/host association index. Inasmuch as a parasite will seldom be found separated from
its host, the reciprocal host/parasite index is not calculated.

It should be noted that in the association index no account is taken of
the number of samples examined in which neither of the species under consideration appears. This lack makes impractical the development of any

statistical evaluation of the significance of these indexes. It is recommended that count should always be made, if possible, of the total number of samples examined, so that in addition to the calculation of the association indexes the data can be treated statistically.

The association index is of particular value in those measures of association where the frequency of occurrence of one species may readily be ascertained, but where the frequency of the other cannot be counted. This is true, for example, of the usual parasite/host examinations. Where the frequencies of occurrence of both species can be ascertained, it will be better to use the coefficient of association. The "coincidence index" (Dice, 1945) seems to have no practical value.

COEFFICIENT OF ASSOCIATION. In any given series of samples the 2 species whose association is being measured would be expected to occur together by chance in a certain number of the samples. Such chance occurrences would, of course, not indicate any ecologic relation between the species concerned. We need, therefore, to measure the amount to which the occurrence together of any 2 given species deviates from that of chance association. For this purpose the coefficient of association (Forbes, 1907) may be used. This coefficient is obtained by dividing the observed number of samples in which the 2 species occur together by the number of samples in which they would be expected to occur by chance alone. Let a be the total number of samples in which a given species A occurs, and b the total number of samples in which another species B appears; also let h be the number of samples in which both species occur, and n be the total number of samples examined. Then the chance of species A occurring in any particular sample is a/n and the chance of B occurring in any sample is b/n. The chance that both species will occur in any given sample is $a/n \times b/n$, and the total number of samples in which both species would be expected to occur is $a/n \times b/n \times n$ or ab/n. Therefore:

$$\text{Coefficient of association} = \frac{h}{ab/n} = \frac{hn}{ab}.$$

Should a coefficient of association of 1.0 be obtained for any 2 species, then these 2 forms have been found together in exactly the number of sample units that would be expected by chance. Should the coefficient be smaller than 1.0, it indicates less frequent association between the 2 species than would be expected by chance, while a coefficient larger than 1.0 indicates a more frequent association than would be expected by chance alone.

CHI-SQUARE TEST OF SIGNIFICANCE OF ASSOCIATION. The statistical reliability of none of these measures of association can be directly determined. We may, however, use the chi-square test (Snedecor, 1940: 16-19) to determine the probability that the combinations of species in the samples of a particular series may be due to chance errors in random sampling. In order to apply the chi-square test we may first determine the number of samples in which each possible combination of the 2 species would be expected to occur by chance. We have already shown that species A and B would be expected to occur together in ab/n samples. The number of samples in which it would be expected that species A should occur alone would be the total number (a) in which it is recorded, minus the number in which it is expected to appear with B ($=a-ab/n$). Likewise, it would be expected that species B should appear alone in b minus ab/n samples. The expectation that species A will not appear in any given sample is $(n-a)/n$ and for species B the chance is $(n-b)/n$. The likelihood that neither A nor B will appear in a given sample is therefore $(n-a)/n \times (n-b)/n$. The total number of samples in which it would be expected that neither species should occur is accordingly $(n-a)/n \times (n-b)/n \times n$ or $(n-a)(n-b)/n$.

TABLE XV

AMOUNT OF ASSOCIATION BETWEEN TWO SPECIES

Association between an isopod (*Trachelipus rathkei*) and a roach (*Parcoblatta pennsylvanica*) during September, 1942, under large boards in a wood lot in Kendall County, Illinois (data from L. A. Cole, 1946a).

Species	Boards	Expected by Chance	Deviation from Expectation	Deviation^2 / Expectation
Trachelipus only.....	14	24.23	−10.23	4.319
Parcoblatta only.....	26	36.23	−10.23	2.889
Both species.........	74	63.77	+10.23	1.641
Neither species.....	24	13.77	+10.23	7.600
Totals...........	138	138.00	00.00	16.449

Association index *Trachelipus/Parcoblatta* = 0.74.
Association index *Parcoblatta/Trachelipus* = 0.84.
Coefficient of association = 1.16.
χ^2 = 16.449 with 1 degree of freedom.

An example of the calculation of chi-square is given in the accompanying table (Table XV). A somewhat simpler but less graphic method for calculating the chi-square of a 2 by 2 table, such as this, is given by Snedecor (1940: 371). The total value of chi-square in the example given in the table is 16.449. This is a significant deviation, far above the 1 per cent level of significance. One concludes, therefore, that the 2 species in this example are associated more frequently than would be expected by chance. In this particular example the 2 species may have had no special attraction for each other, but their association was probably due to similar reactions to some environmental factor (Cole, 1946a: 78).

Attention is called to the fact that the chi-square test is not reliable when the number of expected units in any class is few. Accordingly, if few samples are available, Yates' correction (Snedecor, 1940: 168-69) may be applied.

The values of the coefficient of association and of chi-square are affected by the frequency with which the 2 species concerned appear in the samples which are used as a basis for measuring their association. Neither of these statistics measures association directly, but only the deviation of the amount of association from that expected by chance. Care should be taken not to interpret either of them as measures of the strength of association.

TYPES OF SAMPLES WHICH MAY BE USED. The samples which are used as a basis for the measurement of the association between any 2 given species must be uniform in size, comparable in season and in other temporal features, and must be taken at random. Most of the kinds of samples employed in ecologic field work will be suitable. Sample plots or transects will be satisfactory if they are small enough. Sample catches obtained by sweeps made by an insect net or obtained by a townet or dredge also will often be satisfactory.

For the reliable measurement of association it is essential that the 2 species compared actually are associated in nature if they appear in the same sample. Samples taken from large areas, therefore, will often be unsuitable, as will samples taken from heterogeneous areas which include several community types. Samples based on time intervals can only be used if at the same time they are space units (Dice, 1945).

ASSOCIATION BETWEEN A SPECIES AND A HABITAT FEATURE. The amount of association between a particular species and any selected feature of its habitat can also be measured by the methods described above. One can thus compare the occurrence of a species and the simultaneous presence of rocks, logs, trees, or any other selected feature of the environment. In making such a comparison due attention should be given to the possibility that some secondary factor may affect the measure of association.

EVALUATION OF MEASURES OF ASSOCIATION. The demonstration of a tendency toward association between 2 species does not in itself prove that there is any attraction between the individuals of the 2 forms. The 2 species may be associated only because both have selected the same habitat. The ascertainment of the amount of attraction between 2 species, or of the degree of dependency of one upon the other, would require other kinds of measurements than those here described.

CLASSIFICATION OF ECOLOGIC RELATIONSHIPS

The classification of the ecologic interrelations of the member organisms of communities has been attempted by many biologists. This is shown by the common use of such terms as herbivore, predator, parasite, commensal, competitor, and so on.

Any comprehensive classification of the ecologic relationships within a community, however, is difficult because of the complexity of these interrelations. Many of the classificatory categories that have been proposed grade more or less gradually into one another (T. Park, 1941). Various authors have sometimes employed the same term with differing meanings. Also, a given species may, for example, be at the same time a herbivore, a competitor with other herbivores, the prey of several kinds of predators, the host of several parasites, and a commensal of certain other species living in the same community. A complete classification of the ecologic relations of the member species of any naturàl community seems, at least for the present, to be impractical.

SELECTED REFERENCES

Craig, Charles F., and E. C. Faust. 1945. Clinical parasitology. 4th ed.; Philadelphia: Lea and Febiger.

Daubenmire, Rexford F. 1947. Plants and environment: a textbook of plant autecology. New York: John Wiley and Sons. Chap. 7.

Dice, Lee R. 1945. Measures of the amount of ecologic association between species. Ecology, 26: 297-302.

Mayr, Ernst. 1948. The bearing of the new systematics on genetical problems: the nature of species. Advances in Gen., 2: 212-16.

Pearse, A. S. 1926. Animal ecology, New York: McGraw-Hill Book Co. Chaps. 8 and 11.

Sweetman, Harvey L. 1936. The biological control of insects; with a chapter on weed control. Ithaca, New York: Comstock Publ. Co.

Wheeler, William M. 1910. Ants: their structure, development, and behavior. New York: Columbia Univ. Press. Chaps. 15-17.

XIV

COMMUNITY EQUILIBRIUM

The lives of the numerous kinds of organisms which together constitute each ecologic community are directly and indirectly interrelated in an extremely complex manner, as is evident from the discussion presented in the previous chapters. If any species is added to or subtracted from a community, all the other associated species must immediately adjust themselves to this change. Even a change in the abundance of one species has repercussions on all the other members of the community. In order to determine the conditions required for the existence of any particular species of plant or of animal, it is necessary to consider the direct or indirect relations of this form to all the other species that make up each community in which it lives (Adams, 1915b: 158).

Every community is of necessity constantly in process of change. It is never exactly the same in 2 successive moments. The individuals existing at any given time will all ultimately die one by one, and will be replaced by new individuals. The newly produced individuals will continue to grow for a considerable part of their lives, and they may go through various transformations, in each of which they may occupy a different niche in the community. In their wanderings certain individuals may move out of the community and other individuals may move into the community. The activity of each individual organism also varies from time to time. Thus at certain periods of the day and at certain seasons an individual may be at rest or dormant, while at other times it may be very active.

Although every community varies from year to year, from season to season, and to a considerable extent from hour to hour, yet both in structure and in activities most communities continue to exist over long periods of time. The changes that take place in their composition are chiefly fluctuations or cyclic variations rather than permanent changes. Many communities actually persist over long periods with only minor fluctuations in their composition. Moreau (1944: 308), for example, has pointed out that local bird communities are astonishingly stable and that it is unusual for any species to become locally extirpated. The injurious effects of such a disaster as a hard winter tend to be effaced within a very few breeding seasons.

COMMUNITY REGULATORY MECHANISMS

The ability of most communities to maintain themselves with only relatively minor fluctuations from time to time in their composition is due to their possession of numerous ecologic regulatory mechanisms. An ecologic regulatory mechanism may be defined as any agency that tends to maintain a balance between 2 or more members of a community or between any species and the resources of its habitat. These regulatory mechanisms operate to co-ordinate the several parts of every community and to keep the member species in tune with the conditions of their physical and biotic habitats.

Just as each individual organism, in order to continue to live, must constantly adjust its activities to the conditions of its environment, so each community must continually adjust itself to the ever-changing character of its habitat. Otherwise the community could not continue to exist. Every community, therefore, must contain within itself regulatory mechanisms that operate to prevent any alteration in its composition from becoming so great that it changes the character of the community beyond repair. These ecologic regulatory mechanisms enable each community to continue to exist in spite of constant changes within the community itself and in the adjacent communities, and in spite of continual fluctuations in the physical conditions of the habitat.

The significance of regulatory mechanisms in the steppe communities of the U.S.S.R. has been forcefully summarized by Formozov (1928: 459, quoting from Sukachev, 1926), who pointed out that the activities of the rodents and of the larger herbivores operate to maintain the equilibrium of the steppe association. The relationships existing within the community are advantageous not only to the animals but also to the plants.

The mechanisms that keep the various parts of a given community in balance with one another are of 2 principal types. Those mechanisms that act to reduce the numbers of any species that becomes overabundant in relation to its associates will be considered first. Later those special mechanisms that tend to assist certain species in maintaining themselves as members of the community will be discussed.

Mechanisms That Control the Abundance of Particular Species

Mechanisms are needed in every community to regulate the population densities of each of the member species because every species constantly produces more offspring than can survive. The number of individuals of any given species of plant or animal that can thrive in a particular community is strictly limited. Each habitat can furnish only a certain maximum amount of food, sunlight, space, and the other essentials for life. In any given ecosystem at a particular time, therefore, there is a maximum population density for each species, above which it cannot continue to thrive. Any offspring produced above the number necessary to maintain this optimum population density must be considered surplus. If the community is not to suffer an alteration in character, these surplus individuals must be eliminated.

A stable community composed of plants alone without any animals should theoretically be possible. In such a community the controlling mechanisms might be furnished by plant parasites, bacterial diseases, virus diseases, or other simple types of organisms. Such plant communities may actually have existed in some early geologic age before the appearance of animals. That, however, must have been before the evolution of land plants because the protozoa, which are animals, appeared very early in the history of life on the earth.

In all existing communities animals as well as plants occur, and consequently it is of only theoretical interest to consider what a plant community would be like if there were no animals associated with it. In contemporary terrestrial communities many plants are dependent upon animals for the fertilization of their flowers, for the transportation of their seeds, for the control of their numbers, and for other services. Any existing terrestrial community, therefore, would be changed greatly in character if by some cataclysm all its animals should be eliminated. In aquatic communities, also, plants have many interrelations with the associated animals.

The regulatory mechanisms that eliminate the surplus individuals of a species and thereby preserve a proper balance between the several kinds of associated organisms and the resources of the habitat will be here considered under the headings of (1) physical agencies, (2) feeding by herbivores, (3) predation, (4) parasitism and disease, and (5) competition. Often 2 or more of these factors act simultaneously to reduce the numbers of a given species.

PHYSICAL AGENCIES. Any physical factor in an ecosystem that transgresses either the upper or lower limit of toleration for a given member species causes mortality, which reduces the population density of that species. Most species that exist in a given ecosystem are adjusted to the usual amplitudes of fluctuation of the physical factors in the habitat. Extreme fluctuations in temperature, rainfall, wind, or other physical factors, however, occur from time to time in every habitat and these may cause great mortality to certain species. The mortality suffered by a species due to drought, flood, or storm may, in fact, be so great that at times its population density in a particular community is reduced to a very low level.

Reduction in the numbers of a species by the operation of physical factors usually is no more likely to occur when the species is overabundant than when its numbers are few. In this respect physical factors differ in general from biotic factors, many of which are most effective in producing mortality when population density is high and decrease in effectiveness as population density decreases.

FEEDING BY HERBIVORES. Feeding by herbivores is an important mechanism for regulating the numbers of many kinds of plants. As an example of a simple sort of community regulatory mechanism based on the herbivorous habit, a hypothetical community may be considered, consisting entirely of 2 species, one a food plant and the other a herbivorous animal that feeds only on this one particular species of plant (Forbes, 1880). The herbivore will continuously increase in number and in time will likely become so numerous that it will eat more than the current growth of the plant. In other words, the plant species will be overgrazed or overbrowsed and many of the individual plants will be injured or destroyed. In this condition the productivity of the plant species will be lessened, and the amount of food available to the herbivore will accordingly be reduced. If we assume that there is no other plant species in the community to which the animal can turn for food, then all of the individual animals must sooner or later find themselves on short rations and some of them will starve to death. In time the numbers of the herbivore will be reduced through starvation, and its destruction of the plants will consequently be lessened. Ultimately, when the herbivore has become sufficiently reduced in abundance, the plant can again begin to increase in numbers and in productivity of food. This will start the cycle over again.

Each of the 2 species in the hypothetical example given above acts as a check upon the other. Ultimately the numbers of the herbivore and of its food plant may possibly become stabilized at values where both can exist in maximum numbers. More probably there will be frequent oscillations of greater or lesser magnitude in the numbers of both species. In order that the relationship between the 2 species may continue, it must, of course, be assumed that at no time is the food plant ever completely extirpated from the community. It must also be assumed that either the herbivore is always able to secure at least a small amount of food in the community, sufficient to ensure the survival of the species there, or that it is able from time to time to reinvade the area from adjacent communities.

Such a theoretical example of an ecologic regulatory mechanism is actually much simpler than any situation that ever occurs in a natural community. The relationships in nature between a herbivore and its food species usually are complicated by the presence of other sources of food, by the attacks of predators and of parasites, by competition with other species, by fluctuations in populations due to the lethal effects of the weather and of the other physical factors of the habitat, and by the operation of still other controlling mechanisms.

Sometimes, however, a natural ecologic regulatory mechanism that operates in a fairly simple manner may be observed. An illustration is afforded by the relations in certain situations between snowshoe hares and coniferous seedlings. Following forest fires in certain parts of the northern United States and adjacent areas in Canada, conifers often spring up in dense thickets. These densely crowded thickets of seedlings from 6 inches to 2 feet in height often stagnate in growth and become subject to the hazards of fire and of insect damage. The snowshoe hares, at the times of their peak abundance, thin these conifer thickets by clipping and by girdling. As soon as the thickets have been opened up by the work of the hares to a point where most of the cover is removed, the hares are exposed to the attacks of their predators. Under these attacks the hares either are eliminated or they move on to other thickets, where they repeat their thinning operations. The coniferous plantations are thereby opened up by the hares and the intense competition between the individual plants is removed without the destruction of all the seedlings. The process is a more or less self-regulatory one, which results in a more rapid regeneration of the coniferous forest than would be possible were it not for the services of the hares (Cox, 1938). At the same time the numbers of the hares are regulated by the protection or lack of protection from predators that the vegetation provides.

The effect which animals produce on plants by feeding varies in different places and at different times, from a barely noticeable clipping of certain plant parts to the complete local destruction of a plant species. In extreme instances all vegetation may be destroyed on local areas.

The numbers of certain kinds of plants may be controlled by the eating of their seeds or other reproductive parts by animals. Thus, in a given year all the seed crop of a certain kind of tree may be eaten by squirrels, mice, and other animals. Forest insects play a particularly important part in reducing the number of plant seeds and seedlings to the density of individuals that can survive on a given site (Beeson, 1944).

Most kinds of herbivores are able to subsist on a considerable variety of plants, although they may exhibit preferences for certain kinds. Should the preferred food species be absent or difficult to obtain, the herbivore turns to other kinds of plant food that are present in the community. This results in a certain amount of automatic regulation of the numbers of the several food-plant species. A preferred food plant will be fed upon heavily by its herbivores, while a distasteful species will be eaten proportionately less. If, however, the population of herbivores is so large that the preferred food plants are reduced in abundance and become difficult to find, then the herbivores will turn to the less palatable foods, and the pressure on the preferred species will be reduced. Feeding by herbivores, therefore, may greatly reduce the abundance of certain common plant-food species, but the proportion of utilization of each food species tends to decrease as its abundance falls.

The herbivores in a community accordingly reduce the numbers of the more abundant food plants but have less effect on the rarer forms, even though these may be just as palatable. The herbivorous habit, therefore, is a regulatory mechanism which operates to prevent any kind of plant, except the most unpalatable forms, from becoming overly abundant in a community.

Those herbivores which are closely restricted to one or to a few kinds of food plants will not promote community stability so well as those species which are more adaptable in their feeding habits. A herbivorous species which is limited for its food to a certain plant may be very effective in controlling the numbers of that particular food species. When its own food species becomes reduced in abundance, however, this herbivore cannot transfer its attention to other foods. On the contrary, it must continue to feed on that 1 food plant. A restricted food relationship consequently will produce oscillations in the numbers of both species concerned, and instability in the community will result.

The more adaptable a herbivorous species is in its food habits, the more effective it will be as a regulatory mechanism. An adaptable herbivore will feed most heavily on the abundant plant species and neglect the scarcer forms. The rarer species, therefore, have a chance to survive and to increase in abundance, while the overabundant forms are brought under control.

PREDATION. Just as feeding of herbivorous animals controls the populations of plants, so the feeding habits of predaceous animals keep the numbers of the prey species in check. Predation is actually one of the most important mechanisms for regulating the numbers of animals. It should be emphasized that the term "predator" implies the viewpoint of the prey, while from the viewpoint of the predator the prey is only food.

A predator is not necessarily a member of a species different from the one preyed upon. Many kinds of fishes, insects, and other animals feed upon their own young, their brothers, or their larvae or eggs, if they can obtain them. Thus, especially under crowded conditions, a predaceous species may directly aid in controlling its own numbers.

A predaceous species that feeds upon an herbivore is often in its turn fed upon by a larger or more aggressive kind of predator. Examples of such food chains are present in every community. The effect within the community of such superpredation is to weaken to some degree the regulatory control exercised by each predaceous species on the form next below it in the food chain. Nevertheless, the numbers of every species which appears in any food chain are at least to some degree controlled, excepting only the numbers of the ultimate predator, if there is one, on which no other species feeds.

Those individual animals that for any reason are weak, sluggish, or not fully alert will presumably be more vulnerable to predators than those of the same species that are stronger, more active, or more alert. Animals that are old, diseased, crippled, or weak from starvation, therefore, are more likely to be captured by predators than are young, healthy, and vigorous individuals (Adolph Murie, 1944: 121). If there is competition between the members of a species for the better home ranges, then the weaker individuals will be pushed out onto the poorer sites, where their vulnerability is high.

It is true that sometimes all the individuals in a herd, strong and weak alike, succumb to starvation when the food supply has been exhausted. It is likewise true that predators often capture strong and healthy individuals and that they by no means confine their attention to those which are diseased. Also, the young animal that today is easily captured by a predator might next year, if it had lived, have become one of the strongest individuals of its kind. But it seems logical to believe that on the average the healthier and better adapted individuals have the better chance to survive.

Reliable studies of the kinds of prey secured in nature by predators or destroyed by unfavorable environmental conditions are very scanty, but the evidence, so far as it goes, agrees with the conclusion that the abnormal, weak, crippled, and diseased individuals have a higher mortality rate than those that are healthy and strong (Hibben, 1939). The same regulatory mechanisms that operate to keep the population density of each species within reasonable bounds, therefore, also act to improve the health of the species and to increase its adaptation to the environment.

The loss through predation of breeding females is often especially unfortunate. In many cases the loss of a breeding female will result in the loss also of her eggs or young. The loss of one member of a breeding pair, however, does not always result in any permanent lowering of the reproductive capacity of the population. Certain populations seem, as was mentioned in Chapter XI, to have a reserve of unmated males and females ready to take the place of any breeding individual which may for any reason be eliminated. Furthermore, the loss of their eggs or young is known to stimulate many kinds of birds to increased reproduction, so that often there is compensation for the loss.

The several kinds of predators vary in their ability to capture a particular kind of prey and thereby to control its numbers. Thus, the red fox under certain conditions may be more effective than the mink in securing muskrats (Errington, 1943: 859). Under most conditions, however, the mink will be the more effective of these 2 predators in securing muskrats. Also, the mink will undoubtedly be more effective than the fox at practically all times in capturing certain other types of mink foods. The more successful a predator is in capturing a particular kind of prey, the more efficient it should be as a regulatory mechanism for controlling the numbers of that prey species.

Most predators are rather adaptable in regard to prey and seldom are limited to a single prey species. Small predators, of course, must usually feed on small prey. Also, most kinds of predators, although they are particularly adapted to capture certain kinds of prey, will nearly always accept other prey species when the usual prey are difficult to secure. During times of food scarcity, for instance, many predators feed to a considerable degree on insects, though at other times they may not utilize insects at all.

The tendency for any prey species that is unusually abundant to be taken in heavy proportion was well illustrated during an outbreak of the spruce budworm in Ontario. During the years 1923 and 1924, when the spruce budworm was not noticeably abundant, this species, so far as it could be identified, constituted only 0.5 per cent of the stomach contents of the resident warblers. During a severe outbreak of this insect in 1944, on the contrary, C. E. Hope of the Ontario Department of Lands and Forests noted that the budworm "constituted the chief, and sometimes exclusive, food consumed not only by the warblers, vireos, kinglets, and chickadees, as would be expected, but also by various sparrows, tanagers, grosbeaks, flycatchers, thrushes, nuthatches, sapsuckers, and by 2 species of blackbirds that flew from outside into the community to feed" (Kendeigh, 1947: 42).

Care should be taken, however, as has been pointed out by Errington (1943: 809), not to assume that the availability of a prey species is in direct ratio to its abundance. Many factors enter into availability. An abundant prey species may by virtue of its habits actually be less available to certain predators than are less common forms. Also, the food preferences, seasonal hunting range, aggressiveness, and skill of the predators are factors that determine the proportions of the several kinds of prey taken.

Nor should it be assumed with McAtee (1932) that a given prey species is taken in approximate proportion to its relative abundance compared to the other prey species in the region. Each predaceous individual has limitations of size, equipment, and habits that restrict the prey available to him. Many kinds of predaceous birds and mammals also have preferences for certain kinds of prey, which, if available, they continue to take in large amount, even though an abundance of other kinds of prey is at hand. It has been shown, for example, by Pearson and Pearson (1947) that the possible prey species in a given area are taken in differing proportions by the several species of owls which hunt there.

At times when their food is scarce predators reduce their rate of reproduction, but when their food is abundant they breed at maximum rate (Chap. VIII). This tendency evidently operates as an automatic regulatory mechanism to increase the numbers of predators at such times as they are needed to control an overpopulation of any prey species. Lack (1946a), for instance, has presented evidence that certain birds of prey may raise 2 broods instead of their usual 1 brood and that their clutches of eggs may be double the usual size during years when the lemmings and other rodents which they utilize for food are especially abundant. On the contrary, when food is scarce these birds may not attempt to breed at all.

Nevertheless, in spite of such increases in the reproductive rates of predators and also in spite of immigration of predators from surrounding regions, it sometimes happens that the predators are unable to control a given situation and that a serious plague of a certain prey species occurs. In other words, predation is not always successful in preventing serious fluctuations in the numbers of certain prey species. This is due to the fact that the maximum rates of reproduction of the predatory species are usually less than those of the prey. Predators are accordingly less effective than are parasites and diseases in preventing outbreaks of certain herbivores. Nevertheless, predators serve a most important function in maintaining community stability.

The predators that serve most effectively as community regulatory mechanisms should be those which are numerous, able to reproduce rapidly when needed, adaptable in regard to their food, and efficient in capturing their prey. Such predators will tend to attack and control the numbers of the most abundant prey species and will thereby reduce their numbers. At the same time they will tend to neglect the rarer prey species, with the result that these rarer forms will be allowed a chance to increase in abundance. It must be admitted, however, that these are mainly logical deductions and that we know far too little about community regulation to be sure exactly how the process operates in particular situations.

One of the best studies of the actual effectiveness of predation for the control of animal populations in nature is that of L. Tinbergen (1946). This was a study in Holland of the role that the sparrow hawk (*Accipiter nisus*) plays in the control of several passerine birds. The prey of the hawk was ascertained chiefly from the remains of birds found during the nesting season at the "plucking stations," a method devised by Uttendörfer (1930). The populations and rates of multiplication of the song birds were ascertained mostly in their nesting seasons. It was concluded that predation by the sparrow hawk plays a very great role in the mortality of the house sparrow, exceeding all its other mortality factors. With the chaffinch and great tit the mortality by predation was about 50 per cent, while with the coal tit predation was a negligible factor in the control of its population. Even this study, extensive and valuable though it is, fails to give complete information about the quantitative relations of the several species affected.

On any given area of a particular community there is a limit to the number of individuals of each species able to find suitable home ranges, homesites, shelter, and food. When the population density of any species exceeds this limit, some of the individuals will be forced to occupy home ranges that do not supply adequate essentials for life. Some of the individuals may even be forced into other communities where conditions for their existence may be very unsatisfactory.

Animals which live in home ranges that are inadequately provided with shelter and homesites are, of course, more subject to the attacks of predators than those which live in better situations. Also, if the food supply has been depleted, the animals will be forced to travel farther than usual for food and to search for food in situations where they may be especially exposed to attack. These individuals may then be said to be vulnerable (Errington, 1934). Conversely, the prey in such situations are more available to predators. The term "vulnerability" then implies the viewpoint of the prey, while "availability" implies that of the predator or food utilizer.

Vulnerable animals will be taken at a higher rate than those less vulnerable individuals of the same species which live in the better types of home ranges. Furthermore, those individuals that are forced to live in unsatisfactory home ranges are likely to have poor protection against cold and against the other factors of the physical environment. They are accordingly likely to succumb during periods of unfavorable weather.

This theory of vulnerability, suggested by Errington, is essentially that proposed independently by Naumov (1936), who suggested that when a species is at its lowest density it occupies only the most favorable habitats, which he called, as translated into English, "stations of survival."

F. C. Evans (1942) has, on the contrary, suggested that predation and other mortality factors may be excessively high in the places where a population is densest and that consequently a species may survive best in situations where normally it has low density. Mortality produced by parasites and infectious disease would be greatest in dense populations. Under certain conditions, therefore, the dense populations occupying the most favorable habitats might be wiped out, leaving only the sparse populations in the poorer habitats. The available data, however, are insufficient to show the types of situations in which species usually survive during sudden reductions in their abundance. The prey animals most likely to be taken by predators may be presumed to consist of the more vulnerable individuals in the community. Predation usually results, therefore, in reducing the numbers of a species to a level at which only the more favorable situations are occupied by it. When the population of a species is reduced to a level at which all its individuals occupy favorable sites, predation becomes, according to Errington, only slightly effective against that species. The prey species will thus be given a chance to survive and perhaps to increase again in abundance (Elton, 1927: 122-23).

Most attempts of man to increase the population of a desirable species by campaigns against predators must, accordingly, be ineffective. Predators will in general take only the surplus individuals, which probably would be unable to survive anyway in their unfavorable habitats. Increase in the numbers of an economically desirable species can usually be best secured, therefore, through improvement in the carrying capacity of the habitat so that the desired species is made less vulnerable, rather than through the attempt to eliminate the predators (Errington and Hamerstrom, 1936; Errington, Hamerstrom, and Hamerstrom, 1940; Errington, 1943, 1946).

Actual measures of the variations in the rates of survival of individuals living in home ranges of various degrees of suitability for the species are, it must be admitted, mostly lacking. There are, in fact, no good methods for measuring the suitability of any particular situation for a given species, nor is it known how dense a population of any wild species can be supported on a given area of habitat without overcrowding. Nevertheless, the deduction seems logical that for each species of animal a habitat of a particular type will become saturated at some more or less definite population density. When overcrowding exists in a community, certain individuals of the species concerned must be driven out into less favorable habitats, where they will become vulnerable to predation. On the other hand, when a species is reduced in numbers below the carrying capacity of its habitat, its members will come to occupy only the situations where they will be best able to survive, with the result that their mortality rate presumably will be reduced to a minimum.

In support of these deductions Durward Allen (1947) has shown that even extremely heavy and persistent hunting did not kill all the cock ring-necked pheasants on a certain study area in southern Michigan. In the early part of the hunting season there was a heavy kill, especially of the young males of the year, but the rate of kill rapidly diminished as the hunting season progressed. About 25 per cent of the prehunting cock population on the area studied actually were still alive at the end of the hunting season.

From the viewpoint of the wildlife manager an increase in the abundance of a certain game, food, or fur-bearing species of animal is often desirable. Other associated prey species on which the local predators might feed would then be considered buffer forms, which might absorb some of the predation pressure that otherwise would impinge upon the desired species. It has been noted by Adolph Murie (1944: 140), for example, that the Alaskan caribou (*Rangifer arcticus*) serves as a buffer species, to some extent diverting from the bighorn (*Ovis dalli*) predation by the wolf (*Canis lupus*).

Any considerable abundance of a buffer species, however, may result in attracting a large population of predators, which, when the numbers of the buffer species are reduced for any reason, may then turn on the economically desirable species (Stoddard, 1931). A high population of small mammals, for example, does not serve necessarily as a buffer against predation on bob-white quail. On the contrary, such a population of small mammals may not only attract but also build up a high predator population (Komarek, 1937: 563). In a study of the relations between the muskrat and the mink, Errington (1943: 831) was unable to find satisfactory evidence that the presence of possible buffer species upon which the mink might feed had any appreciable effect in diminishing predation on the muskrat. Nor do buffer species seem to play any considerable part in controlling the fluctuations of bob-white populations in Iowa (Errington, 1945).

PARASITISM AND DISEASE. Plant and animal parasites play an important role in community regulation. Here may be included the parasitic bacteria, protozoa, rusts, molds, viruses, and similar microorganisms, as well as the larger fungi, tapeworms, nematodes, certain insects, and other macroscopic parasites. Many of the small parasitic organisms produce serious diseases in their hosts, often leading to death. Even if the parasites that attack a host individual do not cause its death, they may injure or weaken it so much that it falls a victim to the adversities of the physical environment or to the attacks of its other enemies.

Diseases produced by bacteria, protozoa, rusts, spirochaetes, viruses, and other simple organisms are especially effective mechanisms for the control of the abundance of certain plants and animals. These disease-producing organisms usually multiply very rapidly. Consequently, they may be able to control quickly any excess in the numbers of their hosts.

An individual plant or animal which is seriously ill or which has succumbed to disease often becomes a center of dispersal for the pathogenic organisms concerned. From such a center of reproduction and dissemination adjacent individuals in the community may be attacked in mass and their defenses may perhaps be penetrated. Thus the infection may spread. If the weather and other environmental conditions favor the attacking organism, an epidemic may result which produces widespread reduction in the population of the species which is attacked.

Plants are no less subject to the attacks of parasites and diseases than are animals. Many kinds of rots, blights, wilts, galls, cankers, smuts, rusts, scabs, mildews, and other diseases attack and often fatally injure plants. A considerable number of the more highly organized fungi and a few flowering plants also live as parasites on other plants. Parasites and diseases may serve, therefore, as regulatory mechanisms for plants as well as for animals.

The attacks on plants by certain kinds of insects produce results very similar to those of parasites or other pathogenic organisms. Thus, many of the defoliating or wood-boring insects may seriously injure or kill a considerable proportion of the individual plants they attack. Should these insects be very abundant, they may produce an outbreak having an effect similar to that of a disease epidemic.

An insect outbreak or disease epidemic is sometimes stopped by a change in weather or by a local fluctuation in climate. For example, a grove of hickory trees near Syracuse, New York, was practically destroyed during the years 1913-15 by an outbreak of bark beetles. However, a period of cool and rainy weather in 1915, when the beetles were on the wing and were establishing their brood burrows, acted as a partial check on the insects, and numerous larvae were apparently drowned in their burrows. As a result of this unusual weather the outbreak was stopped and a few hickory trees in the grove survived (Blackman and Stage, 1924: 5).

More frequently, however, an outbreak or epidemic "runs its course" and is stopped only when all the susceptible individuals in the community have been attacked and perhaps destroyed. Certain individuals of the species attacked may prove more resistant than the others and may survive to restock the area. These more resistant individuals may often be presumed to owe their resistance in part to hereditary factors. Their survival then constitutes a step forward in the evolution of disease resistance by the species. If no individuals of the species attacked survive within the stand where the epidemic occurs, restocking must come by immigration from a near-by surviving stand or from some distant region.

One kind of parasite frequently attacks another and thereby the organization of an ecologic community is rendered still more complex. Hyperparasitism is particularly common among insects. Tertiary and even quaternary parasites occur rarely in this class of animals (Sweetman, 1936: 266). It is evident that the attacks of a secondary parasite reduce the numbers of the primary parasite and thereby protect the original host. Likewise a tertiary parasite tends to reduce the numbers of the secondary parasite, with the result that the primary parasite is protected and the existence of the original host is handicapped to that extent. A quaternary parasite in attacking a tertiary parasite thereby protects the secondary parasite and ultimately aids the original host.

As community regulatory mechanisms, infective organisms and other parasites are especially effective because they attack most vigorously those host species that are very abundant. When any species becomes especially abundant in a particular community, the chance of its becoming infected by parasites also becomes great. This is true because the chances of the reproductive units of any parasite reaching a proper host are best when the population density of the host is high. A species living in a crowded situation is accordingly likely to have a large proportion of its individuals infected with parasites (Warming, 1909: 92). This will usually result in a reduction in the numbers of the overabundant species. On the other hand, should a species become rare in a particular community, the chances of its parasites being transmitted from individual to individual become low and consequently only a few of its individuals may become infected.

Should the density of a parasite become overly high in proportion to the density of its host, certain of the host individuals are likely to be attacked by several individual parasites. Too great a concentration of parasites may destroy the host individual, and thereby its parasites may fail to complete their life cycle. Such a result is bad both from the point of view of the host and from that of the parasite. For every particular host density there is a corresponding optimum density for each kind of its parasites. Departures from the optimum relative density of host and parasite produce oscillations in numbers both of the host and of the parasite involved (DeBach and Smith, 1947).

The effectiveness of parasites as community regulatory mechanisms is particularly striking among the insects, where a classic example is given by L. O. Howard (1897). In 1895 an outbreak of the white-marked tussock moth (*Orgyia leucostigma*) defoliated many of the shade trees in Washington, D. C. Soon, however, many of the larvae of the moth became parasitized by other insects. No fewer than 21 species of parasites, both hymenoptera and diptera, were found as primary parasites on these moth larvae. As a result, presumably of the activities of these parasites, the outbreak of tussock moths was soon brought under control. The primary parasites, however, did not have things all their own way, for 11 species of insect secondary parasites attacked them. In their turn the secondary parasites were attacked by 5 species of tertiary parasites; 2 of these were species which served also as secondary parasites. One insect species is recorded as being possibly a quaternary parasite as well as a tertiary parasite. The relations among the parasitic insects supported by this 1 species of herbivorous insect, therefore, are very complex, but their effect from the point of view of the community is to dampen the more violent oscillations in population densities and to prevent these fluctuations from becoming overviolent.

A parasite or disease-producing organism that is restricted to a particular host species is likely to cause violent fluctuations from time to time in the abundance of that host. If the host species, because of a favorable season or a succession of favorable years, becomes much more abundant than usual, its parasites also will increase. Then, by reason of the greater ease of transfer from host to host resulting from the increased population density of the host species, the parasites may cause great destruction of the hosts, leading to an abrupt decline in the density of the host population. With the decline in the density of the host population the parasite will have difficulty in finding its host individuals, the rate of infection will decline, and the parasite will become rare. After a time, however, the host, now being largely free of its parasite, will again increase in abundance and the cycle theoretically may again be repeated.

If, on the other hand, a parasite is able to live in any one of several kinds of hosts within a community, it is not likely to cause such violent fluctuations in the numbers of any one host species. The parasite will live in small numbers in all the hosts that it is able to infect. If any one of its host species becomes unusually numerous, the parasite will increase in that host and will ultimately reduce its numbers. But even the complete local elimination of such a host species will not eliminate the parasite, which continues to exist in its other hosts. A host species that suddenly increases in numbers is likely to be quickly attacked by those adaptable parasites which are able to live in or on other associated species within the same community.

The fluctuations in numbers both of hosts and of parasites should, therefore, be least violent in those relationships where a parasitic species is not completely restricted to a single host species. On the other hand, a parasite that is restricted to a single host species may possibly be more efficient in its attacks on that species than if it were more adaptable and able to parasitize, more or less effectively, several hosts.

COMPETITION. Competition between the individuals of the same or of dissimilar species of plants or animals which live together in the same community is a regulatory mechanism of great importance. Organisms compete for sunlight, soil moisture, food, shelter, breeding places, and other essentials of life. Those individuals which, because of excessive competion, fail to secure a sufficient amount of any essential for life are not likely to survive or to produce offspring. When competition becomes very severe, therefore, a reduction in the population density of some or all of the competing forms must automatically result. The population density must continue to decrease until the pressure of competition is relieved. In this way competition serves as a powerful regulatory mechanism.

Green plants growing in well-watered regions often are in especially severe competition with one another for sunlight. Many seedlings die because they chance to germinate in situations where the light is insufficient for survival. Even if a seedling is able to survive for a time, it may be able to grow only very slowly or may later be killed because its neighbors have overtopped it and thereby shut off most of its supply of sunshine.

Most plants produce many more seeds than can possibly germinate. Likewise many more seedlings germinate than can possibly survive. Thus, as many as 52 seedlings of the southern white cedar may germinate per square foot, or $2\frac{1}{4}$ million per acre. Even on the better sites, however, only 200 to 300 per acre can reach maturity (Toumey and Korstian, 1937: 156). All the other seedlings must be eliminated before they reach full size, mostly through competition for sunlight and for soil moisture.

When a tree in the forest falls or dies, a host of plants that previously had been shaded will receive an increase of sunlight. Certain of these plants may be shade-loving species unable to endure the increased light, and these will be stunted or killed. Many, however, will be sun-loving plants that previously had been suppressed in the shade. These will increase their rate of growth and grow upward until the forest canopy is again closed. In the resulting intense competition, however, only 1 or a very few individual trees will succeed in reaching the forest crown. The new tree or trees that finally fill the space in the forest canopy may not be of the same species as the one that fell, but they will of necessity be members of the same community. At least so far as shade is concerned, the previous character of the community will, therefore, be restored.

In arid regions the competition among plants for water is often more severe than the competition for sunlight. On the desert, for instance, there are usually open spaces between the several plants, and accordingly there is little competition for light. Here the spacing between the plants is mostly dependent upon root competition for soil moisture (W. A. Cannon, 1911). The actual mechanisms regulating plant numbers on a desert, therefore, may be very different from those acting in a temperate forest. In both situations, nevertheless, the established community tends to be perpetuated.

Competition for soil moisture limits particularly the number of young seedlings that can establish themselves in a given situation. As soon as they put down their roots the little plants come into competition for soil moisture with the already established plants which probably will have extensive root systems well adapted to utilize all the moisture available in the vicinity. In many communities, therefore, it is very difficult for a new seedling to establish itself unless a vacancy in the root complex has occurred through the death of one of the older plants.

Competition serves also as an important regulatory mechanism for the animals in every community. This competition may involve individuals not only of the same but also of dissimilar species. The individuals may compete for food, shelter, or breeding sites. In competing for food, for example, those individuals which fail to secure sufficient quantities of the proper kinds of food must either starve or be so weakened that ultimately they may be eliminated by other secondary factors. In any case, the populations of all the competing species will tend to be reduced to densities that can be supported by the ecosystem.

So long as there is an abundance of food and of the other essentials for the life of the several species in a given habitat, there may be little competition between the member individuals. The natural resources of every habitat, however, are limited. If any species increases in numbers, as every species tends to do, it may, unless checked, ultimately reach a level of population density at which there is a shortage, at least during certain seasons or periods of time, of some of its essential requirements (Chap. XIII).

For example, a shortage of a certain food item during 1 season of the year frequently occurs. In that situation, all the individuals of all the species utilizing that kind of food may come into competition with one another. There is then almost certain to be overutilization of the food resources and consequently a depletion of the supply. Certain of the associated species may then be able to turn to other food sources and thereby to survive, but one or more of the species may be unable to utilize other types of food and consequently will suffer from the food scarcity. If the food shortage becomes very serious, many individuals will starve and others will be so weakened that they may fall easy prey to predators, to disease, or to unfavorable weather. The rate of reproduction may also be reduced as a result of food shortage, as has already been pointed out. As a result of the operation of these regulatory mechanisms the populations affected will be reduced in numbers. This reduction very likely will be sufficient to bring the populations affected down to a level at which there is again sufficient food for all the survivors. Competition for food may in this way serve to regulate the population densities of many species of animals (Adolph Murie, 1944: 88).

Competition for breeding sites may sometimes operate to reduce the rate of reproduction of the species concerned. In the crowded breeding colonies of certain marine birds many of the individuals must be unable to complete their breeding activities successfully. Likewise, on crowded spawning sites certain species of fishes hybridize. Inasmuch as many of these hybrid offspring are sterile, the reproductive potentials of the species concerned are locally reduced (Lagler, 1944).

Competition among individual animals for what may be called living space may under certain conditions be an important regulatory mechanism. In overcrowded situations the individuals of many species of organisms fail to thrive and do not reproduce well. This may happen when food is present in abundance and when the physical conditions of the habitat are presumably otherwise fully adequate.

The amount of fighting between individuals is closely related to population density. Under crowded conditions the amount of intraspecific fighting is likely to be greatest. Thus, Bellrose and Low (1943: 183) noted that during a flood in the Illinois Valley, when muskrats were greatly crowded on the available refuge sites, there was much intraspecific strife, and numerous individuals, particularly the young ones, were severely injured or killed. The adults of certain species under crowded conditions may also devour the eggs or the young of their own and of associated species. Furthermore, the accumulation of poisons given off in the secretions of certain species may be deleterious to the individuals of the same or of other associated species (Allee, 1935: 927).

Competition for living space is especially important as a regulating mechanism in those species which establish and defend territories. The territorial habit acts to conserve the resources of the habitat and to ensure that a moderate but not excessive number of offspring shall be produced in each generation. This habit is therefore a powerful regulating mechanism in the community, promoting its stability.

Competition is often especially severe between individuals of the same species because these related individuals have similar habits and requirements. It often happens, however, that in a particular community a given species may have a population density too low to produce any appreciable intraspecific competition. A local population of song sparrows studied by Nice (1937: 205) in Ohio, for example, was always an underpopulation during the 7 years of study. Other factors kept the song-sparrow population in check, and intraspecific competition was never in that community an effective or necessary regulatory mechanism for the species.

Although competition is one of the most powerful ecologic regulatory mechanisms, it does not always operate by itself to produce community stability. A population may increase to a density at which the habitat is overcrowded and a certain essential of life, such as food, has become a limiting factor, yet the population often does not become reduced in abundance through competition until the producing capacity of the habitat has been gravely injured. The operation of competition alone as a regulatory mechanism may consequently result in violent oscillations in the population densities of the species concerned. Such types of regulatory mechanisms as predation and parasitism seem likely, therefore, to promote a greater degree of community stability than does competition.

COMBINATIONS OF SEVERAL ECOLOGIC AGENCIES. Each species in a community usually is exposed at the same time to the operation of several diverse regulatory mechanisms. Thus, the population density of a given animal species may be reduced by the combined operation of physical agents, predators, parasites, and competition, all acting at the same time.

Sometimes the operation of 2 or more mortality factors may produce a drastic reduction in the population density of the species attacked. Thus, the coincidence of a severe drought and a grasshopper plague in 1936 caused the death of approximately 50 per cent of the big sagebrush (*Artemisia tridentata*) plants on a segment of the Little Powder River drainage in northeastern Wyoming and southeastern Montana (Allred, 1941).

Other Mechanisms That Promote Community Stability

Besides the several regulatory mechanisms that operate to reduce the abundance of certain species, there are other mechanisms in the community which aid individuals and species to survive and to succeed. Dispersal, seasonal migration, dormancy, food and water storage, and the services rendered by one species to another, all operate to prevent excessive fluctuations in the structures of populations. These mechanisms, therefore, also act to promote community stability.

DISPERSAL OF INDIVIDUAL ORGANISMS. The dispersal of organisms, which in most species occurs during a particular stage of each generation, tends to achieve uniformity of distribution of the individuals. Should any species, because of temporarily unfavorable conditions, be eliminated from a local stand, it is likely through the normal process of dispersal again to reach and to repopulate that community within a generation or two.

Through its powers of dispersal each kind of organism ultimately reaches every local habitat suitable for its existence unless prevented by a barrier of some kind. Most plants depend upon seeds or upon other types of disseminules for dispersal. Almost all species of animals, on the contrary, are able through the mobility of their individual members to spread out into unoccupied habitats. The mature individuals of most vertebrate species, however, have relatively fixed home ranges, and it is usually the young animals that disperse widely from their place of birth. By their individual dispersal movements mobile animals are able to avoid undue concentration in the locations that are most favorable for reproduction. Dispersal is, therefore, a regulatory mechanism which operates to maintain uniformity and stability in communities.

SEASONAL MIGRATION. Seasonal migration is another mechanism that tends to maintain stability in many communities. Many regions are inhospitable for certain of their member species during a part of the year. By migrating to another more favorable region these species often are able to survive the unfavorable season and are then in a position to return during the next favorable season. By their seasonal migratory habits many kinds of birds and mammals and a few other kinds of animals are thus able to maintain themselves as members of certain seasonal aspects of communities in which otherwise they could not exist.

Most insectivorous birds, for example, emigrate from the cold-temperate zone before the onset of the winter season, when few insects are available for food. These birds return in the spring when their insect food has again become abundant. Many aquatic and riparian birds that breed in cold climates also of necessity migrate to warmer regions when the water in their summer habitats becomes frozen. Those herbivorous mammals which perform local seasonal migrations between adjacent life belts are thereby able during part of the year to become members of communities in which they cannot permanently exist.

Seasonal migration is evidently not the same kind of community regulatory mechanism as is predation, parasitism, or disease, for the migratory movement does not itself control the numbers of any species. Nevertheless, migration does contribute to the stability of communities when similar aspects of successive years are compared. Furthermore, it operates to bring certain species into communities at the proper season for them to serve there as regulatory mechanisms. The migratory insectivorous birds, for example, serve as important regulatory mechanisms during summer in controlling the numbers of insects in many temperate and frigid communities.

DORMANCY. The ability of many kinds of organisms to survive for a time in a dormant condition likewise operates as a stabilizing mechanism for the community, allowing the species concerned to survive periods of unfavorable conditions. If these organisms did not have the ability to become dormant, many types of communities would become permanently altered in composition at each recurrent period of winter, drought, or other unfavorable state of the habitat.

The regulatory importance of dormancy is particularly evident in those species whose seeds, spores, or other disseminules are able to survive over a number of years of unfavorable conditions. Kummer (1945) has pointed out that weed seeds lying dormant in the soil are an important factor in the rapid regeneration of grassland that has been destroyed by drought or by overgrazing.

The seeds of certain species of plants are, in fact, able to germinate after they have lain buried in the soil for many years. Some of the more deeply buried seeds apparently do not germinate until, through erosion or the activities of animals or of man, they are brought again to the surface of the ground and placed in proper position for growth. Should any existing plant community be destroyed by fire, erosion, or other agency, the seeds buried in the soil form a reservoir capable of reconstituting in considerable part the community itself or one of its antecedent successional stages.

The number of seeds present in the surface soil of pasture land in the Province of Quebec, Canada, has been estimated by Dore and Raymond (1942) at nearly 20 million per acre, a number slightly more than the estimated density of living plants in this community. A thick growth of plants of numerous species has been described by Billington (1938) as springing up from the mud of an artificial southeastern Michigan lake bottom which was drained after the seeds had been imbedded in the mud for a period of 25 years.

The maximum period over which plant seeds may remain viable has been given considerable study. Most garden seeds will not germinate after a period of a few years because they quickly lose their viability. The seeds of certain kinds of weeds, however, have an extraordinary power for retaining the spark of life and of germinating after a long period of dormancy. In fully controlled experiments it has been shown by Becquerel (1907), Ewart (1908), H. T. Darlington (1931: 1941), and others that many kinds of seeds retain the ability to germinate after they have lain dormant, either in the soil or in a completely dry state, for over 25 years. The seeds of a number of species will germinate even when they are more than 80 years old, but these extraordinary seeds would have little significance for the regeneration of vegetation. The claims that seeds from the Egyptian tombs have proved capable of germination have proved to be false. All those seeds that are able to germinate when more than 50 years old have very impervious integuments.

Animals of many kinds also are able to survive unfavorable seasons or periods by becoming dormant. Species differ in the stage of the life history in which they are able to become dormant. In mammals of certain species, as for example, bears, ground squirrels, dormice, and jumping mice, the adults regularly spend the winter in a dormant condition. Among the insects, each species has a particular life-history stage in which the individuals usually become dormant. In certain species it is the adults that become dormant, in others it is the pupae, in still others it is the larvae or the eggs. The eggs of certain British mosquitoes when dry are able to remain viable for months and in some cases for years (Marshall, 1938: 19). It has been pointed out by Bates (1945: 25) that the ability of the eggs of certain kinds of mosquitoes to remain dormant enables those species to survive long periods of unfavorable conditions.

The exact stimulus that again initiates development in the egg or in any other dormant stage of an animal, after the unfavorable season has passed, varies among the species but is necessarily adjusted to the cycle of events that usually takes place in the ecosystem.

Adverse conditions of drought or of heat arising at seasons other than winter may induce dormancy in certain kinds of plants and animals. For example, the giant cactus (*Carnegiea gigantea*) and certain other kinds of cacti living on the Arizona desert allow the tips of their superficial roots to die during prolonged periods of drought. Whenever sufficient rain falls to wet the upper layers of the soil a new set of root tips is produced (Spalding, 1909: 61). Other desert plants shed their leaves during dry periods and grow a new set of leaves whenever a heavy rain falls.

Another good example of dormancy related to unfavorable conditions is afforded by certain ground squirrels which live in the Palusian and Artemisian biotic provinces of western North America. On the lower life belts of these provinces rain seldom falls in summer and the grass and herbs, therefore, dry up in the heat. To adjust themselves to these xeric conditions several species of ground squirrels become dormant in June or July and remain dormant all during the summer, fall, and winter, emerging only in February or March, when green vegetation again covers the ground (A. H. Howell, 1938: 6, 7, 12, 14).

Many of the bacteria, simpler plants, and lower invertebrates produce spores, cysts, or other resting stages which are able to survive adverse seasons. Many of these spores and cysts also serve as disseminules, which aid in the dispersal of the species concerned.

FOOD STORAGE. During seasons when food is not readily available many kinds of animals are able to survive on stores of food which they have laid away during a previous period of abundance. Both animals and plants also store food within their bodies as a reserve against times of scarcity. These devices for food storage have been described at more length in an earlier chapter. They are of importance to us here because the storage of food enables many organisms to survive in communities from which they otherwise would be excluded because of the occurrence there of unfavorable seasons.

WATER STORAGE. The storage of water is of particular importance for the survival of plants in situations where drought occasionally or frequently occurs. Many kinds of xeric plants store water in their tissues against a time of need. The cacti are outstanding examples of water-storing plants that can survive long periods of drought. The camel is one of the few animals which can store within its body a sufficient amount of water to last for several days. Most animals that are members of xeric communities, however, survive, not through the storage of water, but by devices and habits that reduce the amount of water loss. A few kinds of xeric animals have reduced their water requirements to such a low level that they can exist in large part on the metabolic water obtained from the oxidation of the food materials provided by air-dry seeds. Such adaptations for xeric conditions enable the species concerned to exist in ecosystems from which they otherwise would be eliminated at the first period of drought.

The various devices of plants and animals for dispersal, for seasonal migration, for dormancy, and for food and water storage, some of which have been mentioned above, enable many communities to survive unfavorable seasons or unfavorable years without undue alteration. These devices are all, therefore, important regulatory mechanisms serving to maintain community stability.

SERVICES OF ONE SPECIES TO ANOTHER. An important group of community regulatory mechanisms includes those services which members of the community render to their associated species, thereby aiding them to survive and to succeed. Some of these services have been described in Chapter XIII. In certain of these beneficial relationships 1 or both species concerned are aided. There are also beneficial relationships of a general sort between

the members of a community. These do not necessarily involve actual contact between the benefactors and the individuals that derive benefit, yet
many of these relationships promote stability in the community.

The woodchuck (*Marmota monax*) of eastern United States, for example, by digging burrows performs a service to several of its associates.
The burrows, when abandoned by the woodchuck, serve as homes or shelters
for the cottontail rabbit (*Sylvilagus*) and for a number of other species of
animals. Although the cottontail utilizes brush piles and other types of
shelter in addition to burrows, nevertheless its abundance in a given area
is in part dependent upon the number of woodchucks living there.

In certain cases of symbiosis both associated species profit by the relationship. The numbers of the 2 associated forms, therefore, will tend to increase and to decrease together. In doing so they will to that degree promote
the stability of the community of which they form a part. Any species which
obtains valuable services from one of its associates cannot afford to become
excessively abundant in relation to the species on which it is partially or
completely dependent because, should it do so, it would lose at least part of
the advantage derived from the symbiotic relationship.

Many additional examples could be given of ways in which a species,
through the services it renders, helps its associated species to thrive. As a
matter of fact, every species receives numerous services from its associates.
Without these services no species could long survive. Many of the ecologic
relations among the several members of a community, therefore, constitute
regulatory mechanisms which are important in maintaining community
stability.

BALANCE OF NATURE

The relationship of the population densities of the diverse species of organisms that make up an ecologic community is often spoken of as the balance
of nature. Of late years the concept of such a balance has been severely
criticized. It has been pointed out that the population density of each of the
several member species of a community may fluctuate more or less widely
from time to time and that the density of no species remains at a fixed value.
Certain ecologists have consequently attempted to deny altogether the existence of a balance of nature. In doing so they have misunderstood, in my
opinion, the meaning of the word "balance." The population densities of
every member species making up a community fluctuate from season to
season and from year to year. The fluctuations in the numbers of each
species, however, usually have fairly definite limits. There is nearly always
a more or less definite upper level of abundance beyond which each species
ceases to increase. Likewise, there is usually a lower limit of population
density; thus a species rarely becomes entirely extirpated from a community
except through the intervention of man.

Ecologic Equilibrium

The balance of nature consequently is a tendency toward an equilibrium, which, though often remaining reasonably close to a mean, is never static. It is a dynamic equilibrium (Lotka, 1925: 143; A. J. Nicholson, 1933; Gerard, 1942: 76). If a species at one time becomes exceptionally abundant, it will later decrease in abundance. All populations have their ups and downs. In spite of the violent oscillations that sometimes occur in the abundance of certain species or more rarely in the character of a whole community, these fluctuations under natural conditions are seldom so great that any species becomes completely eliminated or that the community remains permanently altered. In other words, each community tends to maintain a state of ecologic equilibrium among its various members. Most communities actually maintain a striking degree of stability (Elton, 1930, Chap. I).

The ecologic equilibrium of a community can never be a stable equilibrium (Uvarov, 1931: 161). A stable equilibrium, as the term is used in physics, implies a fixed location of the center of gravity to which a system tends to return. A community, on the contrary, does not have a fixed center of ecologic equilibrium to which the population densities of all the member species tend to return, but has a center which is constantly shifting in accordance with the frequent changes in the physical factors of the habitat and with the fluctuations in the population densities of the several associated species.

Changes in the physical factors of the habitat continually produce fluctuations directly or indirectly in the population densities of every member species of every community. Fluctuations in community composition are accordingly a normal feature of community equilibrium. The fluctuations in the population densities of a few species may be violent, but in other species they are of only slight magnitude. After every change in the composition of a community the numbers of each member species must become readjusted to the new conditions. In making these mutual adjustments there may be a greater or lesser number of oscillations in the population densities of all the associated species.

Although no fixed balance of nature can exist in any community, nevertheless, in all except the very simplest communities the fluctuations in population density to which every species is subject tend to be damped and to center around a more or less shifting intermediate position of dynamic equilibrium. The precise level of population density toward which a given species is moving at any given time is affected by the population densities of all its associated species, as well as by the constantly changing conditions of the physical habitat. The population densities of the several species of plants and animals that together compose a given community are so complexly interrelated that they can never have a fixed relationship to one another. Nevertheless, in order to continue to exist each community must constantly maintain a working ecologic equilibrium among the population densities of all its member species.

OPERATION OF THE COMMUNITY REGULATORY MECHANISMS. Every community, as has been stated, possesses numerous ecologic regulatory mechanisms, some of which act to produce mortality in certain species and thus to hold their numbers in check. Other regulatory mechanisms provide services that aid certain species to survive and to thrive in the community. Not every mortality factor or every service to a species, however, is necessarily a regulatory mechanism for the community. During a period of unfavorable physical conditions in the habitat, for instance, certain of the mortality factors operating against a given species may have a tendency to produce a severe alteration in the community.

The agencies that are most effective in causing a reduction in over-abundant populations differ from species to species, from time to time, and from place to place. Mac Lulich (1937: 125), for example, secured evidence that the epidemics which reduce the numbers of snowshoe hares are not always caused by the same disease at every time and place.

The precise agencies that lead a given species to increase its numbers to a high density and those agencies that later result in its reduction in abundance are as yet little known. The interrelations of the various controlling ecologic mechanisms have, in fact, never been fully ascertained for any species (Elton, 1942, Chap. IX). In the past there has been too much speculation and too few field studies have been carried on for a sufficient number of years to secure precise information about the regulatory mechanisms that control communities.

DENSITY-DEPENDENT AND DENSITY-INDEPENDENT CONTROLLING AGENCIES. The agencies that control populations may be divided into 2 important classes: (1) those that are dependent upon population density, and (2) those that are density independent (Howard and Fiske, 1911; H. S. Smith, 1935; Crombie, 1947: 45). The density-dependent agencies are believed to be the ones that principally determine the equilibrium density of each species. On the contrary, the density-independent agencies operating alone can never produce equilibrium. The density-dependent controlling agencies are mostly biotic in nature, while the density-independent agencies are mainly climatic. But climate also may sometimes act indirectly as a density-dependent agency through the preservation of those individuals that occupy favorable situations, while those individuals forced to live outside these favorable situations are destroyed (H. S. Smith, 1935).

As an example of a density-dependent mortality agency intraspecific competition may be cited. When the population of a given species is at a low density, competition among the individual members of that species will be at a minimum and will have little or no controlling effect on their survival. On the other hand, when population density is high, competition among the individuals also will be high and may result in considerable mortality. A density-dependent mortality agency, therefore, promotes stability of population density by operating to produce heavy mortality when the population density is high and by relaxing this control when the population density is low.

On the contrary, the density-independent agencies produce mortality largely irrespective of the degree of crowding of the population and so do not tend to promote community stability. Examples of density-independent agencies are such climatic factors as severely high or low temperatures, high winds, heavy precipitation, frost, ice, and snow.

The most effective regulatory mechanisms in a community are those density-dependent mortality-producing agencies that reduce the numbers of a given species when it is too abundant and that lessen the mortality pressure against the species when its numbers are low, thus allowing it to survive. Predation, parasitism, disease, competition, and similar mechanisms are usually density dependent. They bear most heavily on those species that are most abundant in a particular community, while they take a proportionately lesser toll of those species whose numbers are few. These mechanisms, therefore, operate to prevent violent oscillations in the population densities of the several species that make up a community. By their damping effect on the swings of population abundance these density-dependent regulatory mechanisms tend to maintain community stability.

In order to compare the operation of the 2 contrasting kinds of regulatory mechanisms the community living in England in the flower heads of the black knapweed (*Centaurea nemoralis*) may be used as an example. An important member of this community is the knapweed gallfly (*Urophora jaceana*). The population density of this gallfly is controlled by the density-dependent attacks of several chalcid parasites. These attacks tend to maintain stability in the community. On the contrary, such a density-independent mortality agency as summer flooding operates to reduce the numbers both of the gallfly and of its parasites. Consequently, these density-independent controlling agencies do not promote stability in this community (Varley, 1947).

COMPLEXITY OF THE ECOLOGIC REGULATORY MECHANISMS. The relationships within a community among its several member species are always extremely complex. The complexity of the interrelation of the numerous species of organisms that make up even the simpler communities will be evident when the possible regulatory mechanisms that may control the numbers of a single species are considered. The numbers of the cottontail rabbit, for example, may be controlled by numerous kinds of predators, parasites, and diseases, by competition for food with other herbivores, by competition with other species for burrows which provide protection in severe weather, by intraspecific competition for food and territories, by services received from its associates, and perhaps by other mechanisms.

Every species has numerous ecologic relationships with the other members of its community. The interrelations within each community among the several associated species of green plants, herbivores, predators, parasites, scavengers, saprophytes, competitors, commensals, and other types of associates are, in fact, so numerous that it is impractical even to list all of them. The usual diagram of a food chain or food pyramid is of necessity greatly oversimplified.

Certain of the regulatory mechanisms in a community may at times oppose one another. A predator that feeds on a herbivore, for instance, diminishes the control by the herbivore of the population densities of those plants on which the herbivore feeds. Likewise, a secondary parasite diminishes the control exercised by a primary parasite on its host species. Mechanisms that operate to reduce the number of individuals of a given species may oppose those mechanisms which operate through services received by the species to increase its rate of survival.

Advantages of Regulation

The regulatory mechanisms that control each community afford either direct or indirect benefit to every member species, including those species whose numbers are kept down. If all the seeds that fall on a given plot of ground should survive, for example, none of the resulting plants could possibly be very thrifty. Because of the consequent crowding it is very likely that none of them would ever be able to reach the fruiting stage. It is to the best interests of each species of seed-bearing plant, therefore, that most of its seedlings should perish so that a few may ultimately reach maturity and produce seeds.

Animal species also profit by having their numbers controlled. Predation, parasitism, disease, and other ecologic regulatory mechanisms are often of advantage to the species preyed upon. If not held in check by predators and by other regulatory agencies, every kind of animal tends to become so abundant that its food supply is exhausted, its habitat is destroyed, and most of its individuals must then emigrate or miserably starve. Even the numbers of the larger carnivores are held in check to at least some degree by parasites and diseases. Agencies, such as certain parasites, that weaken an individual without preventing its reproduction are, of course, harmful to the individual animal without being of any advantage to the species. On the other hand, a certain amount of predation or lethal parasitism may actually be an advantage to a herbivorous species by preventing it from becoming too abundant for its own welfare.

Any species that overutilizes its resources of food, space, shelter, or other necessities for life ultimately harms itself. When there is severe competition for any life essential between the individuals of a species, many or perhaps all of them may be stunted and may fail to develop to maturity. Northern pike (*Esox lucius*) that are reared in overcrowded ponds, for example, may remain dwarfed in size, even though food is present in abundance (Carbine, 1945). The elimination of surplus individuals, therefore, benefits the species which is controlled by giving the surviving individuals a better chance to reach maturity and to perpetuate the stock.

Regulatory mechanisms are of obvious advantage to the community, enabling it to survive without serious harm the seasonal changes and greater variations that are constantly occurring in the characters of its physical habitat and in the composition of the community itself. The rate of multiplication of each species of plant and of animal tends to lead it to become excessively abundant in relation to the numbers of its associates. If these tendencies were not controlled, the organization of every community would constantly be disturbed and violent fluctuations in its composition would be produced. Regulatory mechanisms tend to reduce the oscillations in community composition that otherwise would result from the constant tendency of every species to become overabundant in relation to the resources of its habitat.

If there were no predators, no parasites, and no infectious diseases, it is theoretically possible that each herbivorous species might in time, through natural selection, reduce its rate of multiplication to a point at which only the number of offspring would be produced that could live comfortably in that one special type of community. Likewise, in the absence of herbivores or diseases it might be possible for each kind of green plant to reduce its rate of multiplication to a level which in a particular community would just compensate for deaths and which would permit the survival of the individuals produced without any competition with their associates for light, soil moisture, space, or other essentials for life.

Actually, such a reduction in its rate of reproduction would be extremely dangerous to any species because of the possibility that a natural catastrophe, such as a series of drought years, might wipe out the form entirely. Furthermore, it is evident that a given species could make such an adjustment in its rate of reproduction for only a single type of community. In any other kind of community its rate of reproduction would be either too high or too low.

The tendency for every species to produce a surplus of offspring is essential for the survival of the species during periods of adverse conditions. Overproduction by each species also is important to the community in order that the ecologic equilibrium may quickly be restored after a period of scarcity of any form. For example, if the numbers of an important herbivore have been greatly reduced in a particular community, that community will be more or less out of balance until the numbers of the herbivore have again been restored. This will be particularly true if the herbivorous species has been completely extirpated in certain stands of the community. Should the herbivore have a low rate of reproduction it may take a long time to restore the balance of the community. Errington (1943: 900), for instance, has pointed out that seasonal and periodic drought frequently causes a high muskrat mortality in the prairie marshes of the upper Mississippi Valley and that a high rate of reproduction is desirable for the species in order quickly to fill the resulting gaps in the population. All organisms must, therefore, from the point of view of the welfare both of their own species and of the community, have rates of reproduction considerably in excess of the numbers of individuals of each generation that can survive.

RESULTS OF FAILURE OF CONTROL. Sometimes the natural regulatory mechanisms fail to prevent too great an increase in the population density of a certain species, with a resulting disaster to the species and to the community. On Isle Royale in Lake Superior, for example, moose (*Alces americana*) were very scarce or perhaps entirely absent when the island was examined in 1905. About 1913 the species began to increase on the island or it may have immigrated across the ice from the near-by Canadian shore. No wolves or other predators large enough to attack a moose successfully lived on the island, and hunting by man was prohibited. Food was abundant and the herd increased rapidly in numbers. By 1930 the available moose food on the island had almost all been eaten or destroyed and during the subsequent winters many of the animals starved (Adolph Murie, 1934).

Another example of overpopulation is the great increase in the number of mule deer on the Kaibab Plateau, just north of the Grand Canyon in Arizona. There during the early part of the twentieth century many of the cougars which are the natural deer predators were removed by man, with the result that the population density of the deer greatly increased. Ultimately most of their food was consumed, the habitat deteriorated, and the deer herd suffered disastrous starvation (Rasmussen, 1941: 269).

During periods of particularly favorable weather or for various reasons, 1 or more species may increase greatly in a community in spite of the operation of its usual regulatory mechanisms. If the unusually abundant species is a green plant, it may increase its control over the sunlight falling on the rest of the community. It may, moreover, by competing with other plants cause certain associated species to decrease seriously in abundance. In a community that is of direct importance to man such an increase in the abundance of a particular kind of plant may sometimes reach a level at which that species constitutes a pest.

In natural communities plant pests are always ultimately brought under control by natural agencies. One of the controlling agencies may be competition with other plants for light, for soil moisture, or for space. Bacteria, viruses, or animals may also serve as controls. The prickly-pear cactus (*Opuntia* spp.), for example, spread during the drought period of the 1930's over a great part of the Great Plains of middle North America, where it became a serious pest, tending to replace the native grasses. During the abnormally wet years of 1940-42, however, the cactus was so successfully attacked by a number of species of native insects that it rapidly deteriorated and eventually disappeared completely from many areas (Timmons, 1941-42).

An animal species that becomes so exceptionally abundant as to interfere with the activities of man constitutes a plague. Plagues of grasshoppers
and of other insects, for example, often occur in restricted localities. Many
kinds of rats, mice, lemmings, ground squirrels, and other rodents also
occasionally increase locally to plague abundance. A plague is particularly
likely to be caused by the introduction of a foreign species because no natural regulatory mechanisms may exist in the community to keep this alien
form under control.

Any species that expands its numbers to a high density may cause severe
disorganization of its community and widespread destruction of its habitat.
At the time of plague abundance, furthermore, the animals of the species
concerned spread out from the communities in which they have been produced and disrupt also the adjacent communities.

The most severe plague of any kind of animal, however, will eventually
be brought under control through the operation of ecologic regulatory
mechanisms. The predators that prey upon the plague species will, of course,
have an abundant supply of food and they will consequently multiply
rapidly. Many predators living in the surrounding areas also will flock to the
stricken locality. Parasites and contagious diseases will flourish under the
crowded conditions. The reduction in the food supply (including possibly
necessary vitamins and other accessory food elements) caused by the overpopulation of the habitat, the lack of shelter from predators due to overcrowding, the deterioration of the plant cover, the reduction of breeding
rate due to lack of food and to the crowded conditions, the poisoning due
to the accumulation of animal wastes or to the eating of food that during
times of food abundance would be avoided, and the fighting between the
individual members of the species because of the overcrowding may all be
important regulatory mechanisms increasing the rate of mortality and leading to a reduction in its numbers. The actual causes of death for the individual animals may include starvation, exhaustion, predation, shock disease
(Green, Larson, and Bell, 1939), accidents, and infections. In time, therefore, the plague will be abated and the plague species will likely be reduced
considerably below its usual level of abundance.

Fluctuations in Population Densities

No sharp distinction can be made between the normal fluctuations in numbers that every species exhibits from year to year and those more violent
increases in population density that occur only rarely. The main difference
seems to be that the fluctuations in the numbers of the several species that
make up a community usually are controlled by regulatory mechanisms
other than starvation. When for any reason these usual regulatory mechanisms lose control of a particular species, then that species may increase to
a density at which it harms not only its associates but also itself. Eventually,
after it has exhausted its food supply, the species will be brought back under

control by starvation. Meanwhile, however, during its period of excessive abundance it may have severely damaged its habitat and adversely affected many of its associated species. It is of advantage, therefore, for every community to contain regulatory mechanisms that will be adequate to control any emergency. Every community undoubtedly has a tendency to evolve such mechanisms.

Actual outbreaks, where a species of plant or animal increases so rapidly that its usual regulatory mechanisms fail to control it and severe alteration to the community results, occur only rarely, as S. A. Graham (1939: 67) has emphasized. The existence over large areas of the earth of forests in which the trees are hundreds of years old proves that in those communities destructive outbreaks of injurious insects or other organisms must occur very infrequently, even though many species potentially injurious to the trees are present.

Not all fluctuations in animal and plant abundance, however, are great in amplitude. Numerous species, in fact, exhibit hardly any variation in numbers from year to year. Between these very stable forms and those that pass through great fluctuations in abundance are many species that exhibit only slight to moderate variations. Probably most species fall into this intermediate group, but there are inadequate data on the fluctuations of the populations of most kinds of plants and of animals, and no positive statement can be made. It may be assumed that the regulatory mechanisms which control the populations of those species that show only small fluctuations are more efficient than those of the species that exhibit violent oscillations.

CYCLES OF ABUNDANCE. The fluctuations from year to year in the numbers of certain kinds of animals, and perhaps of certain plants, seem to follow a more or less regular cyclical pattern (Chaps. VI, VIII, IX). The snowshoe hare of northern North America, for instance, is said to have a cycle of abundance from peak to peak averaging about 9.6 years (Elton and Nicholson, 1942b). It should be emphasized that the number of years from peak to peak of the snowshoe-hare cycle is decidedly variable. Some cycles are much shorter and others much longer than the mean of 9.6 years.

Such a cycle of abundance of 1 species of course affects, directly or indirectly, all the other species in its community. At the peak of numbers in a snowshoe-hare cycle, for example, the plants utilized as food will be severely pruned back and many of them will be killed. Predators also will increase in numbers, both by an increased rate of breeding in the area and by immigration. Parasites will become numerous. When the hares suddenly become reduced in abundance, the predators must turn their attention to other prey. If other prey is scarce, as usually is the case, many of the predators must starve. It is probably mostly for this reason that the Canada lynx has a cycle of abundance which averages 9.6 years from peak to peak, the same as its principal prey species (Elton and Nicholson, 1942b). The Indians, who utilize the hares for food, will also be on short rations during the time when hares are scarce. When the cycle of numbers is at its lowest ebb, the vegetation can begin to improve. With food once more available and with predators and parasites reduced to a low point, the snowshoe hare, which has a fairly high rate of multiplication, begins to increase, and the cycle repeats itself.

The snowshoe-hare cycle seems to be controlled chiefly by the operation of biotic factors rather than by any known rhythm in the physical factors of the habitat. Likewise, many of the fluctuations in the population densities of other species that occur in natural communities seem to be only in part produced by changes in the physical factors of the habitat. Even in a completely changeless physical environment it is probable that fluctuations in community composition will constantly occur.

This does not in any way minimize the role of physical factors in initiating changes in community composition. At least in some of the simpler communities, fluctuations in the physical factors of the habitat are known to produce direct changes of considerable magnitude in the numbers of certain species of organisms. Cycles of wet and dry or of warm and cold years may thus produce cyclic changes in many communities, as has been discussed in an earlier chapter. Fluctuations in the physical factors of the habitat, however, are evidently not the sole cause of community changes. In many communities the ecologic regulatory mechanisms may, in fact, be able to compensate for considerable fluctuation in the physical factors and thus to reduce the amplitude of the oscillations in the community.

ECOLOGIC DOMINANCE. An ecologic dominant is a species that to a considerable extent controls the conditions for existence of its associates within a particular ecosystem (Shelford and Towler, 1925: 33, footnote). In certain situations ecologic dominance is due to numbers, as is true of grasses in a prairie, and in other situations to the size or height of the individuals, as is true of trees in a forest (Cooper, 1941: 6). Foresters commonly employ the term "dominance" in a more restricted sense to mean shade dominance. Care should be taken also not to confuse ecologic dominance with social dominance, an entirely different concept which is discussed in a previous chapter.

The relative ecologic dominance of the several species of trees making up a forest can usually be ascertained without great difficulty. In many types of communities, on the contrary, it is no easy matter to determine which kinds of plants are dominant. The dominance relations of the animals are in most communities especially difficult to ascertain (Vestal, 1914: 424). Animals are probably never ecologic dominants in terrestrial communities, though they may be dominant in certain marine ecosystems (Clements and Shelford, 1939: 240). Because of their complex ecologic interrelations, numerous species of plants and animals contribute to the control of most communities.

EQUILIBRIUM MOST STABLE IN COMPLEX COMMUNITIES. In the more complex communities there will usually be found a considerable number of diverse kinds of food plants. Here also there will be a variety of herbivores, carnivores, parasites, and diseases, many of which operate as density-dependent regulatory mechanisms. In such a complex community an increase in the numbers of any one species should not greatly affect the constitution of the community. Any species which exhibits a tendency to expand unduly will probably soon be brought under control by the numerous regulatory agencies at hand.

On the other hand, a simple community made up of only a few important kinds of food plants, herbivores, and predators should theoretically be much more subject to violent fluctuations in numbers. In the most simple communities, where the control of the population densities of the several member species may be largely exercised by the physical factors of the habitat, the oscillations in population densities are likely to be extreme.

In the more complex communities, therefore, where density-dependent ecologic controlling mechanisms of many kinds are present, the greatest amount of stability should theoretically be achieved. No one of the member species of a climax forest, for example, is ever likely to be allowed to increase to the point where the forest would be destroyed (Beeson, 1944: 48). There are, however, few data about ecologic equilibrium in natural communities, and deductions must accordingly be largely tentative.

Minimum Size of Area for Community Organization. Associations that are discontinuous in their distribution often occur in stands that are individually too small to include all the species that are characteristic of the association. Animals, such as the cougar and wolf, that have individual ranges covering many square miles will probably not remain in an otherwise suitable habitat which covers only a few acres. A species usually cannot continue to live in a community which is smaller than the home range of a single individual (Aldo Leopold, 1939: 85). A unit of range of such small size would certainly be a minimum, and it may be doubted that any species would long persist in so restricted an area.

It may be assumed, therefore, that very small stands will often lack certain of the regulatory mechanisms which commonly are present in larger stands of the same type of association. Very small stands accordingly may be assumed to be less stable than larger stands. Again I must confess, however, that precise information on this point is largely lacking.

Ecologic Functions of Member Species

In treating of the ecologic position of a given species in a community it is not sufficient to consider only the life requirements of this one particular species. The food and other services that this species supplies to the associated members of its community must be considered also. Life in a community involves giving as well as taking. A herbivore is not only an eater of plants, but his body may furnish the food needed by a carnivore, and he may be host to various parasites. The burrow that a rodent makes for his own use may also furnish shelter to numerous other kinds of animals.

Any service that 1 species of plant or animal renders to an associate may from the standpoint of community organization be considered an ecologic function. Thus, the green plants, which are the ultimate source of food for almost all the other organisms, perform an important food function in the community. The herbivorous animals in their turn perform the ecologic functions of controlling the abundance of their food plants and of providing food for carnivores. The light-tolerant plants perform the ecologic functions of providing shade and shelter and often breeding places for many kinds of animals and for shade-loving plants. An important function in community regulation is performed by parasites and predators through their destruction of surplus individuals of their host and prey species. Many kinds of insects perform the ecologic function of pollinating the flowers of particular kinds of plants. The ecologic function of soil enrichment is performed by practically all terrestrial organisms.

Each species performs various services for its associates and, therefore, simultaneously performs a number of diverse kinds of ecologic functions in the community. The number of ecologic functions performed by the several members of a community is so great that any attempt at their exact classification seems at the present time to be impracticable. It should, however, be emphasized that the recognition of any ecologic function implies the viewpoint of community organization.

MATHEMATICAL EXPRESSION OF COMMUNITY INTERRELATIONS

Mathematical calculations of the theoretical interrelations of 2 or more associated species have been made by a number of biometricians. Among some of the more noted of these studies are those by Thompson (1922-31), Volterra (1928), Lotka (1925), A. J. Nicholson (1933), Gause (1934a), and Nicholson and Bailey (1935). These calculations consider the numerical relations between 2 or more species that compete for the same food, between a predator and a prey species, between a parasite and its host, and between various other possible combinations of species. Under certain conditions one species may thrive at the expense of the other, leading to the decrease or the complete elimination of the one form. Under certain other conditions there may be oscillations of greater or lesser amplitude in the numbers of both the associated species.

Actual data on the numerical relations of species that form a natural ecologic community are largely lacking. Such data as are available are difficult to organize because of their enormous complexity. Because mathematical ecology is as yet an undeveloped field, it is necessary to consider chiefly the relationships between 2 associated species rather than to attempt an analysis of the tremendously complicated interrelations of all the species that compose a natural community. Furthermore, it is almost always necessary to conduct the studies in the laboratory, where the conditions affecting each experiment can be carefully controlled. It is impossible here to give a summary of these studies, and accordingly attention will be called only to several of the more outstanding lines of investigation.

DYNAMICS OF LABORATORY POPULATIONS. The laboratory study of tiny artificial populations of certain beetles and other arthropods kept in a small measured quantity of flour or grain has yielded valuable information about population dynamics to R. N. Chapman (1928), T. Park (1941), Crombie (1944), and numerous others. A summary of the earlier work on the population dynamics of flour insects is given by Ford (1937). The relations between the numbers of 2 or more species of protozoa, yeasts, bacteria, and like organisms kept within the confines of a test tube or similar small glass container have likewise been investigated by Gause (1934a, 1935a, etc.) and others. All these intensive studies of strictly limited laboratory populations have had the common aim of determining the quantitative relations of the several organisms that are associated to form a miniature community.

COMPETITION BETWEEN TWO SPECIES. In a laboratory population consisting solely of 2 species that are directly competing for food or for any other element essential for life, one species in time completely eliminates the other. This has been demonstrated by numerous studies (Gause, 1934a: 113, 1934b; Park, Gregg, and Lutherman, 1941; Crombie, 1945; T. Park, 1948). Many factors combine to determine which of the 2 competing species will succeed in eliminating its rival. Among these controlling factors may be mentioned the relative rates of reproduction of the 2 forms, the original sizes of the 2 populations, the relative ability of the 2 forms to tolerate unfavorable conditions, and the degree to which each form inhibits its own increase compared to the degree to which it inhibits the increase of its rival.

Direct competition between 2 species, however, is seldom the only factor involved in this relationship. One of the associated species, for example, may give off some secretion which in high concentration is deleterious to the other. Thus, in the competition between 2 species of yeasts the tolerance of each species for a given concentration of alcohol in relation to the amount of alcohol produced by each of the forms becomes of the greatest importance in determining which form shall succeed the better (Gause, 1934a: 89).

When 2 species of grain or flour beetles are kept together in a small laboratory container, the total population density may affect the fecundity of 1 or both forms, even though food is present in abundance. Fecundity is affected also by the accumulation of waste products in the habitat ("conditioned medium"). One species of beetle, furthermore, may prey upon the eggs or larvae of the associated form in addition to competing with it for the normal flour or grain food (Crombie, 1944). Any 2 associated species, therefore, may affect each other in numerous ways.

Two species that utilize the same food only in part and accordingly occupy somewhat different niches in the community may be able to exist together and to form a stable population. This was demonstrated by Gause (1935a, 1935c) in an artificial community composed of the 2 related protozoa, *Paramecium caudatum* (or *P. aurelia*) and *P. bursaria,* together with 2 food species, a bacterium and a yeast. In this community *Paramecium caudatum* consumed more effectively the bacterial components suspended in the upper layer of the liquid, while *Paramecium bursaria* preferred the yeast cells sedimenting on the bottom of the container.

PREDATOR-PREY RELATIONS. When a prey species is exposed to a predatory species without the possibility of escape, the predator tends to multiply until it has utilized all the prey. The prey species is thereby eliminated from the situation. The predators, now left without food, will subsequently all die. Under these conditions, therefore, both the predator and its prey species are eliminated. On the other hand, if there are places of refuge in which a certain number of the prey species can escape the predator, a different result is obtained. The predator increases in abundance until all the readily available prey are consumed, following which the predators all die. A few of the prey are preserved, however, in the places of refuge. With all the predators removed, the prey species will now multiply rapidly and will occupy the whole accessible area, so that the resulting population is made up only of the prey species (Gause, 1934a).

Should a few of the predators be able to survive in spite of the elimination of most of their prey, the predators will multiply as soon as their prey again becomes abundant. There will theoretically be set up then a series of oscillations in the populations of both prey and predators, with the prey species becoming first abundant and then scarce slightly in advance of the increases and decreases in the abundance of the predator. Such oscillations are postulated in the "classical" mathematical formulae by Volterra and by Lotka. This "classical" type of periodic fluctuations in the populations of a predator and its prey species, however, seems rarely or never to be realized in the laboratory (Gause, 1935b).

The violent oscillations of abundance of a predator and its prey species often encountered in laboratory experiments are called by Gause (1934a: 131) "relaxation oscillations." Under laboratory conditions the prey species usually is eliminated during the first oscillation, with the consequent starvation of all the predators, so that no further fluctuation can occur. If the prey and the predator, however, are allowed at intervals to immigrate into the experimental community they can both be periodically maintained there. As a result of such immigration and subsequent multiplication, violent oscillations in the numbers of both species occur.

Mathematical formulae to describe the relaxation fluctuations have been presented by Gause and Witt (1934, 1935). These authors stated that the formulae are in complete accord with the data obtained from their experiments on protozoa in which *Paramecium caudatum* served as prey and *Didinium nasutum* as the predator.

In those species in which the larger individuals prey upon the eggs or young of their own species, fluctuations in the populations somewhat similar to those which occur in attacks of a predator species on its prey may be produced. Thus, in a laboratory population of the fish *Lebistes,* in which the adults are predatory on their young, oscillations were produced, but the studies were not continued long enough to ascertain their type (Shoemaker, 1947).

PARASITE-HOST RELATIONS. The dynamic relations between the population of a parasite and that of its host can also be subjected to laboratory study. DeBach and Smith (1941, 1947) exposed a known number of the pupae of the common housefly (*Musca domestica*) to attack by a known number of its pupal parasite, *Mormoniella vitripennis.* As a result of the parasitic relations between these 2 forms, oscillations were set up in the 2 populations which up to the seventh generation tended to follow those expected from the theoretical calculations of Nicholson and Bailey (1935). Additional studies are needed for a clear understanding of these host-parasite relations.

DIFFICULTIES IN MATHEMATICAL EXPRESSION OF COMMUNITY DYNAMICS. The mathematical treatments of community dynamics presented up to the present time have in the opinion of Thompson (1939) all been based on untenable assumptions. It has usually been assumed in the computations that the finding of the prey is completely at random. This is certainly not true in nature. Likewise, the building up and averaging of the factors operating from place to place and from moment to moment are impossible because the data are heterogeneous. Furthermore, the methods of the infinitesimal calculus are not suitable for studying changes in real populations. These mathematical calculations, therefore, are valuable adjuncts to research but are in no way a substitute for investigations in the laboratory or in nature.

Even in a carefully controlled laboratory community consisting of only 2 species, the relationships between the 2 populations may be extremely complex. The statement of these relations in mathematical terms accordingly must also be complicated. Far too little is known as yet about the quantitative relations of even the simplest association between 2 species to permit them to be satisfactorily expressed in figures or in mathematical symbols of any kind. Not even a beginning can now be made toward stating in mathematical terms the tremendously complex interrelations within any natural community. Decades or perhaps centuries of experimentation and analysis will be required to elucidate the ecologic laws involved. Biologists who have received exceptional training both in mathematics and in ecology may be expected to make important contributions in this field (Sweetman, 1936: 26).

ADJUSTMENT OF THE COMMUNITY TO ITS AVAILABLE RESOURCES

The existence of any community at a given place is obviously dependent upon the resources of its habitat. These resources include, among others, solar energy, chemicals that are capable of being synthesized into plant food, and all the other materials and conditions essential for the life of organisms. The resources of every habitat, however, have definite limitations, and no community can consume its resources faster than they are produced without ultimate disaster. Overutilization of any particular natural resource is likely to result in the abrupt local extirpation or great reduction in the numbers of 1 or more species, followed later perhaps by a rapid multiplication, and this again by a sudden collapse.

It may be assumed that the most efficient utilization of the resources of any given habitat is obtained when the community occupying the habitat is well organized and regulated so that no very violent fluctuations in the populations of the member species are produced, even by considerable variations in the weather or in the other physical conditions of the habitat. The well-regulated community may consequently be assumed to be the most efficient one. Many communities, however, are too temporary to become well organized before they are followed in succession by some other type of community. In those natural types of community that endure over a long period of time, however, it may be presumed that there is in general a fairly efficient organization and that the available resources are being utilized to a reasonably satisfactory extent.

SELECTED REFERENCES

Crombie, A. C. 1945. On competition between different species of graminivorous insects. Proc. Roy. Soc. London, Ser. B, 132: 362-95.

Elton, Charles. 1930. Animal ecology and evolution. Oxford: Clarendon Press. Chap. 1.

Gause, G. F. 1934a. The struggle for existence. Baltimore: Williams and Wilkins Co.

Lotka, Alfred J. 1925. Elements of physical biology. Baltimore: Williams and Wilkins Co. Chaps. 13 and 14.

Sweetman, Harvey L. 1936. The biological control of insects; with a chapter on weed control. Ithaca, New York: Comstock Publ. Co.

XV

EFFECTS OF COMMUNITIES ON THEIR PHYSICAL HABITATS

Every community modifies more or less extensively the physical conditions of its habitat. These modifications of the physical habitat, of course, react in their turn on the community. Certain types of communities are able to modify their physical habitats only slightly, with the result that the raw physical factors of their environments may very largely control the characters of such communities. Many other types of communities, however, are able to modify the physical characters of their habitats to a considerable extent, and consequently these communities themselves are able, at least in part, to control their own environments. The physical conditions in terrestrial habitats are so different from those of aquatic habitats that these 2 types of conditions will here be treated separately.

EFFECTS OF TERRESTRIAL COMMUNITIES ON THEIR HABITATS

The effects of terrestrial communities on their habitats are numerous and varied. Plants modify the local climate in their vicinity. Both plants and animals aid in soil formation and both also may aid in the decrease of erosion. Through the activities of animals large rocks become buried in the soil. On the debit side of the ledger it must be pointed out that large animals through trampling sometimes compact wet clayey soils. Animal activities may also in certain situations initiate soil erosion.

Control of Local Climate

EFFECTS OF PLANTS ON LOCAL CLIMATE. In the shade cast by plants the intensity of the sunlight is reduced. Certain kinds of plants produce relatively little shade, while others, notably the larger broadleaf trees, allow very little sunlight to reach the surface of the ground beneath them. Under very heavy forest the amount of solar energy reaching the ground may be as little as 1 per cent of that in the open (Kittredge, 1948: 51). In passing through green leaves the sunlight is given a greenish hue.

By reducing the amount of solar energy reaching the ground, plants retard and reduce the diurnal rise of temperature characteristic of exposed habitats. The evaporation of water from green vegetation also reduces the temperature in the habitat. Plants likewise act as a partial barrier to the radiation of heat from the ground surface and thus they reduce the amount of cooling to which exposed habitats are subject at night. Under heavy plant cover the air temperature, therefore, remains cooler in the daytime and warmer at night than in the open (Kittredge, 1948: 61). The protective effect of the plant cover may prevent the occurrence of a killing frost at a time when sensitive vegetation not so protected may be badly damaged.

Plants sometimes induce a small amount of precipitation from moisture-laden air. Along the coast of California, for example, there is almost no rainfall during the summer, but fogs are frequent. During these fogs a considerable amount of water may drip from the bushes and trees, sufficient to be important for the vegetation (Kittredge, 1948: 115-19).

Plant stems and plant leaves interfere with the normal movement of the wind, and the wind velocity consequently is reduced within growths of vegetation. In thick growths of plants the reduction in wind velocity may be very considerable, so much so that when strong winds are blowing in the open there may be only slight air movements in the shelter of thickets or forests. The rate of wind movement in forest usually averages only 1 to 2 miles per hour (Kittredge, 1948: 71).

Air humidity in the vicinity of growing plants is often higher than in bare habitats because of the evaporation of moisture. At times, however, the relative humidity may be lower inside a forest than in the open. Under a dense growth of vegetation moist air persists because the wind movement is only slight. As a result of decreased light intensity, reduced daytime temperatures, increased air humidity, and lowered rate of wind movement under dense vegetation, the rate of evaporation from smaller plants and from the soil surface is low (Kittredge, 1948: 72-79, 156).

The effectiveness of plants in controlling the local climate varies both with the denseness of the vegetation and with the seasonal changes that take place in the plants themselves. Seasonal changes occur in almost all plants, but these seasonal variations are least conspicuous in those species that are evergreen. Deciduous trees and shrubs, many perennial herbs, and all annuals vary greatly with the season in their effect on the local climate.

EFFECTS OF ANIMALS ON LOCAL CLIMATE. Animals have only a slight effect on the local climate compared to that exercised by plants. Within the burrows made by certain animals the sunlight is reduced, there is protection from the wind and from rain or snow, the air humidity is greater than in open situations, and the evaporation rate is lower. The nests constructed by some kinds of animals also modify the local climate in varying degrees. If an animal, especially a warm-blooded bird or mammal, is occupying a burrow or nest, the heat of its body increases somewhat the temperature of its immediate surroundings. Parasites that live on or within the bodies of animals benefit greatly by the local climate produced by a warm-blooded animal.

Effects on the Composition of the Atmosphere

In the process of metabolism animals and also all kinds of plants constantly absorb oxygen and give off carbon dioxide. Every terrestrial community consequently depletes the O_2 of the atmosphere in its vicinity and increases the concentration of CO_2. This process, however, is counterbalanced by the activities of green plants. When exposed to sunlight, green plants absorb CO_2 and give off free O_2. The activities of green plants consequently tend to prevent the supply of O_2 in the atmosphere from becoming depleted. The concentration of CO_2 in the atmosphere is controlled in part by geologic processes as well as by plant and animal metabolism. Volcanoes and fires return CO_2 to the atmosphere. Carbonate rocks in their decomposition also release this gas. The ocean, on the other hand, absorbs CO_2 from the atmosphere. It is perhaps the capacity of the ocean to absorb CO_2 that exercises the major control of the concentration of this gas in the atmosphere rather than the activities of organisms (Daubenmire, 1947: 258-59).

Depletion by Plants of Soil Moisture and of Soil Minerals

In their process of living the roots of terrestrial plants absorb moisture and dissolved minerals from the soil. This absorbed water is evaporated from the above-ground parts of the plants. The result is that the amount of moisture in the soil is reduced. The lowered rate of evaporation from the soil surface resulting from the presence of the vegetational cover compensates to some extent for this effect.

The minerals removed from the soil through absorption of the soil solution by the roots of plants accumulate in the tissues of the plants. These minerals may in turn accumulate in the tissues of those animals which eat the plants. The loss from the soil is mostly temporary because the minerals are returned to the soil when the organisms concerned die and decay. Those plants, such as the clovers, that support nitrifying bacteria on their roots actually enrich the soil by fixing nitrogen taken from the air.

In the process of metabolism the roots of plants absorb oxygen and give off carbon dioxide. Subterranean animals also use up O_2 and liberate CO_2. The result is that the supply of oxygen in the soil becomes depleted whereas the concentration of CO_2 is increased. Root growth in most plants is stopped when the O_2 concentration in the pore spaces of the soil drops to 3 per cent. Concentrations of CO_2 of about 1.0 per cent are also likely to be lethal for plants (Daubenmire, 1947: 263-77).

Special Effects of Animal Activities

BURYING OF LARGE ROCKS. The activities of burrowing animals often result in the burying of large rocks, logs, and other similar materials. This result is caused by the habit of many kinds of animals, particularly rodents and ants, of excavating tunnels and nest cavities under large objects. In making their burrows under rocks or other objects these animals remove a certain amount of earth, which is deposited elsewhere. In time, therefore, objects under which the burrows are excavated sink into the ground. Grinnell (1923: 145) cited an observation by Joseph Dixon that a certain large rock on his ranch in California settled 6 inches in a period of 10 years.

In regions where the ground freezes at times in winter certain of the rocks, especially those of small and medium size, tend to "heave" out of the ground. In such climates, therefore, the tendency for rocks of a certain size to sink into the ground because of the burrowing activities of animals may be counteracted by the heaving of the rocks due to frost action.

COMPACTING OF SOIL BY TRAMPLING. The trampling of wet, clayey soils by large mammals unfortunately compacts the clay and interferes with the penetration of water and of air. Thus the soil may become unsuitable for the growth of plants. An area denuded of vegetation, therefore, is likely to occur along trails and in any place where large animals congregate.

Soil Formation

The formation of soil is one of the more important ways in which a community affects its habitat. The plants and animals of the community enrich the soil through their activities and make it more suitable for the growth of vegetation than is the raw unmodified soil of a pioneer habitat.

ROLE OF PLANTS IN SOIL FORMATION. Plants are particularly important agents of soil formation because the plant stems and roots aid in catching and in holding wind-borne or water-borne soil particles. In many arid regions the plants grow in clumps, around which mounds of soil accumulate. The sod of plants in a prairie is especially effective in holding the soil. The plants act in part in a purely mechanical way, reducing the velocity of wind or water and thus causing a deposition of the material being transported by these agencies. Also, the plants by their shading effect may cause the soil at their bases to be somewhat more moist than elsewhere. This moist surface catches wind-borne materials and prevents the soil from drying to such an extent that it can be easily removed by the wind.

ROLE OF ANIMALS IN SOIL FORMATION. Animals likewise play an important role in the formation of soil. In this process the burrowing animals are most effective, but the feces and carcasses of the nonburrowing terrestrial species also contribute to soil enrichment. Burrowing animals of various sizes and belonging to numerous taxonomic classes aid in the formation of soil. These soil-forming animals include protozoa, earthworms, nematodes, mollusks, isopods, millipedes, centipedes, mites, insects, mammals, and others (Jacot, 1936, 1940; Fenton, 1947). The activities of these animals in manuring the soil, mixing it, and providing channels for water penetration are in many regions of primary significance in soil formation.

The importance of earthworms in soil formation was pointed out many years ago by Charles Darwin (1882). The amount of work performed by these animals is almost beyond comprehension. On a climax prairie studied near Fort Worth, Texas, for instance, the air-dry weight of the earthworm casts that form a continuous layer beneath the humic mulch layer amounts to 20,960 pounds per acre (Dyksterhuis and Schmutz, 1947).

In many kinds of soil, however, earthworms are absent and other kinds of animals may then take their place as agents of soil formation. In certain types of deciduous forest, for example, crane-fly larvae are abundant and perform an important function in soil formation (Rogers, 1942: 55-57). Many kinds of burrowing insects likewise aid in forming the soils of the prairies (McColloch and Hayes, 1923). In the warm temperate and tropical zones ants and termites are effective agents in the formation of topsoil, but numerous other kinds of burrowing animals assist in the process (W. P. Taylor, 1935a).

Burrowing rodents are especially effective agents in soil formation because of their size, though in their aggregate effectiveness rodents probably do not equal the more numerous arthropods and other invertebrates. Rodent burrows frequently penetrate to considerable depths, and the total amount of earth excavated by these burrowing mammals is very great.

The pocket gophers living in the subalpine belt of the Wasatch Plateau of Utah, for example, were estimated by Ellison (1946: 103) to bring to the surface of the ground in one year an average of 5 tons or 4.6 cubic yards of earth per acre. The displaced earth covers 3.5 per cent of the surface of the area.

Rodent burrows allow rainfall to penetrate the ground readily and thus help to prevent the runoff that causes erosion. Excrement and animal carcasses accumulate in the burrows. Parts of plants taken into the burrows decay. The excavated soil often buries parts of plants growing on the surface of the ground, and these plant materials then decay. All these animal and plant remains ultimately form humus. The operations of burrowing animals, therefore, result in plowing and enriching the soil and consequently in the formation of a topsoil in which most plants thrive better than in the raw, unworked soil (Formozov, 1928; Formozov and Voronov, 1939: 117).

In confirmation of the statement that certain burrowing rodents enrich the soil, Grinnell (1923: 147) has noted that on lands in California overstocked with domestic animals the plant cover is often most luxuriant in the vicinity of pocket-gopher workings. Likewise, the activities of the giant kangaroo rat *(Dipodomys ingens)* in parts of the San Joaquin Valley in California were estimated by Hawbecker (1944) to increase the amount of red-stemmed filaree and red brome grass more than five times on the small spots worked by the animals. The vegetation on land cultivated by the kangaroo rat remains green longer in the season than that on other areas. Thus more feed is created for domestic sheep at a time of year when food for them is greatly needed.

PRODUCTION OF HUMUS. Humus is produced as the result of the cumulative activities of many members of the community (Lyon and Buckman, 1937, Chap. 5). In a deciduous forest, for example, leaves and stems from plants of various kinds accumulate as litter on the forest floor. The moist leaves and other plant tissues are attacked by bacteria, actinomycetes, molds and other fungi, algae, and various kinds of soil animals. Earthworms, if they are present, pull dead leaves into their burrows and mix organic material with soil in their castings. The feces and carcasses of animals also contribute in an important way to the organic materials present in the soil. The debris which has been softened by moisture is consumed by millipedes, isopods, mites, springtails, beetles, fly larvae, and other arthropods. In a layer of surface soil 1 inch in thickness in a deciduous forest in New York State there may be from 1,200 to more than 8,500 arthropods per square foot (Eaton and Chandler, 1942). The organic materials pass repeatedly through the bodies of the animals that compose the community and are broken down into simpler chemical compounds. The residue accumulates in the surface layers of the soil, where ultimately it is converted into humus and gives the soil a dark color.

Humus is an extremely valuable constituent of the soil. Soils that are rich in humus are able to grow heavy crops of vegetation, while soils that lack this material usually grow only scanty crops. Inasmuch as humus is composed in considerable part of the residues from plant and animal decomposition, it is evident that there is a very close interdependence between the community and the soil of its habitat. Humus is continually being used up and its decomposition products utilized by plants. Accordingly, the production of humus in the soil through the addition of organic material derived from plant and animal debris must be a continuous process (Waksman, 1936).

The presence of humus in the surface soil results also in a decrease of water evaporation from the soil surface and in a better absorption of rainfall. As a result, the amount of moisture stored in the soil increases. The surface soil is made more friable by the presence of humus and offers a better and more moist seed bed for the germination and growth of plants.

The amount of organic matter added annually to the soil in certain types of habitats is very considerable. For example, it is estimated by Dyksterhuis and Schmutz (1947) that on the prairie near Fort Worth, Texas, the total surficial organic matter varied from about 6,000 pounds per acre on April 1, to 9,200 pounds on September 1.

Most of the smaller soil-forming organisms thrive best in fairly moist soil and are greatly reduced in numbers in xeric soils. In xeric climates, furthermore, the amount of plant and animal debris on which these organisms can subsist also is much less than in more humid regions. The type of climate, therefore, has an important relation to the luxuriance of the soil biota and to the rate at which humus is formed. In deserts and in other very arid regions the products of soil formation may be used up, leached out, or washed away as fast as they are produced, and the soil consequently may not show any appreciable improvement with the lapse of time. Even under the best climatic conditions for the growth of vegetation and of soil organisms it may be assumed that there is a maximum condition of the soil beyond which the processes of humus utilization and destruction equal those of humus production, so that no further improvement of the soil beyond this point will take place; however, it may be doubted if many soils ever reach their maximum condition.

Relation to Soil Erosion

PREVENTION OF SOIL EROSION BY PLANTS. The spaces in the soil left vacant by the decay of plant roots provide channels for the absorption of water (Jacot, 1940). The living plant roots also form a thick mat which holds the soil and prevents its washing away. Furthermore, the presence of plant debris on the soil surface decreases the amount of surface runoff of water and increases the ability of the soil to absorb rainfall. The amount of surface runoff of water from bare soil may, in fact, be from 2 to 70 times that from litter-covered soil (Kittredge, 1948: 253). The presence of a good growth of plants is, accordingly, the best insurance against soil erosion.

ANIMAL ACTIVITIES AND EROSION. The activities of animals often affect the rate of soil erosion. On all lands except those that are very flat or those that are receiving additions of soil from higher levels a certain amount of removal of soil is always in progress through the operation of physical agencies. Certain of the activities of animals may in places hasten this process and in other places may delay it.

The paths made on steep slopes by mammals, especially domestic stock, sometimes form channels for the runoff of water. In these paths erosion of the soil is very likely to occur. Also, large mammals often cause destruction by trampling on the vegetation in their trails and congregrating places; as a result the bare earth is easily washed away. The mounds of freshly excavated earth thrown up by certain burrowing mammals are particularly subject to being washed away by runoff water. These mounds, however, usually are quickly occupied by plants, which then protect the soil from further erosion.

Burrowing animals often aid in the prevention of soil erosion by providing channels by which rainfall can readily penetrate the ground. A summary by Jacot (1940) shows that many kinds of animals dig tunnels in the ground. The aggregate number of channels so produced by which water may enter the soil is very great. An enormous amount of surface water is thus directed into the soil, thereby preventing or reducing erosion.

The initiation of erosion on range lands has sometimes been blamed on the burrows of rodents. There is no doubt that under certain conditions, such as along a drainage channel, local erosion can be started by a rodent burrow. Also, on steep slopes in the Caucasus Mountains considerable amounts of local erosion around rodent workings have been reported by Formozov and Prosvirnina (1935). Under conditions of severe overgrazing by domestic stock, when the cover of vegetation has been mostly removed, the presence of rodent burrows seems also to add to the resulting erosion (Renner, 1936).

The steepness of the slope is an important factor in the relationship between the activities of animals and erosion. On very steep slopes any disturbance of the vegetation or of the soil by animals is likely to result in accelerated erosion. Burrowing rodents and other animals, therefore, contribute to the degradation of mountains (Seton, 1919, I: 585). The soil eroded from the steeper slopes is likely to come to rest on the more gentle slopes and in depressions, and accordingly the burrowing animals contribute also to the accumulation of soil in those places (Grinnell, 1923: 144). Furthermore, on gentle slopes animal burrows prevent rather than accelerate erosion because the tunnels lead the runoff water into the ground.

The most comprehensive study of the relationship between a burrowing rodent and erosion in a mountainous area is that of Ellison (1946), who investigated the effect of the work of pocket gophers on soil formation and erosion in the subalpine belt of the Wasatch Plateau, Utah. His conclusions are that the activities of these animals assist the normal erosional creep of the soil through their tendency to displace the earth downhill. On areas overgrazed by domestic stock the activities of the rodents may contribute to accelerated erosion. On range that is in good condition, however, the activities of the pocket gophers contribute to soil formation, and in the area studied these animals are not the primary cause of destructive erosion.

EFFECTS OF AQUATIC COMMUNITIES ON THEIR HABITATS

Those organisms which live in aquatic situations also modify the physical conditions of their habitats in many ways. Among the more important effects of aquatic communities on their habitats may be listed: (1) alteration in the chemical composition of the aquatic medium itself, (2) increase in the turbidity of the water, (3) protection of the land against waves and erosion, and (4) deposition of materials on the bottom.

Alteration in the Composition of the Aquatic Medium

Through their metabolic activities when exposed to sunlight most aquatic plants absorb carbon dioxide from the water and secrete oxygen. Aquatic animals reverse this process and extract oxygen from the water and in turn give off carbon dioxide. Only those aquatic forms, such as the whales, that rise periodically to the surface to breathe, lack this relationship to the surrounding water. At night the aquatic plants also absorb oxygen from the water and secrete carbon dioxide just as animals do. The proportion of oxygen and of carbon dioxide dissolved in the water of the aquatic habitat, therefore, is subject to constant alteration due to the physiologic activities of those organisms which compose the community.

Aquatic animals also release nitrogenous wastes, excreta, and sometimes other chemicals into the water. The decomposition of the dead bodies of plants and of animals likewise produces changes in the chemical composition of the water. The accumulation of these products in enclosed waters often becomes sufficiently concentrated to affect seriously the composition of the aquatic medium. In bog lakes, for example, the water may be stained brown and may have peculiar chemical properties because of the accumulation there of the products of the decomposition of plant remains. Many bog lakes also have a strongly acid reaction (Welch, 1935: 355).

The organisms that live in an aquatic habitat often "condition" the water so that other individuals of the same species are better able to exist in that situation. Thus, an aggregation of individuals of the same species may be able to thrive in an aquatic habitat where a single individual could live only with difficulty or not at all. The exact process by which aquatic organisms "condition" their habitat to make it more suitable for their existence is not well known, but there is no doubt that it often occurs (Allee, 1935: 924). On the other hand, a group of organisms may render a habitat less suited for the existence of themselves or of other organisms of similar kind (Lucas, 1947). Toxic secretory and other products may accumulate in the habitat to such an extent that they harm the inhabitants.

Increase in Turbidity

A pronounced turbidity is often produced in the aquatic habitat by the presence of algae, diatoms, protozoa, entomostracans, and other kinds of small plants and animals, as well as by the presence of dead organisms. In certain habitats the presence of many organisms and their debris greatly hinders the transmission of light to the levels below the surface.

Protection of Land Against Erosion

The water lilies, pondweeds, rushes, sedges, and other kinds of rooted aquatic plants which grow in many shallow, fresh-water situations protect the shore and bottom against the waves and water currents. By their sheltering action they also promote the deposit of water-borne silt and other soil-forming materials. Along marine shores and in shallow seas the seaweeds and other attached marine plants and animals have a similar effect. Along tropical shores, for instance, mangroves often aid in the extension of the land at the expense of the aquatic habitats.

Deposit of Materials on the Bottom

The individual plants and animals that live in the water all eventually die and their remains accumulate on the bottom. In many places this bottom "ooze" forms only a very thin layer, but in other places the deposit of organic materials may become many feet thick. Numerous fossil beds of past ages, composed in part or almost wholly of the skeletons of marine organisms, are hundreds or in some cases several thousands of feet thick. The deposit of organic debris, aided by materials washed in from the adjacent land, slowly fills up shallow bodies of water. Many ponds, lakes, and even shallow seas have thus become dry land.

In the shallow water along the ocean margins thick deposits often are built up through the activities of corals, algae, and other rock-forming organisms. Behind a fringing reef which has been produced by the activities of such organisms, a protected lagoon may be formed in which the physical conditions are very different from those in a similar area exposed to the full force of the waves.

EFFECTS OF THE ACTIVITIES OF MAN

Among the organisms which are active in producing changes in the physical habitats of the world, man is undoubtedly the most effective of all. Through many activities which include cutting down forests, clearing and cultivating the land, setting fires, pasturing domestic animals, constructing towns, roads, canals, dams, and drains, and polluting streams and lakes he has literally remade the face of the earth in many parts of all continents except Antarctica. The operations of man will in the future undoubtedly have a greater effect on the physical habitats of the world than at present. Nevertheless, the other organisms living in all the various communities existing on the earth will also continue to play their very important roles in modifying the physical factors of the habitats in which they live.

SELECTED REFERENCES

Clements, Frederic E., and Victor E. Shelford. 1939. Bio-ecology. New York: John Wiley and Sons. Chap. 3.

Darwin, Charles. 1882. The formation of vegetable mould, through the action of worms. New York: D. Appleton and Co.

Kittredge, Joseph. 1948. Forest influences. New York, Toronto, and London: McGraw-Hill Book Co. Chaps. 4 to 20.

Lutz, Harold J., and Robert F. Chandler, Jr. 1946. Forest soils. New York: John Wiley and Sons. Chaps. 5 to 6.

Waksman, Selman A. 1927. Principles of soil microbiology. Baltimore: Williams and Wilkins Co.

———— 1936. Humus: origin, chemical composition, and importance in nature. Baltimore: Williams and Wilkins Co.

XVI

ECOLOGIC SUCCESSION

Many ecologic communities are only temporary stages that in time will be replaced by other kinds of communities. A lake in the northeastern part of the United States from which a small stream flows may serve as an illustration. Many lakes of this kind were formed as a result of the activities of the continental glaciers that at one time overran this area. These lakes now are being slowly obliterated by the inwash of soil from the surrounding land and by the deposit of the remains of plants and animals. When the water has become sufficiently shallow in any part of such a lake, rooted plants of various kinds invade the situation. Among these early plants water lilies will likely be conspicuous. Later, as the water becomes more shallow, cattails and rushes appear, and then the situation has been transformed into a marsh. As the filling of the lake progresses, sedges of various kinds take control. In those places where soil has completely filled the lake, grasses become an important element in the newly emerged community, which now is probably called a meadow. Small willows and shrubs are likely to appear next. Still later these shrubs will be replaced by trees. Eventually, a mature forest of the type characteristic of the region will occupy the former site of the lake.

A slightly different sequence of communities appears during the filling of a bog lake (Fig. 41), but the process is much the same. The appearance of such a sequence of communities is called succession.

DEFINITION OF SUCCESSION. The definition of ecologic succession as the replacement of one ecologic community by another of different type will not be accepted by such ecologists as Clements (1916) and Tansley (1935), who use the term "succession" only for orderly progressive changes. I am following the recommendation of Cooper (1926: 410) and of Gleason (1927) in considering any replacement of one community by another to be succession, no matter how it is caused and irrespective of whether or not the change tends towards a climax. Temporary changes in a community, however, such as are produced by the progression of the seasonal aspects, are not considered succession.

Succession takes place in communities of every possible kind, size, and rank. The process is perhaps most obvious and striking among communities

368

that cover a considerable area, such as those on a sand dune or those on an
extensive mud bar formed by a large river. Succession also occurs, however,
in communities of very small size. For example, the heap of soil excavated
by a small burrowing mammal is likely to be taken from the subsoil and

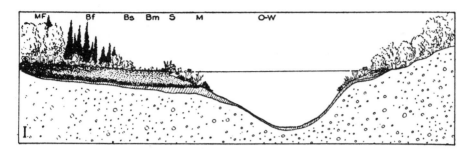

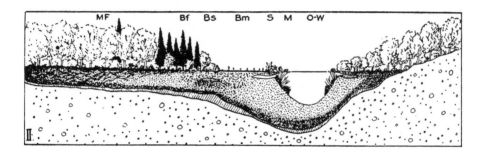

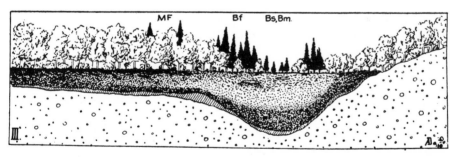

FIG. 41. Three stages of succession in the bog sere in Ohio. The communities are
indicated by the following symbols: O-W, open-water; M, marginal; S, shore; Bm, bog
meadow; Bs, bog shrubs; Bf, bog forest; and MF, mesophytic forest. (After Dachnowski,
1912, by permission of the Ohio Geol. Surv.)

consequently to be somewhat different from the surface soil in chemical
and physical composition. The mound is usually first occupied by plant
pioneers of species different from those that grow on the more mature soil
upon which the heap of new soil is superimposed. Each mound of excavated
earth, therefore, becomes the site of a miniature community, which differs

in character from the surrounding larger and more mature community and which initiates a new cycle of succession leading from bare soil toward the climax of the area (Formozov, 1928).

When a community has changed sufficiently to be in a different category in its classification, succession has taken place. The change that has occurred, however, may be no different in kind, but only in degree, from the changes that were in progress in the community previous to its change of category. Succession, then, is a continuous process, the results of which are recognizable in a procession of communities.

CLIMAXES

Any community that is not in process of further progressive succession is a climax. A climax community, then, is one which is in a state of relative ecologic equilibrium with its habitat. Tansley (1939: vi) stated that any community which is in a condition of relative stability is a climax, though he also agreed that no climax is ever completely stable. Changes in every climax community will constantly be in progress because of the frequent death and replacement of the individual organisms, but the general character of the climax will remain essentially the same so long as no change takes place in the general environmental factors or in the biota of the region.

There are actually several kinds of climaxes, but these are not entirely distinct from one another. Most commonly recognized are the climatic climax, edaphic climax, and topographic climax. Climaxes of certain minor communities could probably also be recognized, but these have not been given special names.

STAGE. Any clearly marked step in succession, whether pioneer, intermediate, or terminal is a stage (Braun-Blanquet, Fuller, and Conard, 1932: 320). For example, in certain regions of eastern North America a pine stage precedes the hardwood forest which forms the climatic climax.

SUBCLIMAX. Any important successional stage below the climatic climax is a subclimax. Thus, an edaphic or topographic climax could also be a subclimax.

SERE. Any sequence of successional stages leading from a definite pioneer stage to a climax of any kind is a sere (Clements, 1916: 4). Several types of seres have been given special names to indicate their beginning stages. The hydrosere is the series of successional stages leading from open water to a terrestrial climax. The xerosere leads from bare soil or rock to a climax. The miniature succession that takes place in a minor habitat, such as an animal dropping, is a microsere (Mohr, 1943: 284).

CLIMATIC CLIMAX. Within any given climatic region succession tends in general toward the ultimate production of a particular climax type of community. In southern Michigan the succession that begins in the open water of a shallow lake leads toward the development of a deciduous hardwood forest dominated by maple and beech, which in this area constitutes the climatic climax. In this same area other sequences of succession may begin on bare rock, on sand, or in a bog lake. When these successions are closely examined it will be found that they all lead toward the same kind of deciduous-forest climax (Shelford, 1913: 310). In any given situation, therefore, several diverse lines of succession may lead toward 1 particular climatic climax, which represents the ultimate limit of succession possible for that particular biota and for that particular climate.

The climatic climax then is the highest phase of ecologic development that the biota and the climate of a given region permit. Although this climax is called the climatic climax, the biota is included as well as the climate. From the climatic climax no further progressive succession is possible, no matter what changes may occur in the habitat, so long as the climate and the biota remain the same. Any important change in the habitat will almost certainly be of a destructive nature, initiating a new sequence of succession, which will again tend toward the production of the same climatic climax.

In any given climatic region at a given time, therefore, there can be, according to this definition, but 1 climatic climax. For instance, in southern Michigan the beech-maple forest is considered the climax and all the other types of communities in that area are presumably more or less temporary stages in succession leading toward this climax. When ecologists speak of climax without a qualifying adjective, it is nearly always the climatic climax of the region that is meant.

EDAPHIC CLIMAX. An ecologic association held through the action of soil factors more or less permanently at a given stage in succession below the climatic climax constitutes an edaphic climax. On sandy soils in northern Michigan (Canadian biotic province), for example, the pine association is very enduring and forms an edaphic climax. Theoretically, the accumulation of forest litter under the pines should ultimately enrich the soil to such an extent that the beech-maple forest, which is the climatic climax of the region, replaces the pines. In certain places this succession of pines by the beech-maple climax does actually take place. In other situations the sandy soil is so porous and so lacking in lime and perhaps in other essential soil elements that the pine stage is very persistent and may never develop into the beech-maple climatic climax.

Other types of edaphic climaxes may be produced by overwetness of the soil caused by lack of drainage, by excess amounts of soil acidity, by the accumulation of alkali and other salts in the soil, and by numerous other kinds of local soil conditions.

TOPOGRAPHIC CLIMAX. A particular type of topography may also produce a topographic climax that is more or less persistent. The associations on steep mountain slopes, for instance, may differ in important respects from those of more gentle slopes. Likewise, the associations on north-facing slopes may differ from those of south-facing slopes. In part, the controlling factors, including soil moisture and soil texture, which distinguish the associations of steep from those of gentle slopes and those of north from those of south slopes, are present in the soil, but they also are based to some extent on the local climate and include especially temperature and rate of evaporation. All these factors are controlled at least in part by topography. Although many ecologists fail to distinguish between edaphic and topographic climaxes, there is actually a fundamental difference between them (Vestal, 1938: 112, footnote).

The distinction between the climatic climax and the edaphic or topographic climaxes is fairly obvious in most regions. Usually the climatic climax is the extensive or regional climax, while the edaphic and topographic climaxes are local in occurrence. Sometimes, however, edaphic climaxes may cover extensive areas. The sand hills of western Nebraska, for instance, cover thousands of square miles over an extensive and generally continuous area (Ostenson, 1947). Edaphic, therefore, is not always synonymous with local (Vestal, 1938: 112, footnote).

AQUATIC CLIMAX. Succession occurs in aquatic ecosystems as on land. Those successions that accompany the filling of bodies of water by soil may lead to the ultimate replacement of the aquatic communities by a terrestrial climax. Other aquatic communities, however, through wave action or other environmental factors, may be held more or less stable for long periods of time, under which circumstance they constitute aquatic edaphic or topographic climaxes (Tutin, 1941). Reverse succession may also occur where a land habitat is eroded by waves or by river currents and is replaced by an aquatic habitat. Climatic climaxes that are seemingly as stable as those of the land occur in the oceans and perhaps also in certain of the larger lakes.

CRITERIA OF A CLIMAX. It is not always easy to determine with certainty whether a given community is a climax. Among the possible criteria for a terrestrial climax the most useful one is the presence of the same species of plants in the understory as in the topmost stratum. If those species that form the upper stratum are able to reproduce in their own shade, it is likely that little succession can be in progress. Another way of stating this criterion is to ask whether the stand is made up of individuals of all ages. If it is, then the species concerned must be reproducing themselves. On the contrary, if those species that form the topmost stratum are not present in the understory as young plants of varying ages, then the stand is not reproducing itself and succession must either be in progress or be likely to appear in the near future.

A knowledge of the growth habits, vigor, length of life, and ability of all the species of plants in the region concerned to endure unfavorable seasons will also aid the observer in deciding which forms are likely to be members of the climax (Hough and Forbes, 1943: 317). The determination of the climax is always subject to the individual judgment of the investigator. Ecologists may not always agree as to which particular community in a given region actually is the climatic climax.

The prediction of the kind of climax that will ultimately be reached on a given area is in some places made difficult by the fact that topographic climaxes may cover considerable areas, particularly in mountainous regions. Furthermore, several life belts, each indicating a different type of climate, may occur close together on a mountain slope. Even in areas of low relief the general climate varies somewhat from place to place and over any large area it usually shows at least a small amount of gradation.

Frequently the ecologist must deduce what the climatic climax will ultimately be from fragmentary evidence presented by the several kinds of communities which he is able to examine. To be accurate he should always specify the conditions of topography and soil which he assumes the climax will occupy and he should designate the precise area covered by his description.

CAUSES OF SUCCESSION

Succession may be initiated by any one of several diverse agencies (Clements, 1916). These agencies may be considered under the general headings of (1) physiographic processes, (2) catastrophes, (3) climatic changes, (4) changes in the biota of the region, (5) evolution of species, and (6) activities of organisms.

PHYSIOGRAPHIC PROCESSES. Many kinds of physiographic processes may initiate ecologic succession. An important pioneer study of that type of plant succession which is initiated and controlled in large part by physiographic processes was made by Cowles (1901a) in the Chicago region. Among those physiographic processes that are important in initiating succession may be mentioned the erosion of soil from one place and its deposition in another. The degradation of highlands and the aggradation of lowlands, therefore, cause many successional changes in the regions affected. The elevation of a mountain range or any other kind of earth movement is almost certain to result in widespread succession. In arid regions the accumulation of mineral salts in particular areas also may produce succession.

Certain physiographic processes are more or less abrupt in their action. For example, a landslide occurs suddenly and immediately initiates a new succession. On the other hand, many physiographic processes, such as most types of erosion, operate slowly, and therefore the resulting succession usually is a slow development.

CATASTROPHES. Various kinds of catastrophes also can initiate succession. A fire, flood, volcanic eruption, drought, freeze, disease, plague of animals, or other type of minor or major disaster may destroy or seriously alter a community, and so open the way to a new sequence of succession. The new community that is thus formed and its succeeding communities may or may not be exactly like the stages in succession shown by other seres in the region.

It is seldom that a catastrophe of any kind completely destroys all the organisms living in any community. A wind storm, for example, that blows down the forest trees in a particular stand seldom destroys more than a part of the plants and animals living in that community. Even a volcanic eruption is completely destructive only to the organisms in the vicinity of the vent (Eggler, 1948). Some of the types of successions started by catastrophes are properly treated under other headings. Here will be emphasized only the role of fire.

Fire is often a most important factor in causing succession. Certain ecologists, as already pointed out, do not consider the catastrophic change in a community caused by fire to be a true succession. Many of the fires that cause succession are started by man, either intentionally or by accident, but numerous fires also are started by lightning and by other natural causes.

Communities differ greatly in their sensitiveness to fire. Certain types of conifer forests, in which the mature trees may be hundreds of years old, often are completely destroyed by fire. Grassland, on the contrary, may owe its continued existence to fires that every few years destroy the shrubs and tree seedlings which otherwise might in time shade out the grass. The underground parts of the grasses are seldom seriously damaged by fire, and the plants spring up again as soon as there is sufficient soil moisture.

The species of trees and shrubs likewise vary greatly in their ability to withstand fire. Many of the pines of the southeastern United States, for instance, have heavy bark when mature, which makes them very resistant to fire. Small trees and shrubs, on the other hand, are likely to suffer considerably from fire. Trees and shrubs tend to be eliminated from areas where fires are frequent unless they are able to sprout again from their roots.

When a community has been destroyed by fire, a new succession begins immediately on that site. Should the destruction be complete, succession may have to begin with bare soil, but if the destruction is only partial, then the first stage in the ensuing succession will depend on the kinds of organisms that remain and on the condition of the habitat.

CLIMATIC CHANGES. The course of succession is necessarily affected by every change of climate which takes place in the region concerned. Any change in climate which is of considerable magnitude may alter the climatic climax of the area and this will, of course, also produce many changes in the subclimax communities.

In past geologic ages major changes in climate have often occurred, with the result that at any given place there has been a succession of climatic climaxes. Such successions have been studied principally in the glacial and interglacial stages of North America and Europe. Other successions of climaxes of an even more profound sort were produced by the evolution of climate during earlier geologic time (Cain, 1944, Chap. 9).

Climatic fluctuations of a less permanent sort may also produce or influence succession. A series of drought years, for example, may seriously change the character of many communities (J. E. Weaver, 1943). Similarly, a series of wet years or of cold years may produce great changes in community composition. It is known that such minor fluctuations in climate are constantly occurring, and it is obvious that they frequently cause minor successions.

Certain major changes in climate have undoubtedly been caused by physiographic processes, such as base-leveling. It is not always possible, therefore, to distinguish sharply between the effects of physiographic and of climatic changes in the production of succession.

CHANGES IN THE BIOTA OF THE REGION. The invasion of a foreign species (Gleason, 1917: 474) is another factor that may initiate succession. The introduction of rabbits into Australia, for instance, produced many important changes in the terrestrial communities of that continent. Important changes in communities may also be caused by the elimination of certain species from a region. Thus, the elimination of the large carnivores and some of the small ones from regions of intensive agriculture results in an increase of herbivores, which may then overgraze the plants and produce considerable alterations in the local ecosystems.

EVOLUTION OF SPECIES. The evolution into new forms of certain of the species making up a community is another possible cause of community change (Cooper, 1926: 398). Often, but not always, specific evolution leads to the production of better adapted forms, with the general result that the community becomes more efficient. Specific evolution usually is presumed to be a very slow process, and the succession caused by it will accordingly also be slow. Nevertheless, during the long period which has elapsed since life first appeared on the earth there have been many great changes in the character of the plants and animals that have made up the successive biotas. The communities of Pennsylvanian time, for instance, must have been very different from those of Recent time, not only in the species of organisms of which they were composed but also in their general physiognomy. Specific evolution has accordingly been, and undoubtedly continues to be, a major factor in succession.

ACTIVITIES OF ORGANISMS. The activity of organisms initiates many kinds of succession. Even the growth of a single plant to a size where it produces an appreciable amount of shade may cause a minor succession on the site where the shade falls. Every tree that falls in the forest initiates at least 2 new successional sequences, one ultimately replacing the tree in the forest canopy and the other consuming the fallen log.

Animals, as well as plants, may initiate successional changes by their activities. Each mound of earth excavated by a burrowing animal, each heap of animal feces, and each animal carcass begins a new microsere. Erosion of the soil caused directly or indirectly by the activities of animals may also initiate a local succession. Animals may indirectly cause local succession through the damage they do to plants in the process of feeding. Trampling of the plants and of the soil by large animals may also initiate local succession. Sometimes the vegetation is injured or destroyed by animal activity over a considerable area. The succession initiated by animal activities, there-fore, is by no means always local.

The beaver may be cited as an example of an animal that often plays an important role in initiating succession. Every time a beaver dam is con-structed a new local cycle of succession is begun. Should the dam remain in place a sufficiently long period of time, the pond above the dam will become filled with silt and organic debris and will in turn be replaced by a beaver meadow. Ultimately the meadow will be transformed by succession into the regional climax. The completion of this succession, however, may be long delayed because the beavers may continue to raise the level of the dam in order to retain a pond about their lodge, or they may build new dams, thereby again flooding certain parts of the beaver meadow. In areas occupied by beavers, therefore, succession is seldom allowed to go to full completion. Under primitive conditions enormous areas in North America and Eurasia were under the control of beavers. It may even be said that until fairly recent times the changes in natural communities produced by the activities of the beaver were greater than those caused by man (Ives, 1942: 194).

The most important of all animals in causing ecologic succession is man. By the reduction in numbers or the complete destruction of certain species of plants and animals, by intentional or unintentional introduction of foreign species, by the alteration or removal of many natural communities through the operations of grazing, agriculture, and lumbering, and by the establishment of new types of habitats in cultivated fields, in waste lands, about buildings, and in other places, man is constantly inducing succession of many diverse kinds in most parts of all the continents except Antarctica. The erosion resulting from unwise use of the land (Fig. 42) is an example of such man-initiated succession.

FACTORS THAT CONTROL SUCCESSION

The initial cause of a succession may have no control whatever over the course of the ensuing succession. Succession nearly always is a complex process that is controlled by the combined operation of many diverse factors. It may happen, therefore, that each of the successive stages in a sere is con-trolled by a different combination of factors. Among the factors that control succession, climate, physiography, soil, plants, and animals demand particu-lar consideration.

CONTROL BY CLIMATE. Climate plays a most important role in control-ling successional change. No community can develop unless it is permitted by the climate of the location. The local climate of a given situation, how-ever, is itself often determined in part by the physiography and to a lesser degree by the organisms, especially the plants, that are present.

CONTROL BY PHYSIOGRAPHY. Physiography also plays a significant part in controlling successional changes. In hilly or mountainous areas the orienta-

FIG. 42. Erosion gully in a small valley near Capitan, New Mexico. Unless it can be controlled, this gully will eventually remove the productive soil from this whole little valley and thereby will initiate a new cycle of succession. (Drawing by Carlton W. Angell, after a photograph by L. R. Dice, taken July 7, 1937.)

tion of each slope in relation to the sun and to the prevailing winds greatly affects the local climate and thereby determines the kind of community that can exist in that situation. On steep slopes erosion may prevent certain species of organisms from maintaining themselves. Likewise, in areas of soil deposition certain species may be unable to exist because they cannot endure being continually buried.

In situations where the physiography is in process of rapid change the course of succession may be almost entirely directed by these changes. This is well illustrated in every active dune area. Here the wind removes sand from one site and deposits it in another place, thus, for a time completely controlling the course of succession. It is only when the movement of the sand in a particular situation has ceased and vegetation has become established on it that the physiographic processes lose control (Cowles, 1901a).

CONTROL BY SOIL. The character of the soil exercises considerable control over succession in certain terrestrial communities, particularly during their pioneer stages. Numerous species of plants can grow only in sand or in very light soil, while other species prefer clay. Likewise, certain burrowing animals, such as the kangaroo rats, are able to excavate their tunnels only in sandy soil, while other species are strong diggers and are able to burrow into heavy soils.

The distribution of many species of plants is largely controlled by the amount of moisture and of dissolved chemicals in the soil. Certain kinds of plants are unable to tolerate wet soil and others cannot endure any considerable concentration of salts. Accordingly, the communities of which such species form a part can develop only on well-drained soils. Other kinds of communities are able to develop only on soils which are constantly wet but which are free from harmful dissolved salts. The plants and animals of still other kinds of communities are able to tolerate a considerable concentration of salts in the soil solution.

Soil characters, however, not only are controlled by the minerals of which the soil is composed, by the climate, and by the physiography, but also may be affected by the organisms that occupy the situation. The improvement in the character of the soil produced by the activities of the organisms has much to do with the trend of succession. It is probable that the climatic climaxes of many regions can develop only on mature soils.

CONTROL BY WAVES. In certain kinds of aquatic habitats the waves may prevent the accumulation of soil and thereby may prohibit succession toward emergent types of communities. (Tutin, 1941). For this reason certain types of aquatic communities, both in fresh water and in the oceans, may become stabilized as climaxes.

CONTROL BY PLANTS. Many kinds of plants and animals are able to influence to a considerable degree the characters of their own environment. By so doing they often are able to control more or less effectively the course of succession. In terrestrial communities the plants are especially important agents for the control of succession because of the shade they produce. Tall plants that bear an abundance of leaves prevent direct sunlight from reaching the shorter plants that may happen to grow beneath them. Low-growing plants that are not tolerant of shade cannot survive under dense shrubs or trees. When shrubs or trees invade a meadow, therefore, they tend to drive out most of the grasses and other shade-intolerant herbs. In situations where plants are able to produce thickets or forests, any species of plant that is able to germinate and to grow in its own shade or in the shade of other plants will ultimately succeed those plants that are able to grow only in full sun. Any climax in which the plants form a closed canopy must accordingly be composed mostly or entirely of species that are able to germinate and grow in their own shade as well as in the shade produced by the plants of the immediately preceding successional stage.

The control which plants exercise over the community is sometimes expressed through other means than by shutting off sunlight. Certain sedge bogs of northern Michigan, for example, are formed through the ability of 1 kind of sedge (*Carex lasiocarpa*) to grow on the surface of the water free from the soil. The mat of vegetation thus produced may sometimes be broken up by storms or by ice action. If it is able to persist, it forms a bog, which in time is invaded by other characteristic bog species. This particular bog succession is consequently dependent upon the ability of a species of plant to transform open water into a mat of vegetation (Gates, 1942).

CONTROL BY ANIMALS. Certain ecologists have a tendency to consider that true succession results only from those processes that are controlled by plants, while animals are treated as intruders or disturbing influences. As has been emphasized in Chapter II, however, animals are an important and natural part of the community; therefore their activities in relation to succession must be carefully considered. For instance, on the arid Great Plains of North America the grazing of domestic stock often results in the production of a short-grass community, while if grazing animals are excluded grasses of midheight will in many places displace the short grasses. Clements concluded from this that the midgrasses constitute the climatic climax, while the short-grass community is a "disclimax" due to overgrazing. Larson (1940), however, argued that bison and other native animals grazed extensively on these plains before the arrival of domestic stock and that the short-grass community is a natural community and not a "disclimax." Formozov (1928) likewise pointed out that the rodents and hoofed mammals are a natural and very indispensable part of the steppe association of Russia and Siberia and that they play an important role in the maintenance of this association. Certain rodents actually assist in the recovery of deteriorated ranges and their regeneration toward the climax (Bond, 1945).

The preferences exhibited by herbivorous animals for certain food plants often control the succession of one type of vegetation by another. If the herbivores are present in considerable numbers, so that there is a tendency toward the overutilization of the habitat, their preferred food plants will tend to decrease. At the same time nonedible types of plants are likely to increase in the community because of the removal of their competitors. For example, in certain areas in England studied by Summerhayes (1941) the activities of voles (*Microtus agrestis*) reduce the luxuriance of the dominant grasses and thereby allow certain other herbs and especially the mosses to grow more abundantly. The voles, therefore, stop the course of succession and tend to preserve a relatively open vegetation, comparatively rich in species.

Rabbits (*Oryctolagus cuniculus*), also, in parts of England are important factors in changing Calluna heath to grassland. They eat the Calluna, which then is replaced by grass. The rabbits do not live in thick Calluna heath and they prefer the grass as food. Consequently, their activities produce a habitat more suited to their own existence (Farrow, 1925). Likewise, in certain fresh-water habitats, the carp, by destroying aquatic vegetation, largely controls the kind of community that can exist (Cahn, 1929).

Overgrazing or selective feeding by herbivores may affect not only the vegetation but also indirectly the fauna. Taylor, Vorhies, and Lister (1935) have pointed out that the overgrazing of range lands by cattle may result in an increase in the numbers of jack rabbits. This is due to the fact that jack rabbits seem to avoid areas covered by coarse ungrazed grasses. If the grasses are closely cropped by domestic stock, then the situation becomes favorable for jack rabbits, which consequently invade the area in numbers. In this case the jack rabbits do not cause the initial overgrazing, but they add to the damage after overuse by domestic stock has started the process.

Grasshoppers of certain kinds also may be exceptionally abundant on overgrazed areas (Treherne and Buckell, 1924). Overgrazed prairies in Oklahoma, for example, may have grasshopper populations 4 or more times as great as land that is not overgrazed (Coyner, 1939; Weese, 1939). Thus, there may be the apparent paradox of the distribution of grasshoppers being controlled by a barbed-wire fence. The fence, of course, does not limit the distribution of the insects directly, but only indirectly through its control of grazing by the large domestic herbivores. Similarly, prairie dogs (*Cynomys*) generally inhabit areas of short grass, but they are able also to invade adjacent tall-grass communities in which the grass has been closely cropped by domestic mammals (B. Osborn, 1942).

Another example of the control of the habitat by the activities of animals is given by the guano islands lying off the coast of Peru. Here certain species of birds, such as the pelicans and cormorants, make their nests on the bare surface of the soil or rocks. As a deposit of manure accumulates, however, the site becomes less suited to these surface-nesting species. At the same time the site becomes more suited to the penguins, diving petrels, and Inca terns that make their nests in burrows excavated in the guano. The character of the community that exists in these situations is changed, therefore, as the result of animal activities and in the complete or practically complete absence of plants (E. H. Graham, 1944: 44).

Through their relationship to soil formation the plants and animals often exercise an important control over succession. As the soil becomes improved through the accumulation of organic debris and through the activities of animals and plants, many kinds of plants are able to thrive that could not exist on raw soil. By the accumulation of a mantle of surface soil, furthermore, the community may become independent to a greater or lesser degree of the character of the subsoil and of the underlying rock (Cowles, 1901b).

The succession of terrestrial animals usually lags somewhat behind the succession of plants. This is a necessary consequence of the fact that plants are the ultimate source of food for all animals and that they also supply shelter and breeding places. Moreover, it takes some time for the animals to find and occupy suitable newly produced habitats. Lack (1933: 245), for example, has pointed out that certain species of birds persist in pine plantations until the young trees have reached a height greater than that usually tolerated by the species. Seemingly there is a reluctance to give up a site which has been suitable.

In certain marine communities, especially those on rocky shores, attached seaweeds may grow in abundance and may locally control the habitat. In many other marine habitats, however, the corals, hydroids, mollusks, crustaceans, echinoderms, annelids, sponges, and other animals are more in control of the environment than are the plants (Clements and Shelford, 1939). Along the Pacific Coast of North America, for example, the sea mussel (*Mytilus californicus*) forms thick colonies on wharf piles and on cliffs exposed to heavy surf, where few other animals or plants are able to attach themselves. The mussels produce conditions that are tolerable for a number of other kinds of organisms and a *Mytilus californicus* association develops. This association includes even some animals that are characteristic of the quiet water behind rocks (Haas, 1943). Along the northern Atlantic Coast of North America a related species of sea mussel (*Mytilus edulis*) and its associates control the community that develops on many exposed shores (Newcombe, 1935).

SUCCESSION IN MICROSERES. The control of succession by the organisms themselves is particularly obvious in many microseres. When, for example, a tree has died, a miniature succession is immediately initiated in its tissues. The wood of the tree is first invaded by various boring insects and by numerous kinds of fungi. The activities of these organisms produce changes both in the physical and in the chemical character of the wood, with the result that the habitat often becomes unsuited to the primary invaders. The dead tree, however, by the activities of these primary invaders is made into a habitat suitable for other secondary invaders, which enter the community in the second or in subsequent years. The tree, consequently, shelters a series of communities which invade it in succession, each community serving to prepare the way for the next. At first the community inhabiting the dead tree or log is composed mostly of wood-boring insects together with their parasites and predators. In later years there is an increase in the proportion of fungi responsible for the decay of the wood and of forms which live upon these fungi (Blackman and Stage, 1924: 11-12).

In most descriptions of succession the microseres have received far too little attention. Numerous kinds of microsuccessions are concurrently in progress in every community of any size. Every time a tree falls in the forest it starts 2 or more new microseres, as has previously been mentioned. There are first the microseres initiated in the wood and bark of the decaying log. If the uprooting of the tree has exposed an area of bare earth, this will be the site of another microsere. Then the fall of the tree has probably left a vacancy in the forest canopy so that more sunlight than formerly will fall on a certain area of the forest floor. This increased light will initiate still another microsere. Even the death of a small tree or shrub may initiate a local microsere. Every rock under which small animals hide or on which lichens or moss grow is the site of a microsere. Every spring of water, every small stream, and every pool also provide the basis for one or more microseres.

A microsere that at any given time occupies only a small part of a particular ecosystem may by repetition ultimately affect all the area. Thus, on the plains of West Kazakhstan, U.S.S.R., each freshly excavated mound of the gray ground squirrel (*Citellus pygmaeus*) initiates a new microsere. The sequence of succession on each mound, however, varies with the chemical character of the excavated soil, with the nature of the surrounding vegetation, and with the invasion of the mound by steppe lemmings. Various stages in succession are represented on the mounds, depending on their ages. In regions where ground squirrels are abundant, practically all the area of the steppe, during the course of the years, is covered by a series of these microseres (Formozov and Voronov, 1939: 120-21).

The local sequences of succession exhibited by diverse types of microseres keep practically every community, no matter what its size, in a state of constant turnover. These microseres, therefore, deserve careful attention in any description of an ecologic community.

DYNAMIC NATURE OF SUCCESSION

Succession is a dynamic process which tends toward the establishment at any given site of that type of community which is best able to maintain itself in competition with those other kinds of communities which may exist there.

TENDENCY TOWARD STABILITY. A tendency toward stability may be assumed to be present in every ecologic community (Lindeman, 1942: 409).

When stability is attained at the pioneer stage, as may happen in the desert and in certain other very rigorous habitats, this pioneer stage may persist indefinitely. Succession does occur in deserts, but here it is controlled mostly by physiographic processes. In such rigorous situations the final community type may be determined almost solely by the physical features of the habitat, including climate, physiography, and soil. In more favorable climates the organisms, particularly the plants, may be able to modify the habitat and accordingly they are able, at least to some degree, to control the succession. In any given region the greatest amount of control that the organisms are able to achieve is exhibited in the climatic climax.

A complex type of association, particularly one of climax type or approaching a climax, may be composed of a considerable number of important species of generally similar ecologic type, no one of which alone is able to control the community. These several important species may recur in all possible combinations and, so far as the character of the community is concerned, it may make little difference which of the controlling species occurs at any particular spot. In some of the complex tropical forests, for example, it is said that the individuals of each species may be widely dispersed, with considerable distances intervening between individuals of the same kind. Because of the numerous species of which it is composed and the complexity of their interrelationships, such an association approaches the maximum of stability in ecologic organization.

In spite of the considerable degree of ecologic stability reached by some of the more complex associations, no community ever achieves complete stability. Local successions caused by such factors as soil conditions, the activities of animals, and accidents are always in progress. Ecologic stability seems, nevertheless, to be the ultimate goal toward which nature strives, but which it never quite reaches.

CLOSED VERSUS OPEN COMMUNITIES. The tendency toward stability in every community often results in a closed community. A closed community is one in which all the possible niches are fully occupied. An open community, conversely, is one in which certain possible niches are not filled by any kind of organism. Theoretically, every climax community may be considered closed. In the climax community all the possible niches available to those species that live in the region may be assumed to be already filled. The invasion of another species, therefore, would be practically impossible. In all subclimax stages, on the other hand, succession is likely to be in progress. This proves that these subclimax communities are not completely closed.

Communities differ greatly, nevertheless, in the readiness with which a foreign species may be able to establish itself. A desert community may be "closed," even though plants occupy only a small fraction of the surface of the soil. In such a situation competition for soil moisture may be so severe that no new invader is likely to obtain a foothold. It has been shown by Robertson and Pearse (1945) that the artificial seeding of desirable plant

grasses in certain natural grassland or sagebrush communities in the western
United States is largely futile because such communities are already closed.
If, however, the natural vegetation is destroyed by artificial means, such as
fire, it may then be possible to establish a desired forage species in the
community.

IRREGULARITIES IN SUCCESSION. Ecologic succession does not always proceed as regularly as certain of the published descriptions would indicate nor
as is implied in the term "sere" (Gleason, 1927: 318). On the contrary,
in any situation where a considerable diversity of ecologic communities
is present there may be numerous possible lines of succession. Short cuts
may be inserted, with 1 or more of the usual successional stages omitted
(Gates, 1926: 181-82). E. H. Graham (1942: 49), for example, has noted that
in certain situations on the Appalachian Plateau a stand of pines may
develop directly on severely eroded soil without the interposition of the
usual sequence through annuals, perennials, and broomsedge, to pine. Also,
additional stages may be inserted (Fig. 43) or retrogressive succession may
take place. Descriptions of terrestrial successions that include only the hydrosere and xerosere, therefore, may nearly always be suspected of being over-
simplifications.

Neither is succession a process that always proceeds at a uniform rate.
When the vegetation has gained control in a certain situation, succession
may be halted at a particular stage for a long period of time. Thus, for example, the prairies of Illinois and of parts of Texas are grassland communities that have long persisted in areas in which deciduous forest forms
the climatic climax (E. H. Graham, 1944: 24). In these areas the plants control the situation so completely that it is impossible for trees to gain entry
except along the very margin of the forest, where the shade of the trees
eliminates the grasses. Tree seedlings have great difficulty in establishing
themselves in the closed sod of a prairie (Clements, Weaver, and Hanson,
1929: 199). On the other hand, it is only when the forest has been destroyed
by fire, by drought, or by other causes that it can be replaced by grassland.
Prairie and forest both resist change and, therefore, succession from one to
the other is usually a very slow process.

Local factors of soil and physiography may likewise halt succession for a
long period of time, or perhaps indefinitely, at a certain particular stage
(Cain, 1947: 192).

The soil type of the habitat often plays an especially important role in
determining the sequence of succession. Following a fire in the hardwood
forest of northern Michigan, for instance, the usual succession on sandy
soil leads through herbaceous, aspen, and pine stages back toward hardwood
forest, the whole process requiring many years. On clay soil, on the contrary,
the hardwood forest may quickly regenerate through herbaceous and shrub
stages and may omit the pine stage entirely (Gates, 1930: 253).

Physiography likewise has an important influence on the sequence and

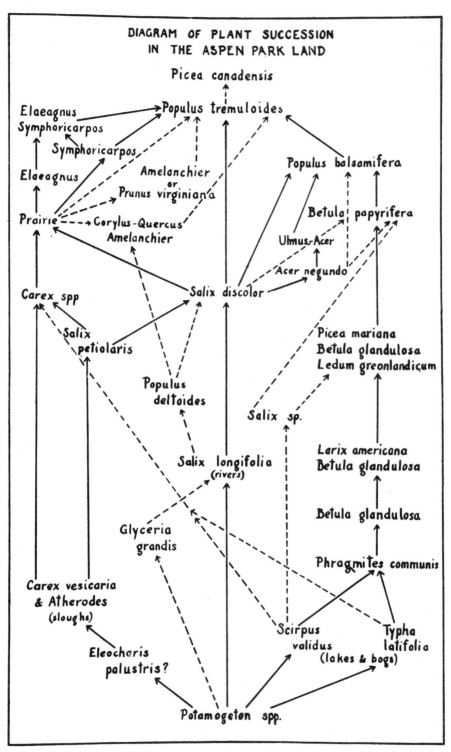

FIG. 43. Irregularities in succession in the aspen park land of Alberta. The arrows indicate the trend of successions, solid lines the most common seres, and broken lines the less frequent sequences. (After Bird, 1930.)

speed of ecologic succession. The angle of slope, for example, affects the character of the soil, and also, through its relation to erosion, controls to some degree the rate of establishment of certain kinds of plants. It has been emphasized by J. H. Davis (1945) that the degree of physiographic maturity of the habitat often determines whether succession shall continue to the climatic climax or remain stalled for a short or long period of time at an edaphic climax. The dune-strand "formation" of the Caribbean, for in-stance, is in certain situations an edaphic climax, but on physiographically unstable sites it may be only a temporary successional stage (V. J. Chap-man, 1944).

Irregularities of succession are particularly evident in many microseres. The course of succession in a microstand, such as an animal dropping, may be influenced by factors including the season, the weather, and the relative abundance in the immediate vicinity of those species that invade the habitat at particular stages (Mohr, 1943). Any given microsere, therefore, may exhibit numerous variations in the sequence of its successional stages.

The external and internal factors that control the succession of ecologic communities are numerous and are very complexly interrelated. Certain of the factors that control succession in a particular community may be in a condition of balance, so that during one stage in a climatic cycle succession will proceed in one direction, while in a later stage of the cycle a reverse succession may occur. Any unraveling of the past history of a community on a particular site, therefore, is difficult and often impossible, except in the most general outline. Likewise, the future of any given community can be predicted with a reasonable degree of reliability for only a brief period. Such predictions must become more uncertain the further into the future they are advanced.

DEGREE OF CONTROL BY ORGANISMS. The degree to which the community is able to modify the physical characters of the habitat and thus to manu-facture its own environment varies greatly according to the situation. Al-though organisms are able to control ecologic succession in many situations and thus are able to direct the course of succession toward a climax, they are not equally effective agents of control in all habitats. In every kind of habitat the physical factors of the environment play at least some part in directing or limiting the course of succession, and often are much more effective than the biotic factors.

The organisms making up a terrestrial community are able to exercise the greatest amount of control over their habitat in those situations where plants grow very luxuriantly. Through their control of the sunlight that falls on the community, the trees, shrubs, and other large plants effectively direct the course of succession. In many situations, also, the plants and animals are able in considerable part to form soil that is suited to their own needs. Where the community is able to do this it may ultimately become largely independent of the character of the soil of the pioneer habitat. The organisms are able, furthermore, to control the local terrestrial climates to some degree, but are never able to control them completely. No terrestrial community is ever independent of the type of sunlight, temperature, precipitation, and rate of evaporation characteristic of its region.

In some shallow fresh-water ponds and in many quiet river pools the growth of aquatic vegetation may be heavy enough to modify the penetration of sunlight to a considerable degree. Aquatic vegetation also tends to aid in the accumulation of soil and thus aids in the succession toward a terrestrial type of community. In shallow-water habitats, therefore, the vegetation and, to a lesser degree, the animals may play an important role in directing the course of ecologic succession.

In certain marine habitats, also, especially along shore, organisms of various kinds, such as corals, mussels, and seaweeds, play an important role in directing the course of whatever succession takes place. Here it is the animals, rather than the plants, which are mostly in control. Much of the succession that occurs in littoral communities, however, is probably due to local physiographic changes. The organisms in a few aquatic ecosystems act to prevent erosion and to accelerate soil deposition, but in general they seem to be less effective than the agents which control succession on land.

ABSENCE OF SUCCESSION IN CERTAIN ECOSYSTEMS. Succession toward a climax seems to be entirely lacking in certain types of ecosystems. In many of the desert communities of the southwestern parts of North America, for example, "the initial, sequential, and final stages of a succession are characterized by the same species, and often by the same individuals" (Shreve, 1925: 102). Muller (1940) concluded that in the strict sense of the word there is no organism-controlled succession in the Larrea-Flourensia Desert Scrub of Brewster County, Texas. He also pointed out that succession controlled by organisms is not important in the arctic tundra. In such rigorous habitats as those of the desert and of the tundra the environmental conditions are so extreme that only the most vigorous and most resistant species are able to exist. In these situations, consequently, the pioneer species tend to persist indefinitely, and there can be little if any progression to a more advanced type of community.

In some situations, both in the ocean and on land, the climax may be reached by the addition of certain species but without the loss of any of the pioneer forms (Shelford, 1932a: 112). In such situations succession is a simple process and the succeeding communities do not differ greatly from one another.

On many rocky marine shores and on rocky shoals seaweeds and marine animals may form communities that are composed of densely crowded individuals. Here the organisms evidently exercise a considerable control over the local environment. Nevertheless, there seems to be little or no succession of communities in such situations, other than that produced by physiographic processes. In the marine communities around the shores of Puget

Sound, Washington, for example, no succession was discovered (Shelford and others, 1935), but the studies were not considered fully conclusive (Clements and Shelford, 1939: 353). On a small area in Monterey Bay, California, from which the *Mytilus californicus* association had been artificially denuded, Hewatt (1935) was able to demonstrate a short sere leading to the re-establishment of the original association. Among the littoral communities of the Woods Hole region, according to Allee (1934: 550), physiographic rather than biotic agencies are responsible for such succession as occurs.

In those fresh-water and marine habitats where the bottom is composed of shifting mud or sand, plants usually are absent or sparse, and the animals that are able to exist are chiefly burrowing forms. That fluctuations occur in the marine communities living on sand or mud bottom is well known (MacGinitie, 1939: 41). There is no good evidence, however, that the changes which occur in the bottom communities follow any regular successional sequence toward a climax. The changes which occur in the communities occupying such unstable habitats may be presumed to be produced mostly by physiographic processes.

The plankton communities, also, obviously cannot control their habitat to any great extent. These communities are in most part composed of floating or feebly swimming organisms that are constantly being drifted about by the winds and currents, though certain animals, such as the fishes, are highly mobile. The course of succession in the open water is influenced by many variable characters (Hutchinson, 1941), and there are frequent changes in the communities that occupy any given site. The successions that occur in plankton communities can seldom be said to form an orderly progression leading toward a climax.

CLIMAX AN IDEAL ONLY. The concept of climax, although a useful working hypothesis, must not be too rigidly applied. Each climax represents a state of dynamic equilibrium. There must accordingly be constant fluctuations, of greater or lesser amplitude, in the characters of every climax community.

S. A. Graham (1941: 361-62) and others have pointed out that many natural agencies, such as fires, insect outbreaks, windstorms, severe seasons, and other cataclysms keep almost every community continuously in a developmental stage. Frequent repetition of the local microseres also keeps most communities in a state of constant change. Furthermore, succession may be stalled for a longer or shorter period of time at some particular stage.

The various phases of the climatic cycles tend to favor first one and later another type of climax (Clements, Weaver, and Hanson, 1929: 201). During the drought cycle of the 1930's, for example, the true prairie climax of parts of eastern Nebraska and Kansas was replaced by the mixed prairie climax, which previously had been restricted to more western areas (J. E. Weaver, 1943).

The progressive modification of climates and the physiographic processes of land elevation and of base-leveling, furthermore, prevent the permanent establishment of any particular type of climax. The ideal which any climax tends to approach is, therefore, subject to constant modification. The climax must accordingly be considered an ideal which may be more or less closely approached but which is seldom or never realized.

The comparison of succession to a braided stream (Cooper, 1926:397) is a very apt one. The series of successions that finally unite to form an extensive climax often originate in diverse conditions of soil and topography, just as do the tributaries of a large river. No extensive community can be static, any more than can a river, and the various parts of the community may diverge in type and later reunite, like the branches of a braided stream. Like the stream, also, there may be eddies and reverse bends in succession, where movement is for a time in a backward direction. The rate of succession, like the rate of a stream flow, varies from place to place and from time to time, but is usually most rapid near the point of origin.

RATE OF SUCCESSION. Many successional progressions take place so slowly that the change from year to year may be almost imperceptible. Many of the early stages in succession, however, can be passed over fairly rapidly. After a fire, for example, the successive stages may follow one another quickly.

The complexity of the successional process makes very difficult any precise measurement of the rate of succession. Nevertheless, it is possible to measure with some accuracy the duration of certain of the stages or the length of a particular sere on a few sites. Thus, if a short-grass community in Colorado is plowed and later allowed to revert to its original condition, a period of about 20 years will be required for the succession from plowed land to the short-grass community, the time depending in part on the type of soil in the locality (Shantz, 1911: 66). On the Piedmont Plateau of North Carolina the time required on upland areas for succession to progress from abandoned field to climax oak-hickory forest is estimated by Oosting (1942: 118) to be 150 to 200 years.

SIGNIFICANCE OF SUCCESSION IN THE HISTORY OF THE EARTH

Whether the rate of succession in any sequence of communities be fast or slow and whether it be regular or irregular, it is evident that every community, no matter how stable it appears to be, will ultimately be replaced by another community of dissimilar type. In every part of the globe the climate, the physiography, the soil, and the species of plants and of animals are constantly changing and evolving, with resultant changes in the ecologic communities. Even the climaxes are not permanent because they, too, change during the course of geologic time. Every community, if it is to remain in adjustment to the constantly changing environment, must of necessity always be in process of change. Succession is more rapid in certain communities, in certain places, and at certain times than at others. Nevertheless, no community can ever be static, for its environment never is static. Every community then, including every climax, represents only a time phase in the continually unfolding history of the earth (Gleason, 1927: 325).

SELECTED REFERENCES

Clements, Frederic E. 1916. Plant succession: an analysis of the development of vegetation. Publ. Carnegie Inst. Wash., 242: i-xiii, 1-512.

Cooper, W. S. 1926. The fundamentals of vegetative change. Ecology, 7: 391-413.

Cowles, Henry C. 1901a. The physiographic ecology of Chicago and vicinity; a study of the origin, development, and classification of plant societies. Bot. Gaz., 31: 73-182.

Elton, Charles. 1927. Animal ecology. New York: Macmillan Co. Chap. 3.

Gleason, Henry A. 1939. The individualistic concept of the plant association. Amer. Midl. Nat., 21: 92-110.

Mohr, Carl O. 1943. Cattle droppings as ecological units. Ecol. Monog., 13: 275-98.

Muller, Cornelius H. 1940. Plant succession in the Larrea-Flourensia climax. Ecology, 21: 206-12.

Shreve, Forrest. 1925. Ecological aspects of California deserts. Ecology, 6: 93-103.

XVII

LOCAL AND GEOGRAPHIC VARIATION WITHIN COMMUNITIES

All communities vary more or less in their composition over the area in which they occur. No single stand or microstand ever is completely uniform. Likewise, the several stands of a particular association that occur in a given region often differ from one another in important respects. The same thing is true of microstands. Should any association or microassociation extend over a wide geographic area, the amount of variation from place to place among the several concrete units is likely to be considerable.

TYPES OF STANDS

PURE STANDS. The simplest type of stand is one in which a single species is so conspicuous that the whole stand seems to be made up of this one form. Such a growth dominated by a single species is called a pure stand. In terrestrial situations pure stands are nearly always dominated by a single species of plant, but in some aquatic communities certain kinds of sessile animals also may grow in pure stands.

No stand, of course, is ever pure in the sense that it is composed entirely of a single species. Such a growth would be a society rather than a community. The conspicuous species in the stand always is accompanied by parasites and by other associates in at least small numbers. Sometimes, in fact, the inconspicuous associated forms may actually be many times more abundant than the conspicuous species that gives the stand its general appearance.

Pure stands are especially characteristic of pioneer communities. The first species that is able to colonize a previously unoccupied habitat is likely to cover it completely and evenly and to hold it for a time against the encroachment of other species. The species that colonizes a previously unoccupied habitat, however, is often unable to reproduce itself there. It frequently happens, therefore, that a pure stand is composed of individuals all of which invaded the situation at the same time and which consequently are all of approximately the same age.

MIXED STANDS. A pioneer community seldom is able to persist very long as a pure stand. Only in certain very rigorous habitats, such as parts of

391

some deserts, will the pioneer community fail to be followed by a more advanced stage consisting of a mixed stand of several species. In most habitats the pioneer pure stand will be able to endure only during the life of the first set of individuals that become established there. It is true that if these pioneer individuals are very long-lived, as Douglas spruce for instance, the stand may continue to be nearly pure for hundreds of years. In time, however, the pioneer species will in most situations be succeeded at least in part by other species and a mixed stand will result. All the individuals of the succeeding species are not likely to germinate or to invade the habitat at the same time. Each mixed stand, therefore, probably will be composed of individuals of diverse ages and of various sizes.

The several species which are associated to form a mixed stand are seldom equally abundant. The native hardwood forests of northern Michigan, for example, often were composed of a mixed stand of sugar maple, beech, yellow birch, and other more rare species. Generally, the sugar maple was the most abundant species, the beech was intermediate in abundance, and the birch was still less common.

The number of species that may live together in a mixed stand varies from 2 to at least several hundred. In the Rocky Mountains one sometimes finds mixed stands of conifer forest made up almost entirely of 2 important species, yellow pine and Douglas fir. Deciduous forests often are composed of a considerable number of species of trees. In parts of the southern Appalachian region of southeastern North America, for example, 15 to 20 tree species may be found in various combinations in the climax mixed mesophytic forest (Braun, 1938: 518). The number of species of trees represented in some of the tropical rain forests may be still greater (P. W. Richards, 1945). In certain Brazilian forests studied by D. E. Davis (1945: 292) over 90 species of trees were noted. Warming (1899) stated that tropical forests are composed of such a large number of species that it often is difficult to locate more than a single individual of any given species. In forest that had been felled, when the identification of species is easier than it is in standing forest, Warming found the number of species to range from 27 to 91 among 50 to 250 trees which he counted. At least 350 tree species were said by W. H. Brown (1919: 30) to live in the Philippine dipterocarp forest near Manila, though these species do not all occur together at any given station.

The composition of mixed stands is seldom fully uniform except over relatively small areas. On the contrary, most communities vary irregularly in composition from place to place. Even a community that appears at first glance to be a nearly even mixture of several species will often be found on closer inspection to exhibit considerable internal variability. A meadow, for instance, that appears to have an even plant carpet usually includes relatively wet spots on which 1 set of species thrives and also relatively dry spots on which a very different set of species may occur.

COMMUNITY MOSAICS. Certain species of plants and animals grow in clumps or colonies, with the result that the community of which they form a part exhibits a mosaic pattern of organization. In wet meadows, for example, coarse grasses often occur in clumps, between which finer types of grasses and other herbs grow. On parts of many deserts the shrubs grow in clumps, between which the ground is covered only by a thin growth of annuals and perennials. Certain delicate herbs grow in the shelter of the shrubs which often are thorny. The vicinity of these shrubs also is a favorite site for the homes of kangaroo rats and other small animals. Certain annual plants grow best in the open spaces between the shrubs (Went, 1942). It may be assumed that some kinds of insects and other animals also inhabit these open spaces between the shrubs. In such a desert situation, then, each stand is composed of an interspersed mosaic of 2 types of microstands represented, respectively, by the shrub clumps and by the more open spaces between them (Fig. 44). Such a type of organization in which a stand is composed of a mosaic pattern of 2 or more interspersed microstands is relatively common in nature (Romell, 1930: 593; Diver, 1938b).

The mosaic type of community organization is sometimes difficult to distinguish from a mixed or a pure stand. Thus, if trees or shrubs occur in a nearly closed stand and if attention is centered on these woody plants rather than on the openings between them, the stand may be considered pure or mixed, depending upon whether 1 or more species of woody plants are present. Also, in a forest stand the forest crown may be formed by 1 or by several species of trees in either a pure or a mixed stand, but the microstands on the forest floor may alternate in a mosaic pattern. Whether a given community shall be called a mixed stand or a mosaic depends in considerable part on the point of view of the observer and on the emphasis he wishes to give to a certain feature of community organization.

VARIATION WITHIN STANDS

Numerous factors operate to produce variability within stands. Among these the most important are variations from spot to spot in the physical factors of the habitat, irregularities in the distribution, activities, and heredity of the several species of member organisms, and inequalities in the relation of the stand to adjacent stands of differing community types. Because of the numerous factors that operate to produce variability within stands, uniformity of composition throughout a stand is rarely found. On the contrary, most stands vary more or less in their make-up from spot to spot and many types of stands are highly variable.

VARIATIONS IN THE PHYSICAL HABITAT. The physical factors of the habitat seldom are uniform over any large area. Within the limits of a single stand of a terrestrial community, for example, there always are small to large variations in soil type, drainage, exposure to sun and to wind, temperature, likelihood of frost, relative humidity, and other factors. The con-

FIG. 44. Mosaic distribution of plants in creosote-bush association near Tucson, Arizona. The prevailing shrub is creosote-bush (*Covillea tridentata*), but there are a few individuals of the cholla cactus (*Opuntia*). The shrubs grow in open stands, between which there is a growth of low herbs, here mostly plantain (*Plantago*). The growth of herbs forms a secondary mosaic, with open spaces of bare soil between the plants. (Redrawn by Carlton Angell from Coville and MacDougal, 1903, by permission of the Carnegie Inst. of Washington.)

ditions toward the edges of a stand are particularly likely to differ from those within the main body of the community. These local variations in the physical factors of each habitat inevitably produce irregularities in the characters of every stand.

IRREGULAR DISTRIBUTION OF THE ORGANISMS. The individuals of each species seldom are evenly distributed throughout any stand. On the contrary, the individuals of most species tend to occur thinly in certain spots and more thickly in others. Certain species form social groups or colonies, with the result that their distribution within the stand is very irregular. The distribution of mobile animals frequently changes because of movements of the individuals; thus the composition of the stand at any given point is in a constant state of fluctuation.

Many kinds of animals live in either small or large social groups, which are called colonies when they are stationary. If the population of such a social species has a low density in the community, its colonies may be situated at considerable distance from one another. Sometimes the isolated locations of the several colonies of a species in a particular community are correlated with the corresponding isolated occurrence of special types of local habitats. At other times, however, the position of the colony seems to be determined largely by chance. Such marine birds as the herring gull, for instance, nest in large and crowded colonies in spite of the occurrence only a short distance away of habitats which are apparently just as suitable for nesting (Darling, 1938: 48). It is also true that a given colony may change its location from time to time.

Plants, as well as animals, often occur in groups that are distributed irregularly in the stand. Sometimes these plant groups, like some animal groups, are correlated in their distribution with a particular type of local habitat. At other times a group may result from the aggregation of young plants around a parent individual. Plants that reproduce vegetatively are particularly likely to form clumps, but so also are many forms with heavy seeds that are not easily distributed by the wind.

A certain amount of irregularity is introduced into communities also by random distribution. It must be emphasized that random distribution is not likely to be uniform (Romell, 1930: 592). Only when the individuals of every member species are spaced evenly apart will a stand be fully uniform in its composition.

EFFECTS OF ANIMAL ACTIVITIES. Animals often play a considerable role in distributing the seeds of plants and sometimes the disseminules of other animals. Colonies of certain kinds of plants and animals, therefore, spring up along trails and around the homes and roosting places of animals. As an example may be cited the growth of seedlings of red cedar, sumac, arrowwood, dogwood, cherry, sassafras, and other plants which may spring up around a dead tree that is used as a roosting place by birds. The seeds of the plants are eaten by the birds and deposited in their droppings beneath the tree (E. H. Graham, 1944: 34).

HISTORIC ACCIDENTS. A further amount of variability within every stand is produced by what may be called historic accidents. In a forest, for example, a tree may be killed by lightning or by the attacks of parasites. The death of the tree leaves an opening in the forest crown through which sunlight may penetrate to the forest floor. The removal of the tree causes a local change in the habitat, with the result that certain light-loving species may be encouraged, while certain light-intolerant forms may be suppressed. In its history every stand has been subjected to innumerable accidents of various kinds, each of which has a temporary effect on the composition of the local community.

INDIVIDUAL VARIATIONS IN HEREDITY. The individual organisms that make up any given population vary among themselves in their heredity. Except for identical twins and for organisms produced by asexual methods, no 2 individuals ever carry exactly the same combination of genes. The considerable amount of individual variability exhibited by every species has been well described by R. J. Williams (1946). This individual variability is expressed both in morphologic and in physiologic characters and produces a large amount of variation within every stand.

INTERGRADATION BETWEEN COMMUNITIES. The intermingling of 2 adjacent stands of dissimilar type along the ecotone where they come into contact introduces irregularities into both stands. Only rarely is there a sharp boundary to any stand. Sharp community limits are most likely to occur where a terrestrial stand meets an aquatic stand at the bank of a stream or along the shore of a lake. Even here, however, there often is a narrow zone of intergradation. In those frequent situations where there is a wide zone of intergradation between 2 adjacent stands of diverse type the characters of both may be intermingled over a considerable area.

EFFECTS OF SUCCESSION. The successional changes that are in progress in many existing communities also contribute to community variability. It is evident that during the process of succession any given site may be inhabited by members from at least 2 different communities. If succession is proceeding rapidly and if certain of the individuals are long-lived, then members of more than 2 successive communities may for a time occur in the same stand. During a period of rapid succession, therefore, the stands affected are likely to exhibit a high degree of variability.

In certain situations succession may proceed so rapidly that a microhabitat suited for a given species remains favorable for only 1 or a few years. If this particular species is not able to reach and to occupy the microhabitat quickly, it may never become a part of that stand. It is accordingly evident that the powers of dispersal of species have an important relation to the make-up of certain stands. In general, the more ephemeral microhabitats must be occupied by those species which have the most effective means of dispersal, while those species which have weak powers of dispersal will be limited to the more stable communities. For example, the fireweed community that in northern North America so quickly springs up following a forest fire is dependent upon the wide dispersal of the wind-borne seeds of the fireweed (*Epilobium angustifolium*).

Ecotypes

Those individuals which exhibit a distinctive type of inherited morphology or physiology which is adaptive in relation to a particular ecosystem constitute an ecotype (Turesson, 1922*a*, 1922*b*, 1925; Gregor, 1944). For example, certain plants that grow in exposed places along the ocean shore tend to have a low habit of growth, whereby they escape in part the drying winds that blow in such a situation (Turesson, 1922*b*). Likewise, in alpine areas many kinds of plants tend to mature in a shorter season than lowland forms of the same species (Clausen, Keck, and Hiesey, 1940; 1948). Rodents that live on local areas of dark-colored soil are usually darker than their relatives that live on pale-colored soil (Dice and Blossom, 1937). Insofar as such local adaptations are inherited, they constitute ecotypes. The strains of parasites that are adapted to particular host species (Bodenheimer, 1938: 167) are probably also to be classed as ecotypes.

According to the definition of ecotype given above, only those individuals which exhibit the particular adaptation concerned belong to that ecotype. Other members of the same population which fail to exhibit the adaptation do not belong to that ecotype, even though they may in part carry the underlying heredity. I disagree here with Clausen, Keck, and Hiesey (1940, 1948) and with Gregor (1947), who treat whole populations with complex heredity as ecotypes.

In his original use of the term "ecotype" Turesson (1922*a*, 1922*b*) referred to a growth form or other inherited character adapted to a particular kind of habitat. He noted that certain populations were composed wholly of 1 ecotype, but he also described other populations which were mixtures of ecotypes. Turrill (1946) has pointed out that the ecotypes described by Turesson are of a much lower taxonomic status than those described by Clausen, Keck, and Hiesey. It seems best to adopt the original concept of Turesson and to consider as ecotypes only those individuals which exhibit the particular inherited adaptation concerned. Other terms are available for populations and for geographic races.

The natural selection of individuals carrying combinations of genes that are favored by a local ecosystem should theoretically produce a special ecotype in each distinctive kind of habitat that a species occupies, that is, if a species has a considerable range of tolerance and is able to live in several kinds of habitats, then that species is likely to develop a series of ecotypes (Fig. 45), each adapted to a particular type of ecosystem that occurs within its geographic range (Clausen, Keck, and Hiesey, 1940). On the other hand, those noninherited modifications of growth form which are produced by the direct influence of the environment are not classed as ecotypes.

It is not necessary to assume that all the individuals which exhibit the same ecotype necessarily have exactly the same genetic constitution. The narrow-leaved ecotype of *Hieracium umbellatum* characteristic of Swedish shift-

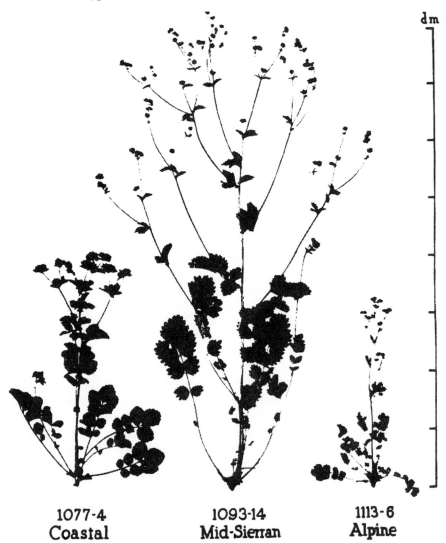

dm

1077-4
Coastal

1093-14
Mid-Sierran

1113-6
Alpine

FIG. 45. Ecotypes of *Potentilla glandulosa* from 3 life belts of the California biotic province. The plants were all grown together in a garden at Mather, elevation 1,400 meters. (After Clausen, Keck, and Hiesey, 1940, by permission of the Carnegie Inst. of Washington.)

ing dunes, for example, differs from locality to locality in the detailed shape of its leaves (Turesson, 1922*b*: 339). This indicates that the several local races involved differ from one another in heredity, to at least some degree. Very similar phenotypes likewise can be produced in the laboratory by entirely different genes or by dissimilar gene combinations. Nevertheless, it is probable that a given ecotype usually has much the same heredity no matter where it occurs within a given biotic province.

The tendency of a special ecotype to evolve in each local ecosystem is combated by interbreeding with adjacent local populations living in habitats in which other ecotypes may be favored. Random genetic drift may also in a small population run counter for a time to the trend of selection toward a given ecotype. The changes that are constantly in progress in the characters of every local habitat also militate against all the individuals in any given situation ever having exactly the same heredity. The size of the local population, the degree of its isolation from its neighbors, the stability of the local ecosystem, the intensity of natural selection, and the length of time the population has been isolated are among the factors which affect the evolution of ecotypes.

Latin names, such as *alpinus, arenarius,* and *campestris,* have been given to ecotypes by certain authors. It seems best, however, not to give taxonomic status to these ecotypic variations. In order to avoid confusion with taxonomic terms, I recommend that only colloquial names be applied to particular ecotypes. No confusion should result from a reference to an alpine, a sand, or a field ecotype. If an additional name is needed, some geographic or local term may be applied. Far too little is known as yet about ecotypes to justify any attempt at their classification.

Ecophenes

In response to the conditions of their local environment, the individuals of many kinds of plants and of animals are able to change their characters to at least a slight degree, thereby producing ecophenes. An ecophene may be defined as a particular type of modification of a genotype produced in response to the influence of the local environment (Turesson, 1922b: 347). For example, a plant grown in the shade often presents a strikingly different appearance from a plant with the same heredity grown in full sun. Also, a plant growing in wet soil may exhibit a very different ecophene from the same plant growing in dry soil. Two organisms with identical hereditary constitution but exposed to different local environments, therefore, may come to differ considerably in their structure and behavior. The responses of individual plants to the conditions of their environment are more evident than those of most animals, although animals also exhibit ecophenes. This is shown by the stunted condition of an animal which has not received an adequate amount of food of proper quality during its period of growth. These individual responses of organisms to the conditions of their environment produce an additional amount of variability in ecologic communities.

DIFFERENCES BETWEEN STANDS

Not only does each stand tend to vary in composition from spot to spot within itself, but each stand differs more or less from every other stand of the same association. The differences between stands are in considerable part produced by the same factors that produce variability within stands; these differences, however, are likely to be greater than those within stands. This is true because partial isolation of stands prevents the free mixing of their populations of plants and animals, with the result that the population densities of one stand may fluctuate to a great extent independently of the densities of any other stand of the same association. A species may even become eliminated from one stand of a particular association, while the same species is still an important member of other stands in the same area.

The amount of variation from stand to stand may be very great. Even the most uniform associations are composed of only a few species which are usually present in every stand (Curtis and Greene, 1949: 90). The majority of the species which are members of any given association are occasional or rare in their occurrence. Consequently, the relative frequencies of the several member species usually vary greatly from stand to stand. Notwithstanding this variability in composition according to species, the several stands of 1 association often exhibit a high degree of uniformity in physiognomy and in other general characters.

VARIATIONS IN ASPECT. Dissimilarities in the aspects presented at a given moment often produce considerable variation among the stands of a given association. The time of appearance of any given aspect depends upon the exposure of the local habitat to the sun and wind, upon the drainage of the soil, and upon the other biotic and physical characters of the situation. The greatest amount of variation between stands in the sequence of the aspects occurs, therefore, in those situations that have the most variability in habitat characters.

LOCAL RACES. Local races often develop in those situations where part of the population of a species is more or less isolated from the rest. Each isolated stand tends to develop a local race of each of its member species. This tendency to produce local races is combated by interbreeding between the populations of adjacent stands and by changes from time to time in the characters of each local habitat. Consequently, it is probable that individual stands only rarely develop recognizable local races. Our knowledge about local races is, however, very inadequate.

The term "race" is here used in its usual biological sense to refer to any population the majority of whose members are distinguished from the members of other populations of the same species by 1 or more inherited characters (Davenport, 1917; Dobzhansky, 1941: 63-64). Every race, of course, varies in its characters, and certain members of a race may not show the diagnostic racial characters. Many members of a given race, therefore, may not be distinguishable from certain members of other races. This is true because races are distinguishable from one another mostly by differences of averages in their measurements. All the individual members of a given population which are potentially free to interbreed are considered members of the same race, whether or not they exhibit the typical racial characters.

The distinctive characters of some races are known to be adaptive in relation to certain features of their ecosystems. The same character, therefore, may sometimes distinguish both a race and an ecotype. It is possible, however, that some racial characters are not adaptive (Dobzhansky, 1941, Chap. 5). Local races, therefore, may differ in this respect from ecotypes, which by definition always are adaptive. There is the further distinction that several ecotypes may occur within a single population, but only 1 race can occur at a given geographic location.

Each small population of a given species that inhabits an isolated stand should in time evolve into a local race. Natural selection is presumed to be most effective in producing evolution in small populations because each individual that is eliminated constitutes a considerable proportion of the population. The fixation of hereditary factors through the random elimination of genes also theoretically proceeds most rapidly in small populations (Wright, 1931).

Many stands are only incompletely isolated from their neighbors; furthermore, changes in the degree of isolation of the local habitats are constantly in progress. A local population which inhabits a particular stand may accordingly be completely isolated at one time, but at some later time it may again become united with the rest of the population of the species. Fluctuations in population density and changes in the trend of selection in each local habitat must also occur frequently. We may assume, therefore, that the pool of hereditary characters possessed by each local race is constantly in process of alteration.

VARIATIONS BETWEEN MICROSTANDS. The microstands of the same microassociation are even more subject to variation in their composition than are stands. The distribution of the several species of plants and animals that make up each microstand is affected by numerous local biotic and physical factors (Clapham, 1936: 249). Because they are usually small, isolated, and often ephemeral, microstands tend to be highly variable.

When the several microstands of the same microassociation are effectively isolated from one another, they may at any given time vary markedly both in their composing species and in the relative population densities of their several member species. Wesenberg-Lund (1930: 53) stated, for example, that in an old peat bog every little water hole may have its own peculiarities of flora and fauna. Certain of these local variations in microstand composition undoubtedly are due to local differences in the rate of progression of the seasonal aspects, with the result that a maximum local population of a given species may be reached earlier in one microstand than in others of the same type. Also each microhabitat probably differs slightly from every other in its food resources and in the other factors that control the productivity of the several species. In addition, the regulatory mechanisms of each microstand may, by chance alone, operate differently from those of the other microstands of the same microassociation, so that the seasonal maximum reached by any given species may vary among the microstands.

Many microstands have only a very temporary existence. This is especially true of some of the aquatic microstands. A fleeting burst of phytoplankton productivity that occurred in a Connecticut pond, for instance, has been described by G. A. Riley (1940).

Those microstands that are formed as the result of animal activities also are likely to be highly variable in their composition. The microstands that flourish on the mounds of earth thrown up by burrowing mammals, insects, and other animals must have a composition far from uniform. The mounds themselves vary in size and in type of soil, and they are located under varying conditions of exposure to the sun, winds, precipitation, and the attacks of herbivores and predators. Furthermore, succession at any given time will probably be at a different stage in each microstand of the same microassociation. All these factors make such microstands extremely variable.

GEOGRAPHIC VARIATION WITHIN ASSOCIATIONS AND MICROASSOCIATIONS

Geographic variation within associations is produced by all those factors that cause variability within and between stands. Factors which produce geographic variation in microassociations and in associations are similar and need not be described separately.

The greater the distance that separates 2 stands of the same association, the more the conditions of their habitats are likely to differ. Differences in heredity between local populations of each member species also are likely to increase with distance. Certain species, furthermore, may be limited in their distribution to a part only of the geographic area inhabited by an association. In certain districts such a species may consequently be absent from stands of the association, while elsewhere it is conspicuous.

Geographic Variations in Physical Factors

Those stands of an association that are far separated from one another geographically are likely to occupy habitats that are more or less dissimilar in climate, physiography, and soil. These geographic variations in the physical habitat must often be reflected by geographic variations in the characters of the stands. A sphagnum bog that occurs in the Carolinian biotic province of southern Michigan, for example, differs somewhat in its physical habitat from a similar bog in the Hudsonian biotic province or even from one in the Canadian province of northern Michigan. The individual sphagnum-bog stands, therefore, cannot be expected to be exactly the same in southern as in northern Michigan.

Limitations to the Geographic Ranges of Species

Probably the most important factor of all in producing geographic variability within associations is the failure of the several member species to have exactly the same geographic ranges. A species that in 1 place is an important member of an association may have only a limited geographic distribution and accordingly may be absent from extensive areas where that association occurs.

EFFECT OF PHYSICAL BARRIERS. A physical barrier to the distribution of a certain species, for example, may prevent it from reaching all parts of the area of distribution of a particular association. A body of water thus often forms a barrier to the spread of terrestrial animals and plants. Conversely, a body of land may form a barrier to the distribution of aquatic forms. Physical barriers to distribution, however, may not be equally effective against all the various kinds of plants and animals that compose a given association. For instance, volant birds and insects and those plants that have wind-dispersed seeds may easily cross a river that forms a positive barrier to the distribution of certain other terrestrial organisms.

A particular physical barrier may affect only 1 or a few species and consequently the associations affected may differ very little on the opposite sides of that barrier. The encelia and rocky-creosote associations of the Colorado Desert, for example, are slightly different in California from those in Arizona (Table XVI) because the Colorado River here forms a barrier to the distribution of a few species of rodents (Grinnell, 1914a: 101). Also, ecologic associations on islands usually are composed of fewer species of land organisms than similar associations on the adjacent mainland (A. R. Wallace, 1880: 233). Where closely related species or subspecies live in very similar communities on opposite sides of a barrier, it may be assumed that because of isolation produced by the barrier, divergent evolution has operated to produce these distinct forms (Emerson, 1943: 103).

EFFECT OF CLIMATIC BARRIERS. Climatic barriers operate somewhat differently from those physical barriers that abruptly limit the distribution of animals and plants. A climatic barrier seldom forms as sharp a limit to the distribution of a species as a physical barrier, such as a large body of water, does for a terrestrial species. In fact, the exact location of a climatic barrier may vary from year to year, depending upon the changes of climate. During a series of mild winters, for instance, certain frost-sensitive plants, such as the creosote bush, may spread some distance to the northward, but the northern pioneers of these species may be seriously injured or killed during the next severe winter (W. P. Cottam, 1937).

Climatic and edaphic barriers to the distribution of species often have only a gradual effect; consequently a species may occur in reduced numbers

far beyond its optimum habitat. As a result, a species that is in 1 area an
important member of a given association may occur only infrequently in
an adjacent area.

The effectiveness of a given climatic barrier is, of course, not the same
for all the member species of an association. A climatic barrier, such as frost,
that may positively limit the distribution of a particular kind of organism
in a certain geographic direction, may have no effect at all on an associated
species. In fact, a particular climatic barrier may affect only 1 or a very few
of the species making up an association. For instance, the *Mytilus californi-*

TABLE XVI

Rodents to Which the Lower Colorado River Is an Absolute Barrier

(From Grinnell, 1914a, by permission of the University of California Press.)

Associations	Arizona side		California side	Associations
Encelia and Rocky Creosote	{ *Ammospermophilus harrisi harrisi*		*Ammospermophilus leucurus leucurus* }	Encelia and Rocky Creosote
			Peromyscus crinitus stephensi }	Encelia
Sandy Creosote	{ *Thomomys chrysonotus*	Colorado River		
			Thomomys albatus }	Saltbush
			Perognathus formosus }	Encelia and Rocky Creosote
Encelia and Rocky Creosote	{ *Perognathus intermedius*			
			Perognathus spinatus spinatus }	Encelia and Rocky Creosote

cus or sea-mussel association has an extensive distribution along the shores
of the Pacific Coast of North America. It occurs both in the cold waters
north of Point Conception, California, and in the warmer waters south of
that point. The species of mussel that largely controls the community, and
from which the community derives its name, is able to thrive both in warm
and in cold sea water. Several of the associated species also have a wide
distribution and a few of them accompany the sea mussel over its whole
range. Others of the associated species are more restricted in range. Certain
of these more restricted forms live only in the warm waters south of Point
Conception and others only in the colder waters to the north (Haas, 1943).

EFFECT OF BIOTIC BARRIERS. The presence or absence of a particular
species may affect the occurrence of another related form. Thus, the existence of an obligate parasite as a member of any community is dependent

on the presence there of its host species. On the other hand, the presence of a seriously infective organism may prevent a susceptible species from existing in a given area. Numerous species are dependent for essential services upon associates without whose aid they cannot succeed. Certain relationships between associated species consequently operate as biotic barriers to produce geographic variability in associations.

The control of the distribution of a particular species by biotic barriers is, of course, always based ultimately on control by climate or by other physical barriers. This is true because those organisms which operate as biotic barriers to other forms are themselves directly or indirectly controlled in their distribution by physical barriers.

The types of barriers which a given species encounters may vary from place to place along the borders of its geographic range. For instance, the prairie vole (*Microtus ochrogaster*) of the Illinoian biotic province is believed to be prevented from spreading westward by the occurrence of increasing aridity in that direction. It is probably prohibited from extending its range southward by the intolerably high temperatures that at times occur there in the open fields in summer. It is prevented from spreading eastward by the lack of its open-field habitat (Dice, 1922: 46-47).

SPECIES OF RESTRICTED RANGE. Many species of plants and of animals have a very restricted geographic distribution. They may be numerous or even abundant in a particular type of local situation, but rare or absent elsewhere (G. L. Stebbins, 1942). A few species exist only in a single very restricted stand, such as on an island or on a mountain top.

Certain of these species of restricted range may be ancient forms that are approaching extinction and that now are able to persist only on 1 or a few especially favorable spots. Others may be new species just evolved which have not yet had time to spread far from their place of origin. Still others may be restricted in distribution because of their high specialization to particular types of local habitats. Whatever the factors that produce localization in the distribution of each particular species, there results a considerable degree of geographic variation within associations.

GEOGRAPHIC VARIATION GREATEST FOR MINOR SPECIES. From the preceding discussion it will be evident that the assemblage of species that compose a particular association will seldom remain associated over any large geographic area. Associations vary geographically in their composition because of the subtraction of certain species and the addition of others. A rare species is especially likely to be present in one stand but absent from another. The greatest part of the geographic variation in the composition of associations is undoubtedly caused by irregularities in the distribution of these less common species.

Most rare species play only an insignificant role in community organization and their presence or absence may accordingly be of little ecologic importance. Nevertheless, they must be considered in the complete description of any association and the amount of geographic variation produced by their irregular distribution should not be minimized.

WIDE-RANGING SPECIES. The barriers to the spread of each species differ at least in part from those that limit the distribution of every other member of its association. Accordingly, it is rare for any 2 species to remain associated throughout the range of both. Nevertheless, several species that play an important part in the organization and in the regulation of a particular association may remain together over a wide area. If the variations in the composition of the association produced by additions and subtractions from place to place of those species that play only a minor role are disregarded,

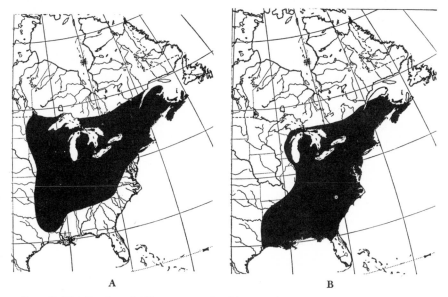

A   B

FIG. 46. Distribution of (A) sugar maple (*Acer saccharum*) and of (B) beech (*Fagus grandifolia*), showing the differences between the geographic ranges of these 2 important members of the beech-maple community. (After Nichols, 1935.)

this particular association may be said to have a widespread distribution. This is a wholly useful and practical procedure, so long as one remembers that the association actually is not exactly the same in all the areas where it is mapped as occurring.

As an example of a wide-ranging type of community may be cited the beech-maple association of eastern North America. Over a wide area the beech and the sugar maple are associated in the climax forest, though the other associated climax trees vary from region to region and include yellow birch, American elm, basswood, hemlock, white pine, chestnut, yellow tulip, sweet gum, various oaks, and other species (Weaver and Clements, 1938: 511; G. E. Nichols, 1935: 407). The beech and the sugar maple, however, do not have exactly the same geographic ranges (Fig. 46). In northwestern Michigan, for example, the beech is absent from the climax forest, but the sugar maple remains a very important member of the climax (Dice, 1943: 15). There is thus a considerable amount of geographic variation in the distribution of the more important trees of the beech-maple association, but over an extensive geographic area this community retains a fair degree of ecologic uniformity.

IRREGULARITIES DUE TO INVASIONS. At the time when a species is expanding its range a certain amount of irregularity is likely to be introduced into any association which it enters because of the time required to spread over the whole area of that association. Organisms that have a high rate of dispersal and which are able to establish themselves quickly, produce irregularities in community composition for a shorter time than those species whose invasion proceeds more slowly. Climax associations are less likely to be invaded by newcomers than are the earlier stages in succession. In this respect, then, climax associations tend to be more uniform than subclimax associations (Gleason, 1920: 22-23).

Geographic Races

Another source of geographic variation in associations is the variation from place to place which many species exhibit in their hereditary characters. Most species of plants and of animals exhibit at least a small degree of geographic variation in their morphology. Numerous species also are known to vary geographically in their physiology and habits. For example, the behavior of the yellow-breasted chat (*Icteria virens*), of the American robin, and of other birds is said by Brooks (1942) to vary considerably from region to region.

An especially good example of the occurrence of geographic variation within a single species of animal is afforded by the deermouse (*Peromyscus maniculatus*). This species has a wide range over the continent of North America. Nearly every population of this small rodent seems to differ in 1 or more characters from every other population (F. B. Sumner, 1932; Dice, 1940b). In this species geographic variation occurs in pelage color, in body proportions, in behavior, and in the type of habitat selected.

Plants likewise may vary geographically in the height of stem attained, number of stems produced, erectness of growth, type of branching, possession of herbaceous or woody stems, and other features of their structure. They may also differ in their resistance to severe winter cold, in their season of growth, in the ability of their foliage to withstand frost, in their times of blooming and fruiting, in their type of leaves (deciduous or evergreen), and in other physiologic characters (Clausen, Keck, and Hiesey, 1940).

SUBSPECIES. The more conspicuous geographic variants of a species are usually named by taxonomists as subspecies. In the usage of vertebrate zoologists and of many invertebrate zoologists and botanists a subspecies is always a geographic race. This convention is coming to be standard practice among all taxonomists. For example, about 50 geographic races of *Pero-myscus maniculatus* have been named by mammalogists as subspecies.

By cuttings taken from an individual plant and grown in different life belts in California it has been demonstrated that many of the geographic variations exhibited by plants are based on heredity (Clausen, Keck, and Hiesey, 1940). Likewise it has been shown by F. B. Sumner (1932) and by Dice (1940b) that the subspecies of the mice of the genus *Peromyscus* collected in widely separated areas maintain their characteristics when bred under controlled conditions in the same laboratory. It is evident, therefore, that although some degree of individual modification in structure and in behavior is possible in response to the conditions of the local habitat, a considerable part of the geographic variation exhibited by organisms in nature must be due to hereditary factors.

It may be assumed that each geographic race has evolved in response to the conditions in a particular ecosystem or group of related ecosystems. This does not mean that each subspecies is necessarily perfectly adapted to the conditions of its habitat but only that it is at least able to tolerate them. In general, therefore, if a geographic race of a particular species occurs in a given biotic province, it should occur throughout the province in those associations suitable for its existence. The boundaries of biotic provinces, however, are in many places poorly defined and furthermore the ranges of subspecies often do not end abruptly at the boundaries of biotic provinces. Consequently, it sometimes happens that 2 or even more different subspecies of a species may occur in the various parts of a single biotic province.

Whether or not any particular geographic variation in structure or behavior exhibited by a species is called a subspecies by taxonomists, each such variation changes to at least some slight degree the relations of the individuals concerned to their communities.

CLINES. The geographic variation exhibited by certain species of organisms is of a gradual sort, with no abrupt change at any place. A geographic gradient in a given character or in a group of characters of a given species may be called a cline (Huxley, 1938b). Such a cline in a particular species often is correlated with a parallel gradient in some feature of the environment. Thus a cline may be correlated with a gradient in any one of the various features of the climate, soil, or other habitat factors, including the biotic ones. Many clines, however, have no known relation to any gradient in the habitat.

Not all the geographic variation of species, however, is of a gradual sort. Along a climatic gradient there often occurs a series of ecotypes, each more or less distinct from the others. Thus, as has already been mentioned, in going from sea level to the alpine belt in California several species of plants present a series of ecotypes (Clausen, Keck, and Hiesey, 1940). Many animals exhibit a similar sort of geographic variation. In going from east to west across North America, for example, one will encounter a series of named subspecies of many kinds of mammals, birds, reptiles, and insects. Perhaps this step-by-step form of geographic variation is due to a tendency for certain genetic combinations to be more stable than others, but its precise basis has not been ascertained.

VARIABILITY OF COMMUNITIES COMPARED TO THAT OF OTHER BIOLOGIC UNITS

The high variability of all kinds of communities which is described in the preceding paragraphs is by no means an unusual phenomenon in biology. Variability is a natural feature of all kinds of life. The individual organisms making up every population differ more or less from one another in their morphology, physiology, and behavior. Communities are much more loosely organized than are individual organisms. In view of the great variations in climate, soil, and other physical factors to which communities must adjust themselves, it is to be expected that the composition of every type of community will exhibit a considerable amount of variation from place to place.

SELECTED REFERENCES

Clausen, Jens, David D. Keck, and William M. Hiesey. 1940. Experimental studies on the nature of species. I. Effect of varied environments on western North American plants. Publ. Carnegie Inst. Wash., 520: i-vii, 1-452.

Grinnell, Joseph. 1914a. An account of the mammals and birds of the lower Colorado Valley, with special reference to the distributional problems presented. Univ. Calif. Publ. Zool., 12: 66-110.

Livingston, Burton E., and Forrest Shreve. 1921. The distribution of vegetation in the United States, as related to climatic conditions. Publ. Carnegie Inst. Wash., 284, P. I.

Turesson, Göte. 1922b. The genotypical response of the plant species to the habitat. Hereditas, 3: 211-350.

XVIII

RELATIONS BETWEEN COMMUNITIES

The composition of every community is affected not only by the factors operating within that particular ecosystem but also by the conditions in neighboring and even in distant situations. No community, no matter how distinct its characters may be, can ever be independent of its neighbors.

An example of interrelations between 2 adjacent communities has been described by Piemeisel (1945). In southern Idaho the beet leafhopper (*Eutettix tenellus*) carries from plant to plant the virus which produces "curly top" of sugar beets, beans, tomatoes, and other valuable cultivated plants. The simplest way to control the virus is to eliminate the beet leafhopper that transmits it. Control, however, is rendered difficult by the fact that the leafhopper thrives also on weeds of several kinds that grow in the adjacent uncultivated communities, from which it moves into the cultivated fields to infect the growing plants. Under natural conditions the uncultivated fields would revert in a few years to annual and perennial grasses and the weeds that harbor the leafhoppers would disappear. Unfortunately, however, these uncultivated fields are now for the most part heavily grazed by domestic stock, by jack rabbits, and by rodents of several kinds, with the result that the natural succession is prevented and the fields remain covered with weeds. The overgrazing of these uncultivated communities consequently results indirectly but effectively in damage to .the crops grown at considerable expense in the adjacent cultivated fields.

Another example of the interrelations of communities is provided by the beaver pond. By building a dam across a small stream a family of beavers may change a terrestrial habitat into a beaver pond, a very considerable ecologic change. The beaver pond, as one of its functions, serves as a settling basin which removes the soil and organic materials which are being carried by the stream. The beaver pond, when it becomes shallow, also may serve in summer to raise the temperature of the water. The stream below a beaver pond may consequently be both clearer and warmer than the stream above the pond. For this reason a somewhat different stream community may live below the pond from that living above it.

410

AGENCIES THAT TRANSPORT ORGANISMS AND MATERIALS

Communities affect one another through the interchange of member organisms, of organic debris, and of inorganic materials. Wind and water both are very efficient agents for transporting organisms and materials from one ecosystem to another. Many animals also are able to move from community to community by their own exertions.

Wind as an Agent

The wind is an important agent for transporting from one community to another the seeds and spores of plants and also small animals of various kinds, such as spiders and insects. These wind-borne organisms have important effects on the ecosystems in which they come to rest. They provide food for certain animals, they may change the conditions of the surface soil, and the invaders may compete with the resident members of the community.

TRANSFER OF ORGANISMS BY THE WIND. Organisms of very light weight and those provided with special devices for riding the wind may be carried for a great distance away from their place of origin (Ridley, 1930). The dandelion seed is very small and is provided with a tuft of fine branching bristles which adapt it for being carried by the wind. Certain spiders and other animals likewise have special devices for dispersal by the wind. Such wind-dispersed organisms may affect far-distant communities. Many seeds and most animals, however, are too heavy to be transported by the wind.

Few studies have been made of the actual distance of dispersal of organisms from their place of origin. One of the best studies of the dispersal of bacteria, spores, seeds, pollen, and insects through the agency of wind is that of Wolfenbarger (1946). Certain of the more buoyant organisms reach a great height above the ground and are carried long distances by the wind.

Many of the seeds and spores that are transported by the wind are unable to germinate successfully in the ecosystems where they come to rest. Even if they are able to germinate, they may be unable to grow to maturity. On the other hand, wind-borne animals arriving at a new site are usually in a more fortunate position than are wind-borne plants. If the new site is not suitable for their existence, the animals often will be able under their own power to move on to a more favorable habitat.

Any wind-borne organisms, either plants or animals, that are able to survive successfully in their new situations, will usually come into competition with certain of the previously established members of the invaded community. Only when an invading species by good fortune finds an unoccupied ecologic niche will it be able to avoid competition in its new home. In any case the establishment of a new form, or even the arrival of new immigrants of forms previously present, must cause numerous readjustments in the organization of the invaded community.

TRANSFER OF ORGANIC DEBRIS BY THE WIND. The wind not only transports organisms of various kinds but often transports organic debris from one ecosystem to another. Dead leaves and similar organic materials may be carried by the wind from their place of origin to distant ecosystems. Wind-blown tumbleweeds, for example, may travel for miles before coming to rest. Such wind-carried organic debris enriches the ecosystem in which it is finally deposited.

TRANSFER OF SOIL BY THE WIND. The lighter particles of the soil of one ecosystem also may be picked up by the wind and later deposited in an adjacent or even in a far-distant ecosystem. Soil particles are especially likely to be picked up by the wind in arid regions where the vegetative covering does not completely protect the ground surface. The materials most frequently carried by the wind are derived from the topsoil. The removal of part or all the topsoil, of course, depletes the resources of the ecosystem concerned. The deposit of this material in another ecosystem may enrich the site where it comes to rest if the deposit is very thin. If the deposited material forms a thick layer, however, it may directly or indirectly destroy many of the plants and animals in the ecosystems where it falls.

Water as an Agent

Currents of water serve for the dispersal of many kinds of organisms and of materials from one aquatic community to another in much the same manner that winds serve to transport terrestrial organisms and materials.

TRANSFER OF ORGANISMS BY WATER. Aquatic organisms as a class actually depend much more on water dispersal than terrestrial organisms do on wind dispersal (Ridley, 1930). A great proportion of those aquatic plants and animals which are attached to the substratum during most of their lives have a free-floating or free-swimming stage in some part of their life histories. Numerous kinds of aquatic organisms are never attached to the bottom but are always subject to dispersal by currents of water. The dispersal of organisms by water currents consequently plays a large role in the interrelations of aquatic communities.

Terrestrial organisms as well as aquatic forms may be transported by streams or by the currents in lakes and oceans. On a lake beach or on a river bar, for example, one often sees windrows made up of myriads of seeds of terrestrial plants or of the bodies of terrestrial animals. The transported seeds often germinate in their new sites. Some of the animals deposited by the water also may be still alive and able to take up residence in a near-by community.

Many of the terrestrial organisms that are carried by water currents are blown into the water by the wind, so that certain individuals may be both wind borne and water borne. Numerous terrestrial organisms, however, fall directly into the water from overhanging vegetation or are washed from the land into the water without ever being wind borne. The cocoanut palm is an example of a terrestrial plant that depends largely on currents of water for its dispersal, yet this plant is widely distributed along the shores of the tropical oceans.

TRANSFER OF ORGANIC DEBRIS AND OF SOIL BY WATER. Water is a still more effective agent for the transportation of organic debris and of soil than is the wind. Rivers and streams of all sizes transport organic and inorganic materials, which ultimately are deposited in a new situation. Through soil erosion certain terrestrial ecosystems are depleted of valuable topsoil, which is carried away by the water. Materials already present in aquatic ecosystems also may be picked up to be redeposited elsewhere. Through the deposit of silt in thin layers the fertility of the soil is increased in many riparian ecosystems; however, if the soil is deposited in a thick layer, it may seriously injure the organisms on which it falls. Since rivers often transport light materials for great distances, the organic debris and soil originating in one ecosystem may affect other ecosystems which are far distant.

The materials transported by water affect not only aquatic communities but also many adjacent terrestrial communities. The organic debris thrown up on beaches by wind and waves, for example, forms an important part of the food of many beach animals. Even man makes use of driftwood and of other jetsam deposited along shores. Sand thrown up on the beach by waves may dry and then later be transported by the wind to be deposited in adjacent communities. Floods which spread out over riparian ecosystems often deposit a layer of silt or sometimes of coarse materials. Through the agency of water, food which originates in one ecosystem may be transported into another. In these and many other ways, then, materials and organisms transported by water affect communities other than those in which they have originated.

Movements by Organisms Themselves

Many individual organisms, especially those of terrestrial communities, are not dependent upon either wind or water currents for their dispersal, but are able to move about through their own exertions. The movements of individual animals from one community to another produce especially important effects on both the community from which the animal emigrates and the community into which it immigrates. A few of the simpler kinds of plants also are able to move themselves from place to place by their own activities. The range of individual movement by such plants, however, is usually small.

EFFECTS OF DAILY LOCAL MOVEMENTS. Communities that lie adjacent to one another tend to have an especially close interrelation because of the daily local movements of many of their animal members. It has earlier been pointed out, for example, that many animals feed in 1 ecosystem but roost or nest in a different ecosystem in the same region. Many individual animals are consequently members almost simultaneously of 2 or more communities, in each of which they perform different functions. The larger mammals and birds and especially the predators tend thus to travel back and forth between neighboring communities.

An individual animal may in the course of its daily and seasonal travels become temporarily a member of many different stands and these may include a number of dissimilar associations. Even though an individual has a more or less fixed home range, he may still become successively a member of several different minor communities. A colony of nest-building ants, for example, has a fixed position, but because the individual ants and their associated myrmecophiles forage over a considerable area around their nest, they temporarily become members of many diverse microstands. The microstands adjacent to such an ant colony are affected in numerous ways by the activities of the ants and their guests.

EFFECTS OF DISPERSAL. During the process of the dispersal of individual organisms from their places of origin they are likely to invade many neighboring communities. Thus the seeds and other disseminules of plants often are carried by wind, by water, or by animals into types of communities other than those in which they originated. Dispersing animals, especially the young, often travel or are carried considerable distances and invade many neighboring or distant communities. Even though the conditions in the invaded ecosystems may be unsuited for the continued existence of the immigrants, nevertheless these plants and animals temporarily become members of the invaded communities.

The surplus individuals produced by every animal species are likely to spread out from their place of origin into adjacent communities, where often the species does not live permanently or where it may be present only in scanty numbers. The dispersal movements of strong-flying or wind-dispersed species of animals may carry the individuals long distances away from their birthplaces and into very strange surroundings. The cotton moth (*Alabama argillacea*), for example, sometimes occurs in numbers in New York City, which is a long distance from places where cotton grows (Lutz, 1941: 19). The cotton moth thus becomes temporarily a member of certain northern communities in which it is unable to reproduce. By reason of this tendency of individual animals to disperse from their birthplaces, most communities serve as reservoirs from which temporary populations of various animal species are supplied to neighboring stands or even to distant communities.

EFFECTS OF SEASONAL MIGRATIONS. Great variations in the composition of certain communities may be caused by the regular seasonal migrations which are performed by many animals. For example, the arrival of the migratory birds in interior Alaska in summer almost completely transforms the organization of the communities of that region. Because of the inhospitable nature of the arctic habitat in winter, very few birds are year-round residents. The bird population consequently is tremendously increased by the influx of the summer breeders, which are of many species and occupy many diverse ecologic niches.

EFFECTS OF MASS MIGRATIONS. An extreme example of the effects of movements by animals from community to community may be seen in the descent of a plague of a certain species, such as grasshoppers or lemmings, upon a stand that previously was almost or completely free of these animals. Upon arrival in the new community the invaders will proceed to eat certain plants and in so doing they may destroy not only the plants attacked but also the food and shelter of numerous other kinds of animals. Reduction in the abundance of these forms results. The predators and parasites of the affected animal species will then likewise be made more scarce unless they can turn to other prey and to other hosts. At the same time the natural predators of the invading pest are likely to be attracted to the stand, thereby still further upsetting the previous ecologic balance (Elton, 1942: 134, 150). The whole organization of a community may, in fact, be completely disrupted by such an immigration.

When a species has increased to extraordinary numbers in a particular region and has exhausted its food supply, it may emigrate in many directions from its center of overabundance. The emigrating individuals often travel many miles, and accordingly they may cause alterations in communities long distances away from the original center of overpopulation (Fig. 47).

The movements of predators away from a locality following an abrupt decline in the numbers of a prey herbivore are especially likely to have profound effect on numerous near-by communities and may disturb even those at a considerable distance. Elton (1942: 469), for example, stated that the emigration of snowy owls from an arctic locality after a crash in lemming numbers is one of the remarkable features of the cycle. Such an emigration may affect the equilibrium of communities hundreds of miles away from the original source of the disturbance.

INTERRELATIONS BETWEEN COMMUNITIES IN RESOURCES

Communities often are related to their neighbors through sharing certain of their resources, as, for example, food and water. Certain other resources of one ecosystem also are sometimes utilized by members of a neighboring community.

Interrelations in Food Resources

It is in their food resources that adjacent communities often are most closely interrelated. Almost never does any community form an isolated unit which is dependent solely on the food produced by itself and which furnishes no food to its neighbors. The nearest approach to such a condition perhaps is found in certain lakes that have no outlets and in certain desert oases (Hesse, Allee, and Schmidt, 1937: 138). Even an isolated lake, however, receives

some food materials by inwash from the surrounding land and every oasis
receives from the surrounding desert a number of visitors who utilize its
water or its food.

The members of many communities actually derive a considerable part
of their food from neighboring ecosystems. Many marine birds that nest

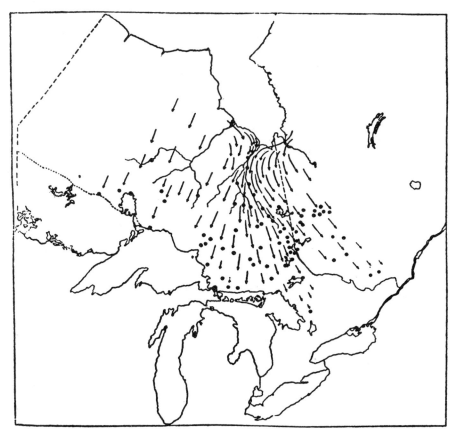

FIG. 47. Dispersal of a species from an area of overpopulation. The emigration in 1932
of the sharp-tailed grouse (*Pedioecetes p. phasianellus*). (After L. L. Snyder, 1935, by permission of the Ontario Mus. Zool.)

and roost on land, for instance, derive most or all of their food from near-by
aquatic communities. Likewise, many terrestrial birds that breed and roost
in trees find part of their food in adjacent open-field ecosystems. The animals that compose a cave community directly or indirectly derive all their
food outside the cave (Banta, 1907). The members of abyssal communities
derive all their food from organic materials originating in higher levels.
The food resources of neighboring communities consequently have many
important interrelations. From a broad point of view the food productivity

of each community affects the operations of every other community in the same region.

WIND-BORNE FOOD. The organisms and organic debris carried by the wind are a source of food to those ecosystems in which the materials come to rest. The amount of food provided by any single wind-borne spore, seed, animal, or piece of organic debris is slight because any material that is carried by the wind can have but little weight. In the aggregate, nevertheless, the amount of food transported into certain ecosystems by the wind may be considerable. In fact, on certain pioneer sites, such as bare rock or a snow surface, the food deposited by the wind may constitute the major part or all of the food resources available to the community living there.

WATER-BORNE FOOD. Water currents also transport much food from one ecosystem to another. Rivers, in particular, discharge food organisms and organic debris into lakes and oceans. Because currents of water in the ocean distribute organisms and organic debris, materials originating in a marine ecosystem often nourish the members of other communities. Most of the food that supports the bottom communities and ultimately most of the fisheries of the fjords and other sheltered waters of the North Atlantic region originate in communities along the ocean shores (Petersen and Jensen, 1911; P. B. Jensen, 1915; T. C. Nelson, 1947). One of the most important contributors to this food supply is the eelgrass (*Zostera*). From a study of a marine estuary in California, MacGinitie (1935: 649) concluded that the main source of food supply to all the bottom communities in that situation was the organic debris suplied by *Zostera* and other littoral plants.

Interrelations in Water Resources

Neighboring terrestrial communities often are tied together also through their relations to free water. The occurrence of open water not only affects the aquatic and semiaquatic life able to exist in the water itself but also attracts many kinds of terrestrial animals that require water to drink. The raccoon, for instance, is never found far from water because it requires water to drink and also has the habit of washing its food in water. The tiger is said to drink large quantities of water while it is engaged in eating a "kill" and accordingly it is never found far from water.

In arid regions water has especial importance for many kinds of mammals and birds, some species of which regularly travel long distances to drink from water holes. Sheep and cattle need to drink every day in hot weather and consequently are unable to utilize pastures in summer that are more than a few miles from a water supply. On the other hand, horses and mules can utilize much more distant pastures, not only because they can travel faster than cattle but also because they can remain away from water for 2 or even more days at a time, except in very hot weather.

Because open water is often very irregularly distributed in terrestrial habitats, those animals that must drink frequently must also be irregular in their distribution. The distribution of free water consequently affects the composition of all the communities of which such animals form a part. In the big game part of Africa, for example, the large mammals may be forced to leave extensive sections of otherwise favorable habitat during drought periods because of the drying up of the water holes (Roosevelt and Heller, 1914: 680).

Interrelations Involving the Soil

The enrichment of the surface soil by the deposit of wind-borne organisms and organic debris is of considerable significance to certain ecosystems. Wind-borne leaves and other organic debris, for example, often form a mat over the ground in ecosystems adjacent to those in which they have originated. The surface mat formed at times by such wind-borne materials affects the rate of evaporation of moisture from the soil, sometimes interferes with the movements of small terrestrial animals, and contributes to the enrichment of the soil. In most situations the contribution to soil enrichment by wind-borne organisms and debris is slight in any 1 year, except under very special conditions, but its cumulative effect is often considerable.

The erosion of soil from terrestrial ecosystems may have an important effect on those lowlands or aquatic ecosystems that receive the deposited materials. The amount of runoff and of erosion from terrestrial ecosystems is dependent in part on the vegetative cover and on the activities of animals. The characters of certain communities may consequently be indirectly affected by the activities of numerous kinds of organisms which live in neighboring habitats.

Interrelations in Other Resources

Certain members of a community may make use of resources of neighboring ecosystems other than food or water. Thus, certain kinds of animals may temporarily seek shelter in an ecosystem adjacent to the one in which they spend most of their time. Likewise, certain birds and bats may roost in ecosystems where they do not feed.

SPECIAL TYPES OF COMMUNITY INTERRELATIONS

At the margins of its habitat a community comes into close contact with its neighbors. Communities of diverse types that occur in relatively small patches interspersed with one another consequently have especially close interrelations.

Marginal Communities

Where habitats that are markedly different in character lie adjacent to one another there often occur marginal communities which themselves may have pronounced individuality. Thus, along the shores of the ocean or of a large lake there may be beaches of various types and often also dunes, eroded cliffs, and other shore features. If there are tides, an intertidal zone having peculiar communities will be produced. Under the surface of the water along the shore there will also be a series of subsurface communities. Likewise, along the valley of a large river there is usually an extensive development of riparian communities, which often differ in important characters from those of the surrounding uplands. Where the Colorado River, for instance, crosses the Colorado Desert of California and Arizona, the river and riparian communities are very different from those of the adjacent desert communities on each side (Grinnell, 1914a).

Another example of a marginal community that exhibits special characters of its own is the sumac association, which in many places in the Illinoian biotic province forms an ecotone between forest and prairie. The sumac shrubs produce more shade than the herbs of the prairie, but less shade than the adjacent forest. A considerable number of prairie plants and animals are found in the sumac community associated with a few from the forest. The sumac itself is not a regular member either of the prairie or of the forest. The sumac association, therefore, while it is somewhat intermediate in character, is distinct both from prairie and from forest (Dice, 1923b: 48-49).

SPECIES OF THE MARGINS. Certain kinds of animals reach their greatest abundance at the borders of an ecosystem, while in the main body of the ecosystem they may be less numerous or absent (Shelford, 1913: 262; Lay, 1938). This tendency sometimes produces an "edge-effect" (Aldo Leopold, 1939). Not every species of animal, however, is most numerous at the borders of an ecosystem. Certain birds, like the meadow lark and bobolink (Beecher, 1942: 40), and certain mammals, such as the prairie deermouse (Blair, 1940b: 300), shun edges. Wildlife managers have in recent years tended to overemphasize the importance of "edge" communities for game species. According to Davison (1946), relatively few species actually thrive best at the borders of ecosystems.

Interspersed Communities

A certain amount of confusion has arisen in the minds of some field ecologists because of a failure to distinguish between community edges and interspersed communities. Many kinds of communities occur only in small patches or in narrow zones which are interspersed among communities of a dissimilar type, thus forming a mosaic pattern. Such interspersed communities can be expected to have a greater number of interrelations with their neighbors than communities that occur only in large masses and which consequently come into contact only along an "edge." In an area of interspersed communities the daily and seasonal movements of various kinds of mammals, birds, insects, and other animals bind the adjacent communities together and produce many interdependencies.

The interspersion of communities has especial importance for those mobile animals that find their essentials for life in several diverse types of ecosystems. A particular species of animal may perhaps feed in one ecosystem, find suitable shelter in another, and secure its best breeding sites in a third ecosystem. Such a species will, of course, succeed best in a diversified area where the several types of ecosystems preferred by it are interspersed. Aldo Leopold (1939: 130), for example, has pointed out that the eastern bobwhite quail requires an interspersion of woodland, brushland, grassland, and cultivated fields for optimum success.

The valley quail of California likewise is said by Emlen and Glading (1945: 7-8) to require at least 3 types of cover for its most successful exist-

FIG. 48. Four types of cover used regularly by the California Valley quail. For best success the birds need to have all these habitat types in proximity. (After Emlen and Glading, 1945, by permission of the Dept. Agric. Information, Univ. Calif.)

ence (Fig. 48). These birds prefer to feed in clearings or in sparse vegetation that affords them an open view of the sky. They may also nest in such a situation. Between periods of feeding they like to loaf under rather thick cover which protects them from the sun, wind, and rain, and from the eyes of predators. Cover suitable for loafing is good protection from predators, but these birds may also utilize more open habitats for protection from enemies. In their foraging excursions the quail seldom wander more than 50 feet from brushy cover of some sort, to which they can retreat to escape the attacks of predators. At night the quail roost among the dense foliage of trees or shrubs 5 to 30 feet tall. The most satisfactory habitat for valley quail, consequently, must have these several types of cover in proximity.

Interspersion of communities frequently occurs in the successional stages following fires or clearings. Consequently, it may happen that certain species, including several of importance as game, may thrive especially well after extensive fires. Game managers have accordingly sometimes recommended the clearing of forests or even the intentional setting of fires as a means of increasing game. Such a procedure will probably succeed under some conditions in increasing for a time the numbers of certain desired species. The setting of fires must, however, be applied with great caution and with due consideration of the effects on all the members of the several ecosystems involved, including the deterioration of the soil that results from the removal of humus-forming materials.

Ecologic Series of Communities

Certain communities that occur close together may be arranged in a sequence corresponding to a gradient of variation in 1 or more of the controlling environmental factors. Ecologic series have been especially emphasized by such Soviet ecologists as Alechin and Sukachev (Cain, 1939). An ecologic series of communities, for example, is often encountered in a wet meadow. Here the gradient of saturation of the soil by water tends to arrange the communities into an ecologic series based on soil moisture. With cyclic changes in water level the whole of such a series may be shifted upward or downward.

Ecologic series of communities may be produced by gradients in many kinds of habitat factors, including soil moisture, amount of humus in the soil, amount of soil aeration, amount of shade produced by the vegetation, or concentration of chemical substances in the soil or in the aquatic medium. An ecologic series of communities is likely to develop only in those situations where there is a gradient of a particular physical factor which is important in the control of the community type.

Community Boundaries

Community boundaries are likely to be sharper where the community exercises considerable control over the habitat than where such control is weak or lacking. Forests, for example, usually control the habitat to a very considerable degree and accordingly the edges of forest stands are often fairly sharp. On the contrary, in situations where the plants and animals have little control over the habitat, as generally is true in the desert, the margins of the communities are often difficult to determine except where they are controlled by soil factors. Wide areas of intergradation between adjacent communities, consequently, are of frequent occurrence in areas where the organisms do not control the habitat (Gleason, 1917: 469).

EFFECT OF SUCCESSION. A community that is in process of being succeeded by another community of different type will likely have areas of transition with 1 or more of its neighbors. Succession tends, therefore, temporarily to produce indistinct boundaries to the communities affected.

EFFECT OF FLUCTUATIONS IN HABITAT FACTORS. The degree of distinctness of the boundaries of certain kinds of communities sometimes varies also in response to fluctuations in the factors of the habitat. In the mature prairies of Nebraska, for example, certain widespread plant species appear as dominants in several types of prairie communities. Although distinct communities occur, they are difficult to delimit with precision. During the dry cycle from 1934 to 1940, however, many of the dominant species were destroyed or greatly reduced in abundance. Under these temporary conditions the several grassland communities formed a mosaic in which the community boundaries often could be definitely mapped (Weaver and Darland, 1944).

Ecotones

Ecotones between communities may be of several types. Between certain communities there is a broad zone of intermediate conditions. In such situations one community may pass gradually and almost imperceptibly into the other. In other situations there may be a sharp limit to each community, with the result that the ecotones are narrow and the boundaries of each community can be clearly identified.

In the ecotone between 2 very distinct types of associations there often occurs a marginal community, which may have distinctive characters of its own, as has been pointed out. Sometimes the characters of this marginal community are sufficiently distinctive for it to be recognized as a separate association. More frequently, however, the ecotone is not itself classed as a distinct community, but its presence introduces variability into both adjacent communities.

In the ecotone between 2 life belts or 2 biotic districts no intermediate type of community may occur, but the ecotone may take the form of an alternation of the principal types of communities represented in the adjoining belts or districts. Thus, where conifer forest meets grassland in the Rocky Mountains, there is likely to be an alternation of these 2 community types, with grass occupying the exposed slopes of the mountains and with yellow pine together with other conifers occupying the more sheltered slopes. In a region of rolling hills or low mountains such a mosaic type of ecotone may have a width of many miles.

GENERAL PRINCIPLES OF COMMUNITY INTERRELATIONS

Few detailed studies have been made of community interrelations. The general principles that apply to these interrelations must accordingly be deduced mostly from what we know about ecologic relations in general.

Influence of a Community Increases with Its Area

Communities that cover a considerable proportion of the area of a given region will, in general, have more influence on their neighbors than com-

munities that cover only .small areas. This is true because the more extensive communities nearly always are composed of large populations of numerous species. The seeds and spores of the numerous plants in these extensive communities are likely, as a consequence, to be carried to all the communities in the region. The mobile animals originating in an extensive
community also will probably wander into and perhaps cross most of the
neighboring communities. On the other hand, a community that covers
only a small area and is made up of only a few individual plants and animals will not be able to send out its offspring widely and so can have only
minor effects on its neighbors.

Certain communities may exert an influence on their neighbors that is
very great in proportion to their size. The presence of a water hole in a
desert region, for example, may enable many animals to live in the adjacent
arid communities which otherwise could not exist in that region. The water
hole may thereby greatly influence the characters of communities for miles
around.

Influence of a Community Decreases with Distance

The influence of a community on its neighbors will of necessity decrease
with distance. Adjacent communities will usually have the most influence
on one another. Although certain communities, through the movements of
migratory animals and through the dissemination of wind-borne and water-
borne organisms, influence others which are hundreds or even thousands
of miles distant, yet in general these long-range influences must be relatively
slight, except for the effects of the migratory birds.

No mathematical statement can be made of the precise rate of decrease
in the influence of communities on one another in relation to their distance
apart. It may be expected, however, that in general the influence of a community will decrease according to the square of its distance. Many exceptions to this rule can be cited, especially for those communities that lie
along the path of seasonal migration of certain birds. Nevertheless, the rule
should hold in general, because the area available increases as the square
of the distance from the point of origin.

Competition Among Communities

Neighboring communities constantly compete with one another for space,
as was pointed out long ago by Warming (1909). The succession of one community by another is clear evidence of such a struggle. During the process
of succession one community succeeds in expanding its area at the expense
of another.

Every community continually extends its range through the dispersal of
its seeds or other disseminules and through emigration of its individual
members. The majority of the individuals that invade an alien ecosystem

must perish because the conditions in which they find themselves are likely to be unsuited for their existence. A few individuals, however, may succeed in establishing themselves. Should the individuals of several characteristic species of a particular community thus become established within an adjacent community, they will thereby tend to produce succession and to expand the area of their own type of community.

It must accordingly be assumed that a struggle among all adjoining communities is constantly in progress. Should the boundary between 2 particular communities remain stationary for a time, this will indicate that the forces of aggression and of resistance are more or less equally balanced along that boundary. Some types of communities seem to be well able to defend themselves against aggression. Thus, a prairie is not easily invaded by trees or shrubs, even in a climate in which forest is the climatic climax. Many pioneer communities, on the contrary, seem to have little resistance to competition, but are quickly replaced by other successional stages.

Ecologic Unity of the World

It has been pointed out in the previous discussion that neighboring communities have many ecologic interrelations. The influence of a community decreases with distance, but communities that lie considerable distances apart may, nevertheless, have many ecologic interrelations, either directly through the interchange of individual organisms or indirectly through interactions with the intervening communities. All the communities in 1 local area actually constitute an interrelated regional community, as is implied by the recognition of biotic provinces and biotic districts.

From a broader point of view all the communities of a continent or of an ocean are related ecologically. In fact, it may be said that ecologically the whole world is a unit. Directly or indirectly every biotic event in 1 community ultimately, to at least a slight degree, affects every other community on the earth. The whole world of life actually forms 1 comprehensive community, of which the various subdivisions are very complexly interrelated.

SELECTED REFERENCES

Petersen, C. G. J., and P. B. Jensen. 1911. Valuation of the Sea. I. Animal life of the sea-bottom, its food and quantity. Rept. Danish Biol. Sta., 20: 3-81.

Warming, E. 1909. Oecology of plants. An introduction to the study of plant-communities. Oxford: Clarendon Press. Pp. 348-73.

Wolfenbarger, D. O. 1946. Dispersion of small organisms: distance dispersion rates of bacteria, spores, seeds, pollen, and insects; incidence rates of diseases and injuries. Amer. Midl. Nat., 35: 1-152.

XIX

CLASSIFICATION OF ASSOCIATIONS AND MICROASSOCIATIONS

The high degree of variability that occurs within ecologic communities of every rank and the general lack of precise boundaries between adjacent communities make their classification difficult. Ecologists have not yet been able to agree on any classification of communities according to rank. The system of classification here described will accordingly not be acceptable to all ecologists.

Several ecologists have attempted to devise statistical methods for ascertaining the rank in ecologic classification of any given community. These attempts have all been failures. I agree, therefore, with Ashby (1936) that statistical methods for classifying vegetation are not practical. On the contrary, the classification of communities must be based largely on the good sense of the experienced field ecologist. Quantitative methods for describing communities are, nevertheless, extremely useful and should be employed whenever possible.

Certain kinds of communities are assemblages in which the member organisms actually are directly or indirectly associated with one another. Each stand and each microstand is a concrete community of this kind. Certain other kinds of communities, however, are based on abstractions, being composed of those concrete communities which in our opinion are sufficiently similar in character to be classed together. An association does not exist as a unit in nature, but is formed only in someone's mind of those stands which are considered to be of generally similar type. If I believe forest trees to be important indicators of ecologic conditions, I shall probably recognize a number of forest associations. If, on the contrary, I believe soil type to be most important in the control of ecologic distribution in the area under consideration, I shall probably classify the communities under a wholly different array of associations. Because the classification of communities is based upon opinion, there is no "right" classification for any area. Community classification must change as information accumulates and as ecologists modify their opinions about the relative importance of the features which distinguish communities.

425

RANKS OF CONCRETE COMMUNITIES

At least 3 ranks of concrete communities can be distinguished in every region. The first and largest of these is a regional community that covers a considerable geographic area, perhaps including the whole of the region under study. In my terminology a regional community occupies a biotic province, a biotic district, or a life belt. The classification of regional communities will be discussed in Chapter XX. In this chapter I shall consider only associations and more minor communities.

Within each regional community certain types of stands recur with sufficient frequency to be recognized as associations. The stand then is a concrete community of lesser rank than the regional community. The third and lowest rank of concrete community usually recognized is the microstand.

Neither the stands nor microstands are categories that have hard and fast limits in classification. Frequently it is difficult to decide whether a particular concrete community should be considered a stand or whether it is of minor rank and should be classed as a microstand. The microstands are themselves of several degrees of importance. Nevertheless, the recognition of microstands in addition to stands greatly simplifies our classification of communities.

Stand

The most important unit of ecologic classification is the stand. Each stand is an actual concrete community which exists at a given time and covers a particular area. Considerable variability in composition may occur within a single stand, as has been pointed out in Chapter XVII. Adjacent stands of dissimilar types also may influence one another in various ways, as was described in Chapter XVIII. The numerous individual organisms of the several species which together compose each stand, however, have numerous direct and indirect ecologic relationships with one another. Considered together the members of a stand constitute a clearly recognizable ecologic unit.

The term "stand" is not applied to a minor concrete community but only to a community of considerable importance that covers an appreciable area. A grove of trees together with its associated plants and animals, for example, is a stand. On the contrary, a single tree or a clump of plants is not usually called a stand. A meadow of a particular type could be a stand and so could a marsh or bog. I apply the term also to important concrete aquatic communities, as a stand of water lilies or a stand of sea mussels.

STRATUM. The several strata that may be represented within a particular stand rarely are uniform over any considerable area, and often it is difficult to locate precisely the boundaries of the several layers. In a forest stand, for example, the shrubs and the small trees may in one place form 2 distinct strata, but in another part of the same stand these 2 strata may be indistinguishable. In still another place small trees and shrubs may both be wholly lacking. Strata, therefore, are useful in the description of communities, but they are not to be treated as rigid units of ecologic classification.

Strata, especially, should not be considered independent of one another, like the floors of a building. Each stratum, on the contrary, is intimately related to all the strata below and above it. A single large animal, for example, may at a given time occupy several strata. The trunks and stems of a tree likewise may pass through several above-ground strata while its roots penetrate the subterranean stratum. Only the epiphytes among plants are usually limited to a single stratum (Cain, 1934: 531). Among animals, a few species may be restricted for a particular season to a single stratum, but most animals occur in several strata.

TABLE XVII

ABUNDANCE OF INVERTEBRATES IN RELATION TO DEPTH FROM THE SOIL SURFACE
Duke Forest, Durham, North Carolina (data from Pearse, 1946).

Type of Soil and of Forest	Percentage of All Invertebrates Collected		
	Surface Litter	0-2 Inches	2-5 Inches
Clay soil			
Oak forest........	68	27	5
Pine forest........	74	21	5
Sandy soil			
Oak forest........	55	39	6
Pine forest........	66	30	4
Average........	65	30	5

Strata are by no means confined to the vegetation that grows above the ground but are present in the soil and in water. The great majority of soil-inhabiting forms occupy only the upper layers of the soil. In a study, for example, of the invertebrates of the Duke Forest, North Carolina, Pearse (1946: 133) found that 65 per cent of the invertebrates were in the surface litter and only 5 per cent in the layer between 2 and 5 inches below the surface (Table XVII). A few species burrow to greater depths, but there is a very evident stratification of these soil-inhabiting animals. The roots of plants also exhibit stratification, with those of certain species occupying the surface layers of the soil and the roots of other species penetrating more deeply. A few kinds of plants have both shallow and deep roots.

In aquatic ecosystems likewise there is a very obvious stratification of life. Sunlight penetrates only a relatively short distance into water and consequently photosynthesis is effective only near the surface. Nearly all aquatic plants that have chlorophyll are accordingly concentrated near the upper levels. Many aquatic animals also live near the surface. At greater depths are found other kinds of organisms that are not directly dependent upon the radiant energy from the sun. Stratification is especially conspicuous along the ocean shores, where many of the organisms are attached to the substratum.

The daily vertical movements that are characteristic of many plankton organisms produce frequent changes in the composition of each stratum of an open-water community. This frequent interchange of individuals up and down between the several depths makes it necessary, in my opinion, to recognize the several important layers at any given situation as strata rather than as separate associations. The several strata that may be recognized in the plankton communities seem to parallel closely the similar strata that occur in terrestrial communities, except that the movement of the individuals from stratum to stratum is often more frequent in aquatic than in terrestrial ecosystems.

Ecologists, however, are not agreed on the terms to be applied to these vertical divisions of aquatic communities. For example in the *Balanus–Mytilus californicus* community of Puget Sound, Washington, Shelford labels as "fasciations" 4 divisions, all of which occur within a vertical distance of 190 centimeters (Clements and Shelford, 1939: 328).

UNION. Certain plant ecologists consider each association (as here defined) to be composed of 1 or more elementary, 1-layered units, usually called unions, which are more or less independent of one another. The plants that compose any 1 union belong to a single or at most to 2 related life forms (Lipmaa, 1939: 118). I have already called attention to the difficulty of classifying animals according to life form. Animals, also, because of their mobility, are seldom closely restricted to 1 stratum. It is, accordingly, difficult or impossible to apply the concept of unions when the animals are considered part of the community.

ASPECT. The aspect constitutes a temporal division of a stand or microstand which usually is correlated with a particular season. A good example of seasonal change in community aspect is given by the plants of the Sonoran desert. This desert has 2 principal rainy seasons, one in winter and the other in summer. Certain species of the desert annual plants are adjusted in their growth period to the winter rains. In response to the moisture provided by these rains the seeds germinate, the plants grow, flowers and seeds are produced. After this period of activity the plants die. Thornber (1909) listed 122 species of annual plants which appear on this desert only in winter (W. P. Taylor, 1935b: 300). In response to the summer rains a wholly different set of annual plant species germinates, grows, and fruits (W. A. Cannon, 1911). The aspects of winter and summer on this desert consequently are considerably different from each other as far as the annual plants are concerned. The perennials, of course, are present on the desert throughout the year, but they also vary with the season in the amount of foliage they expose. Their periods of flowering and of fruiting likewise are tied to the seasons.

Seasonal aspects are very difficult to classify. Just as the seasons themselves have no sharp beginning or ending, so the aspects change gradually and sometimes almost imperceptibly from day to day and from week to week. Many species of plants have a long season of growth and some also have a long period of blooming and fruiting. Other species grow quickly, produce their flowers and fruit in a brief season, and then disappear. Animal species also may differ greatly from one another in the duration of their several life-history stages. The result is that the aspects of every community are constantly changing. It is seldom possible to specify any particular date when a given aspect has begun or ended. Only when some important change in the weather occurs suddenly, such as the first heavy freeze in the autumn, can a sharp limit be set to an aspect.

The progression of the seasonal aspects does not always have the same rate in all the stands of an association or in all the microstands of a micro-association, as has been pointed out in Chapter XVII. Consequently, the several communities of similar type within a region may at any given time vary more or less in the aspect which they exhibit. Due to the variability in aspects from place to place and from year to year, it seldom is possible to classify them very precisely. The recognition in any community of only the usual 4 seasonal aspects will, as a rule, be an oversimplification.

Microstand

The microstands that occur in any given region are of various types and sizes and of numerous grades of ecologic importance. As an example of the smaller type of microstand may be cited each individual plant or animal which, together with its parasites and other associated species, constitutes a separate microstand. A single plant, for instance, often has numerous symbionts that live in or on its leaves, flowers, fruit, bark, or stems. Still smaller microstands may inhabit only a single part of a plant. Thus, Needham (1948) has described a microassociation composed of those seed eaters, juice suckers, nectar feeders, gall makers, predators, parasites, scavengers and seekers of temporary shelter, which inhabit the flower heads of one species of beggar-ticks (*Bidens pilosa*). Each separate flower head shelters a separate microstand. Microstands of still smaller size also are common. At the other extreme of size, certain microstands approach the stands in size and importance.

The microstand is not to be considered as a subdivision of the stand, although each microstand occurs within a stand. Each stand is a unit in itself which is not completely divisible into subunits of any kind. The microstands, furthermore, are of such diverse types that they cannot be treated as subunits. It is better, therefore, to treat each microstand also as a unit by itself, recognizing, of course, that it has numerous relationships to the stand in which it occurs and also to neighboring microstands.

RANKS OF ABSTRACT COMMUNITIES

The abstract communities composed of stands and of microstands are called associations and microassociations, respectively.

Association

In any given biotic province a certain type of stand may recur frequently and in the aggregate may cover an important proportion of the regional area. The abstract community composed of an assemblage of stands of similar types is an association, as I use that term. For example, in the region near Tucson, Arizona, the following associations have been described: aquatic, cottonwood-willow, mesquite forest, desert wash, salt bush, cholla-mesquite-hackberry, creosote-bush, Franseria, paloverde-brittlebush, upper bahada, rock hill, aerial, and edificarian (Dice and Blossom, 1937).

It is important to keep in mind that an association, as the term is used in this book, is always an abstract concept and that the stand is the concrete unit of community classification (Pavillard, 1935). The relationship between the stand and the association is similar to that between the individual organism and the species. An association is composed of more or less similar stands, just as a species is composed of more or less similar individual organisms.

The term "association" unfortunately has been employed by ecologists for a number of diverse concepts. The earliest use of the term for a plant community seems to have been by Humboldt (1805: 14), as was mentioned in Chapter I. The early ecologists, however, used the term rather loosely and without full consideration of the diversity of communities that now are known to exist in the world.

In calling each important type of community in a given region an association, whether or not it is a climax, I here follow the usage of most ecologists (Warming, 1909; Flahault and Schröter, 1910, 1912; Vestal, 1914; G. E. Nichols, 1923; Gleason, 1925; Braun-Blanquet, 1928; Conard, 1939; Tansley, 1939). Clements (1916) and his followers, on the contrary, indicate by the term "association" a climatic climax together with all its antecedent successional stages. Some other ecologists give a still different definition for the term.

The reason for limiting each association to a single biotic province is that biotas and physical conditions vary from province to province and that, therefore, no community is exactly the same in different provinces. Associations, of course, vary within provinces also, but the variations are much greater between provinces than within a single province. In limiting each association to the limits of a single biotic province I believe I am in essential agreement with Cain (1947: 194).

One of the associations that can be recognized in each biotic province is the regional climatic climax; others are subclimax stages. Certain of the subclimax associations may represent edaphic or topographic climaxes. It should be emphasized, however, that the term "association," as here used, has no necessary relationship to succession.

Climax associations are relatively stable and highly permanent, while a subclimax association may be relatively impermanent at any particular location. For example, many pioneer stages exist only a very few years at any one spot. These pioneer communities, however, often are distinct in composition and in character from the later stages in succession. Certain species that are abundant in a given region may, in fact, occur only in the pioneer or early successional stages. These temporary stages, therefore, may be important communities which deserve to be recognized as associations. A pioneer community, through its successive occupation of constantly appearing new pioneer sites, may actually cover every year a very appreciable part of the area of a region, although it may exist only a short time at any given spot.

No group of stands will in general be recognized as an association unless the stands are important because of the proportional area that they cover in their particular region and unless they are reasonably similar to one another and at the same time are generally distinct from their neighbors. The degree of similarity to one another and of distinctness from other communities that members of a group of stands must have before the group may be ranked as an association, however, cannot be exactly specified. Neither can any hard and fast rule be laid down for the minimum proportional area of a region that an association must cover. Certain associations deserve recognition because of their distinctness, even though they cover only a proportionally small area. On the other hand, a particular type of stand may cover an extensive area but may be so nearly like some other type of community in its component species and its characters that it is hardly worth while to recognize both as associations. The decision as to which types of recurrent stands in a given region are to be classed as associations must, therefore, depend largely upon the judgment of the field student. Actually, it may not make a great deal of difference how the communities of a region are classified so long as all the more important types of communities and their variations are adequately described.

BIOCENOSIS. The term "biocenosis" (Möbius, 1877, *biocönose*), with its various modifications, is used by numerous European ecologists for a community of a rank approximately similar to that of association as above defined. The usage of the term varies, however, and certain ecologists use biocenosis in much the same sense as community.

FACIES. Many types of stands are composed in part of 2 or more conspicuous species, which often vary from stand to stand in their relative abundance. Thus, in the beech-maple association of Michigan the hard maple may in 1 stand make up most of the forest canopy, while in a neighboring stand the beech may outrank the maple in abundance. In one district the yellow birch may be an important member of the association, but in another district this species may be inconspicuous or absent. Each such well-marked variation in the relative.abundance of the more important species within an association is a facies (plural, also facies). Foresters often designate the more important facies of forest associations as forest types, but they also list whole associations as forest types.

The definition of a facies as a well-marked variation of an association will not be accepted by all ecologists. For a contrary opinion see Groom in Warming (1909: 146, footnote). The "systasis" of Klugh (1923: 369) seems to be a synonym of facies.

The occurrence of a facies often indicates a local variation in the physical factors of the habitat. For this reason, facies often are most numerous and most distinct in type in those situations where the local habitat is highly variable. Because the facies are based on variations in the relative abundance of the more conspicuous members of an association, it is evident that seldom will there be sharp boundaries between adjacent facies. Simple types of associations, especially those in which a single species is most conspicuous, may not be divisible into facies.

The failure of a conspicuous member of an association to range over the whole geographic area in which that association occurs may sometimes produce facies. In those districts where an important member species of an association is absent the composition of the stands will be different from the composition found in places where that species is present. A particular facies may in such a case be characteristic of a particular geographic area, and thus the association may be divided into facies on a geographic basis. Facies may, therefore, either be local, when they distinguish stands of the same association that occur close together, or they may be geographic in extent, when they distinguish stands of the same type of association that occur in different districts.

Microassociation

Because of the diverse sizes and various degrees of ecologic importance of the numerous types of microstands that occur in every region, the abstract microassociations which they compose also are of unequal importance. A particular difficulty in the classification of microassociations is that 1 kind of microstand may be made up in part of other microstands of still smaller size. It does not seem practical, at least at this time, to divide the several microassociations into grades of any kind. Any concrete community of lesser importance than a stand, therefore, is called a microstand. Likewise any abstract group of microstands of the same type which occurs within a single regional community is called a microassociation without regard to its relative importance.

Certain microassociations are composed of microstands which recur frequently and which in the aggregate cover a considerable area. The microstands of other kinds of microassociations may recur frequently, but because of their small size, the total area covered may be relatively small. The micro-stands of still other microassociations may occur only rarely. Certain kinds of microstands nearly always occur on isolated sites, as, for example, those that inhabit animal droppings. Other kinds of microstands, such as some of the riparian communities, occur in very long but narrow zones.

Any attempt to classify the microhabitats within a regional community and thereby to secure an ultimate basis for the classification of the micro-associations seems to be impracticable because of the enormous number of possible microhabitats. Each kind of tissue and each organ in each indi-vidual organism is a possible microhabitat for some other organism. Many other kinds of microhabitats are available on the surfaces of organisms. Thus, there are numerous different possible microhabitats on the trunks, stems, leaves, flowers, and fruits of plants and on the various parts of the bodies of animals. The physical habitat likewise offers innumerable possible microhabitats such as the surface of the soil, beneath the surface of the soil in crevices and holes, on and under rocks of various sizes, on the surface of the water, beneath the water at various depths, and on or beneath bottom materials which are of various textures. These physical and biotic microhabitats occur in various complex combinations. It is obvious, then, that the number of microhabitats which possibly are suited for the life of organisms is so great that their classification is not practicable.

SOCIETY. The term "society" has been used by certain ecologists (Clem-ents and Shelford, 1939: 245) for both concrete and abstract minor com-munities which correspond in part to the microstand and microassociation as previously defined. The term "plant society" is also in current use by botanists to designate strata and aspects and sometimes other minor com-munities. No serious objection can be raised to the use of "plant society" when only the plants are being considered. When the animals as well as the plants are considered, then the use of the term "society" in this sense is confusing, for the word has a very different meaning to zoologists. It has been pointed out that, at least when animals are being considered, a society is an aggregation composed of members of a single species which derive mutual benefit from their association and which usually exhibit social be-havior. In order to avoid ambiguity it seems best to avoid the use of the term "society" except when social groups are under consideration.

COMMUNITIES ESPECIALLY DIFFICULT TO CLASSIFY

Certain kinds of communities are especially difficult to classify. Among these I shall briefly discuss mobile communities, several kinds of imperma-nent communities, marginal communities, and artificial communities.

Mobile Communities

Certain communities are not fixed in position but move about from place to place. A band of driver or legionary ants accompanied by its associated symbionts is an example of such a mobile community (Wheeler, 1910: 246-66). The ant army is accompanied not only by its insect parasites and commensals but also by a number of species of birds which feed on the invertebrates driven from their hiding places by the ants (Skutch, 1934: 9). A wandering herd of caribou accompanied by its parasites and predators is another example of a community whose position is not fixed. The distinction between stationary and mobile communities, however, is not always sharp. Sometimes a mobile animal aggregation composed of mixed species may remain for a time in a particular region, which then becomes temporarily its home range.

A mobile community that is composed in part of animals of large size, such as the caribou mentioned above, may during the course of a year wander over many diverse types of habitats which shelter numerous kinds of communities. In its wanderings the mobile community will tend to remain in the same general community type, but may successively occupy numerous kinds of associations. Such a mobile community, therefore, may form a part of a particular association for only a very short time. All this adds to the difficulty of distinguishing and classifying communities.

Aquatic Communities

Communities seem to be less easily recognizable in water than on land. Although many aquatic communities have been described, both in fresh water and in the ocean, aquatic biologists in general have given much less attention to the description of communities and community relationships than have terrestrial biologists.

One reason for this neglect undoubtedly is that many aquatic communities are only temporary in character. The open-water habitat in particular is unstable. Because of its constant exposure to the action of winds and waves the plankton community is subject to frequent vicissitudes. The shores of many bodies of water also are unstable because of erosion or because of the frequent deposition of materials. In fresh-water habitats only a few communities are able to control the environment sufficiently to reach a climax stage (Clements and Shelford, 1939). Many fresh-water communities are in fact only stages in a sere leading to a terrestrial climax. Along some marine shores, on the other hand, the habitat is relatively stable and here Shelford has recognized a number of marine climaxes. Nevertheless, in these littoral climaxes the organisms have by no means as much control of the habitat as they have in certain of the better organized terrestrial ecosystems.

Many open-water organisms are subject to being drifted about by winds and currents and consequently do not live at any fixed location. Open-water communities fluctuate in their composition not only because of these involuntary shifts of position by their members but also through the swimming movements of those member organisms which are mobile. The reproductive units and larvae of many attached plants and animals may likewise for short periods of time become temporary members of open-water communities that occur near shore or in shallow water.

In spite of frequent changes in their composition, open-water communities often are very distinct in their characters and they may cover wide areas. Owing to their distinctness and importance it is necessary to treat at least some of them as associations. For example, the pelagic community of the offshore waters of the Gulf of Maine described by Bigelow (1926) certainly deserves to be called an association. Although this pelagic association exhibits seasonal aspects, is composed of several important strata, and has many local variations of facies, nevertheless it has the same general composition from year to year.

Those communities that occupy the open waters of streams are often very temporary in their composition. Because many of the individuals that make up such communities are constantly drifting downstream with the current, the individuals at any given site are constantly changing. Only strong swimmers, such as the fishes, are able to maintain their position. At those places where a stream empties into a lake or other body of water in which the animals from the stream are unable to live, these drifting organisms are being continually destroyed (Dendy, 1944). Nevertheless, the aggregation of species characteristic of the open water of particular streams may remain constant over appreciable periods of time. Probably some of these communities of running water, therefore, also deserve to be classed as associations.

Aerial Communities

Aerial communities are still more impermanent than are any of the aquatic communities. In fact, many ecologists refuse to recognize aerial communities at all, placing them as strata of the terrestrial or aquatic communities that happen to lie beneath them. This may have the ludicrous result of listing a woodpecker as a member of an aquatic community, just because he happens to fly over a small lake.

Many animals feed in the open air and certain kinds of insects mate there. In carrying out these essential activities they are members temporarily of an aerial community. The fact that no individual organism can maintain itself permanently or carry out its complete life cycle in the air does not alter the fact that the aerial community does constitute an important and distinct aggregation of interrelated organisms.

Many kinds of flying animals, especially the birds and insects, use the air as a route of travel, sometimes to escape their enemies. To list all of these flying species in any given aerial association would necessitate including nearly all the birds and insects and also some other kinds of animals that inhabit the region. I have as a practical expedient, therefore, usually

listed in the aerial association only those animals that carry out in the open
air above the earth some important activity, such as feeding or mating.

Marginal Communities

The practical problem often arises whether to recognize a particular marginal community as distinct from its neighbors, or whether to consider that
it is only an intermediate condition between them, not worthy of special
description. Such problems are especially troublesome in the classification
of associations. Each such case must be solved individually. If an intermediate type of association is recognized, then the problem of boundaries
has not been solved, for one must now determine the boundaries on each
side of the intermediate association. There are twice as many boundaries to
be delimited as there would have been if the intermediate association were
not recognized. If the proposed intermediate association contains several
species that do not occur or are rare in the adjacent associations and if it
covers an appreciable proportion of the area of the region, then it probably
should be recognized as distinct. In general, however, it is best to keep the
number of associations recognized in any region as small as possible and to
rank as associations only those communities that are of distinct type.

ZONES. A zone is a community that exists as a narrow belt, much longer
than it is wide. Zonation of communities often is conspicuous in places
where the controlling factors of the habitat occur in zones or belts. Zones are
most likely to occur along the shores of bodies of water. Around the margin
of a lake that is being silted up, for instance, there often occur concentric
zones of varying widths, which are dependent in large part upon the water
content of the soil. Zones of vegetation dependent upon the concentration
of chemicals in the soil also occur around alkaline lakes or playas. Zones
may be found in places far removed from water. For instance, a zone of
brush is likely to border the edge of a forest where this adjoins grassland.

The ecologic classification of any particular zone depends upon its degree
of ecologic distinctness, upon its uniformity, and upon its actual width.
Care should be taken not to confuse these minor ecologic zones with life
belts, which are vertical subdivisions of biotic provinces, or with the large
climatic zones of the earth, usually called tropical, temperate, and frigid.

A zone that is only a few feet in width may often be considered only a
microstand. A zone that intergrades broadly with the remainder of an association may be considered a facies. On the other hand, a zone that is wide
and is composed of distinctive species of plants and animals may itself be
called a stand. Zones, therefore, may be of diverse ecologic ranks.

Community Complex

Not all the area of any given region can successfully be classified into
associations. The transitional areas that lie between 2 adjacent stands often
cannot be assigned to either. In situations where succession is in rapid prog-

ress there may be great difficulty in locating the boundaries of the various successional stages. Furthermore, situations will sometimes be found in which several associations are inextricably mingled. In a dune area, for instance, where blowouts are active and where dunes in various stages of development are present, it may be impossible to map the distribution of the several communities, even though elsewhere in the same area several dune associations may be clearly distinct from one another. In such a situation it is usually best to describe the area as a community complex, which in the example given would be called a dune complex.

Artificial Communities

Many of the natural communities of the world have been greatly modified by the activities of man. When, for example, a forest has been cleared and the land planted to a cultivated crop, the resulting community is an artificial one, even though a number of the native species may still be present. Even primitive man produced local changes in natural communities through the removal of certain species of plants and animals, through the local planting of crops, and through the setting of fires. Modern man has caused extensive changes in most of the natural communities of the world and has produced many types of artificial communities.

The artificial communities that arise as a result of the activities of man are particularly difficult to classify. This difficulty is in considerable part due to the highly variable and often impermanent nature of such communities. The communities of cultivated fields, the edificarian communities in and around the habitations of man, and the communities of industrial areas are particularly likely to fluctuate in their characters from time to time. In such situations man is continually interfering with the natural regulatory mechanisms and thereby keeps these artificial communities in continual turmoil.

ECOLOGIC CLASSIFICATION

Each individual concrete microstand and each concrete stand can be recognized more or less clearly and can be described as a unit. These concrete units must serve as the basis for any classification of the communities that occur within a given region. Any combination of these concrete units to form larger categories must of necessity be only abstractions.

Abstract classifications are common in everyday life. Thus a familiar article of household furniture is called a table. A particular table can easily be identified and described. Furthermore, the class term "table" is useful, even though tables may be of many diverse shapes and kinds and though they may intergrade with other types of furniture, such as desks. Similarly, the combination in one's mind of concrete communities to form abstract communities may be useful in description. It must be remembered, however, that only arbitrary limits can be established for any abstract community.

The ecologist who first describes the ecology of any given region is likely to describe as associations and microassociations those communities which appear to be important from the standpoint of the particular organisms in which he is especially interested. An ornithologist, therefore, will be likely to classify the communities somewhat differently from a botanist, an entomologist, or an ichthyologist. Nevertheless, after the communities of a region have been described by specialists in the various branches of plant and animal ecology, there will seldom be much difficulty in securing rather general agreement as to which of the communities are most important, and which, therefore, deserve to rank as associations, and which are microassociations.

The main difficulty in classifying communities comes from the tremendous variation in the size and in the mobility of the diverse kinds of organisms that live in the world. The 1-celled organisms, for example, such as the bacteria, the protozoa, and the 1-celled algae, can exist in communities that occupy a minute amount of space. On the other hand, a large plant, such as a forest tree, or a large and mobile animal, such as a large mammal, requires a considerable amount of space. The habitats of those communities which are composed of large organisms must, therefore, be many times larger than those microscopic communities which are composed of the smallest organisms. Large and small organisms, however, may have close ecologic relations, as happens when a bacterium infects a tree or a large mammal. There seems to be no practical way by which communities can be divided into ranks according to the size or mobility of the organisms of which they are composed. Small, intermediate, and large organisms, in fact, often occur in the same communities.

In view of the considerable variations that are exhibited by all types of communities, the very practical question arises: How much may a community vary and still be given the same name? No good answer can be given to this question, for ecologists are by no means agreed on the methods for the classification of communities. My own practice is to consider that each association and each microassociation is limited always to a particular life belt and to a particular biotic province. Although somewhat similar types of communities often recur in adjacent life belts and in adjacent provinces, a given assemblage of species seldom extends over any great geographic area. In regions of high ecologic diversity, as in the desert parts of southwestern North America, it may often be desirable to limit each described association and each microassociation to a single biotic district (Dice, 1943: 3-4). When referring to a particular community the ecologist should always be careful to specify its geographic location as well as its name, for in no other way can future workers know with certainty what community is meant.

In spite of the difficulty of classifying microassociations, associations, and biotic provinces, it is possible to devise classifications that are useful for particular purposes. Foresters, for example, have developed practical classifications of forest types. Wildlife managers constantly utilize classifications of cover types. Furthermore, useful maps of the distribution of forest types or cover types in particular areas can be made without undue effort. There is no doubt that maps of the distribution of other types of communities can similarly be drawn with sufficient accuracy for the needs of any special study. The difficulties involved in the classification of communities are, therefore, not insuperable.

SELECTED REFERENCES

Braun-Blanquet, J., George D. Fuller, and Henry S. Conard. 1932. Plant sociology: the study of plant communities. New York and London: McGraw-Hill Book Co. Chap. 2.

Elton, Charles. 1927. Animal ecology. New York: Macmillan Co. Chap. 2.

Pavillard, J. 1935. The present status of the plant association. Bot. Rev., 1: 210-32.

Tansley, A. G. 1946. Introduction to plant ecology; a guide for beginners in the study of plant communities. London: George Allen and Unwin. Chap. 3.

XX

LARGER UNITS OF COMMUNITY CLASSIFICATION

A number of methods have been proposed for classifying the diverse ecologic communities that occur in the world. Four of these proposed methods deserve special attention. The major units of these 4 classifications are: (1) the community type, (2) the life zone, (3) the biome, and (4) the biotic province.

COMMUNITY TYPE

One of the major units of ecologic classification employed by certain early ecologists was the community type, though various terms were used for the concept. The term "community type" here used is a modification of the "association-type" of G. E. Nichols (1923: 156). A community type is an abstract unit composed of stands or microstands which are of generally similar character in their physiognomy, but which are not necessarily composed of the same species.

The several concrete microstands or stands which are grouped to form an abstract community type do not necessarily require any geographic contact with one another. They do not even need to occur on the same continent. The more conspicuous plants in each of the several communities that are combined into one community type, however, will have similar growth forms. All the sedge-marsh communities of the world may, for example, be combined as a single abstract community type. The sedge-marsh communities on one continent may be composed of entirely different species of plants from those on other continents. The animals, also, that live in sedge marshes will differ greatly from region to region. Nevertheless, all sedge-marsh communities resemble one another in their growth form; they all occupy habitats of similar kinds; and the kinds of food, shade, and shelter for animals which they produce are much the same in all of them.

LIFE ZONE

The life-zone concept of geographic distribution was developed by C. Hart Merriam (1890, 1892, 1894, 1898). It is based on the hypothesis that temperature is the most important factor controlling the distribution of plant and animal species. On this hypothesis the major units for the classification of plant and animal distribution should constitute zones of life which parallel the isotherms. The life zones accordingly are arranged in a regular sequence as one goes from the tropics to the arctics or as one ascends a high mountain. In North America, where the system has been best developed, the life zones commonly recognized are the Tropical, Lower Austral, Upper Austral, Transition, Canadian, Hudsonian, and Arctic (Merriam and others, 1910).

BIOME

A third possible method for classifying the major ecologic divisions of the world is by biomes (Fig. 49). A biome is a major ecologic community distinguished by the ecologic physiognomy of its climaxes (Shelford, 1930: 219; 1932a). This unit of classification is sometimes called a formation, especially when only the plants are considered (Clements, 1920). Many plant ecologists, however, use the term "formation" in a different sense from that in which Clements uses it. Tansley (1939: vi-vii), for instance, limited a formation to a single climatic and floral area. Climaxes based on similar life forms, but occurring in geographically separated areas and composed of different dominant species, are by Tansley called a "formation-type" rather than a formation.

All those climatic climaxes which have similar physiognomies, together with all the successional stages leading to those climaxes, belong to the same biome. The term "similar physiognomy" means that the climaxes making up a common biome look alike and that their member species presumably have similar adaptations. The dominant plants of the several climaxes of the same biome also will have similar life forms. There may be, for example, a grassland biome, a deciduous-forest biome, a tundra biome, and many others. Climaxes that are far removed from one another geographically will presumably belong to the same biome if they have similar ecologic physiognomies. This will be true even though the species of plants and animals that make up each of the member climaxes are taxonomically very dissimilar. No attempt has yet been made by anyone to classify the biomes of the whole world, but it may be assumed, for instance, that the grasslands of all the continents, including Australia, constitute a common grassland biome.

"Association"

Each biome usually is composed of 2 or more "associations," though it may be possible for a biome to include only 1. An "association" in this sense is a climatic climax community together with all the successional stages leading toward the climax (Clements and Shelford, 1939: 243). Care should be taken not to confuse this usage of the term "association" with the more usual one by ecologists for an abstract community, whether climax or not, composed of stands of similar type within a given region.

It is not entirely clear how the boundaries are drawn between adjacent climaxes or between adjacent biomes. From the descriptions of certain biomes, formations, and "associations" that have been published by Clements (1920), by Weaver and Clements (1938), by Shelford and others (1935), and

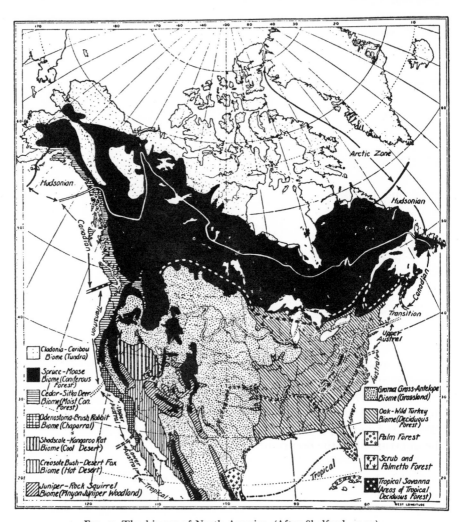

FIG. 49. The biomes of North America. (After Shelford, 1945.)

by Clements and Shelford (1939), however, it is evident that 2 or more biomes may occupy the same general area. For example, in a mountainous area several biomes often alternate with one another. Also, a small area of one biome is frequently completely surrounded by a biome of another type. Neither the biomes nor their climaxes, therefore, are necessarily continuous geographically. For this reason it is difficult to map accurately in any detail the distribution of the several biomes that may occur in an area of complex physiography.

The several divisions ("associations") of a biome often differ considerably from one another in their component species of plants and animals. Clements and Shelford (1939: 243, 257), however, have pointed out that certain species and certain genera recur in a number of the climaxes that make up the grassland biome in North America. There are, nevertheless, many important differences in the species that compose these climaxes.

FASCIATION. Each of the climaxes ("associations") into which a biome is divided, may itself be subdivided into fasciations, and these fasciations in their turn into communities of lesser rank (Clements, 1920; Shelford and others, 1935; Clements and Shelford, 1939). In descriptions of biomes, however, relatively little attention usually is given to these lesser communities.

AQUATIC COMMUNITIES. Marine communities constitute biomes which differ from the terrestrial communities that occupy the adjacent shores (Shelford and others, 1935). The fresh-water communities in some of the larger lakes and in rivers also are considered to form independent ecologic climaxes. It is not clear, however, how these fresh-water climaxes are to be combined to form biomes. The smaller bodies of water, such as ponds, small lakes, and marshes, are merely seral stages in terrestrial climaxes, and such communities, therefore, are classified under the appropriate terrestrial biomes (Clements and Shelford, 1939).

BIOTIC PROVINCE

A fourth method of classifying ecologic communities is by biotic provinces (Vestal, 1914; Dice, 1943). Each biotic province covers a considerable geographic area which is characterized by the occurrence of 1 or more important ecologic associations that differ, at least in proportional area covered, from the associations of adjacent provinces. The term "association" here refers to an abstract group of relatively important stands, whether climax or not. Terrestrial biotic provinces are always continuous, except where they may be interrupted by the occurrence of bodies of water. Aquatic biotic provinces probably are often interrupted by the presence of land. They have as yet received only slight attention.

A biotic province may best be thought of as a considerable geographic area over which the climate is relatively uniform, though often locally modified by physiographic features. Obviously, the climate cannot be generally uniform over any region unless there is also general uniformity of physiography. The climate will determine to a considerable extent the kinds of soils that are produced. Each biotic province, therefore, is a unit of climate, of physiography, and of soil types (Fig. 50).

A region that is distinguished by its climate, physiography, and soil is certain to develop characteristic types of ecologic communities. This is especially true of the edaphic and climatic climaxes. Furthermore, in each region

that exhibits peculiar ecologic conditions the plants and animals develop
certain adaptations and differentiate into local species and subspecies. Each
biotic province, therefore, is also a center of taxonomic differentiation. For
example, the differentiation centers of the birds of Baja California outlined
by Grinnell (1928b, Fig. 1) evidently correspond closely to the biotic provinces and biotic districts of that peninsula.

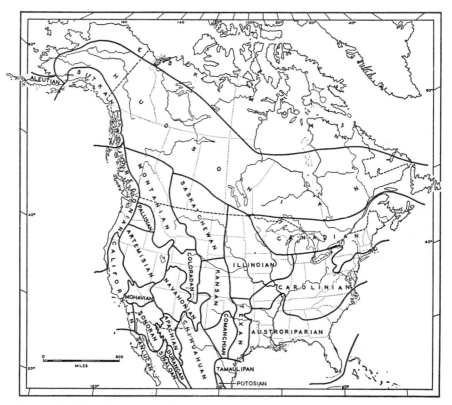

FIG. 50. The biotic provinces of part of North America. (After Dice, 1943, by permission of the Univ. Mich. Press.)

The areas occupied by the floras and faunas of the biogeographers correspond in large part to the biotic provinces as here defined. As a matter
of fact, most of the information we have about the species of plants and
animals that occupy biotic provinces has come from the labors of the taxonomists.

Many types of ecologic communities are able to modify the natural
habitat and thus to a greater or lesser extent to manufacture their own environment. Through succession they may spread, therefore, from their place
of development to adjacent areas. A biotic province thus may be considered
a center of ecologic dispersal.

The boundaries between adjacent biotic provinces sometimes follow natural physical barriers to the distribution of species. A large body of water, for example, often forms a boundary to a terrestrial biotic province. More frequently, however, the boundaries to biotic provinces are formed by climatic barriers, though these are seldom so effective as are physical barriers. An inspection of the maps of the distribution of boreal plants in North America presented by Raup (1947) will show, nevertheless, that actually many species do find their limits to distribution at closely similar lines. In such situations the boundaries of the biotic provinces can often be located with considerable precision.

In many places, on the contrary, there is no natural boundary between adjacent biotic provinces. Species, races, and ecologic communities that have developed in a particular biotic province in response to the climate and to the other environmental conditions existing there tend to spread beyond the limits of the province in which they have originated. It frequently happens also that small patches of habitats similar to those characteristic of a given province will occur far·beyond its borders. In such isolated habitats communities may occur which are similar to those that are widespread in a distant biotic province. The small bogs of the Canadian and Carolinian provinces in Michigan and Ohio, for example, constitute ecologic communities in which many of the species of plants and of animals are identical with those characteristic of the Hudsonian biotic province, which lies much farther north.

It is obvious then that, lacking any natural place of division between biotic provinces, the boundary lines between adjacent units must often be drawn more or less arbitrarily. The best way to locate roughly the boundary between 2 adjacent biotic provinces is to draw the line at the place where the area covered by the most widespread association of the one province equals the area covered by the most widespread association of the other province.

The classification of ecologic communities according to biotic provinces has been developed mostly with terrestrial communities (Dice, 1943). It is assumed that somewhat similar biotic provinces can be recognized in the oceans of the world. The classification of some fresh-water communities is a matter of more difficulty. Many fresh-water communities actually are successional stages leading toward terrestrial climaxes. Nevertheless, the communities of the larger lakes and of many streams have ecologic characteristics that undoubtedly deserve special recognition in community classification.

Each lake, stream, or other small body of water, because of its isolation from similar habitats, constitutes a more or less independent ecologic community. In the language of Forbes (1925), each lake forms a "microcosm." Each of these ecologic units may be self-contained and largely independent of the adjacent land (Welch, 1935: 308). Furthermore, there is sometimes very little intercommunication of one lake or one stream and its neighbors.

The ecologic processes of one such isolated ecologic unit, therefore, may be very little affected by the activities of any other similar unit.

All the aquatic communities within one connected stream system constitute an evolutionary unit, so far as the strictly aquatic species are concerned. Each aquatic species living in a stream system tends by dispersal to occupy all the suitable habitats within that system. The biotas of separate stream systems, however, often differ in their included species, and consequently the ecologic communities of separate stream systems also differ more or less from one another. There would be an advantage, therefore, in having some unit of ecologic classification to apply to each stream or to each related group of streams which have closely similar biotas and similar ecologic communities. It might perhaps be possible to recognize certain of the stream systems together with their larger lakes as biotic districts separate from those of the land, but so little is yet known about the ecologic communities of fresh water that any attempt to classify these fresh-water communities would at this time be premature.

Islands also constitute regional terrestrial communities that are more or less independent of other islands and of the mainland. Many terrestrial animals, however, are able to fly or to swim, and the seeds or spores of many terrestrial plants are carried by the wind or water. Islands, therefore, are seldom so independent of one another as are stream systems and other isolated aquatic communities. A continental island, in fact, can usually be assigned without difficulty to the same biotic province that occupies the adjacent mainland.

The classification of biotic provinces and their subdivisions should properly be based upon the distinctness and distribution of the several included associations. For most parts of the world, unfortunately, descriptions of the associations that include both the plants and animals and also the physical conditions of the habitat are nearly always inadequate, and often are wholly lacking. At the present time the classification of the major terrestrial communities must be based chiefly on the vegetation. Animals are dependent upon the plants directly or indirectly for food and often also for shelter and breeding places. Even where plants do not control the distribution of the animals, they often indicate the characters of climate and soil upon which the animals are dependent (Dice, 1931b). The vegetation, accordingly, offers for the present the most satisfactory basis for the recognition and classification of the major terrestrial communities.

The area covered by each biotic province is without doubt continually changing because of the slow but more or less permanent modifications of climate that are presumably in progress everywhere. Any general alteration of the topography, such as the elevation or degradation of a mountain chain, will, of course, alter the local climate. Any modification of climate will in its turn affect the geographic distribution of all the biotic provinces concerned. The biotic provinces themselves are in process of slow evolution and occasionally a new one may appear or an old one become extinct. The boundaries of the provinces, therefore, are not stationary, but they are constantly, though very slowly, changing their position.

Biotic District

Some biotic provinces can be subdivided into biotic districts. A biotic district is a continuous part of a biotic province distinguished by ecologic differences of lesser importance than those that separate biotic provinces. The Chihuahuan biotic province in southeastern Arizona, for example, is divided into the Santa Catalina, Chiricahua, Huachuca, and Santa Rita biotic districts (Dice and Blossom, 1937). This is an area in which large mountain masses are separated by wide plains of lower elevation. On account of its isolation each mountain mass tends to evolve peculiar races, species, and communities. It is to distinguish these variations within the biotic province that biotic districts are described.

Life Belt

A life belt is a vertical subdivision of a biotic province (Fig. 51). The distribution of a life belt often is not continuous, and a given belt may thus recur, under proper conditions of altitude and slope exposure, on widely separated mountains within 1 biotic province. It seems best to consider that each life belt is limited to a single province because each province is more or less distinct in its environmental factors and also in its fauna and flora. Similar kinds of life belts, however, sometimes occupy corresponding positions in adjacent biotic provinces. On the other hand, in a biotic province which has considerable ecologic variability a life belt may remain relatively uniform only within a single biotic district (Dice and Blossom, 1937:45).

The several belts of life that are so conspicuous on high mountains are correlated in large part with altitude and often run parallel for long distances. The communities of these adjacent life belts have many interrelations. Numerous species of animals perform seasonal migrations between 2 or more neighboring life belts. Certain of the larger mammals and birds even move up and down between adjacent belts in their daily travels. The seeds of plants frequently are transported from belt to belt, either blown by the wind or carried by animals or by running water. The more important communities of 1 life belt often recur in a more subordinate position in the adjacent belts. These ecologic interrelations between the adjacent life belts of each region tend to unify the biotic district or biotic province of which the belts are subdivisions.

SECTION. A vertical division of life belts into sections has been proposed by Larrison (1946). Thus he divides the alpine belt of the Oregonian biotic province into the following sections: (1) subalpine, (2) intermediate-alpine, (3) barren-alpine, and (4) arctic-alpine. There is no doubt that such sub-

FIG. 51. Life belts on the western side of Indian Divide, 12 miles east of Carrizozo, New Mexico. Here the sabinal life belt with its prominent pinyon-juniper association occupies the upper parts of the mountains and the arid grassland belt, made up mostly of the short-grass association, occupies the adjacent plains. (Drawing by Carlton Angell, from a photograph taken by L. R. Dice, July 12, 1937.)

belts can be distinguished within certain life belts, especially in regions of
high relief where there are very steep slopes. In regions of low relief, however, factors other than altitude often control the distribution of the communities, and subbelts, therefore, are seldom conspicuous in such areas.

CRITICISM OF THE SEVERAL SYSTEMS OF CLASSIFICATION

The 4 systems described above for classifying the major ecologic communities of the world are not mutually exclusive. All of them contain elements
of value. If their limitations are kept in mind it is possible to classify communities according to several of them at the same time.

Emphasis on Adaptations

The grouping of concrete communities into community types serves to
emphasize the similar adaptations that often are developed by plants and
animals of diverse taxonomy in response to similar environments. Thus, on
the plains of Africa the antelopes and other large herbivorous artiodactyls
have developed certain striking adaptations for feeding and for escape from
enemies. In Australia, where artiodactyls are absent, somewhat similar
adaptations are exhibited by the kangaroos and perhaps by other large
marsupials (Shelford, 1913: 314). Classification by community type mini-
mizes the taxonomic relations of the species that make up the several communities involved. It also ignores the geographic relations between the communities that are included within a single community type.

Classifications based on a community type have proved difficult to construct (Shelford, 1932a: 115). A chief stumbling block is that ecologic similarity is almost impossible to define and to measure, and consequently the
limits of every category in the classification are more or less vague. Nevertheless this kind of classification, if not applied too strictly, is very useful in
description. The term "alpine meadow," for instance, gives to the ecologist
a useful picture of a particular community type. Although classifications
based on community type are now seldom attempted, the concept is used a
great deal in the descriptions of communities.

Emphasis on Control by Temperature

The life-zone classification emphasizes the effect of temperature in controlling the distribution of species. The importance of temperature, however,
is recognized also in several of the other systems of classification. Certain of
the climaxes that make up biomes correspond locally to life zones and so
also do the life belts in certain biotic provinces. The greatest weaknesses of
the life-zone method are (1) the rigid limit on the number of zones recognized, and (2) the insistence that all the life zones are transcontinental in
extent. It is a defect of this classification also that the life zones largely
ignore the aquatic communities.

As the limit of toleration of the various species of plants and animals to low temperatures is approached, temperature often becomes the major factor controlling their geographic distribution. In the arctic and subarctic climates and on high mountains, accordingly, belts or zones of life often follow certain isotherms. In warm-temperate and tropical climates, on the contrary, factors other than temperature, such as available water, often control the distribution of life. In regions of this kind, therefore, zones of life based on temperature may be of only local importance.

No serious attempt has been made by anyone to classify any considerable proportion of the ecologic communities of North America or of any other continent according to life zones. The life-zone concept itself has been severely criticized by a number of ecologists (F. B. Sumner, 1915; Dice, 1916, 1923a; Ruthven, 1920; Livingston and Shreve, 1921; Kendeigh, 1932; Shelford, 1932b, 1945; Daubenmire, 1938; Pitelka, 1941). The life-zone method, therefore, does not seem to be suited for the classification of ecologic communities.

Emphasis on the Life Forms of the Climatic Climaxes

It is evident that the classification of ecologic communities according to biomes gives special emphasis to the life forms of the climatic climax communities. Because the attention is so strongly directed toward the climax communities, the successional stages receive less attention than they deserve. This is unfortunate because certain of the seral stages may be of great importance in the ecology of the areas concerned.

Many striking adaptations actually are exhibited by the members of subclimax communities. The plants and animals of sand dunes, of caves, and of riparian communities, for example, are often of particular ecologic interest, yet none of these are ever climax communities. In fact, some of the species of a given region which are most interesting ecologically live only in certain successional stages and never in the climax community. Many successional communities also have very extensive distributions. The Austro-riparian subclimax pine forests, for example, cover far greater areas than the hardwood forest which is the climax of southeastern North America.

Those climatic climaxes that have similar physiognomy are classed together to form a single biome. To this extent a biome resembles a community type. The grouping of climax communities to form biomes, therefore, is subject to the same difficulties to which the classification of community types is subject. It is often difficult to decide whether a particular climax, such as a savanna, is to be placed in one kind of biome or in another. Where 2 biomes alternate in a given region, a confused state of ecologic classification must of necessity result.

In the biome system the basing of ecologic classification on the trend of succession sometimes makes the classification of the ecologic communities of a given region uncertain and difficult. Ecologists often are not agreed as to

the trend of succession in a particular area. Two ecologists might consequently classify the biomes of a particular area differently, depending upon
their opinions of the trend of succession in the region. It also is difficult to
draw lines between adjacent biomes, because of the uncertainty of the place
where the trend of succession changes from one type to the other. With
fluctuations of climate an area now classed in 1 biome might 5 years from
now theoretically belong in a different biome. The mapping of biomes in
regions of considerable physiographic diversity is particularly difficult because of the interdigitation and alternation of communities.

Taxonomic relations among the several species that make up ecologic
communities are of necessity largely ignored when these communities are
classified according to biomes, just as they are when the classification is
according to community type. The neglect of these taxonomic relations is
probably not of great importance, so long as the composition of all the
communities, successional as well as climax, is equally well described. In
that case the taxonomist can discover the ecologic distribution of those
species in which he is particularly interested. If, however, an ecologist describes only the climax communities that make up a biome and neglects the
successional stages, then his description is to that extent incomplete.

Emphasis on Geographic Area

Each biotic province is a unit of ecologic classification that covers a rather
compact geographic area. In contrast to the units of classification employed
in the other systems described above, each biotic province occupies a continuous geographic area, except for islands. The mapping of biotic provinces, therefore, is somewhat more simple than the mapping of community
types, life zones, or biomes. The biotic-province method also emphasizes
centers of specific evolution and differentiation to a greater degree than any
of the other systems of ecologic classification proposed. Nevertheless, the
biotic province corresponds in part to some of the units of classification
used in the other systems. Certain biotic provinces, for example, are nearly
identical in distribution with certain climaxes ('associations") of certain
biomes. Where well-marked life belts occur within a biotic province, however, each of these is usually placed in a different climax ("association"). The
boundaries of certain of the biotic provinces correspond in places also with
the limits of certain life zones.

One criticism of community classification according to biotic provinces
is that corresponding life belts in different provinces are separated. For instance, the biota of the montane life belt in the Californian biotic province
probably more closely resembles that of the montane life belt of the Coloradan province than that of its adjacent grassland belt of the Californian
province. Nevertheless, there are numerous differences in climate, in species,
and in ecologic characters between the montane belts of the Californian
and Coloradan provinces. Also, some of the communities of adjacent life

belts in each biotic province are interrelated through the seasonal migration of certain species of animals and through the common possession of other regional species. Division of the life belts into geographic units of some sort, therefore, is certainly desirable. The treatment of the life belt as a subdivision of the biotic province makes this possible. The use of the same or similar names for homologous life belts in the different provinces will make their relationship to one another sufficiently clear.

The occurrence and distribution of biotic provinces is based ultimately on climate. This is true in considerable part also of life zones and of biomes. It is the climate that determines the character of the vegetation and limits the types of plants and of animals that are able to exist in any given area. In any extensive area of fairly uniform climate there will occur not only adaptations to the prevailing environments, but also taxonomic differentiation of the plants and animals into forms specially fitted for life in that climate. Any extensive climatic unit consequently is almost certain to become also a biogeographic unit characterized by the occurrence of unique subspecies, species, and perhaps genera. This tendency toward taxonomic differentiation is emphasized in the classification according to biotic provinces. Because each biotic province is to a considerable degree a center of taxonomic differentiation, these provinces often cover much the same areas as the faunal and floral biogeographic units previously recognized by taxonomists.

Diversity of Included Communities

A considerable diversity of kinds of ecologic communities is included within the major unit employed in each of these methods of classifying communities, except the community-type. A life zone, a biome, or a biotic province may each include 2 or more climaxes of somewhat dissimilar type, together with all the successional stages and associations. Although the several climaxes included within a biome have the same general physiognomy, their successional stages may differ considerably from climax to climax, and the total amount of ecologic variability included within one biome may not be much less than that included within a life zone or within a biotic province.

Relations of the Several Systems

The community-type system of classification, as has been stated, is of value for description but does not provide a suitable basis for a comprehensive classification of communities.

The life-zone system seems to be of little value for the classification of ecologic communities. The zonal features of biogeographic distribution which it emphasizes are much better treated as climaxes ("associations"), which are subdivisions of biomes, or as life belts, which are subdivisions of biotic provinces.

Biomes and biotic provinces are not necessarily to be considered as mutually exclusive and competing systems of ecologic classification, but rather as more or less supplementary to each other. Biomes emphasize climatic climaxes and their physiognomic similarities. There can be no question of the desirability of such recognition. Biotic provinces, on the contrary, emphasize geographic relations and taxonomic differentiation. Ecologic communities that lie close to one another geographically have of necessity close ecologic interrelations, either directly or indirectly, even though they may lie in different life belts and in different biomes. It may often be desirable, therefore, to classify ecologic communities both according to biomes and according to biotic provinces. In addition, it may often be desirable to classify communities according to their community type because this method of classification emphasizes adaptations and similarities in the ecologic responses of organisms of diverse ancestry.

SELECTED REFERENCES

Clements, Frederic E., and Victor E. Shelford. 1939. Bio-ecology. New York: John Wiley and Sons. Chaps. 7 to 10.

Dice, Lee R. 1943. The biotic provinces of North America. Ann Arbor: Univ. Mich. Press.

Livingston, Burton E., and Forrest Shreve. 1921. The distribution of vegetation in the United States, as related to climatic conditions. Publ. Carnegie Inst. Wash., 284: i-xvi, 1-590.

Merriam, C. Hart. 1898. Life zones and crop zones in the United States. Bull. Div. Biol. Surv., U. S. Dept. Agric., 10: 1-79.

XXI

COMMUNITIES OF THE PAST

A sequence of communities may be expected to appear on any given site as a result of ecologic succession. Even a climax community is not permanent, for it may be destroyed by various accidents, or, if the climate changes, another climax community of a dissimilar type may take its place. Furthermore, the processes of evolution and of migration are continually producing changes in the species and races of plants and animals that live in any given region. When the history of a particular site is studied, it always becomes apparent that the communities of earlier ages were different from those that now exist.

Tremendous changes in the ecologic communities of the world are known to have occurred during the course of past time. The northern hemisphere, for example, is just now recovering from a series of severe glaciations. It is not improbable that within a few tens or hundreds of thousands of years a new period of glacial advance may again overwhelm parts of the northern world. The recent glacial period itself included several distinct "ice ages," after each of which the glaciers partly or completely disappeared and the climate became warm again. Previous to the Pleistocene glacial period there is a long history of climatic changes which were in part caused by invasions and recessions of the seas over the continent and by the rise and subsequent erosion of mountain ranges.

In the early part of the Cenozoic era the general climate of western North America was warm and moist. A subtropical type of forest at that time covered wide areas on the Pacific Coast, and a warm-temperate type of forest was present in the Rocky Mountain and Great Plains regions. Only much later were the forests of the Great Plains replaced by the grasslands that now occupy that area (Clements and Chaney, 1936). From a study of the fossil plants, Axelrod (1948) concluded that a major change in climate and vegetation occurred in western North America just prior to the Middle Pliocene and that in this area the climate of the Middle Pliocene was semi-arid and somewhat warmer than at present. Climatic changes of similar magnitude are undoubtedly still in progress, though they take place so slowly that they are detected only from geologic evidence and from the records of past communities.

454

METHODS FOR ASCERTAINING THE CHARACTERS OF PAST COMMUNITIES

Information about the kinds of communities that existed on a particular site at a particular earlier time may be derived from various types of evidence (Berry, 1916; Clements, 1916; Case, 1919; Cooper, 1942; Cain, 1944). Obviously, the information available about a formerly existing community is likely to be more scanty and more difficult to evaluate the further back in past time the paleoecologist carries his studies.

In spite of the very serious difficulties in the reconstruction of the communities and habitats of past ages, notable advances are being made in the study of paleoecology. As additional fossil horizons become known and as additional information is secured about the previously discovered deposits, knowledge of past conditions steadily becomes more complete and more dependable. Unfortunately, the number of working paleoecologists is very small. The elucidation of the ecology of past time is, therefore, proceeding very slowly.

Succession as Evidence

The usual successional sequences of a given region can generally be deduced from observations of the relationships of the various kinds of communities existing there. It will, therefore, frequently be possible to ascertain what stages immediately preceded any particular existing stand. This ascertainment will often be aided by the presence of living relict individuals from the preceding stages or by their dead remains (Clements, 1934). Fire scars on stumps, logs, or living trees give indication of a past fire. An even-aged stand of a certain species of tree may also indicate a past fire, which then can perhaps be dated by tree-ring counts. The thickness of a particular tree ring or group of rings may also give useful information about the occurrence of past wet and dry seasons (Douglass, 1914). A stand of a very long-lived tree, such as the big tree (*Sequoia gigantea*) of California, may thus furnish information about the characters of the habitat and of the community over the past several thousand years. Most forest communities, unfortunately, do not supply much direct information about their history prior to the last few hundred years, and herbaceous communities seldom give historical information covering more than a very few years.

In reconstructing the past ecologic history of a given region from successional evidence the ecologist must keep in mind the possibility that the climate of the area may have changed more or less greatly in the recent past. As an example of a climatic change that is still affecting the sequence of succession in certain parts of the world may be cited the recent retreat of glaciers from parts of northern North America. In parts of southeastern Alaska the actual times of the more recent advances and retreats of the glaciers can be estimated more or less accurately by plant successions, tree-ring counts, and other ecologic and geologic methods (Cooper, 1923). The retreat of the last glaciers has been so recent that the vegetation over considerable areas has not yet become adjusted to the change. On the Alaskan Peninsula and on the adjacent Kodiak Island, as well as on other islands, spruce forest is still encroaching on the tundra and is spreading westward at a fairly rapid rate (Griggs, 1934; 1946).

Pollen Analysis as Evidence

The analysis of pollen in bog deposits has been developed rather recently as a very useful method in reconstructing the history of certain past ecosystems (Erdtman, 1943; Cain, 1944: 122; Potzger, 1946). Small samples of the peat from successive depths in the bog are prepared for microscopic analysis. The pollen grains from each sample are then identified according to species and are counted. By this means an estimate of the species composition of the community existing at each level of deposition of the bog is obtained. It is then possible to trace the succession that has occurred during the period of formation of that particular bog. A correlation of the time sequences represented by different bogs occurring in the same region can also sometimes be established. Numerous factors influence the deposition and preservation of pollens, and due attention must be given to these factors in any analysis of fossil pollens.

Organic Remains as Evidence

In reconstructing the communities of past ages from the remains or evidences of organisms found in fossil deposits the paleoecologist must exercise great caution as well as a high degree of imagination. The remains of species that in life inhabited very diverse types of ecologic communities may, by the action of flood waters or other geologic agencies, be deposited in the same fossil bed. Materials that float in water may be carried many miles by a stream. Beds deposited in the lower course of a river, therefore, may contain fossil materials derived from various parts of the stream system, possibly representing diverse life belts and several biotic provinces.

In any analysis of a fossil biota due attention must be paid to the relative abundance of the remains of the several species represented. The several species and communities of a given region, however, will rarely be equally represented in a fossil biota. Certain kinds of organisms are easily destroyed and, therefore, are seldom preserved as fossils. Also, the species living in certain types of communities are more likely to be preserved than those of other communities (Chaney, 1925). The fossil remains of the members of riparian communities, for example, are likely to be best represented in a stream deposit, while the plants and animals of the adjacent uplands have much less chance of being preserved. If the ecologist should judge solely from the proportional number of specimens of the various species preserved in a given deposit, he might erroneously conclude that at the time the deposit was formed the region was well watered and had a humid climate, while actually these conditions might have been present only in a narrow valley.

Other factors concerned with the preservation of fossils may also affect the proportional numbers of the several kinds of organisms preserved. Those species that in life are most abundant in a given situation are not always the ones that will be most commonly preserved as fossils. In the tar beds of California, for example, the remains of bird and mammal predators and scavengers are much more abundant than are those of the herbivores on which they must have preyed (Stock, 1929). Some feature of their behavior presumably made the predators and scavengers particularly likely to be trapped by the tar (J. C. Merriam, 1911; Hildegarde Howard, 1930).

Fossils deposited in one bed sometimes are later exhumed by natural agencies and redeposited in another bed. Here they may be associated with materials representing not only a different geographic area but also a different geologic age. Unless the paleoecologist is able to detect these false relationships, he may be misled entirely as to the character of the communities in which the fossil forms originally lived. Paleoecologists, therefore, exercise special care to be sure that the fossil beds they examine have been deposited in an orderly fashion and that the fossil remains have not been subjected to disturbance or wear.

One great difficulty in the reconstruction of fossil ecosystems is the possibility that the species represented in the fossil beds might have had somewhat different habitat preferences from those of their living relatives. It is not safe to assume that the elm or the bison whose remains are found as fossils necessarily lived in exactly the same types of habitats that their living relatives inhabit today. Living species often have subspecies or related species which live in several dissimilar kinds of habitats. The various races of the North American deermouse (*Peromyscus maniculatus*), for example, may be found in such diverse habitats as deciduous forest, conifer forest, prairie, chaparral, and semidesert. So also a single species of plant may range from sea level to the upper life belts of the mountains. Even when a living species is now closely restricted to a particular type of habitat, there is always the possibility that some earlier relative may have lived in a very dissimilar kind of situation. Reconstructions of past habitats and communities based on a presumed coincidence in habits between species or genera living today and those of an earlier age must, therefore, always be of doubtful validity.

Somewhat more confidence may be felt in deducing the ecologic relations in earlier ages of a taxonomic family or order the members of which all occupy generally similar habitats. Thus, the presence in a fossil deposit of the remains of a duck or of a goose would probably indicate the former presence of at least small bodies of open water (A. H. Miller, 1944). A fossil beaver would indicate the presence of a stream or a lake. A fossil fish of any kind would certainly indicate the presence of water. Care must be taken, however, not to lean too heavily on family or group relationships. Other species than those now known might have had aberrant habits.

When most of the species making up a fossil fauna or flora still live in the same general area, it is reasonably safe to conclude that conditions have not changed greatly since the time when the fossils were deposited (Dice, 1925*b*; A. H. Miller, 1937). Such cases, however, are rare. Biotas that existed prior to the Pleistocene period will almost certainly contain important species that differ from those living in that situation today.

ELEMENTS. A fossil flora or fauna often is composed of a mixture of species whose modern representatives do not now live together. For example, many of the Pliocene floras of the western United States include a number of species of which the nearest relatives are now found in the deciduous forest of the eastern United States. That part of a fossil biota of which the modern related species and subspecies occupy a major geographic and climatic province is called an element (Wulff, 1943: 202-13). In some of the Tertiary floras of western North America, for example, there is represented an East American element of broad-leafed deciduous trees and rarer conifers (Chaney, 1944: 6-12).

COMPONENTS. Within such an element it is sometimes possible to recognize subdivisions called components, which correspond to important modern ecologic communities. Thus, in the Pliocene floras of California and Oregon it is possible to distinguish components of the East American element made up of groups of species of which the nearest living relatives are found in the beech-maple, oak-hickory, coastal pine, and swamp cypress communities (Chaney, 1944: 6-12). This method of analyzing a fossil biota has great value in interpreting its characters. In reconstructing the characters of a fossil ecosystem care obviously must be taken not to rely too heavily on the presence of a single or of only a few species representing a particular element or component.

ADAPTIVE CHARACTERS. The best basis for the reconstruction of the habitat conditions existing in a particular past age is given by the adaptive characters of the fossil forms themselves. Most animals and plants are more or less adapted in structure to their habitats. For example, there is a striking difference between the teeth of browsing and of grazing mammals. The teeth of browsing animals have large cusps and are low crowned. Grazing animals, on the contrary, have many low ridges on their teeth, which are high crowned. The silica spicules present in the leaves of grass would quickly wear out a tooth that does not grow constantly from its roots, a process which the term "high crowned" describes. The presence of a fossil mammal with high-crowned teeth, therefore, may be taken to indicate the presence of grassland in the habitat of the animal (Hibbard, 1941).

The characters of fossil plants give evidence about the types of habitats and of the climate in which the plants grew. Species with tough, thick leaves, such as the oaks, may usually be assumed to have lived in a much drier type of habitat than those with thin, broad leaves, like the maple or banana. If the leaves have "dripping points," they indicate a heavy rainfall. Growth rings in the wood of the tree trunks indicate an alternation of seasons. The growth form of the plants and their other characters, therefore, may tell a great deal about the characters of the past environment (Berry, 1930; Cain, 1944: 70; Axelrod, 1948: 133).

Certain species are very adaptable and are able to live in a wide variety of habitats. Such species when preserved as fossils give very little information about the characters of the habitat in which they lived. The paleoecologist consequently must beware of placing too much reliance on the presence of any one species. In reconstructing the communities and habitats of a past age he must take account of all the species represented and of the relative numbers of their remains. When the fossil assemblage is scanty, little can be done to reconstruct the ecologic conditions of that past situation, but when there is an abundance of material a fairly dependable picture of the conditions existing at the time the deposit was made can usually be reconstructed.

Characters of Fossil Beds as Evidence

The paleoecologist, fortunately, is not wholly dependent upon the remains of plants and animals for evidence concerning the habitat conditions during a past age. The materials in which the fossils are deposited and the position of the strata also give evidence of value. If the fossils are lying in beds of shale it will indicate that quiet water was present, otherwise the mud would have been washed away. Similarly, if the fossils are in sandstone or conglomerate it will indicate that the waters were in more rapid motion. If the deposit is only a small lens it was probably laid down in a stream, but if the deposit is a broad bed, a lake or ocean-shore situation may be indicated. The materials of which the deposit is formed may also give evidence of its origin and thereby suggest the physiography of the region at the time the deposit was laid down (Chaney, 1918; 1922). For example, layers of volcanic ash indicate the presence of an active volcano in the vicinity at the time the beds were formed.

METHODS FOR DATING THE TIME OF OCCURRENCE OF PAST COMMUNITIES

The age of certain existing forest communities may be estimated from the age of the trees as ascertained from tree-ring counts. Unless the trees are all of the same age, however, such an estimate will give only the minimum age of the community. In a stand of uneven-aged trees it may be assumed that the oldest tree now standing probably germinated some time after the community was established. If relict trees from a preceding successional stage occur in a community, counts of their rings may indicate the age when that stage was in control of the site.

In deposits of peat where the conditions are favorable, it is possible by special methods to count fairly accurately the layers that have been deposited annually and thus to secure an estimate of the period of time since a given type of community has occupied the site (Sears, 1932). In certain lakes, similarly, the annual layers (varves) of mud deposited may enable an estimate to be made of the age of the deposit (Ernst Antevs, 1922). These methods, however, enable the age of a site to be determined for only a few past centuries or at most for several thousand years.

Estimates of the time at which a still more ancient ecosystem was in existence can be based in part on calculations of the rate at which physiographic changes have taken place in the area under study. Also, the determination of the proportion of radioactive minerals and their decomposition products in the rocks of a particular geologic stratum provides an estimate of the age of that stratum. This is a very reliable method that is especially valuable for the more ancient rocks.

SELECTED REFERENCES

Berry, Edward W. 1916. The Lower Eocene floras of southeastern North America. Prof. Paper U. S. Geol. Surv., 91: 133-40.

Cain, Stanley A. 1944. Foundations of plant geography. Part II. New York and London: Harper and Brothers.

Case, E. C. 1919. The environment of vertebrate life in the late Paleozoic in North America: a paleogeographic study. Publ. Carnegie Inst. Wash., 283. Chap. 1.

Chaney, R. W. 1925. A comparative study of the Bridge Creek flora and the modern redwood forest. Publ. Carnegie Inst. Wash., 349: 1-22.

Clements, Frederic E. 1916. Plant succession: an analysis of the development of vegetation. Publ. Carnegie Inst. Wash., 242. Chaps. 12-14.

Hibbard, Claude W. 1941. Paleoecology and correlation of the Rexroad fauna from the Upper Pliocene of southwestern Kansas, as indicated by the mammals. Univ. Kans. Sci. Bull., 27: 94-102.

Miller, Alden H. 1937. Biotic associations and life-zones in relation to the Pleistocene birds of California. Condor, 39: 248-52.

XXII

EVOLUTION OF COMMUNITIES

The complex ecologic interrelations of the numerous kinds of organisms that together compose each well-organized microstand, stand, and biotic province must have originated through a long course of interco-ordinated evolution. Every community that has achieved a measure of equilibrium contains not only green plants but also parasites, herbivores, carnivores, and other ecologic types, some of which operate as ecologic regulatory mechanisms. A carnivore cannot be a member of a community unless its prey also is present, nor can a parasite exist without its host. It is evident also that during the course of their evolution the plants have become adjusted to the damage caused by herbivores and by parasites. Herbivores are adjusted to the losses caused by predators, by parasites, and by other mortality factors. Any predatory species that utilizes more than the natural increase of its prey injures itself. Natural selection compels the adjustment of the rates of mortality and of reproduction of the several species that make up a community, and in so doing promotes their common interest (Forbes, 1925: 549-50). Further evolution is undoubtedly now in progress in most, if not all, existing communities.

EVOLUTION OF VARIOUS RANKS OF COMMUNITIES

The most important units for the evolution of communities are (1) the association, (2) the microassociation, and (3) the regional community. From a broad point of view the whole world is the largest unit of evolution, but I shall not here discuss this unit further.

Evolution of Associations

The association is evidently a very important unit of ecologic evolution. Stands of the same type which occur within a given region tend to operate as a unit in ecologic evolution. Individuals and reproductive units are frequently interchanged between neighboring stands of the same association. Although no one stand may at any given time contain all the species that are members of a particular association, nevertheless, all the members of the association are potentially able to live in every stand of the association which covers a sufficient area. All the species which are members of a given association consequently are adjusted more or less perfectly to one another and all are able to exist in the same community.

The fluctuations in composition which take place constantly in the individual stands are evidently of little significance in the evolution of the association. The fluctuations in the population densities of the several member species of each stand are a normal part of the process of maintenance of community equilibrium. Even though a member species may temporarily be eliminated from a particular stand, that species will probably soon reinvade from a neighboring stand. No serious or permanent alteration in the character of a stand usually results, therefore, from these frequent changes in its composition. Only in a completely isolated situation will the individual stand form an independent unit of ecologic evolution.

It is not only the climax associations that are subject to evolution but the successional stages as well. Each successional association, no less than each climax, is the resultant of interactions between the habitat existing at the moment and the kinds of organisms that are at hand. Each successional stage has its own regulatory mechanisms and each, therefore, has an organization of at least a simple kind. A great many species of organisms occur only in successional communities or they reach their greatest abundance there. The conclusion must accordingly be reached that all kinds of associations, successional as well as climax, have been produced by evolution.

Care must be taken to distinguish the evolution of a new type of association from the succession of one association by some other seral stage leading toward a climax. Succession may proceed rapidly, but the succeeded association nearly always persists on other sites in the same region, and the association itself is accordingly neither lost nor changed. A newly evolved association, on the contrary, is one that previously has not existed anywhere. It must be assumed that the evolution of a new type of association usually is a very gradual process.

Evolution of Microassociations

Another important unit of ecologic evolution is the microassociation. Individual organisms are frequently interchanged between the several micro-stands of the same type that together form a microassociation, just as they are between stands. As a result of this interchange of individuals, each micro-association forms a unit of ecologic evolution similar to the association but on a smaller scale.

Each microassociation is influenced in its evolution by the characters of the association or associations in which it occurs, as well as by the other microassociations with which it may be in contact. Each microassociation, nevertheless, has at least a considerable degree of independence in its evolution. For example, the terrestrial microassociation that lives on or in decaying small vertebrate carcasses may in part draw its members from other adjacent types of communities, but some of its members are completely restricted to it.

Evolution of Regional Communities

The evolution of a regional community must evidently follow much the same process as the evolution of an association. This is true because each regional community is itself composed of a number of associations. More species of plants and animals are, of course, represented in the flora and fauna of a regional community than will be members of any one included association. Many species, however, are simultaneously members of 2 or more associations; consequently, the number of species making up a regional community is not the sum of the member species of all its associations.

Much has been written about the origins of certain member species of particular regional communities. Through the efforts of biogeographers and paleontologists considerable information has been acquired about the lines of evolution, speciation, migration, and time relationships of numerous genera, families, and orders of plants and animals. It is even possible to trace somewhat vaguely over a brief period of past time the histories of certain existing communities. Knowledge about many important members of most past communities, however, is still scanty or lacking. It is impossible as yet to trace very far back in time the course of evolution of any existing association or regional community.

WAYS IN WHICH A COMMUNITY MAY CHANGE

There are 2 principal methods by which evolution may take place in a community. First, the composition of the community may be changed, either by the addition of a new member species or by the elimination of a former member; or, second, one of the member species of the community may through evolution become modified in its adaptive structure or habits, thus changing to some degree the ecologic composition of the whole community.

Addition of a New Species

Biotic provinces, associations, and microassociations frequently become modified by the invasion of alien species. The geographic ranges of many kinds of plants and of animals thus are known to have changed in the past (McClanahan, 1940). Among the causes of expanding ranges may be mentioned the changing of physiographic conditions due to land elevation or to base-leveling, the removal of physical barriers to migration, climatic changes, decrease in numbers or removal of enemy species, evolution of new adaptive characters by the species concerned, accidental introduction into new regions, and transfer by man to new habitats.

A species that is expanding its range is certain to invade new communities sooner or later, in which, if it is able to establish itself, it will set in motion new sequences of evolution. Each invaded community must immediately undergo greater or lesser changes in its organization in order to adjust itself to the presence of the invader.

DISTURBANCE PRODUCED BY AN INVADING SPECIES. The amount of disturbance produced in a community by the invasion of a strange species will depend upon the character of the newcomer as well as upon the make-up of the community that is invaded. Sometimes the invading species will be of a similar ecologic type to 1 or more of the previous members of the community. In such a case there is likely to be severe competition between the new and old members, which may lead to the elimination or suppression of 1 or more of the species. If the invading species is ecologically identical with a species that it replaces, theoretically little change in the community should result from the replacement.

No invading species, however, is likely to be ecologically identical with any previous member of a biotic province in all its requirements for light, food, water, shelter, or breeding sites, and also in the services it supplies to the other species of the region. Even closely related species usually differ from one another in some feature or other of their behavior, especially in their degree of restriction to particular ecosystems. No invading species, therefore, is likely to occupy exactly the same ecologic position as some already established member of the province. If an invading animal, for example, has food habits similar to those of an established member of an association, it is likely to have different habits of nesting, or it may be more adaptable in its requirements. An invading species, therefore, nearly always makes new ecologic contacts directly or indirectly with numerous members of the communities it invades. The addition of a new species to a biota is almost certain, consequently, to cause numerous readjustments in the ecologic organization of 1 or more communities within the area invaded. A common result is the elimination of certain native species from the invaded communities (G. M. Thomson, 1922: 505-35).

Should an invading species be very different in its ecology from any previous member of an invaded biotic province, it may produce very serious alterations in the characters of 1 or more of the local ecosystems. The introduction of goats and of other domestic animals on certain oceanic islands, for instance, has resulted in great destruction of the island vegetation and the consequent elimination of numerous native animals and plants (Huey, 1925). The destruction of vegetation by introduced herbivores may also open the way to soil erosion, which in its turn may produce further changes in the characters of the affected communities.

RATE OF SPREAD OF A SPECIES. Whenever a new species is introduced into or invades a region from which it was previously absent, it will usually at first be restricted to the edge of the region. From its point of entry it will then gradually spread to other suitable ecosystems in the same geographic area. This process of invasion takes an appreciable time, even when no barriers prevent free movement of the invading species. During the period of invasion, therefore, certain stands of an association which is being invaded may have received the invader, while in other near-by stands of the same association it may not yet have gained an entrance.

The rate of spread of a species is determined by the mobility of the individuals, including that of their reproductive units, and by the barriers to their movements. When a species has been able to pass a barrier to its distribution, it is likely to expand its range rapidly until it has occupied all the ecologically suitable area within its reach. The introduced English sparrow thus occupied most of the suitable parts of North America within less than a century (Grinnell, 1916). Ultimately each invading species will reach barriers beyond which it cannot pass, at least for a time.

The best information available on the rate of invasion of a foreign species is obtained from the history of the spread in North America of certain introduced birds. Aldo Leopold (1939, 79-80) stated that the spread of the introduced Hungarian partridge was at the rate of 5, 3.5, 2, and 28 miles per year in various parts of North America. The starling, which is another introduced bird, spread from New York City to Madison, Wisconsin, a distance of 800 miles, at the rate of 21 miles per year. The last 700 miles, however, were covered in 14 years, or at the rate of 50 miles per year.

EVOLUTION STIMULATED BY INVASION OF AN ALIEN SPECIES. The changes produced in the organization of an established community by the introduction of a new species theoretically may stimulate certain of the old members to new evolution. The invasion of a community by a foreign species, therefore, may not only alter the community by the addition of the new member, but the whole equilibrium of the community may require readjustment. As a result, a new cycle of evolution by several or all of the member species may be initiated. Although this conclusion is a logical one, there is no positive evidence that evolution of the members of a community actually does follow the introduction of new forms. Such evidence would be almost impossible to secure because of the difficulty of observing evolution in progress in nature.

EVOLUTION OF ECOLOGIC CONTROLS FOR AN INVADER. When an alien species has newly invaded a region and has become established, it may at first multiply vigorously, often causing serious alterations in certain of the native communities. When it has lived in the new region for a number of years, however, the usual history is that the introduced species becomes reduced in numbers to a point of moderate abundance or it may even become rare. The European rabbit, for instance, when first introduced into New Zealand increased enormously and was a great pest, but after the lapse of a considerable number of years it became much less numerous (G. M. Thomson, 1922: 88).

The explanation of the great burst in the numbers of a species following its introduction into a new region seems to be that the natural parasites and other ecologic controls of the invader have not come with it (W. R. Thompson, 1928: 108), or at least not in sufficient numbers for its control, and that it takes some time for the ecologic communities invaded to evolve suitable controls for their new member. In time, however, ecologic controls do become developed and the community again becomes stabilized, but with a somewhat changed composition.

Subtraction of a Member Species

Whenever for any reason a species becomes eliminated from a region, this likewise necessitates a reorganization of the communities of which it was formerly a member. Large carnivores which are native to a region usually are promptly eliminated when that region is thickly inhabited by man. In consequence, the herbivores which formerly were preyed upon and kept in check by these large carnivores are likely to increase and may cause considerable damage to crops and to pasture lands. In densely populated and intensively cultivated districts, therefore, man himself must assume the expense of controlling both the carnivores and the herbivores.

Certain species of plants and of animals are known to have suffered a reduction in their geographic ranges within historic time, and a few species of animals have fairly recently become entirely extinct. Numerous other species are in imminent danger of extermination (G. M. Allen, 1942). Any reduction in the range of a given species will eliminate it from certain of the communities of which it previously was a member.

ABRUPTNESS OF EXTERMINATION. Little is known about the rate at which species become alienated from communities, but the extermination of a species often seems to be an abrupt event. At least, it is known that the extinction of several kinds of animals took place rather suddenly. The passenger pigeon of North America, for example, seems to have passed from abundance to extinction within a very few years.

RELATIVE IMPORTANCE OF THE MEMBER SPECIES. The effect produced on a community by the invasion of a new species or by the loss of a former member depends to a great extent on the relative importance of the form concerned. The several species that make up any given community are, of course, not all equally important ecologically. For example, if a plant species that furnishes a considerable amount of shade is eliminated, the character of the ecosystem may be greatly altered unless some other species, by expanding its shade production, can compensate for the one removed. On the other hand, if a rare and ecologically unimportant form is either removed from or added to a community, the characters of that community may be very little altered.

Due caution, however, must be used in assuming that any species is of only slight importance in a community. Actually, the roles that the several species play in most communities are not fully known. An inconspicuous species may possibly perform some function which is important in community organization.

Evolutionary Change in a Member Species

In addition to the changes in communities produced by the addition or loss of species, every community must change to some degree whenever any one of its component species evolves a new structure or new habit. Each of the species making up a community has direct or indirect ecologic relations with all its associates, as well as with the physical environment. If one of the organisms making up a community evolves a new adaptive character, then all its associates must adjust themselves to this new development. For instance, if a species of herbivore becomes better adapted for concealment or for defense against its predators, then the predators, if they are to continue to utilize this food, must evolve more efficient methods for detecting and capturing the prey species.

VARIABILITY OF HEREDITARY CHARACTERS WITHIN POPULATIONS. Every population of wild plants or animals that has been carefully investigated has been found to contain a considerable amount of variability in its heredity. If samples of wild plants are grown in experimental gardens or if wild animals are brought into the laboratory, their offspring are not all alike but vary in important respects, even though the conditions for their growth are made essentially identical. Because of the store of genetic variability possessed by every population, evolution can proceed rapidly, whenever needed, through the action of natural selection alone, without waiting for the appearance of suitable new mutations.

ROLE OF ECOTYPES IN EVOLUTION OF COMMUNITIES. An indication of the amount of genetic variability present in nature is given by the occurrence in certain populations of 2 or more ecotypes. Should the conditions in a given ecosystem change so that at any given time 1 ecotype is favored in survival over the others, then natural selection will direct the trend of evolution toward that ecotype. Evolution will be expected to proceed most rapidly where a more or less suitable ecotype is already present in the population. Ecotypes, therefore, undoubtedly play an important role in the evolution of species and consequently of communities.

Should a population be subjected to a change in its ecosystem for which it has no suitable ready-made ecotype at hand, then it will probably still be able to produce, from the store of hereditary factors that it contains, a combination somewhat suited to the new situation. In other words, it will tend to produce a new ecotype. If the genetic combinations first produced are not fully suited to the changed conditions, new recombinations will continually be produced by each generation, and from among these combinations natural selection will presumably produce continually better adapted individuals.

Two different ecotypes, theoretically, cannot long exist together in the same population. Competition between them will be expected quickly to eliminate one or the other. The occurrence of 2 ecotypes in a population, therefore, means that (1) in this situation there is a mixture of 2 or more types of local habitats, (2) the situation lies on an ecotone between 2 dissimilar kinds of habitats, or (3) insufficient time has elapsed since the ecotypes came into competition for 1 to be eliminated.

The swings of climatic cycles and other fluctuations in the characters of habitats, however, may operate to favor first one and then another of the ecotypes that may be present in a given population. It should be expected, accordingly, that the proportions of the several ecotypes of a given species which may be present in a particular situation would also fluctuate. Little is known, however, about actual changes in the proportional abundance of several competing ecotypes in nature.

SPECIAL FEATURES OF COMMUNITY EVOLUTION

Adaptive Radiation

Every ecologic niche within a community tends to be occupied by some kind of organism. Thus Grinnell (1924b: 227) said that "if a new ecologic niche arises, or if a niche is vacated, nature hastens to supply an occupant, from whatever material may be available. Nature abhors a vacuum in the animate world as well as in the inanimate world." The same idea in another form was expressed by H. F. Osborn (1902) in his *Law of Adaptive Radiation*.

An excellent example of adaptive radiation is provided by the Hawaiian honey creepers of the family Drepaniidae. Although the several species of these birds are closely related and presumably are all descended from a common ancestry, they now occupy a number of diverse ecologic niches. Various structures and habits are represented by these birds on the islands of the Hawaiian group. One small bird (*Loxops virens chloris*) has a small, delicate, decurved bill adapted to searching for insects among foliage and to extracting nectar and small insects from flowers. A larger bird (*Hemignathus obscurus*), now probably extinct, had a much longer, more decurved bill and a relatively shorter tail. The bird hitched along the trunks or large limbs of trees in the manner of a creeper or woodpecker and used its long, slender bill to probe for insects in the crevices of the bark. Another species of the same genus (*Hemignathus lucidus wilsoni*), also probably extinct, had a long and slender upper mandible, but the lower mandible was short and heavy and was used like a chisel, driven by the powerful neck muscles, to pry off pieces of bark. The bird thus secured its insect prey. Still another member of the family (*Pseudonestor xanthophrys*) has very heavy upper and lower mandibles, which are used for crushing dead twigs in order to secure the larvae of cerambycid beetles. In 5 species of the genus *Psittirostra* the bills are to varying degrees heavy and finchlike and are adapted for crushing seeds (Amadon, 1947). Thus, in 1 family of birds there have evolved structures and habits fitting the animals to widely diverse niches.

The law of adaptive radiation is illustrated also by many other groups of organisms. Nevertheless, it must not be assumed that the process of evolution ever is completed. Many possible resources in every ecologic community still lack full utilization. For example, it is well known to field naturalists that conifer forests, as a rule, shelter a much smaller assemblage of animal life than an equal area of deciduous forest. Only a relatively few kinds of animals are able to use the food offered by the conifers. It is fortunate for man, of course, that the conifers are not attacked by a greater number of organisms, for otherwise our wood resources might be greatly depleted. But the food resources in the conifer needles and wood is not fully utilized by other organisms. The tendency for organisms to occupy every available niche, therefore, is a trend only and one that always falls somewhat short of fulfillment.

It may be presumed that any vacant habitat tends to be occupied by a new community which is evolved for the situation. In other words, adaptive radiation applies to communities as well as to geographic races, species, and larger taxonomic units. Actually, new types of communities are continually being evolved in pasture lands, in forest plantations, about the habitations of man, and in other artificial and natural habitats. Relatively little study from the ecologic point of view has yet been made of these newly evolved communities.

Role of Natural Selection in the Evolution of Communities

Natural selection undoubtedly is an important agent directing the evolution of communities, just as it also directs the evolution of species. Should 2 species in a given community come into competition for any life essential, one or the other is likely to be eliminated. In the frequent competition for sunlight among species of plants, for example, that species of which the individuals grow the tallest is likely to shade out its competitors. It will accordingly thrive, while its competitors will be eliminated. Each community through the action of natural selection consequently comes to be composed of those species which are best able to thrive under the conditions present in that ecosystem.

The further inference may be drawn that the possible degree of adaptation of communities will be greatest in those regions where a considerable variety of species is present. In biotic provinces containing a high diversity of species of plants and animals, natural selection will have abundant material from which to choose. As a result, the level of adaptation achieved by each type of community in that region should be high. On the contrary, in regions of scanty flora and fauna, such as small isolated islands, the range of possible selection between species will be narrow, and consequently the opportunity for evolutionary improvement in the characters of each kind of community presumably will be limited.

Effect of Size of Area and of Isolation

The rate of evolution of each species of plant or animal is dependent in part upon the size of the population concerned and upon the degree of its isolation from other populations with which it may interbreed. Large, freely interbreeding populations are believed to change their characters very slowly, even under considerable pressure from natural selection. Very small, closely inbred populations may change their characters rapidly but tend to fixation of characters, which may or may not be adaptive. Most rapid progress toward adaptive evolution is theoretically made by those species whose constituent populations occur in partly isolated subgroups. A small population living in a partly isolated community of moderate size and distinctive habitat type, therefore, may be expected to develop rather promptly a local race adapted to that situation. On the other hand, if the local population is not isolated to some degree from the adjacent populations of the same species, the incipient new ecotype or race will tend to be swamped by constant inbreeding with its neighbors and it may never come into existence.

Most stands are relatively small and are incompletely isolated from other stands of the same association. Microstands often are even more isolated from one another than are stands. The occurrence of most associations and microassociations in relatively small units incompletely isolated from one another constitutes, according to the deductions of Sewall Wright (1931), especially favorable conditions for the evolution of species and consequently of communities.

COMPLETE ISOLATION. Under conditions of nearly complete isolation, such as occur on many oceanic islands, unique types of communities may develop. Isolation often encourages the evolution of races and of species. Each isolated part of a species tends to diverge from its relatives and to evolve distinctive characters (Mayr, 1942, Chap. 9). Each completely isolated community, therefore, will come in time to be composed at least in part of species and subspecies which are more or less different from those of any other existing community.

LARGE VERSUS SMALL AREAS. Under conditions of nearly complete isolation the size of the area covered by a given ecosystem becomes very important in relation to the number of species which are associated to form its community. It has earlier been pointed out (Chap. III) that some of the species characteristic of large stands may be absent from small stands and that fewer species may be represented in a small stand than in a stand that covers a larger area. The size of the area covered by a geographically continuous type of habitat, therefore, affects the number of species that can live there (P. J. Darlington, 1943: 43).

It would be expected that on a large area in which a number of stands of a particular type of community are more or less isolated from one another, a given member species would probably not be eliminated from all the stands at any one time. Even though the species may have severe fluctuations in numbers and may be at times eliminated from some of the stands, it will likely survive in others. From the stands where it survives the species will tend to spread again over the area, probably reaching all the stands. But on small, isolated areas, such as islands or mountain tops, where a few stands or perhaps only a single stand occurs, any species whose numbers become locally reduced is likely to be eliminated from the community. Once eliminated from such an isolated area, reinvasion will be retarded or prevented by the barriers which are present. The fauna of the locality will accordingly be reduced by the loss of that species. Communities which occupy small areas will consequently be composed of fewer member species than will more extensive communities.

Effect of Changes in Climate or Physiography

Each important change in the climate of a region must usually initiate evolution in its communities. No climate is ever fully stable for any long period of time. On the contrary, cycles of wet and dry or cold and warm years frequently occur. The extensive climatic changes that may take place during a geologic period should be especially effective in producing evolution in communities.

CLIMATIC CHANGES. Every time the climate of a region becomes permanently changed the climatic climax association of the area must give place to a new climax adjusted in its characters to the new conditions. Many of the successional communities leading toward the climax will also be affected and will be forced to modify their composition in response to the climatic change.

CHANGES IN PHYSIOGRAPHY. Physiographic changes in a region likewise may initiate evolution in communities by altering the physical conditions of the local ecosystems. Physiography often has a direct relationship to the local climate, to soil formation, and to soil erosion. Every change in physiography, whether produced by the elevation or by the degradation of the land, must consequently result in modification of 1 or more of the local communities.

Each Community a Unit in Evolution

In its evolution each biotic province, association, and microassociation must act to a large degree as a unit, although, as has previously been pointed out, every community also is more or less related to the adjacent and even to the distant communities on the earth. Every evolutionary change in 1 member species in a community compels corresponding changes in every associated species. Should, for example, a predator evolve improved equipment for capturing its prey, then those prey species which are most easily secured must theoretically decline in numbers, increase their rate of reproduction, or evolve improved methods for escaping capture. Such changes in the predator-prey relations between 2 species cannot fail to force, directly or indirectly, changes in all the other members of the community. Consequently all the members of each community must evolve together.

Rate of Evolution of Communities

CLIMAX COMMUNITIES. Little is known about the rate of evolution of communities, but certain suggestions may be offered. It may be assumed with some confidence that in a complex and well-organized community, such as a climax deciduous forest, many of the constituent species are changing their characters only very slowly or not at all. Any change in a species that already is well adjusted to such a community would be likely to render it less rather than better fitted for success. Accordingly, most of the changes that are occurring in the characters of the member species of such a community would be expected to be correlated with the extremely slow, progressive evolution of the whole community.

NEW HABITAT TYPES. The evolution of a new community may, on the other hand, theoretically occur rapidly whenever a new type of habitat suddenly becomes available. Such a new habitat will presumably be occupied quickly by plants and animals of various kinds. Certain of these will be forms that already occupy somewhat similar types of habitat in the same region. Others may be inhabitants of near-by or even of distant regions, which in their wanderings find the vacant habitat largely by chance. Only those species adapted to the ecosystem, however, will be able to survive. The aggregation of species from diverse sources thus brought together will constitute a new type of community. It may be assumed that a new type of community tends to evolve promptly whenever a new type of habitat is produced.

URBAN COMMUNITIES. As an example of the rapid evolution of communities in new kinds of habitat I may point to the evolution of the special communities of urban situations. Although the urban communities of the whole world have a few species in common, including man, each region has its own special urban communities, many of which must have evolved during recent centuries. Excellent descriptions of the urban and suburban communities of London, England, have been given by Fitter (1945), but for most other regions such information is largely lacking.

A few of the species that become associated to form a new community may flourish exceedingly because they find conditions in the new ecosystem more favorable than in their previous habitats. Other species may change their physiology or behavior in certain respects in order to succeed in the new situation. Thus, in urban communities many species of birds are much less shy of man than they are when encountered in natural communities. Even a bird usually so shy as the wood pigeon may in London become very tame (Fitter, 1945: 141). Any animal which is unable to adjust itself to the vicinity of man would, of course, be unable to thrive in a city.

Certain species of organisms are so adaptable in their behavior that each individual is able to adjust itself to a considerable range of conditions. These species may thus be able immediately to invade a new type of habitat that becomes available. It is probable, however, that in order to succeed as a member of a new kind of community a species must change its heredity to at least some degree.

Ultimate Limits to the Evolution of Communities

The trend of evolution in every community is toward the most effective utilization of all the resources of its habitat. In part, these resources can be measured in terms of energy. Certain resources of the climate and soil, however, cannot be expressed in terms of energy alone.

AVAILABLE ENERGY. Various kinds of energy are present in every ecosystem. There is first of all the incident energy that comes from the sun. If not immediately absorbed by the habitat or by organisms, this incident energy is likely to be radiated back into space and to be lost. A certain amount of energy is also present in every habitat as stored heat. This store of heat is being continually dissipated by radiation and by conduction. The food and other organic materials that are present in each ecosystem may also be measured in terms of stored energy. This is true of the materials in the bodies of living organisms no less than of those in dead and decaying organic substances.

All organisms are continually consuming energy in order to live. In other words, the energy contained within an ecosystem is organized on a number of different levels, but the maintenance of life demands a constant loss of energy. If it were not for the input of solar energy at the proper diurnal and seasonal periods, no community could long continue to exist.

The physical features of the habitat are unable to change themselves to make more effective use of the energy that is present. Organisms, on the contrary, do have the unique ability to improve themselves through evolution in order more effectively to utilize the resources of their habitats. No species of organism, however, can follow a course of evolution independent of that of its associates. The members of the whole community must evolve together and during this process the associated species of plants and animals must be kept continually in adjustment with one another.

No community is able to utilize more than a small fraction of the solar energy that falls upon it. As previously mentioned in Chapter VII, it has been estimated by G. A. Riley (1944) that over the whole earth the efficiency of green plants in utilizing solar energy is only 0.18 ± 0.12 per cent. There are, therefore, very great potentialities for the further improvement of every ecosystem through evolution. Such improvements might take the form of more effective methods for the photosynthesis of food stuffs, more complete utilization of the food resources at times of abundance, or more efficient storage of food materials during periods of surplus.

LIMITING PHYSICAL FACTORS. The trend of evolution of each community must be toward its better adaptation to the conditions of the physical environment, as well as toward the most effective utilization of the resources of the habitat. In certain situations it is true that the organisms making up a community may be able in part to control the environment and to manufacture to a considerable degree their own soil and their own local climate. The amount of control, however, that any community is able to exercise over its environment is distinctly limited. No rain-forest type of community, for example, can ever develop in a desert climate. Many communities, in fact, are able to modify the physical environment only slightly. In any given situation the community that can best succeed will be the one that is best adapted to the physical conditions of the habitat, however much the community may be able to modify those conditions.

Adaptations of Communities

Adaptation to its environment is essential for the existence of every community, just as it is for every race and species. Adaptation is, of course, a relative term and no species or community can be expected ever to become adapted perfectly to its habitat. The changes in member species and in physical habitat that are continually in progress make adaptation an ideal that is constantly approached, but never fully attained by any community.

EFFECTIVENESS OF THE ADAPTATIONS OF SPECIES. Special adaptations which fit various species of plants and animals to their physical habitats or which aid them in their relations with their associated species have been described by many authors (Hesse, Allee, and Schmidt, 1937; Van der Klaauw, 1948). It is a logical assumption that every species must have numerous adaptations to enable it to survive. Few critical studies, however, have been made of the actual effectiveness of any particular adaptation in aiding a given species of plant or animal to succeed in a given ecosystem. Such studies are difficult to carry out because of the complex interrelations of every species with its environment, but they are by no means impossible.

As an example of a study of the effectiveness of a particular adaptation may be cited the observations by S. A. Graham (1930) on the numbers of sawfly larvae taken by birds on some experimental plots in Minnesota during 1 summer. The position of these larvae on the slender tips of the tamarack branches is believed to be an adaptation that protects them from the attacks of most birds. Nevertheless, a few of the larvae disappeared from time to time, presumably through the attacks of insectivorous birds. Three series of samples comprising, respectively, 20, 15, and 10 groups of larvae were kept under observation. Each group consisted of those larvae which had hatched on the tip of a particular tamarack branch. Only 4 of the 45 groups of larvae were attacked by birds, though all the larvae in 1 group were taken. The percentages of larvae taken in the 3 series were, respectively, 0.3, 8.0, and 0.0 per cent of those present. Evidently the adaptations of these larvae were very effective in preserving them from the attacks of birds.

In considering the adaptations of species it should be emphasized that many of the most important adaptations involve physiology or behavior and that adaptations are by no means restricted to morphological specializations. For instance, the habit of many animals of producing their young at the season when suitable food is becoming abundant is an important adaptation. Not only is such an adaptation of value to the animal species concerned, but it also operates to prevent the food species from being over-utilized and thereby damaged.

DIVERSITY IN METHODS OF ADAPTATION. The several species that live in a particular ecosystem may exhibit many diverse types of adaptations to the conditions of their habitat. This diversity of adaptations is especially evident in those situations where the conditions of life are severe. In the Arizona desert, for instance, the animals and plants must have special adaptations to survive the extreme heat and aridity of the long summer. Vorhies (1945) has shown that in this desert several kinds of mammals have each developed a different set of habits and structures to meet these severe conditions. The kangaroo rats and pocket mice, for instance, live in burrows, which they leave only at night when the heat of the desert is lower and the humidity higher than during the day. By careful control of water elimination from their bodies and by conserving the metabolic water derived from the oxidation of their foods, these rodents are able to subsist mostly on dry seeds. The desert wood rats, on the other hand, live in "houses" which are not so well protected against heat as are the burrows of the kangaroo rats, but they secure a considerable amount of water from their food, which includes cacti and other succulent plants. The jack rabbits make no burrows at all, but they are largely crepuscular or nocturnal and they lie in "forms" in the shade during the daytime. They also eat succulent vegetation. The desert ground squirrel (*Citellus tereticaudus*) is diurnal in habit, but in summer it is not active in the hottest part of the day. It lives in burrows and eats succulent plants. Each of these kinds of mammals, therefore, is adapted to life in the desert, but each has solved in a different manner the problem of existing under extremely difficult conditions.

Should attention be directed to the plants, to the insects, or to any other group of desert organisms, it would be seen that each species likewise has evolved a particular set of adaptations which enable it to survive. The same is true in any other type of rigorous habitat.

NOT ALL SPECIFIC EVOLUTION IS ADAPTIVE. Not all the characters or habits of species and subspecies are necessarily adaptive in relation to the ecosystems in which they live. As a result of mutation pressure and random loss of genes, minor changes of a neutral sort must frequently occur in local populations. In isolated populations there may even be fixation of certain genes or gene combinations that are deleterious to a mild degree (Wright, 1931; Dobzhansky, 1941, Chap. 10). Recessive characters that are positively harmful may be carried for many generations in heterozygous condition, even though all the homozygous individuals that exhibit the character in each generation are prevented from breeding (Dice, 1940a). Characters that are mildly deleterious may theoretically persist in a population for a considerable time because of chance or the presence in the individual phenotypes of other useful compensating characters.

Certain authors have gone so far as to state that most or all subspecific or varietal characters are nonadaptive. The fallacy of this idea has been well exposed in a summary by Kalabukhov (1941), who emphasized the widespread occurrence of ecologic variation among animals and the undoubted importance of natural selection in the evolution of local forms.

ADAPTATIONS OF THE WHOLE COMMUNITY. No satisfactory study has yet been made of the adaptations of a whole community to the conditions of its habitat. In fact, such studies have hardly been attempted. Too little is known about the effectiveness of the adaptations of individual species in fitting them to their particular niches in the community, to enable one to attempt any critical consideration of the adaptations of a whole community. Nevertheless, in time this information can be assembled and an analysis made of the effectiveness of each community as a whole in utilizing the resources available to it.

Good adaptation in a community means not only the adjustment of each member species in tolerable degree to the conditions of the physical and biotic habitat, but also close integration between the several member species to form a stable organization of the community.

A community composed of a limited number of species can seldom have the stability that a more diversified community will have because of the fewer possible adjustments among its members. It may be assumed, therefore, that the trend of evolution in each community will usually lead toward an increase in the number of member species. The addition of new species to the community should continue until every possible niche in the ecosystem is filled. No actual study of the trend of evolution in any community has, so far as I am aware, ever been made.

Evolution Is Inherent in Life

The tendency for communities to become fitted to the conditions of their habitats is inherent in life itself. Just as every organism must continually adjust itself to the changing conditions of its environment, so every community must continually accommodate itself to the conditions of its habitat. The community, like the species, however, does more than merely become adapted to the conditions of its immediate environment. It tends to improve itself, that is, to evolve, so that it becomes better able to adjust itself to the environment. The organic world made up of individuals, species, and communities could not have come into existence without this inherent property of life, the ability to continually improve the effectiveness of its adaptation to the environment.

SELECTED REFERENCES

Dobzhansky, Theodosius. 1941. Genetics and the origin of species. 2d ed. rev.; New York: Columbia Univ. Press. Chap. 6.

Fitter, R. S. R. 1945. London's natural history. London: William Collins Sons & Co.

Mayr, Ernst. 1942. Systematics and the origin of species from the viewpoint of a zoologist. New York: Columbia Univ. Press. Chap. 9.

Osborn, Henry F. 1902. The law of adaptive radiation. Amer. Nat., 36: 353-63.

XXIII

PHILOSOPHY OF COMMUNITIES

If every individual plant and animal were able to live equally well in every existing type of habitat and could thrive in association with every other kind of organism, then the resulting aggregations of individuals should be formed entirely at random. Under such a theoretical condition there might occur any possible combination of individuals and of species, and communities would not exist, but only random aggregations of individuals.

It is obvious, however, that the various kinds of plants and animals are not distributed over the face of the earth at random. On the contrary, each kind of organism has very specific habitat limitations. Also, most organisms tend to occur in association with certain other particular kinds of plants and animals, and the resulting communities often are more or less uniform over geographic areas of appreciable size.

Ecologists are agreed, therefore, that concrete communities actually exist in nature (G. E. Nichols, 1929; Gleason, 1929b). They are by no means agreed, however, about the factors that produce and control communities nor about the importance of the community in the drama of life.

THE COMMUNITY AS A UNIT

Practically all communities are composed of both plants and animals. With a few negligible exceptions all animals are dependent directly or indirectly upon plants for food. Many animals also obtain from plants other essentials for their existence. Most kinds of plants likewise are dependent upon animals for important services, including the regulation of their numbers. Any complete description of a community, therefore, must include consideration of all the animals and all the plants that are associated.

A COMMUNITY IS MORE THAN THE SUM OF ITS PARTS. Every community is more than the mere sum of its component individuals and species. This is shown particularly by the influence of the community on its habitat. A stand of trees, for example, is much more effective in producing shade, in decreasing wind action, in controlling temperature and evaporation, and in the accumulation of duff and leaf mold than would be the same number of individual trees each standing alone (Clements and Shelford, 1939: 68-69).

The concept of the community as a unit of organization and of evolution

478

is of basic importance in every study of organisms living in nature. Communities differ in type, as is shown by differences in the species that compose them; they differ in size as reckoned by the number of included individual member organisms; they vary in the area of habitat that they occupy; they vary in the complexity of their organization; and they differ from one another in numerous other ways. Nevertheless, the concept of the community as a unit which is more than the sum of the individuals which compose it is a most fruitful one.

DIVISION OF LABOR. Every well-organized community exhibits the phenomenon of division of labor. The several species that make it up perform different essential functions in the community. Certain member species produce food stuffs by photosynthesis; others modify the habitat in various ways to make it tolerable for the life of the community; still others serve as ecologic regulatory mechanisms to keep the various parts of the community in equilibrium. The several associated species can operate most efficiently because each is specialized for particular functions in the community. By working in co-operation with one another the species which constitute a community, therefore, are able to thrive better than any one of them could alone. Every one of them derives certain benefits from membership in the community.

ADAPTATIONS FOR COMMUNITY LIFE. In addition to the behavior patterns and physiologic characters that fit organisms for life as individuals and as members of social groups, most species also possess characters that fit them for life in a particular type of community. Each organism must have reactions and responses that enable it to live more or less in harmony with its associates. A species that causes widespread destruction to the other members of its community tends to destroy its own habitat and thus injures itself. Although very little is known about the actual process of community evolution, it may be assumed that the effect of natural selection is to produce communities made up of organisms all of which have types of behavior that enable them to live together with mutual benefit or at least with mutual tolerance.

COMMUNITY ORGANIZATION. In the course of time many types of communities have become highly organized. In certain ecosystems the general environment is to a large extent produced or controlled by the organisms that make up the community. In such a highly organized community certain of the constituent species may be wholly unable to exist except within this
1 community type. The complexity of organization within the community, however, varies greatly. It is greatest in climax communities and is particularly obvious in climax hardwood forests. It is much less apparent in some other climaxes. Many pioneer communities have relatively simple organization.

A simple pioneer community that is only a random aggregation of individuals is usually quickly succeeded by a more complex community that exhibits at least some trace of organization. When more than a very few species live together to form a microstand or stand, most of these species will probably be ecologically related to certain of their associates. This will constitute interdependence and accordingly will be a beginning in community organization. In fact, it may be doubted that more than a single species of organism can exist in any ecosystem without the development there of some degree of ecologic interrelationship resulting in the emergence of organization.

Because of the numerous interrelations of the associated individuals and species, the organization of most communities is extremely complex. The living beings that are associated to form a community have their common existences so linked and interwoven that a change in the relationship between any 2 species may produce far-reaching changes in the whole community (Warming, 1909: 366). The complexity of organization of a community is actually much greater than that of any single organism because the community is itself composed of many individual organisms.

COMMUNITY REGULATION. One of the most important features of a community is that it possesses mechanisms for self-regulation. All communities, except possibly the very simplest types, contain within themselves regulatory mechanisms which enable them constantly to adjust themselves to the changing conditions of their physical environments. This ability for self-regulation is found also in individuals and in societies and is called homeostasis (W. B. Cannon, 1939; Brody, 1945). Homeostasis may be defined as the ability of an individual, society, or community to regulate itself so that it is able to exist in a frequently changing environment. In thus constantly adjusting itself to the conditions of its environment each community operates as a more or less independent unit.

PHILOSOPHIC BASIS OF THE COMMUNITY CONCEPT

Certain ecologists maintain that communities are simply aggregations of individuals controlled by the inorganic and organic habitat (Gleason, 1939; Mason, 1947). Others consider certain communities to be complex organisms (Clements, 1916: 3). Most ecologists hold a position between these extremes and agree that all communities are aggregations controlled more or less by the characters of the habitat, that some communities are highly organized, but that none of them can rightly be considered organisms (Vestal, 1938: 111), although it may be proper to call at least certain ones epiorganisms.

Individualistic Concept of the Community

The principal proponent of the individualistic concept of the community is Gleason (1939: 108), who holds that a community is an aggregation of those individuals which happen to live together. This statement should not be interpreted to mean that Gleason does not believe in the occurrence of concrete communities, which he emphatically does.

In a situation where the habitat is constantly changing, an organized community has little chance to develop. Shelford (1932a: 108), for instance, pointed out that in fresh-water streams with shifting bottoms, communities can hardly be said to occur. Likewise, on a dune of constantly moving sand no community can long endure. In such situations there can at most be only temporary aggregations of certain species of organisms.

The control that the physical habitat exercises over certain communities is very clearly exhibited in those simple pioneer aggregations composed of only a few species which are newly invading a previously unoccupied site. An example is the community formed on a rock surface freshly exposed by erosion. It is obvious that the pioneer community in such a situation is controlled to a considerable extent by the physical characters of the habitat, including the climate of the area. The community is largely a chance aggregation of those individual organisms which reach that particular site and are able to maintain themselves there.

The composition of such a pioneer community depends upon the ability of the reproductive units of various kinds of organisms to reach the situation, their tolerance for the environmental factors they encounter there, and the resources of the habitat in relation to the requirements of the organisms. Diverse kinds of plants and animals vary considerably in their ability to colonize any given habitat. The habitat, therefore, even in very simple situations, is never in complete control of the community. It can at most only accept or reject those organisms that reach the site. While the selective effect exercised by the habitat may play a major role in determining the character of the community that develops on a pioneer habitat, it cannot produce a community of any kind in the absence of organisms.

Even in the simplest communities, moreover, the several member species will be related ecologically to one another. Predators and parasites, as well as herbivores, will nearly always arrive promptly. The associated species will also be dependent upon one another in numerous other ways. Many of the species, moreover, will exhibit adaptations for coexistence. In other words, even in the simplest ecosystems certain ecologic interrelations of the species assist in controlling the formation of the community. It must be a rare event, then, for any community to exist for any great length of time as a simple aggregation of species brought together and selected solely by the physical factors of the habitat.

The relationships between certain members of particular communities are of a highly specialized character which cannot be due to chance aggregation alone. In a community composed of 1 or more species of obligate parasites and their host, each individual host together with its parasites constitutes a microstand. All the individuals of this host species together with their parasites form a microassociation. The important thing here is that the same organization is repeated in each microstand time after time in essentially the same form. There may be differences from host to host (microstand to microstand) in the associated species of parasites and in the number of individuals of each species represented; nevertheless, all communities, each represented by a host individual and its parasites, will be of generally similar character. Furthermore, the parasites will have evolved adaptations for this one particular host species and the host will likewise exhibit means of defense in order that it may not be completely destroyed by its parasites.

Similarly, in almost every other kind of community the several member species have evolved adaptations which enable them to live together and sometimes to exploit one another. Every food chain is an illustration of such relationships. The literature is full of examples of symbiotic relationships between species, many of them the evident result of mutually adaptive evolution.

In selecting their habitats many kinds of animals presumably make use of responses and reactions that are definitely directive. Certain species must be able to detect from a distance the location of a preferred type of habitat and to orient their movements so as to reach that habitat. It is true that in the selection of a habitat many kinds of animals operate largely by trial and error. It also is true that chance plays a large part in determining which particular individual shall reach any particular site or even whether he shall reach a suitable site of any kind. Many of the reactions by which individual animals reach their preferred habitat are of a mechanical sort, not necessarily involving consciousness. Nevertheless, the purposive movements that many animals make in reaching a particular ecosystem do not fit well with the individualistic concept of the community. In thus criticizing the individualistic concept of the community, I recognize that Gleason in propounding this concept did so entirely from the point of view of the plants and that he did not include the animals as part of the community.

Most communities seem, therefore, to be more than just aggregations of those individual organisms that happen to occur together. In most communities, in fact, many of the members are closely dependent for their existence upon certain other associated species. The individualistic concept of the community may be considered, therefore, to apply only to a very few of the more simple aggregations that occur in nature.

Organismic Concept of the Community

That the climax community together with its successional stages is "an organic entity" has been propounded by Clements (1916: 3). He believes that, like an individual plant or animal, this unit "arises, grows, matures, and dies," and that furthermore the climax "is able to reproduce itself, repeating with essential fidelity the stages of its development." The entity may be destroyed at any stage of growth (that is, at any stage in succession), but in Clements' opinion succession itself is never retrogressive (p. 145). If the destruction of the community at any stage is only partial, succession may, however, start again from some intermediate stage and so does not have to repeat the whole succession from the very beginning. This concept of Clements that the climax and its successional stages represent a kind of organism has been adopted by a number of ecologists. Tansley (1935), however, holds that the climax community is only a quasi-organism and that succession can be retrogressive as well as progressive. He does not consider the catastrophic destruction of a community to represent succession.

Although the analogy between a community and an individual plant or animal is stimulating to thought, this analogy must not be forced too far, for there are many evident differences between them. One important difference between a community and an individual organism is in their outer limits. A community nearly always intergrades more or less with its neighbors, and there is seldom any definite boundary between 2 adjacent communities. An individual organism, on the contrary, has a skin, bark, or other kind of envelope which forms a fixed outer boundary. Except in certain colonial forms, it is relatively easy to determine the boundary of each individual organism. Communities, on the contrary, tend to merge with one another at their edges and consequently their boundaries are often difficult to define.

Another important difference between organisms and communities lies in the permanence of their component parts. The component cells, tissues, and organs of one individual organism seldom can be transferred in nature to another individual, except in reproduction. Mobile animals, on the contrary, frequently move from one community to another and in this manner 1 animal may at successive times be a member of many different communities. There are so many mobile organisms in most types of habitats that a considerable and important part of many communities may not be permanent.

Another difference between communities and organisms lies in the age they attain. Every individual organism in time becomes senile and ultimately dies. There is no evidence that communities ever become senile. On the contrary, old communities seem generally to be better organized and to thrive as well as or better than younger communities of the same type.

Neither can the reproduction of communities be considered the same sort of process as the reproduction of individual organisms. The climax community, which presumably represents maturity, may not include in its membership any species which is able to colonize a pioneer habitat and thus to initiate a new sequence of succession leading to the production of the climax. The pioneer species that colonize newly available habitats often are absent from the mature climax. In other words, the initial stages in succession are seldom derived from the most mature community of the sequence.

The ecologic relations between the several species that compose a community also are much less obligatory than are the physiologic relations between the organs that make up an organism. The addition or elimination of a species from a community seems sometimes to have only a slight effect on the operation of the community. The practical elimination, for example, of the chestnut from the hardwood climax of certain parts of the eastern United States, due to the chestnut blight, caused a major change in the composition of the community, but the general character of the climax was not greatly altered. The removal of any important organ from an individual organism, on the contrary, nearly always results in its death.

The analogy of a highly integrated community to an organism is nevertheless useful, if it be kept in mind that this is an imperfect analogy only and not a homology. Clements himself has not made the mistake of calling the community an organism, but instead has defined the climax together with its successional stages as a "complex organism" (Clements, Weaver, and Hanson, 1929: 314). Nevertheless, the use of the term "organism" has led many persons, probably including Clements himself, to make too much of the analogy and to attempt to find more of a homology between a community and an organism than actually exists.

The dispute as to whether or not a community is an organism is in large part due to a double meaning for the term. There are in English 2 uses for "organism." Biologists in general restrict the term to an individual plant or animal. Philosophers, however, use the term for a natural unit with distinctive characteristics, though it may be separable into more or less independent parts (Egler, 1942: 246).

In order to avoid confusion it is best to designate as an epiorganism any natural entity composed of individual organisms (Gerard, 1940: 404; 1942: 76). Colonies, social groups, and communities are clearly epiorganisms, all of which have special characteristics that are more than the sum of the characters of the individual organisms of which they are composed.

Each climatic climax association and all the successional associations and microassociations that occur together within a given climatic region form a unit of organization and of evolution. It is justifiable, therefore, to treat each regional community as an epiorganism.

Each local concrete stand as well as each microstand is a unit of organization. As such, each of these concrete communities deserves also to be treated as an epiorganism. The abstract associations and microassociations form other ranks of organization, which may also be recognized as epiorganisms. At the extreme of size, the community comprising the whole world of organic life is an enormous epiorganism.

The concept that most communities are composed of more or less independent individual organisms which are interrelated and to some extent co-ordinated so that the whole community forms a unit of organization, agrees well with what is known of ecology. To this extent I accept the organismic concept of the community. I emphatically disagree, however, with the procedure of Clements in singling out the climatic climax community together with its successional stages as the most important unit of community organization. The regional community is merely 1 of the types of communities which are important units of organization and which constitute epiorganisms.

PLACE OF THE COMMUNITY IN EMERGENT EVOLUTION

From the philosophical point of view called emergent evolution all matter is organized on a number of levels, each of which has its own particular laws. Among important levels of emergence may be mentioned: (1) inorganic matter, (2) organic compounds, (3) one-celled organisms (4) many-celled organisms, (5) social groups of organisms of the same species, and (6) communities composed of several associated species (Fig. 52). This list by no means includes all the stages in the evolution of community organization, but only a few of the more important emergences.

Each level of emergence has natural laws differing from those of any other level, superimposed on the laws that apply also to the lower levels (Wheeler, 1926; Jennings, 1927). For example, the chemical compound water has properties and laws of behavior different from those of the elements oxygen and hydrogen of which it is composed. Similarly every organism has properties and laws different from those of the organic compounds from which its various organs are built. The laws of physics and chemistry are operative on the molecules and compounds of which each organism is composed, but the behavior of the organism as a whole is something beyond the sum of these physical and chemical laws. A knowledge of physics and chemistry alone could never enable the physical scientist to predict what an organism would be like nor how it would act.

COMMUNITIES
↑
SOCIETIES
↑
MANY-CELLED ORGANISMS
↑
ONE-CELLED ORGANISMS
↑
ORGANIC COMPOUNDS
↑
INORGANIC MATTER

FIG. 52. Important levels in the emergent evolution of communities.

A community likewise is a unit of organization that has laws and functions which are in addition to the laws and functions of the individual organisms and species of which it is composed. In the process of its continual adjustment to a changing environment the community forms a unit which is at a higher level of organization than the individual or the species.

From the point of view of the emergence of community organization there are various levels of communities. First, there are many kinds of micro-associations, certain of which constitute separate levels of emergence. The association also constitutes an important level of organization. The biotic province, with its trend toward a climax or toward a series of climaxes corresponding to several life belts, constitutes a level of emergence of still higher grade. Then all the communities of the whole world may be considered a supercommunity that embraces all living plants and animals.

One of the most significant characteristics of the community is that it is able through progressive evolution to improve its adaptation to its habitat. In this ability the community parallels the species, which likewise is able through evolution to improve its efficiency.

No community has ever evolved a perfect organization, nor are the resources of any habitat fully utilized. Often there are maladjustments between the several member species. A state of constant and complete health has not yet been achieved anywhere in the organic world, a fact which is true of communities no less than of individuals. Nevertheless, each community contains within itself the possibility of improvement. Through the process of organic evolution there may be assumed to be constant, though usually exceedingly slow, improvement in the structure of every kind of community. Evolution tends ultimately to make each kind of community as stable and efficient as possible in utilizing effectively all the resources of its habitat.

The evolution that occurs in communities takes place primarily through changes in the characters and behavior of the several member species. The community, however, directs the evolution of each member species through its control of natural selection. The evolution of every species is thus shaped to the character of the community as a whole. Each community tends to evolve the highest degree of adjustment to its habitat that is possible within the limitations of the species available in its region.

Communities generally represent, therefore, a very high level of emergent evolution (Emerson, 1939). Plants and animals themselves represent high levels of emergent evolution, but every individual organism, including man, exists only as a member of some community. Through emergent evolution the community has come to occupy the highest level of organization attained in the organic world.

SELECTED REFERENCES

Clements, Frederic E., and Victor E. Shelford. 1939. Bio-ecology. New York: John Wiley and Sons. Chap. 2.

Gleason, Henry A. 1939. The individualistic concept of the plant association. Amer. Midl. Nat., 21: 92-110.

Jennings, Herbert S. 1927. Diverse doctrines of evolution, their relation to the practice of science and of life. Science, 65: 19-25.

Wheeler, William M. 1926. Emergent evolution and the social. Science, 64: 433-40.

LITERATURE CITED

No attempt is made to present here a complete bibliography of community ecology.

Adams, Charles C.

 1913 Guide to the study of animal ecology. New York: Macmillan Co.

 1915*a* An outline of the relations of animals to their inland environments. Bull. Ill. State Lab. Nat. Hist., 11: 1-32.

 1915*b* An ecological study of prairie and forest invertebrates. *Ibid.*, pp. 33-280.

Albrecht, William A.

 1944 Soil fertility and wildlife—cause and effect. Trans. N. Amer. Wildlife Conf., 9: 19-28.

Aldous, A. E.

 1930 Effect of different clipping treatments on the yield and vigor of prairie grass vegetation. Ecology, 11: 752-59.

Aldous, Shaler E.

 1938 Beaver food utilization studies. Journ. Wildlife Manag., 2: 215-22.

 1944 A deer browse survey method. Journ. Mammal., 25: 130-36.

Allan, Philip F., and P. R. Sime

 1943 A hawk census on Texas Panhandle highways. Wilson Bull., 55: 29-39.

Allee, W. C.

 1919 Note on animal distribution following a hard winter. Biol. Bull., 36: 96-104.

 1923 Studies in marine ecology. IV. The effect of temperature in limiting the geographical range of invertebrates in the Woods Hole littoral. Ecology, 4: 341-54.

 1927 Animal aggregations. Quart. Rev. Biol., 2: 367-98.

 1932 Animal life and social growth. Baltimore: Williams and Wilkins Co.

 1934 Concerning the organization of marine coastal communities. Ecol. Monog., 4: 541-54.

 1935 Relatively simple animal aggregations. *In* A handbook of social psychology. Ed. Carl Murchison. Worcester, Mass.: Clark Univ. Press. Pp. 919-46.

 1938 The social life of animals. New York: W. W. Norton and Co.

 1940 Concerning the origin of sociality in animals. Scientia, 67: 154-60.

 1942 Group organization among vertebrates. Science, 95: 289-93.

 1943*a* Animal population cycles. Sci. Mo., pp. 561-64.

 1943*b* Where angels fear to tread: a contribution from general sociology to human ethics. Science, 97: 517-25.

Allee, W. C., A. E. Emerson, O. Park, T. Park, and K. P. Schmidt

 1949 Principles of animal ecology. Philadelphia and London: W. B. Saunders Co. (This large work was published after the manuscript for this book was completed.)

Allen, A. A.

 1924 A contribution to the life history and economic status of the screech owl (*Otus asio*). Auk, 41: 1-16.

Allen, Durward L.
    1943 Michigan fox squirrel management. Publ. Mich. Game Div., 100: 1-404.
    1947 Hunting as a limitation to Michigan pheasant populations. Journ. Wildlife
            Manag., 11: 232-43.

Allen, Glover M.
    1925 Birds and their attributes. Boston: Marshall Jones Co.
    1939 Bats. Cambridge, Mass.: Harvard Univ. Press.
    1942 Extinct and vanishing mammals of the Western Hemisphere, with the marine
            species of all the oceans. Spec. Publ. Amer. Comm. Wild Life Protection,
            11: i-xv, 1-620.

Allen, Robert P.
    1942 The roseate spoonbill. Res. Rept. Nat. Audubon Soc., 2: i-xviii, 1-142.

Allen, W. E.
    1934 The primary food supply of the sea. Quart. Rev. Biol., 9: 161-80.

Allred, B. W.
    1941 Grasshoppers and their effect on sagebrush on the Little Powder River in
            Wyoming and Montana. Ecology, 22: 387-92.

Alverdes, Friedrich
    1927 Social life in the animal world. London: Kegan Paul, Trench, Trubner and Co.

Amadon, Dean
    1947 Ecology and the evolution of some Hawaiian birds. Evolution, 1: 63-68.

Anderson, Kling L.
    1942 A comparison of line transects and permanent quadrats in evaluating composi-
            tion and density of pasture vegetation of the tall prairie grass type. Journ.
            Amer. Soc. Agron., 34: 805-22.

Anderson, Paul
    1947 Observations on the denning habits of the prairie rattlesnake, *Crotalus viridis
            viridis* (Rafinesque). Nat. Hist. Misc. Chicago Acad. Sci., 9: 1-2.

Andrushko, S. I.
    1936 Methods and technique of reptilian censuses in deserts. Probl. Ecol. Biocenol.
            Leningrad, 3: 158-67. (In Russian, with English summary.)

Antevs, Ada
    1947 Towhee helps cardinals feed their fledglings. Condor, 49: 209.

Antevs, Ernst
    1922 The recession of the last ice sheet in New England. Res. Ser. Amer. Geog. Soc.,
            11: i-xiii, 1-120.

Arey, Leslie B., and W. J. Crozier
    1921 On the natural history of *Onchidium*. Journ. Exper. Zool., 32: 443-502.

Arnold, Joseph F.
    1942 Forage consumption and preferences of experimentally fed Arizona and antelope
            jack rabbits. Tech. Bull. Ariz. Agric. Exper. Sta., 98: 51-86.

Arrhenius, A.
    1921 Influence of soil reaction on earthworms. Ecology, 2: 255-57.

Asdell, S. A., R. Bogart, and G. Sperling
    1941 The influence of age and rate of breeding upon the ability of the female rat
            to reproduce and raise young. Mem. Cornell Univ. Agric. Exper. Sta., 238:
            1-26.

Ashby, Eric
    1935 The quantitative aspects of vegetation; with an appendix by W. L. Stevens. Ann.
            Bot., 49: 779-802.
    1936 Statistical ecology. Bot. Rev., 2: 221-35.

Axelrod, Daniel I.
1948 Climate and evolution in western North America during Middle Pliocene time. Evolution, 2: 127-44.

Babcock, S. M.
1912 Metabolic water: its production and role in vital phenomena. Res. Bull. Univ. Wis. Agric. Exper. Sta., 22: 87-181.

Bailey, Vernon
1923 Sources of water supply for desert animals. Sci. Mo., 17: 66-86.

Baker, John A.
1930 The breeding season in British wild mice. Proc. Zool. Soc. London, 1: 113-26.

Baldwin, Mark, C. E. Kellogg, and J. Thorp
1938 Soil classification. Yearbook U. S. Dept. Agric. Pp. 979-1001.

Ball, E. D., and W. E. Stone
1928 A puzzling butterfly migration. Science, 68: 110-11.

Ball, Gordon H.
1943 Parasitism and evolution. Amer. Nat., 77: 345-64.

Banta, Arthur M.
1907 The fauna of Mayfield's Cave. Publ. Carnegie Inst. Wash., 67: 1-114.
1939 Studies on the physiology, genetics, and evolution of some Cladocera. *Ibid.*, 513: i-x, 1-285.

Barnes, H. F., and J. W. Weil
1944 Slugs in gardens: their numbers, activities, and distribution. Pt. I. Journ. Animal Ecol., 13: 140-75.

Bartlett, H. H.
1933 The nomenclature of plant associations. Ecology, 14: 157-62.

Bartholomew, George A., Jr.
1942 The fishing activities of double-crested cormorants on San Francisco Bay. Condor, 44: 13-21.
1943 Contests of double-crested cormorants for perching sites. *Ibid.*, 186-95.

Bates, Marston
1945 Observations on climate and seasonal distribution of mosquitoes in eastern Colombia. Journ. Animal Ecol., 14: 17-25.

Baumgartner, F. M.
1939 Territory and population in the great horned owl. Auk, 56: 274-82.

Baumgras, Philip S.
1943 Winter food productivity of agricultural land for seed-eating birds and mammals. Journ. Wildlife Manag., 7: 13-18.

Baweja, K. D.
1939 Studies of the soil fauna, with special reference to the recolonizaton of sterilized soil. Journ. Animal Ecol., 8: 120-61.

Beall, Geoffrey
1935 Study of arthropod populations by the method of sweeping. Ecology, 16: 216-25.
1940 The fit and significance of contagious distributions when applied to observations on larval insects. *Ibid.*, 21: 460-74.

Beck, D. Elden
1942 Life history notes on the California gull, No. 1. Great Basin (Provo, Utah), 3: 91-108.

Becquerel, Paul
1907 Recherches sur la vie latente des graines. Ann. Sci. Nat. Paris, ser. 9, Bot., 5: 193-311.

Beebe, C. William
  1916 Notes on the birds of Pará, Brazil. Zoologica, 2: 55-106.
Beecher, William J.
  1942 Nesting birds and the vegetation substrate. Chicago: Chicago Ornithol. Soc.
Beeson, C. F. C.
  1944 The influence of insects on the regeneration, composition and destruction of forests. Proc. Royal Entom. Soc. London, Ser. C, 8 (11): 48-51.
Bellrose, Frank C., Jr., and H. G. Anderson
  1943 Preferential rating of duck food plants. Bull. Ill. Nat. Hist. Surv., 22: 417-33.
Bellrose, Frank C., Jr., and J. B. Low
  1943 The influence of flood and low water levels on the survival of muskrats. Journ. Mammal., 24: 173-88.
Bennett, L. J., and G. O. Hendrickson
  1938 Censusing the ringneck pheasant in Iowa. Trans. N. Amer. Wildlife Conf., 3: 719-23.
Berg, Irwin A.
  1947 Chronic vitamin B_1 deprivation. Science, 105: 252.
Berger, Bruno
  1907 Über die Widerstandsfähigkeit der Tenebriolarven gegen Austrochnung. Arch. f. Ges. Physiol. (Pflüger's Arch.), 118: 607-12.
Berry, Edward W.
  1916 The Lower Eocene floras of southeastern North America. Prof. Paper U. S. Geol. Surv., 91: 1-481.
  1930 Revision of the Lower Eocene Wilcox flora of the southeastern states. Ibid., 156: i-iv, 1-196.
Bigelow, H. B.
  1926 Plankton of the offshore waters of the Gulf of Maine. Bull. U. S. Bur. Fish., 40, No. 2: 1-509.
Billington, Cecil
  1938 The vegetation of Cranbrook Lake bottom. Bull. Cranbrook Inst. Sci., 11: 1-19.
Birch, L. C.
  1948 The intrinsic rate of natural increase of an insect population. Journ. Animal Ecol., 17: 15-26.
Bird, Ralph D.
  1930 Biotic communities of the aspen parkland of central Canada. Ecology, 11: 356-442.
Birge, E. A.
  1897 Plankton studies on Lake Mendota. II. The crustacea of the plankton, July, 1894–December, 1896. Trans. Wis. Acad. Sci. Arts Let., 11: 274-451.
Birge, E. A., and C. Juday
  1922 The inland lakes of Wisconsin. The plankton. I. Its quantity and chemical composition. Bull. Wis. Geol. Nat. Hist. Surv., 64, Sci. Ser., 13: i-vi, 1-222.
Bishop, James S., and George P. Skinner
  1946 Quantities of weed seed produced in Connecticut cornfields. Journ. Wildlife Manag., 10: 300-303.
Bissonette, Thomas H.
  1938 Experimental control of sexual photoperiodicity in animals and possible applications to wildlife management. Journ. Wildlife Manag., 2: 104-18.
Blackman, F. F.
  1905 Optima and limiting factors. Ann. Bot., 19: 281-95.

Blackman, F. F., and A. M. Smith
  1911 Experimental researches on vegetable assimilation and respiration. IX. On assimilation in submerged water-plants, and its relation to the concentration of carbon dioxide and other factors. Proc. Royal Soc. London, Ser. B, 83: 389-412.

Blackman, G. E.
  1935 A study by statistical methods of the distribution of species in grassland associations; with an appendix by M. S. Bartlett. Ann. Bot., 49: 749-77.

Blackman, M. W., and H. H. Stage
  1924 On the succession of insects living in the bark and wood of dying, dead and decaying hickory. Tech. Paper N. Y. State Coll. Forestry, 17: 3-240.

Blair, W. Frank
  1940a Home ranges and populations of the jumping mouse. Amer. Midl. Nat., 23: 244-50.
  1940b A study of prairie deer-mouse populations in southern Michigan. *Ibid.*, 24: 273-305.
  1940c Notes on home ranges and populations of the short-tailed shrew. Ecology, 21: 284-88.
  1940d Home ranges and populations of the meadow vole in southern Michigan. Journ. Wildlife Manag., 4: 149-61.
  1941 Techniques for the study of mammal populations. Journ. Mammal., 22: 148-57.
  1942 Size of home range and notes on the life history of the woodland deer-mouse and eastern chipmunk in northern Michigan. *Ibid.*, 23: 27-36.
  1943a Activities of the Chihuahua deer-mouse in relation to light intensity. Journ. Wildlife Manag., 7: 92-97.
  1943b Populations of the deer-mouse and associated small mammals in the mesquite association of southern New Mexico. Contrib. Lab. Vert. Biol. Univ. Mich., 21: 1-40.

Blanchard, Barbara D.
  1941 The white-crowned sparrows (*Zonotrichia leucophrys*) of the Pacific seaboard: environment and annual cycle. Univ. Calif. Publ. Zool., 46: 1-178.

Bliss, C. I.
  1941 Statistical problems in estimating populations of Japanese beetle larvae. Journ. Econ. Entom., 34: 221-32.

Blumenstock, David I., and C. W. Thornthwaite
  1941 Climate and the world pattern. Yearbook U. S. Dept. Agric. Pp. 98-127.

Blythe, Richard H., Jr., and Joseph F. Pechanec
  1943 Sampling methods in forestry. Ecology, 24: 414-15.

Bodenheimer, F. S.
  1938 Problems of animal ecology. London: Oxford Univ. Press.

Bogorov, B. G.
  1934 Seasonal changes in biomass of *Calanus finmarchicus* in the Plymouth area in 1930. Journ. Marine Biol. Assoc. U. Kingdom, 19: 585-612.

Bond, Richard M.
  1945 Range rodents and plant succession. Trans. N. Amer. Wildlife Conf., 10: 229-33.

Borror, Donald J.
  1948 Analysis of repeat records of banded white-throated sparrows. Ecol. Monog., 18: 411-30.

Bosma, Nelly J.
  1931 *Alaria mustelae*, sp. nov., a trematode requiring four hosts. Science, 74: 521-22.

Boyce, Janet M.
  1946 The influence of fecundity and egg mortality on the population growth of *Tribolium confusum* Duval. Ecology, 27: 290-302.

Bradt, Glenn W.
  1938 A study of beaver colonies in Michigan. Journ. Mammal., 19: 139-62.

Brady, F.
  1943 The distribution of the fauna of some intertidal sands and muds on the Northumberland coast. Journ. Animal Ecol., 12: 27-41.

Bragg, Arthur N.
  1945 The spadefoot toads in Oklahoma with a summary of our knowledge of the group. II. Amer. Nat., 79: 52-72.

Brambell, F. W. R.
  1944 The reproduction of the wild rabbit *Oryctolagus cuniculus* (L.). Proc. Zool. Soc. London, 114: 1-45.

Braun, E. Lucy
  1938 Deciduous forest climaxes. Ecology, 19: 515-22.

Braun-Blanquet, J.
  1928 Pflanzensoziologie: Grundzüge der Vegetationskunde. Berlin: Julius Springer.

Braun-Blanquet, J., George D. Fuller, and Henry S. Conard
  1932 Plant sociology: the study of plant communities. New York and London: McGraw-Hill Book Co.

Braun-Blanquet, J., and J. Pavillard
  1930 Vocabulary of plant sociology. (Translated by R. R. Bharucha.) Cambridge: Published by the authors.

Brecher, Leonard C.
  1943 The relation of vegetational life-forms to the distribution of breeding birds. Warbler, 19: 41-49.

Breder, C. M.
  1936 The reproductive habits of the North American sunfishes (Centrarchidae). Zoologica, 21: 1-48.

Brierley, W. B., S. T. Jewson, and M. Brierley
  1928 The quantitative study of soil fungi. Proc. Papers 1st Internat. Cong. Soil Sci. Wash., 3: 48-71.

Brody, Samuel
  1945 Bioenergetics and growth. New York: Reinhold Publ. Corp.

Brooks, Maurice
  1942 Birds at the extremities of their ranges. Wilson Bull., 54: 12-16.

Brown, Dalton M.
  1941 Vegetation of Roan Mountain: a phytosociological and successional study. Ecol. Monog., 11: 61-97.

Brown, William H.
  1919 Vegetation of Philippine mountains: the relation between the environment and physical types at different altitudes. Publ. Philippine Bur. Sci., 13: 1-434.

Brues, Charles T.
  1946 Insect dietary. Boston: Harvard Univ. Press.

Burns, Frank
  1900 Monograph of the flicker. Wilson Bull., 31: 1-82.

Burt, William H.
1940   Territorial behavior and populations of some small mammals in southern Michigan. Misc. Publ. Mus. Zool. Univ. Mich., 45: 1-58.
1943   Territoriality and home range concepts as applied to mammals. Journ. Mammal., 24: 346-52.

Cabrera, Ángel
1932   La incompatibilidad ecológica: Una ley biológica interesante. Ann. Soc. Cient. Argentina, 114: 243-60.

Cagle, Fred R.
1944   Home range, homing behavior, and migration in turtles. Misc. Publ. Mus. Zool. Univ. Mich., 61: 1-34.

Cahalane, Victor H.
1941   A trap-removal census study of small mammals. Journ. Wildlife Manag., 5: 42-67.
1942   Caching and recovery of food by the western fox squirrel. Ibid., 6: 338-52.

Cahn, A. R.
1929   The carp as a dominant. Ecoloy, 10: 271-74.

Cain, Stanley A.
1932   Concerning certain phytosociological concepts. Ecol. Monog., 2: 475-508.
1934   Studies on virgin hardwood forest. II. A comparison of quadrat sizes in a quantitative study of Nash's Woods, Posey County, Indiana. Amer. Midl. Nat., 15: 529-66.
1938   The species-area curve. Ibid., 19: 573-81.
1939   The climax and its complexities. Ibid., 21: 146-81.
1943   Sample-plot technique applied to alpine vegetation in Wyoming. Amer. Journ. Bot., 30: 240-47.
1944   Foundations of plant geography. New York and London: Harper and Brothers.
1945   Travelling disturbances as a climatic control. Journ. Tenn. Acad. Sci., 20: 218-23.
1947   Characteristics of natural areas and factors in their development. Ecol. Monog., 17: 185-200.

Calhoun, John B.
1944-46.   Twenty-four hour periodicities in the animal kingdom. Journ. Tenn. Acad. Sci., 19: 179-200, 252-62; 20: 228-32, 291-308, 373-78; 21: 208-16, 281-82.
1945   Diel activity rhythms of the rodents, Microtus ochrogaster and Sigmodon hispidus hispidus. Ecology, 26: 251-73.

Canfield, R. H.
1941   Application of the line interception method in sampling range vegetation. Journ. Forestry, 39: 388-94.

Cannon, W. A.
1911   The root habits of desert plants. Publ. Carnegie Inst. Wash., 131: 1-96.
1913   Botanical features of the Algerian Sahara. Ibid., 178: i-vi, 1-81.

Cannon, Walter B.
1939   The wisdom of the body. Rev. ed.; New York: W. W. Norton & Co.

Cantrall, Irving J.
1943   The ecology of the Orthoptera and Dermaptera of the George Reserve, Michigan. Misc. Publ. Mus. Zool. Univ. Mich., 54: 1-182.

Carbine, William F.
1945   Growth potential of the northern pike (Esox lucius). Papers Mich. Acad., 30: 205-20.

Carpenter, C. R.

    1934   A field study of the behavior and social relations of howling monkeys. Comp. Psychol. Monog., 10: 1-168.

    1935   Behavior of red spider monkeys in Panama. Journ. Mammal., 16: 171-80.

    1942   Societies of monkeys and apes. Biol. Symposia, Lancaster, 8: 177-204.

Carpenter, J. Richard

    1934   Diurnal fluctuations in communities adjoining the forest edge near Urbana, Illinois. Proc. Okla. Acad. Sci., 14: 29-31.

    1935   Fluctuations in biotic communities. I. Prairie forest ecotone of central Illinois. Ecology, 16: 203-12.

    1939   The biome. Amer. Midl. Nat., 21: 75-91.

Carpenter, J. Richard, and John Ford

    1936   The use of sweep net samples in an ecological survey. Journ. Soc. Brit. Entom., 1: 155-61.

Carr-Saunders, A. M.

    1922   The population problem; a study in human evolution. Oxford: Clarendon Press.

Case, E. C.

    1919   The environment of vertebrate life in the late Paleozoic in North America: a paleogeographic study. Publ. Carnegie Inst. Wash., 283: 1-273.

Cater, Milam B.

    1944   Roosting habits of martins at Tucson, Arizona. Condor, 46: 15-18.

Chaney, Ralph W.

    1918   The ecological significance of the Eagle Creek flora of the Columbia River gorge. Journ. Geol., 26: 577-92.

    1922   Notes on the flora of the Payette Formation. Amer. Journ. Sci., 4: 214-22.

    1925   A comparative study of the Bridge Creek flora and the modern redwood forest. Publ. Carnegie Inst. Wash., 349: 1-22.

Chaney, Ralph W. (ed.)

    1944   Pliocene floras of California and Oregon. Publ. Carnegie Inst. Wash., 553: i-vii, 1-407.

Chapin, J. P.

    1932   Birds of the Belgian Congo. Bull. Amer. Mus. Nat. Hist., 65: i-x, 1-725.

Chapman, Royal N.

    1928   A quantitative analysis of environmental factors. Ecology, 9: 111-22.

    1931   Animal ecology. New York and London: McGraw-Hill Book Co.

Chapman, Royal N., and W. Y. Whang

    1934   An experimental analysis of the cause of population fluctuations. Science, 80: 297-98.

Chapman, V. J.

    1944   Cambridge University expedition to Jamaica. Journ. Linn. Soc. Bot., 52: 407-533.

Chitty, Dennis, and Helen Chitty

    1941   Canadian arctic wild life enquiry, 1939-1940. Journ. Animal Ecol., 10: 184-203.

Chitty, Dennis, and Charles Elton

    1940   The snowshoe rabbit enquiry 1938-39. Can. Field-Nat., 54: 117-24.

Clapham, A. R.

    1932   The form of the observational unit in quantitative ecology. Journ. Ecol., 20: 192-97.

    1936   Over-dispersion in grassland communities and the use of statistical methods in ecology. *Ibid.*, 24: 232-51.

Clarke, C. H. D.
  1936 Fluctuations in numbers of ruffed grouse, *Bonasa umbellus* (Linné), with special reference to Ontario. Univ. Toronto Studies, Biol. Ser., 41: 1-118.

Clarke, George L.
  1943 Sea life. *In* Science from shipboard. Washington: Sci. Serv. Pp. 180-206.
  1946 Dynamics of production in a marine area. Ecol. Monog., 16: 321-35.

Clarke, G. L., W. T. Edmondson, and W. E. Ricker
  1946 Mathematical formulation of biological productivity. Ecol. Monog., 16: 336-37.

Clausen, Curtis P.
  1916 Life-history and feeding records of a series of California Coccinellidae. Univ. Calif. Publ. Entom., 1: 251-99.
  1936 Insect parasitism and biological control. Ann. Entom. Soc. Amer., 29: 201-33.

Clausen, Jens, David D. Keck, and William M. Hiesey
  1940 Experimental studies on the nature of species. I. Effect of varied environments on western North American plants. Publ. Carnegie Inst. Wash., 520: i-vii, 1-452.
  1948 Experimental studies on the nature of species. III. Environmental responses of climatic races of *Achillea. Ibid.*, 581: i-iii, 1-129.

Clements, Frederic E.
  1916 Plant succession: an analysis of the development of vegetation. Publ. Carnegie Inst. Wash., 242: i-xiii, 1-512.
  1920 Plant indicators: the relation of plant communities to process and practice. *Ibid.*, 290: i-xvi, 1-388.
  1934 The relict method in dynamic ecology. Journ. Ecol., 22: 39-68.

Clements, Frederic E., and R. W. Chaney
  1936 Environment and life in the Great Plains. Suppl. Publ. Carnegie Inst. Wash., 24: 1-54.

Clements, Frederic E., and Frances L. Long
  1923 Experimental pollination: an outline of the ecology of flowers and insects. Publ. Carnegie Inst. Wash., 336: i-vii, 1-274.

Clements, Frederic E., and Victor E. Shelford
  1939 Bio-ecology. New York: John Wiley and Sons.

Clements, Frederic E., John E. Weaver, and Herbert C. Hanson
  1929 Plant competition: an analysis of community functions. Publ. Carnegie Inst. Wash., 398: i-xvi, 1-340.

Cleveland, L. R.
  1923 Symbiosis between termites and their intestinal protozoa. Proc. U. S. Nat. Acad. Sci., 9: 424-28.
  1924 The physiological and symbiotic relationships between the intestinal protozoa of termites and their host, with special reference to *Reticulitermes flavipes.* Biol. Bull., 46: 178-227.

Cleveland, L. R., and others
  1934 The wood-feeding roach *Cryptocercus*, its protozoa, and the symbiosis between protozoa and roach. Mem. Amer. Acad. Arts Sci., 17: iii-x, 185-342.

Cliff, Edward P.
  1939 Relationship between elk and mule deer in the Blue Mountains of Oregon. Trans. N. Amer. Wildlife Conf., 4: 560-69.

Coker, R. E.
  1947 This great and wide sea. Chapel Hill: Univ. N. C. Press.

Cole, LaMont C.
> 1946a A study of the cryptozoa of an Illinois woodland. Ecol. Monog., 16: 49-86.
>
> 1946b A theory for analyzing contagiously distributed populations. Ecology, 27: 329-41.

Collias, N. E.
> 1944 Aggressive behavior among vertebrate animals. Physiol. Zool., 17: 83-123.

Colquhoun, M. K.
> 1940   The density of woodland birds determined by the sample count method. Journ. Animal Ecol., 9: 53-67.
>
> 1942a Notes on the social behavior of blue tits. Brit. Birds, 35: 234-40.
>
> 1942b A natural population of *Coccinella septempunctata* in Norfolk. Entomologist, 75: 40-41.
>
> 1942c The habitat distribution of the grey squirrel (*Sciurus carolinensis*) in Savernake Forest. Journ. Animal Ecol., 11: 127-30.

Colquhoun, M. K., and Averil Morley
> 1943   Vertical zonation in woodland bird communities. Journ. Animal Ecol., 12: 75-81.

Conant, James B.
> 1948   The role of science in our unique society. Science, 107: 77-83.

Conard, Henry S.
> 1939   Plant associations on land. Amer. Midl. Nat., 21: 1-27.

Conn, H. J.
> 1928   Bacterial population of soil. Proc. Papers 1st Internat. Cong. Soil Sci. Wash., 3: 92-95.

Cooke, May T.
> 1923   Report on bird censuses in the United States, 1916 to 1920. Bull. U. S. Dept. Agric., 1165: 1-34.
>
> 1927   The purpose of bird censuses and how to make them. Rev. Circ. U. S. Dept. Agric., 261: 1-4.

Cooper, W. S.
> 1923   The recent ecological history of Glacier Bay, Alaska. I. The interglacial forests of Glacier Bay. Ecology, 4: 93-128.
>
> 1926   The fundamentals of vegetative change. *Ibid.*, 7: 391-417.
>
> 1941   Man's use and abuse of native vegetation: the lessons of the past and the prospects for the future. Univ. Penn. Bicentennial Conf., "Conservation of renewable nature resources." Pp. 5-18.
>
> 1942   Contributions of botanical science to the knowledge of postglacial climates. Journ. Geol., 50: 981-94.

Cottam, Clarence
> 1934   Eelgrass disappearance has serious effects on waterfowl and industry. Yearbook U. S. Dept. Agric. Pp. 191-93.
>
> 1935   Economic ornithology and the correlation of laboratory and field methods. Wildlife Res. and Manag. Leaflet, U. S. Biol. Surv., 30.

Cottam, Walter P.
> 1937   Has Utah lost claim to the Lower Sonoran Zone? Science, 85: 563-64.

Coville, Frederick V., and Daniel T. MacDougal
> 1903   Desert Botanical Laboratory of the Carnegie Institution. Publ. Carnegie Inst. Wash., 6: i-vi, 1-58

Cowan, Ian McTaggart
> 1945   The ecological relationships of the food of the Columbian black-tailed deer, *Odocoileus hemionus columbianus* (Richardson), in the Coast Forest region of southern Vancouver Island, British Columbia. Ecol. Monog., 15: 109-39.
>
> 1947   The timber wolf in the Rocky Mountain National Parks of Canada. Can. Journ. Res., Ser. D, 25: 139-74.

Cowles, Henry C.
1901*a* The physiographic ecology of Chicago and vicinity; a study of the origin, development, and classification of plant societies. Bot. Gaz., 31: 73-182.
1901*b* The influence of underlying rocks on the character of the vegetation. Bull. Amer. Bur. Geog., 2: 163-76, 376-88.

Cowles, Raymond B., and Charles M. Bogert
1944 A preliminary study of the thermal requirements of desert reptiles. Bull. Amer. Mus. Nat. Hist., 83: 261-96.

Cox, W. T.
1938 Snowshoe hare useful in thinning forest stands. Journ. Forestry, 36: 1107-9.

Coyner, Wallace R.
1939 A report on the influence of overgrazing on the Acrididae. Proc. Okla. Acad. Sci., 19: 83-85.

Craig, Charles F., and E. C. Faust
1945 Clinical parasitology. 4th ed.; Philadelphia: Lea and Febiger.

Cramp, S., and J. H. Ward
1934 A census of house martins and swallows near Manchester, 1933. Journ. Animal Ecol., 3: 1-7.

Crawford, M. P.
1939 The social psychology of vertebrates. Psychol. Bull., 35: 407-66.

Crew, F. A., and L. Mirskaia
1931 The effects of density on an adult mouse population. Biol. Gen., 7: 239-50.

Crombie, A. C.
1944 The effect of crowding upon the natality of grain-infesting insects. Proc. Zool. Soc. London, 113A: 77-98.
1945 On competition between different species of graminivorous insects. Proc. Royal Soc. London, Ser. B, 132: 362-95.
1947 Interspecific competition. Journ. Animal Ecol., 16: 44-73.

Culley, Matt J., R. S. Campbell, and R. H. Canfield
1933 Values and limitations of clipped quadrats. Ecology, 14: 35-39.

Curtis, J. T., and H. C. Greene
1949 A study of relic Wisconsin prairies by the species-presence method. Ecology, 30: 83-92.

Dachnowski, Alfred
1912 Peat deposits of Ohio, their origin, formation, and uses. Bull. Geol. Surv. Ohio, Ser. 4, 16: 1-424.

Dalke, Paul D.
1935*a* Dropping analyses as an indication of pheasant food habits. Trans. N. Amer. Game Conf., 21: 387-91.
1935*b* Carrying capacity of pheasant range. Amer. Game, 24 (2): 23, 31-32.

Darling, F. Fraser
1937 A herd of red deer; a study in animal behavior. London: Oxford Univ. Press.
1938 Bird flocks and the breeding cycle; a contribution to the study of avian sociality. Cambridge: Cambridge Univ. Press.

Darlington, H. T.
1931 The 50-year period for Dr. Beal's seed viability experiment. Amer. Journ. Bot., 18: 262-65.
1941 The sixty-year period for Dr. Beal's seed viability experiment. *Ibid.*, 28: 271-73.

Darlington, P. J., Jr.
1943 Carabidae of mountains and islands: data on the evolution of isolated faunas, and on atrophy of wings. Ecol. Monog., 13: 37-61.

Darwin, Charles
  1859 The origin of species by means of natural selection, or, the preservation of favored races in the struggle for life. London: John Murray.
  1882 The formation of vegetable mould, through the action of worms. New York: D. Appleton and Co.

Daubenmire, Rexford F.
  1938 Merriam's life zones of North America. Quart. Rev. Biol., 13: 327-32.
  1947 Plants and environment: a textbook of plant autecology. New York: John Wiley and Sons.

Davenport, C. B.
  1917 The effects of race intermingling. Proc. Amer. Philos. Soc., 56: 364-68.

Davenport, L. A., Warren Shapton, and W. Carl Gower
  1944 A study of the carrying capacity of deer yards as determined by browse plots. Trans. N. Amer. Wildlife Conf., 9: 144-49.

Davis, David E.
  1941 The belligerency of the kingbird. Wilson Bull., 53: 157.
  1942 The phylogeny of social nesting habits in the Crotophaginae. Quart. Rev. Biol., 17: 115-34.
  1945 The annual cycle of plants, mosquitoes, birds, and mammals in two Brazilian forests. Ecol. Monog., 15: 243-95.
  1946 A seasonal analysis of mixed flocks of birds in Brazil. Ecology, 27: 168-81.

Davis, John H., Jr.
  1945 Jamaican shore-line ecology, especially mangroves. Ecology, 26: 312.

Davison, Verne E.
  1940a An 8-year census of lesser prairie chickens. Journ. Wildlife Manag., 4: 55-62.
  1940b A field method of analysing game bird foods. Ibid., 4: 105-16.
  1946 False principles delay advancement in wildlife techniques. Ibid., 10: 296-99.

DeBach, Paul, and Harry S. Smith
  1941 Are population oscillations inherent in the host-parasite relation? Ecology, 22: 363-69.
  1947 Effects of parasite population density on rate of change of host and parasite populations. Ibid., 28: 290-98.

Deevey, E. S., Jr.
  1947 Life tables for natural populations of animals. Quart. Rev. Biol., 22: 283-314.

Demoll, R.
  1927 Betrachtungen über Produktions Berechnungen. Arch. f. Hydrobiol., 18: 460-63.

Dendy, Jack S.
  1944 The fate of animals in stream drift when carried into lakes. Ecol. Monog., 14: 333-57.

Dethier, V. G.
  1941 Chemical factors determining the choice of food plants by *Papilio* larvae. Amer. Nat., 75: 61-73.

Dice, Lee R.
  1914 The factors determining the vertical movements of Daphnia. Journ. Animal Behavior, 4: 229-65.
  1916 Distribution of the land vertebrates of southeastern Washington. Univ. Calif. Publ. Zool., 16: 293-348.
  1921 A bird census at Prescott, Walla Walla County, Washington. Condor, 23: 87-90.
  1922 Some factors affecting the distribution of the prairie vole, forest deer mouse, and prairie deer mouse. Ecology, 3: 29-47.

1923*a* Life zones and mammalian distribution. Journ. Mammal., 4: 39-47.

1923*b* Notes on the communities of the vertebrates of Riley County, Kansas, with especial reference to amphibians, reptiles, and mammals. Ecology, 4: 40-53.

1925*a* The mammals of Marion Island, Grand Traverse County, Michigan. Occ. Papers Mus. Zool. Univ. Mich., 160: 1-8.

1925*b* Rodents and lagomorphs of the Rancho La Brea deposits. Publ. Carnegie Inst. Wash., 349: 119-30.

1930 Methods of indicating relative abundance of birds. Auk, 47: 22-24.

1931*a* Methods of indicating the abundance of mammals. Journ. Mammal., 12: 376-81.

1931*b* The relation of mammalian distribution to vegetation types. Sci. Mo., 33: 312-17.

1938*a* Some census methods for mammals. Journ. Wildlife Manag., 2: 119-30.

1938*b* The Canadian biotic province with special reference to the mammals. Ecology, 19: 503-14.

1940*a* The theoretical effectiveness of adverse selection. Contrib. Lab. Vert. Biol. Univ. Mich., 14: 1-6.

1940*b* Ecologic and genetic variability within species of Peromyscus. Amer. Nat., 74: 212-21.

1941 Methods for estimating populations of mammals. Journ. Wildlife Manag., 5: 398-407.

1942 Ecological distribution of Peromyscus and Neotoma in parts of southern New Mexico. Ecology, 23: 199-208.

1943 The biotic provinces of North America. Ann Arbor: Univ. Mich. Press.

1945 Measures of the amount of ecologic association between species. Ecology, 26: 297-302.

1948 Relationship between frequency index and population density. *Ibid.*, 29: 389-91.

1952 Measure of the spacing between individuals within a population. Contrib. Lab. Vert. Biol. Univ. Mich., No. 55.

Dice, Lee R., and Philip M. Blossom

1937 Studies of mammalian ecology in southwestern North America, with special attention to the colors of desert mammals. Publ. Carnegie Inst. Wash., 485: i-iv, 1-129.

Diver, C.

1938*a* The distribution of natural populations. Proc. Zool. Soc. London, 108C: 61-62.

1938*b* The plant carpet in relation to animal distribution. Proc. Linn. Soc. London, Sess. 150: 124-35.

1940 The problem of closely related species living in the same area. *In* The new systematics, ed. by Julian Huxley. Oxford: Oxford Univ. Press. Pp. 303-28.

1944 Insects limited by the general conditions imposed by plant communities. Proc. Royal Entom. Soc. London, Ser. C, 8 (11): 44-48.

Dixon, A.

1939 The protozoa of some East Greenland soils. Journ. Animal Ecol., 8: 162-67.

Dixon, J. S.

1934 A study of the life history and food habits of mule deer in California. Calif. Fish and Game, 20: 182-282, 315-54.

Dobzhansky, Theodosius

1941 Genetics and the origin of species. 2d ed., rev.; New York: Columbia Univ. Press.

Dore, W. G., and L. C. Raymond

1942 Pasture studies. XXIV. Viable seeds in pasture soil and manure. Sci. Agric., 23: 69-79.

Douglass, A. E.

1914 A method of estimating rainfall by the growth of trees. Bull. Amer. Geog. Soc., 46: 321-35.

Dowdeswell, W. H., R. A. Fisher, and E. B. Ford
    1940   The quantitative study of populations in the lepidoptera. I. *Polyommatus icarus*
           Rott. Ann. Eugenics, 10: 123-36.

Dowdy, W. W.
    1944   The influence of temperature on vertical migration of invertebrates inhabiting
           different soil types. Ecology, 25: 449-60.

Duck, L. G.
    1943   Seasonal movements of bobwhite quail in northwestern Oklahoma. Journ. Wild-
           life Manag., 7: 365-68.

Duncan, Carl D.
    1939   A contribution to the biology of the North American vespine wasps. Stanford
           Univ. Publ. Biol. Sci., 8: 1-272.

Dusi, Julian L.
    1949   Methods for the determination of food habits by plant microtechniques and
           histology and their application to cottontail rabbit food habits. Journ. Wild-
           life Manag., 13: 295-98.

Dutton, H. J., and W. M. Manning
    1941   Evidence of carotenoid-sensitized photosynthesis in the diatom *Nitzschia
           closterium*. Amer. Journ. Bot., 28: 516-26.

Dyksterhuis, E. J., and E. M. Schmutz
    1947   Natural mulches or "litter" of grasslands: with kinds and amounts on a southern
           prairie. Ecology, 28: 163-79.

Eaton, Theodore H., Jr., and Robert F. Chandler, Jr.
    1942   The fauna of forest-humus layers in New York. Mem. Cornell Agric. Exper.
           Sta., 247: 1-26.

Edmondson, W. T.
    1945   Ecological studies of sessile Rotatoria. II. Dynamics of populations and social
           structures. Ecol. Monog., 15: 141-72.

Eggler, Willis A.
    1948   Plant communities in the vicinity of the volcano El Parícutin, Mexico, after
           two and a half years of eruption. Ecology, 29: 415-36.

Egler, Frank E.
    1942   Vegetation as an object of study. Philos. Sci., 9: 245-60.

Einarsen, Arthur S.
    1946   Management of black-tailed deer. Journ. Wildlife Manag., 10: 54-59.

Ellison, Lincoln
    1946   The pocket gopher in relation to soil erosion on mountain range. Ecology, 27:
           101-14.

Elton, Charles
    1927   Animal ecology. New York: Macmillan Co.
    1930   Animal ecology and evolution. Oxford: Clarendon Press.
    1932   Territory among wood ants (*Formica rufa* L.) at Picket Hill. Journ. Animal
           Ecol., 1: 69-76.
    1939   On the nature of cover. Journ. Wildlife Manag., 3: 332-38.
    1942   Voles, mice, and lemmings; problems in population dynamics. Oxford: Claren-
           don Press.
    1946   Competition and the structure of ecological communities. Journ. Animal Ecol.,
           15: 54-68.

Elton, Charles, and Mary Nicholson
    1942a Fluctuations in numbers of the muskrat (*Ondatra zibethica*) in Canada. Journ.
           Animal Ecol., 11: 96-126.
    1942b The ten-year cycle in numbers of the lynx in Canada. *Ibid.*, 11: 215-44.

Emerson, Alfred E.
    1939 Social coordination and the superorganism. Amer. Midl. Nat., 21: 182-209.
    1943 Ecology, evolution, and society. Amer. Nat., 77: 97-118.

Emlen, John T., Jr.
    1938 Midwinter distribution of the American crow in New York state. Ecology, 19:
         264-75.
    1939 Seasonal movements of a low-density valley quail population. Journ. Wildlife
         Manag., 3: 118-30.
    1940 Sex and age ratios in survival of the California quail. *Ibid.*, 4: 92-99.

Emlen, John T., Jr., and Ben Glading
    1945 Increasing valley quail in California. Bull. Univ. Calif. Agric. Exper. Sta., 695:
         1-56.

Erdtman, G.
    1943 An introduction to pollen analysis. Waltham, Mass.: Chronica Botanica Co.

Erickson, Mary M.
    1938 Territory, annual cycle, and numbers in a population of wren-tits (*Chamaea
         fasciata*). Univ. Calif. Publ. Zool., 42: 247-334.

Errington, Paul L.
    1934 Vulnerability of bob-white populations to predation. Ecology, 15: 110-27.
    1939 Reactions of muskrat populations to drought. *Ibid.*, 20: 168-86.
    1941 Notes on winter-killing of central Iowa bob-whites. Ia. Bird Life, 11: 46-49.
    1942 On the analysis of productivity in populations of higher vertebrates. Journ.
         Wildlife Manag., 6: 165-81.
    1943 An analysis of mink predation upon muskrats in north central United States.
         Res. Bull. Ia. Agric. Exper. Sta., 320: 797-924.
    1945 Some contributions of a fifteen-year local study of the northern bobwhite to
         a knowledge of population phenomena. Ecol. Monog., 15: 1-34.
    1946 Predation and vertebrate populations. Quart. Rev. Biol., 21: 144-77, 221-45.

Errington, Paul L., and F. N. Hamerstrom, Jr.
    1936 The northern bob-white's winter territory. Res. Bull. Ia. Agric. Exper. Sta., 201:
         301-443.

Errington, Paul L., Frances Hamerstrom, and F. N. Hamerstrom, Jr.
    1940 The great horned owl and its prey in north-central United States. Res. Bull.
         Ia. Agric. Exper. Sta., 277: 757-850.

Eskey, C. R.
    1938 Flea infestation of domestic rats in San Francisco, Calif. U. S. Publ. Health
         Rept., 53: 948-51.

Espinas, A. V.
    1924 Des sociétés animales. 3d ed.; Paris: Felix Alcan. (First ed. in 1877.)

Evans, F. C.
    1942 Studies of a small mammal population in Bagley Wood, Berkshire. Journ. Ani-
         mal Ecol., 11: 182-97.

Evans, F. C., and R. Holdenried
    1943 A population study of the Beechey ground squirrel in central California. Journ.
         Mammal., 24: 231-60.

Evans, Llewellyn T.
   1938   Cuban field studies of territoriality of the lizard, *Anolis sagrei*. Journ. Comp.
          Psychol., 25: 97-125.
Ewart, A. J.
   1908   On the longevity of seeds. Proc. Royal Soc. Victoria, 21: 1-210.
Fal'kenshtein, B. Yu.
   1939   Some ecologo-geographical laws governing the population dynamics of mouse-
          like rodents. Plant Protection, Leningrad, 18: 3-14. (In Russian, with English
          summary.)
Farner, Donald S.
   1945   Age groups and longevity in the American robin. Wilson Bull., 57: 56-74.
Farrow, E. Pickworth
   1925   Plant life on East Anglican heaths: being observational and experimental studies
          of the vegetation of Breckland. Cambridge: Cambridge Univ. Press.
Fennell, R. A.
   1945   The relation between heredity, sexual activity and training to dominance-sub-
          ordination in game cocks. Amer. Nat., 79: 142-51.
Fenton, G. R.
   1947   The soil fauna: with special reference to the ecosystem of forest soil. Journ.
          Animal Ecol., 16: 76-93.
Fisher, Arne
   1915   The mathematical theory of probabilities and its application to frequency
          curves and statistical methods. New York: Macmillan Co.
Fisher, Harvey I., Robert W. Hiatt, and William Bergeson
   1947   The validity of the roadside census as applied to pheasants. Journ. Wildlife
          Manag., 11: 205-26.
Fisher, R. A.
   1930   The genetical theory of natural selection. Oxford: Clarendon Press.
   1936   Statistical methods for research workers. 6th ed.; Edinburgh and London:
          Oliver and Boyd.
   1941   Statistical methods for research workers. 8th ed.; Edinburgh and London:
          Oliver and Boyd.
Fitch, Henry S.
   1940   A field study of the growth and behavior of the fence lizard. Univ. Calif. Publ.
          Zool., 44: 151-72.
   1948a Ecology of the California ground squirrel on grazing lands. Amer. Midl. Nat.,
          39: 513-96.
   1948b Habits and economic relationships of the Tulare kangaroo rat. Journ. Mammal.,
          29: 5-35.
Fitch, H. S., F. Swenson, and D. F. Tillotson
   1946   Behavior and food habits of the red-tailed hawk. Condor, 48: 205-37.
Fitch, H. S., and Howard Twining
   1946   Feeding habits of the Pacific rattlesnake. Copeia, pp. 64-71.
Fitter, R. S. R.
   1945   London's natural history. London: William Collins Sons & Co.
Flahault, Charles, and C. Schröter
   1910   Phytogeographical nomenclature: reports and propositions. Zurich: Zurcher
          and Furrer.
   1912   Rapport sur la nomenclature phytogéographique. Actes IIIᵉ Congrès Internat.
          Bot. Bruxelles, 1910, 1: 131-42.

Flanders, Stanley E.
1947 Elements of host discovery exemplified by parasitic hymenoptera. Ecology, 28: 299-309.

Flattely, F. W., and C. L. Walton
1922 The biology of the seashore. London: Sedgwick and Jackson.

Fleisher, W. E.
1935 The relation between chlorophyll content and rate of photosynthesis. Journ. Gen. Physiol., 18: 573-97.

Forbes, S. A.
1880 On some interactions of organisms. Bull. Ill. State Lab. Nat. Hist., 1 (3): 3-17. (Reprinted in 1903.)
1907a An ornithological cross-section of Illinois in autumn. *Ibid.*, 7: 305-35.
1907b On the local distribution of certain Illinois fishes: an essay in statistical ecology. *Ibid.*, pp. 273-303.
1909 The general entomological ecology of the Indian corn plant. Amer. Nat., 43: 286-301.
1925 The lake as a microcosm. Bull. Ill. Nat. Hist. Surv., 15: 537-50.

Ford, John
1937 Research on populations of *Tribolium confusum* and its bearing on ecological theory: a summary. Journ. Animal Ecol., 6: 1-14.

Formozov, A. N.
1928 Mammalia in the steppe biocenose. Ecology, 9: 449-60.
1933 The crop of cedar nuts, invasions into Europe of the Siberian nutcracker (*Nucifraga caryocatactes macrorhynchus* Brehm) and fluctuations in numbers of the squirrel (*Sciurus vulgaris* L.). Journ. Animal Ecol., 2: 70-81.
1934a The lake region of the forest-steppe and steppe of western Siberia as a breeding area of the waterfowl. Bull. Soc. Nat. Moscow, Biol. Ser., 43: 256-86. (In Russian, with English summary.)
1934b On competition between species. Mutual relations between the squirrel (*Sciurus vulgaris* L.), the crossbill (*Loxia curvirostra* L.), and the great spotted woodpecker (*Dryobates major* L.). Doklady Akad. Nauk SSSR, 1934, 3: 197-201. (In Russian, with English summary.)
1937 Materials on the ecology of aquatic birds according to observations made on the lakes of the State Naurzum Reservation territory (northern part of the Kasach SSR). M. A. Menzbier Memorial Vol. Moscow. Pp. 551-95. (In Russian, with English summary.)
1939 The snow covering as an environment factor and its importance in the ecology of mammals and birds. Bull. Soc. Nat. Moscow, 48: 60-68.
1942 A study of the fluctuations in numbers of licensed animals and the organizing of "prognoses of yield" in the hunting economy of the USSR for the period 1917-1942. Zool. Zhur., 21: 251-58. (In Russian.)
1946 La couverture de neige comme facteur intégrant du milieu et son importance dans l'écologie des mammifères et des oiseux. Material for Fauna and Flora USSR, Moscow, n.s., Zool., 5: 1-152. (In Russian, with French summary.)

Formozov, A. N., and I. B. Prosvirnina
1935 Activity of rodents on pastures and hay-mowing property. Bull. Soc. Nat. Moscow, Biol. Ser., 44: 82-89. (In Russian, with French summary.)

Formozov, A. N., and A. G. Voronov
1939 The activity of rodents on the pasture and meadow lands of west Kazakhstan and its economic importance. Uchen. Zap. Moscow St. Univ., 20: 3-122. (In Russian, with English summary.)

Fracker, S. B., and H. A. Brischle
    1944   Measuring the local distribution of Ribes. Ecology, 25: 283-303.

Friedmann, Herbert
    1928   Social parasitism in birds. Quart. Rev. Biol., 3: 554-69.
    1929   The cowbirds. Springfield, Ill. and Baltimore, Md.: C. C. Thomas.
    1935   Bird societies. *In* A handbook of social psychology. Ed. Carl Murchison. Worcester, Mass.: Clark Univ. Press. Pp. 142-84.

Gabrielson, I. N.
    1913   Nest life of the catbird, *Dumetella carolinensis* Linn. Wilson Bull., 25: 166-87.
    1941   Wildlife conservation. New York: Macmillan Co.

Gams, H.
    1918   Prinzipienfragen der Vegetationsforschung. Ein Beitrag zur Begriffsklärung und Methodik der Biocoenologie. Vierteljahrsschr. Naturf. Ges. Zürich, 63: 293-493.

Garner, W. W.
    1936   Photoperiodism. *In* Biological effects of radiation. Ed. B. M. Duggar. Pp. 677-713.

Garner, W. W., and H. A. Allard
    1920   Effect of the relative length of day and night and other factors of the environment on growth and reproduction in plants. Journ. Agric. Res., 18: 553-606.

Gates, Frank C.
    1926   Plant successions about Douglas Lake, Cheboygan County, Michigan. Bot. Gaz., 82: 170-82.
    1930   Aspen association in northern lower Michigan. *Ibid.,* 90: 233-59.
    1942   The bogs of northern lower Michigan. Ecol. Monog., 12: 213-54.
    1949   Field manual of plant ecology. New York: McGraw-Hill Book Co.

Gause, G. F.
    1934*a* The struggle for existence. Baltimore: Williams and Wilkins Co.
    1934*b* An experimental investigation of the struggle for existence between *Paramaecium caudatum, Paramaecium aurelia,* and *Stylonychia mytilus.* Zool. Zhurn., 13: 1-17.
    1935*a* Vérifications expérimentales de la théorie mathématique de la lutte pour la vie. Actual. scient. et indust., 277. Paris: Hermann et Cie.
    1935*b* Experimental demonstration of Volterra's periodic oscillations in the numbers of animals. Journ. Exper. Biol., 12: 44-48.
    1935*c* Behavior of mixed populations and the problem of natural selection. Amer. Nat., 69: 596-609.
    1942   The relation of adaptability to adaptation. Quart. Rev. Biol., 17: 99-114.

Gause, G. F., and A. A. Witt
    1934   On the periodic fluctuations in the numbers of animals: a mathematical theory of the relaxation interaction between predators and prey and its application to a population of protozoa. Izvestia Akad. Nauk USSR. Pp. 1551-59. (In Russian, with English summary.)
    1935   Behavior of mixed populations and the problem of natural selection. Amer. Nat., 69: 596-609.

Gerard, R. W.
    1940   Organism, society, and science. Sci. Mo., 50: 340-50, 403-12, 530-35.
    1942   Higher levels of integration. Biol. Symposia, 8: 67-87.

Gerstell, Richard
    1939   Certain mechanics of winter quail losses revealed by laboratory experiments. Trans. N. Amer. Wildlife Conf., 4: 462-67.

Ginsburg, B., and W. C. Allee
    1942   Some effects of conditioning on social dominance and subordination in inbred
            strains of mice. Physiol. Zool., 15: 485-506.

Glading, Ben
    1941   Valley quail census methods and populations at the San Joaquin Experimental
            Range. Calif. Fish and Game, 27 (2): 33-38.

Glading, Ben, Harold H. Biswell, and Clarence F. Smith
    1940   Studies on the food of the California quail in 1937. Journ. Wildlife Manag.,
            4: 128-44.

Glasgow, J. P.
    1939   A population study of subterranean soil Collembola. Journ. Animal Ecol., 8:
            323-53.

Gleason, Henry A.
    1917   The structure and development of the plant association. Bull. Torrey Bot. Club,
            44: 463-81.
    1920   Some applications of the quadrat method. *Ibid.*, 47: 21-33.
    1925   The structure of the maple-beech association in northern Michigan. Papers
            Mich. Acad., 4: 285-96.
    1927   Further views on the succession-concept. Ecology, 8: 299-326.
    1929a   The significance of Raunkiaer's law of frequency. *Ibid.*, 10: 406-8.
    1929b   Plant associations and their classification: a reply to Dr. Nichols. Proc. Internat.
            Cong. Plant Sci., Ithaca, N. Y., 1926, 1: 643-46.
    1939   The individualistic concept of the plant association. Amer. Midl. Nat., 21:
            92-110.

Glinka, K. D.
    1935   The great soil groups of the world and their development. Translated from the
            German by C. F. Marbut. Ann Arbor: Edwards Brothers.

Godsil, H. C.
    1948   A preliminary study of the yellowfin tuna and the albacore. Fish Bull. Calif.
            Div. Fish and Game, 70: 1-90.

Godwin, H.
    1936   Studies in the ecology of Wicken Fen. III. The establishment and development
            of fen scrub (carr). Journ. Ecol., 24: 82-116.

Gordon, Kenneth
    1936   Territorial behavior and social dominance among Sciuridae. Journ. Mammal.,
            17: 171-72.
    1943   The natural history and behavior of the western chipmunk and the mantled
            ground squirrel. Ore. State Monog., Studies Zool., 5: 1-104.

Gowen, John W., and Leslie E. Johnson
    1946   On the mechanism of heterosis. I. Metabolic capacity of different races of
            Drosophila melanogaster for egg production. Amer. Nat., 80: 149-79.

Graham, Edward H.
    1942   Soil erosion as an ecological process. Sci. Mo., 55: 42-51.
    1944   Natural principles of land use. London, New York, and Toronto: Oxford Univ.
            Press.

Graham, Samuel A.
    1925   The felled tree trunk as an ecological unit. Ecology, 6: 397-411.
    1930   Ornithology and forest entomology. Papers Mich. Acad., 11: 389-97.
    1939   Principles of forest entomology. 2d ed.; New York: McGraw-Hill Book Co.
    1941   Climax forests of the Upper Peninsula of Michigan. Ecology, 22: 355-62.

Gray, Reed, and James Bonner
    1948a An inhibitor of plant growth from the leaves of *Encelia farinosa*. Amer. Journ.
           Bot., 35: 52-57.
    1948b Structure determination and synthesis of a plant growth inhibitor, 3-acetyl-
           6-methoxybenzaldehyde, found in the leaves of *Encelia Farinosa*. Journ. Amer.
           Chem. Soc., 70: 1249-53.

Green, R. G., and C. A. Evans
    1940 Studies on a population cycle of snowshoe hares on the Lake Alexander area.
           Journ. Wildlife Manag., 4: 220-38, 267-78, 347-58.

Green, R. G., C. L. Larson, and J. F. Bell
    1939 Shock disease as the cause of the periodic decimation of the snowshoe hare.
           Amer. Journ. Hygiene, 30: 83-102.

Greenbank, John
    1945 Limnological conditions in ice-covered lakes, especially as related to winter-kill
           of fish. Ecol. Monog., 15: 343-92.

Greenwood, Major
    1928 "Laws" of mortality from the biological point of view. Journ. Hygiene (Cam-
           bridge), 28: 267-94.

Gregor, J. W.
    1944 The ecotype. Biol. Rev., 19: 20-30.
    1947 Some reflections on intra-specific ecological variation and its classification. Trans.
           Bot. Soc. Edinburgh, 34: 377-91.

Griggs, R. F.
    1934 The edge of the forest in Alaska and the reasons for its position. Ecology, 15:
           90-96.
    1946 The timberlines of northern America and their interpretation. *Ibid.*, 4: 275-89.

Grinnell, Joseph
    1908 The biota of the San Bernardino Mountains. Univ. Calif. Publ. Zool., 5: 1-170.
    1914a An account of the mammals and birds of the lower Colorado Valley, with
           especial reference to the distributional problems presented. *Ibid.*, 12: 51-294.
    1914b Barriers to distribution as regards birds and mammals. Amer. Nat., 48: 248-54.
    1916 The English sparrow has arrived in Death Valley: an experiment in nature.
           Ibid., 53: 468-73.
    1917 The niche-relationships of the California thrasher. Auk, 34: 427-33.
    1923 The burrowing rodents of California as agents in soil formation. Journ.
           Mammal., 4: 137-49.
    1924a Wild animal life as a product and as a necessity of national forests. Journ.
           Forestry, 22: 837-45.
    1924b Geography and evolution. Ecology, 5: 225-29.
    1928a Presence and absence of animals. Univ. Calif. Chron., 30: 429-50.
    1928b A distributional summation of the ornithology of Lower California. Univ. Calif.
           Publ. Zool., 32: 1-300.
    1936 Up-hill planters. Condor, 38: 80-82.

Grinnell, Joseph, and Tracy I. Storer
    1924 Animal life in the Yosemite; an account of the mammals, birds, reptiles, and
           amphibians in a cross-section of the Sierra Nevada. Berkeley: Univ. Calif.
           Press.

Grisebach, A.
    1838 Ueber den Einfluss des Climas auf die Begränzung der natürlichen Floren.
           Linnea, 12: 159-200.

Haas, Fritz
   1943   Malacological notes. III. Field Mus. Nat. Hist. Zool., 29: 1-23.

Haldane, J. B. S.
   1932   The causes of evolution. New York and London: Harper and Brothers.

Hall, E. Raymond
   1927   An outbreak of house mice in Kern County, California. Univ. Calif. Publ. Zool., 30: 189-203.

Hamerstrom, F. N., Jr.
   1939   A study of Wisconsin prairie chicken and sharp-tailed grouse. Wilson Bull., 51: 105-20.

Hamerstrom, F. N., Jr., and James Blake
   1939   Winter movements and winter foods of white-tailed deer in central Wisconsin. Journ. Mammal., 20: 206-15.

Hamilton, W. J., Jr.
   1937   The biology of microtine cycles. Journ. Agric. Res., 54: 779-90.
   1943   Winter habits of the dusky salamander in central New York. Copeia, p. 192.

Hammond, E. C.
   1938-39   Biological effects of population density in lower organisms. Quart. Rev. Biol., 13: 421-38; 14: 35-59.

Hanson, Herbert C., and L. Dudley Love
   1930   Comparison of methods of quadratting. Ecology, 11: 734-48.

Hardy, Ross
   1945   The influence of types of soil upon the local distribution of some mammals in southwestern Utah. Ecol. Monog., 15: 71-108.

Harvey, H. W.
   1933   Measurement of phytoplankton populations. Journ. Marine Biol. Assoc. U. Kingdom, 19: 761-73.

Hasel, A. A.
   1941   Estimation of vegetation-type areas by linear measurements. Journ. Forestry, 39: 34-40.

Hatt, Robert T.
   1943   The pine squirrel in Colorado. Journ. Mammal., 24: 311-45.

Haugen, Arnold O.
   1942a   Home range of the cottontail rabbit. Ecology, 23: 354-67.
   1942b   Life history studies of the cottontail rabbit in southwestern Michigan. Amer. Midl. Nat., 28: 204-44.
   1943   Management studies of the cottontail rabbit in southwestern Michigan. Journ. Wildlife Manag., 7: 102-19.

Hawbecker, Albert C.
   1944   The giant kangaroo rat and sheep forage. Journ. Wildlife Manag., 8: 161-65.

Hayne, Don W.
   1949   Calculation of size of home range. Journ. Mammal., 30: 1-18.

Hayward, C. Lynn
   1948   Biotic communities of the Wasatch chaparral, Utah. Ecol. Monog., 18: 473-506.

Heady, Harold F.
   1942   Littoral vegetation of the lakes on the Huntington Forest. Roosevelt Wildlife Bull., 8: 5-32.

Herold, Werner
    1928 Kritische Untersuchungen über die Methode der Zeitfänge zur Analyse von
          Landbiocönosen. Zeit. Wiss. Biol., Abt. A, Zeit. f. Morph. u. Ökol. der Tiere,
          10: 420-32.
    1929 Weitere Untersuchungen über die Methode der Zeitfänge. *Ibid.*, 14: 614-29.

Herrick, F. H.
    1912 Organization of the gull community. Proc. 7th Internat. Zool. Cong., Boston.
          Pp. 156-58.

Herrington, W. C.
    1944 Factors controlling population size. Trans. N. Amer. Wildlife Conf., 9: 250-63.
    1947 The role of intraspecific competition and other factors in determining the popu-
          lation level of a major marine species. Ecol. Monog., 17: 317-23.

Hess, A. D., and J. H. Rainwater
    1939 A method for measuring the food preference of trout. Copeia, pp. 154-57.

Hesse, Richard
    1924 Tiergeographie auf ökologischer Grundlage. Jena: Gustav Fischer.

Hesse, Richard, W. C. Allee, and Karl P. Schmidt
    1937 Ecological animal geography. New York: John Wiley and Sons.

Hewatt, Willis G.
    1935 Ecological succession in the *Mytilus californicus* habitat as observed in Monterey
          Bay, Calif. Ecology, 16: 244-51.
    1940 Observations on the homing limpet, *Acmaea scabra* Gould. Amer. Midl. Nat.,
          24: 205-8.

Hiatt, Robert W.
    1942 A frequency distribution of eastern and western kingbirds in Montana. Great
          Basin Nat., 3: 109-14.

Hibbard, Claude W.
    1941 Paleoecology and correlation of the Rexroad fauna from the Upper Pliocene of
          southwestern Kansas, as indicated by the mammals. Univ. Kans. Sci. Bull., 27:
          79-104.

Hibben, Frank C.
    1939 The mountain lion and ecology. Ecology, 20: 584-86.

Hicks, E. A.
    1942 Some major factors affecting the use of two inventory methods applicable to the
          western fox squirrel, *Sciurus niger rufiventer* (Geoffroy). Journ. Sci. Iowa
          State Coll., 16: 299-305.

Hill, Ralph R.
    1946 Palatability ratings of Black Hills plants for white-tailed deer. Journ. Wildlife
          Manag., 10: 47-54.

Hingston, R. W. G.
    1933 The meaning of colour and adornment. London: Edward Arnold and Co.

Hofmann, J. V.
    1920 The establishment of a Douglas fir forest. Ecology, 1: 49-53.

Holmes, S. J.
    1911 The evolution of animal intelligence. New York: Henry Holt and Co.

Holscher, Clark E.
    1945 The effects of clipping bluestem wheatgrass and blue grama at different heights
          and frequencies. Ecology, 26: 148-56.

Honess, Ralph F., and Edward M. Frost
    1942 A Wyoming bighorn sheep study. Bull. Wyo. Game and Fish Dept., 1: i-vi, 1-127.

Hooker, H. D., Jr.
    1917 Leibig's law of the minimum in relation to general biological problems. Science, n.s., 46: 197-204.

Hopkins, Andrew D.
    1938 Bioclimatics: a science of life and climate relations. Misc. Publ. U. S. Dept. Agric., 280: i-iv, 1-188.

Horn, E. E., and H. S. Fitch
    1942 Interrelations of rodents and other wildlife of the range. Bull. Univ. Calif. Agric. Exper. Sta., 663: 96-129.

Hough, A. F.
    1945 Frost pocket and other microclimates in forests of the northern Allegheny Plateau. Ecology, 26: 235-50.

Hough, A. F., and R. D. Forbes
    1943 The ecology and silvics of forests in the high plateaus of Pennsylvania. Ecol. Monog., 13: 299-320.

Hovanitz, William
    1948 Differences in the field activity of two female color phases of Colias butterflies at various times of day. Contrib. Lab. Vert. Biol. Univ. Mich., 41: 1-37.

Howard, H. Eliot
    1920 Territory in bird life. London: John Murray.

Howard, Hildegarde
    1930 A census of the Pleistocene birds of Rancho La Brea from the collections of the Los Angeles Museum. Condor, 32: 81-88.

Howard, L. O.
    1897 A study in insect parasitism: a consideration of the parasites of the white-marked tussock moth, with an account of their habits and interrelations, and with descriptions of new species. Tech. Ser. U. S. Dept. Agric., 5: 5-57.

Howard, L. O., and W. F. Fiske
    1911 The importation into the United States of the parasites of the gipsy moth and brown-tail moth. Bull. Bur. Entom. U. S. Dept. Agric., 91: 1-344.

Howard, Walter E.
    1949 Dispersal, amount of inbreeding, and longevity in a local population of deermice on the George Reserve, southern Michigan. Contrib. Lab. Vert. Biol. Univ. Mich., 43: 1-50.

Howard, Walter E., and John T. Emlen, Jr.
    1942 Intercovey social relationships in the valley quail. Wilson Bull., 54: 162-70.

Howell, Arthur H.
    1924 Revision of the American pikas. N. Amer. Fauna, 47: i-iv, 1-57.
    1938 Revision of the North American ground squirrels, with a classification of the North American Sciuridae. *Ibid.*, 56: 1-256.

Howell, Joseph C.
    1942 Notes on the nesting habits of the American robin (*Turdus migratorius* L.). Amer. Midl. Nat., 28: 529-603.

Hoyt, J. S. Y.
    1948 Observations on nesting associates. Auk, 65: 188-96.

Hubbell, T. H.
    1936 Monographic revision of the genus Ceuthophilus. Univ. Fla. Publ. Biol., Sci. Ser., 2: 1-551.

Hubbs, Carl L., and Boyd W. Walker
    1942 Habitat and breeding behavior of the American cyprinid fish *Notropis longirostris*. Copeia, pp. 101-4.

Huey, L. M.

    1925 Guadalupe Island: an object lesson in man-caused devastation. Science, 61: 405-7.

Humboldt, Al. de

    1805 Essai sur la géographie des plantes; accompagné d'un tableau physique des régions équinoxiales. Paris: Levrault, Schoell et Cie.

Huntington, Ellsworth, and Stephen S. Visher

    1922 Climatic changes; their nature and causes. New Haven: Yale Univ. Press.

Hursh, C. R., and F. W. Haasis

    1931 Effects of 1925 summer drought on southern Appalachian hardwoods. Ecology, 12: 380-86.

Hutchinson, G. Evelyn

    1941 Ecological aspects of succession in natural populations. Amer. Nat., 75: 406-18.

    1944 Limnological studies in Connecticut. VII. A critical examination of the supposed relationship between phytoplankton periodicity and chemical changes in lake waters. Ecology, 25: 3-26.

Huxley, Julian S.

    1934 A natural experiment on the territorial instinct. Brit. Birds, 27: 270-77.

    1938a Darwin's theory of sexual selection and the data subsumed by it, in the light of recent research. Amer. Nat., 72: 416-33.

    1938b Clines: an auxiliary taxonomic principle. Nature, 142: 219.

Hyslop, J. A., R. L. Webster, and W. E. Hinds

    1925 Report of the committee on estimating insect abundance. Journ. Econ. Entom., 18: 24-32.

Issakov, J. A., and A. N. Formozov

    1946 Unperiodical migrations of flamingoes in the USSR. Zool. Zhurn., 25: 473-80. (In Russian, with English summary.)

Ives, Ronald L.

    1942 The beaver-meadow complex. Journ. Geomorph., 5: 191-203.

Jackson, C. H. N.

    1939 The analysis of an animal population. Journ. Animal Ecol., 8: 238-46.

    1940 The analysis of a tsetse-fly population. III. Ann. Eugenics, 10: 332-69.

Jacot, Arthur P.

    1935 Molluscan populations of old growth forests and rewooded fields in the Asheville Basin of North Carolina. Ecology, 16: 603-5.

    1936 Soil structure and soil biology. Ibid., 17: 359-79.

    1940 The fauna of the soil. Quart. Rev. Biol., 15: 28-58.

Jameson, E. W., Jr.

    1947 Natural history of the prairie vole (mammalian genus Microtus). Univ. Kans. Publ. Mus. Nat. Hist., 1: 125-51.

Jenkins, Dale W.

    1944 Territory as a result of despotism and social organization in geese. Auk, 61: 30-47.

Jennings, Herbert S.

    1904 Contributions to the study of the behavior of lower organisms. Publ. Carnegie Inst. Wash., 16: 1-256.

    1927 Diverse doctrines of evolution, their relation to the practice of science and of life. Science, 65: 19-25.

    1942 The transition from the individual to the social level. Biol. Symposia, 8: 105-19.

Jensen, Herbert A.
    1947 A system for classifying vegetation in California. Calif. Fish and Game, 33:
          199-266.
Jensen, P. Boysen
    1915 Studies concerning the organic matter of the sea bottom. Rept. Danish Biol.
          Sta., 1914, 22: 1-39.
Johnsen, Siguard
    1945 Studies on variation in fish in North-European waters. I. Variation in size.
          Bergens Museums Årbok, 1944, Naturvitenskapelig rekke, Nr. 4: 1-129.
Johnston, Verna R.
    1942 Factors influencing local movements of woodland birds in winter. Wilson Bull.,
          54: 192-98.
Jones, Sarah E.
    1946 Variations in abundance of certain invertebrates in William Trelease Woods,
          1933-38. Amer. Midl. Nat., 35: 172-92.
Judd, Sylvester D.
    1902 Birds of a Maryland farm; a local study of economic ornithology. Bull. Div.
          Biol. Surv. U. S. Dept. Agric., 17: 1-116.
Kalabukhov, N. I.
    1937 Principal laws of the dynamics of mammal and bird populations. Uspekhi
          Sovremenmoi Biologii (Advances in Modern Biology), 7: 505-31. (In Russian.)
    1941 Variation and mass increase. Zhur. Obsch. Biol., 2: 381-93. (In Russian, with
          English summary.)
Kalmbach, E. R.
    1939 Nesting success: its significance in waterfowl reproduction. Trans. N. Amer.
          Wildlife Conf., 4: 591-604.
Kashkarov, D. N.
    1927 The quantitative method in the field study of vertebrate fauna and analysis
          of the data obtained. Acta Univ. Asiae Mediae, Ser. VIII-a., Zool., Fasc. 1:
          3-24. (In Russian, with English summary.)
    1938 Principles of animal ecology. Moscow and Leningrad. (In Russian.)
Kearney, T. H., L. J. Briggs, H. L. Shantz, J. W. McLane, and R. L. Piemeisel
    1914 Indicator significance of vegetation in Tooele Valley, Utah. Journ. Agric. Res.,
          1: 365-417.
Keeler, Clyde E., and Helen D. King
    1942 Multiple effects of coat color genes in the Norway rat, with special reference
          to temperament and domestication. Journ. Comp. Psychol., 34: 241-50.
Kelker, George H.
    1947 Computing the rate of increase for deer. Journ. Wildlife Manag., 11: 177-83.
Kellogg, Charles E.
    1938 Soil and society. Yearbook U. S. Dept. Agric. Pp. 863-86.
Kendeigh, S. Charles
    1932 A study of Merriam's temperature laws. Wilson Bull., 44: 129-43.
    1941a Length of day and energy requirements for gonad development and egg-laying
          in birds. Ecology, 22: 237-48.
    1941b Birds of a prairie community. Condor, 43: 165-74.
    1941c Territorial and mating behavior of the house wren. Ill. Biol. Monog., 18: 1-120.
    1942 Analysis of losses in the nesting of birds. Journ. Wildlife Manag., 6: 19-26.
    1944 Measurement of bird populations. Ecol. Monog., 14: 67-106.
    1945a Community selection by birds on the Helderberg Plateau of New York. Auk, 62:
          418-36.

Kendeigh, S. Charles (*Cont.*)

1945*b* Nesting behavior of wood warblers. Wilson Bull., 57: 145-64.

1947 Bird population studies in the coniferous forest biome during a spruce budworm outbreak. Biol. Bull. Ontario Dept. Lands and Forests, 1: 1-100.

Kendeigh, S. Charles., and S. Prentiss Baldwin

1937 Factors affecting yearly abundance of passerine birds. Ecol. Monog., 7: 91-123.

Kenk, Roman

1944 The fresh-water triclads of Michigan. Misc. Publ. Mus. Zool. Univ. Mich., 60: 1-44.

Kenoyer, Leslie A.

1927 A study of Raunkiaer's law of frequence. Ecology, 8: 341-49.

King, Ralph T.

1937 Ruffed grouse management. Journ. Forestry, 35: 523-32. (Reprinted 1943 in Roosevelt Wildlife Bull., 8: 63-80.)

Kirkman, F. B.

1937 Bird behavior; a contribution based chiefly on a study of the black-headed gull. London and Edinburgh: T. Nelson & Sons and T. C. & E. C. Jack.

Kittredge, Joseph

1948 Forest influences. New York, Toronto, and London: McGraw-Hill Book Co.

Klugh, A. Brooker

1923 A common system of classification in plant and animal ecology. Ecology, 4: 366-77.

Köppen, W.

1936 Das geographische System der Klimate. *In* Handbuch der Klimatologie, Bd. 1, Teil C. Berlin: Gebrüder Borntraeger. 44 pp.

Komarek, E. V.

1937 Mammal relationships to upland game and other wildlife. Trans. N. Amer. Wildlife Conf., 2: 561-69.

Korringa, P.

1947 Relations between the moon and periodicity in the breeding of marine animals. Ecol. Monog., 17: 347-81.

Korstian, C. F., and Theodore S. Coile

1938 Plant competition in forest stands. Bull. School Forestry Duke Univ., 3: 1-125.

Kosmunski, Zygmund

1938 Amount and distribution of the chlorophyll in some lakes of northeastern Wisconsin. Trans. Wis. Acad. Sci. Arts Let., 31: 411-38.

Krefting, Laurits W., and Eugene I. Roe

1949 The role of some birds and mammals in seed germination. Ecol. Monog., 19: 269-86.

Kropotkin, P.

1902 Mutual aid, a factor of evolution. New York: McClure Phillips & Company.

Krumholz, Louis A.

1948 Variations in size and composition of fish populations in recently stocked ponds. Ecology, 29: 401-14.

Kummer, Anna Pedersen

1945 The role of weeds in maintaining the plains grassland. Chicago Nat., 8: 23-27.

Kylin, Harald

1926 Über Begriffsbildung und Statistik in der Pflanzensociologie. Bot. Notiser, 1926: 81-180.

Lack, David
    1933 Habitat selection in birds; with special reference to the effects of afforestation on the Breckland avifauna. Journ. Animal Ecol., 2: 239-62.
    1937 A review of bird census work and bird population problems. Ibis, ser. 14, 1: 369-95.
    1940a The behavior of the robin. Population changes over four years. *Ibid.*, 4: 299-324.
    1940b Pair-formation in birds. Condor, 42: 269-86.
    1943 The age of the blackbird. Brit. Birds, 36: 166-75.
    1944 Ecological aspects of species-formation in passerine birds. Ibis, 86: 260-86.
    1945 The ecology of closely related species with special reference to cormorant (*Phalacrocorax carbo*) and shag (*P. aristotelis*). Journ. Animal Ecol., 14: 12-16.
    1946a Competition for food by birds of prey. *Ibid.*, 15: 123-29.
    1946b Do juvenile birds survive less well than adults? Brit. Birds, 39: 258-64.
    1947 Darwin's finches. Cambridge: Cambridge Univ. Press.
    1948 Natural selection and family size in the starling. Evolution, 2: 95-110.

Lack, David, and Lambert Lack
    1933 Territory reviewed. Brit. Birds, 27: 179-99.

Lack, David, and R. M. Lockley
    1935 The breeding bird population of British heaths and moorland; together with an account of a census over seven years of Skokholm, Pembrokeshire. Journ. Animal Ecol., 4: 43-57.

Laessle, Albert M.
    1942 The plant communities of the Welaka area with special reference to correlations between soils and vegetational succession. Univ. Fla. Publ. Biol., Sci. Ser., 4: 1-143.

Lagler, Karl F.
    1944 Problems of competition and predation. Trans. N. Amer. Wildlife Conf., 9: 212-19.

Lagler, Karl F., and B. T. Ostenson
    1942 Early spring food of the otter in Michigan. Journ. Wildlife Manag., 6: 244-54.

Lagler, Karl F., and William E. Ricker
    1943 Biological fisheries investigations of Foots Pond, Gibson County, Indiana. Invest. Ind. Lakes and Streams, 2: 47-72.

Larrison, Earl J.
    1946 Biotic areas in the Pacific Northwest. Murrelet (Seattle, Wash.), 27: 19-24.

Larson, Floyd
    1940 The role of the bison in maintaining the short grass plains. Ecology, 21: 113-21.

Laskey, Amelia R.
    1947 Evidence of polyandry at a bluebird nest. Auk, 64: 314-15.

Lay, Daniel W.
    1938 How valuable are woodland clearings to birdlife? Wilson Bull., 50: 254-56.
    1940 Bob-white populations as affected by woodland management in eastern Texas. Bull. Texas Agric. Exper. Sta., 592: 1-37.

Lay, Daniel W., and Hilbert R. Siegler
    1937 The blue jay as link between acorn and quail. Trans. N. Amer. Wildlife Conf., 2: 579-81.

Leach, Frank A.
    1925 Communism in the California woodpecker. Condor, 27: 12-19.

Lehmann, Valgene W.
    1941 Attwater's prairie chicken; its life history and management. N. Amer. Fauna, 57: i-v, 1-65.

Leopold, Aldo

    1931   Report on a game survey of the North Central States. Madison, Wis.: Sporting
          Arms and Ammunition Mfr. Inst.

    1939   Game management. New York and London: Charles Scribner's Sons.

    1942   The last stand. Outdoor America, 7: 8-9.

    1943   Deer irruptions. Publ. Wis. Dept. Cons., 321: 3-11.

Leopold, Aldo, T. M. Sperry, W. S. Feeney, and J. A. Catenhusen

    1943   Population turnover on a Wisconsin pheasant refuge. Journ. Wildlife Manag.,
          7: 383-94.

Leopold, A. Starker

    1944   The nature of heritable wildness in turkeys. Condor, 46: 133-97.

Leslie, P. H., and R. M. Ranson

    1940   The mortality, fertility, and rate of natural increase of the vole (*Microtus
          agrestis*) as observed in the laboratory. Journ. Animal Ecol., 9: 27-52.

L'Héritier, Ph., and Georges Teissier

    1933   Étude d'une population de Drosophiles en équilibre. C. R. Acad. Sci. Paris, 197:
          1765-67.

Liebig, Justus von

    1862   Die Chemie in ihrer Anwendung auf Agricultur und Physiologie. 7th ed.;
          Braunschweig: Friedrich Bieweg und Sohn. 2 vols.

Lincoln, Frederick C.

    1930   Calculating waterfowl abundance on the basis of banding returns. Circ. U. S.
          Dept. Agric., 118: 1-40.

    1939   The migration of American birds. New York: Doubleday, Doran and Co.

Lindeman, Raymond L.

    1942   The trophic-dynamic aspect of ecology. Ecology, 23: 399-418.

Linduska, J. P.

    1942   Winter rodent populations in field-shocked corn. Journ. Wildlife Manag., 6:
          353-63.

Linsdale, Jean M.

    1928   A method of showing relative frequency of occurrence of birds. Condor, 30:
          180-84.

    1946   The California ground squirrel; a record of observations made on the Hastings
          Natural History Reservation. Berkeley and Los Angeles: Univ. Calif. Press.

Lipmaa, Theodor

    1939   The unistratal concept of plant communities (the unions). Amer. Midl. Nat., 21:
          111-45.

Livingston, Burton E.

    1908   A simple atmometer. Science, 28: 319-20.

Livingston, Burton E., and Forrest Shreve

    1921   The distribution of vegetation in the United States, as related to climatic con-
          ditions. Publ. Carnegie Inst. Wash., 284: i-xvi, 1-590.

Lorenz, K.

    1935   Der Kumpan in der Umwelt des Vogels. Journ. f. Ornithol., 83: 137-213; 289-413.

Lotka, Alfred J.

    1925   Elements of physical biology. Baltimore: Williams and Wilkins Co.

Low, Jessop B., and Frank C. Bellrose, Jr.

    1944   The seed and vegetative yield of waterfowl food plants in the Illinois River
          Valley. Journ. Wildlife Manag., 8: 7-22.

Lowrie, Donald C.
    1942   The ecology of the spiders of the xeric dunelands in the Chicago area. Bull. Chicago Acad. Sci., 6: 161-89.

Lucas, C. E.
    1947   The ecological effects of external metabolites. Biol. Rev. Cambridge Phil. Soc., 22: 270-95.

Lutz, Frank E.
    1941   A lot of insects; entomology in a suburban garden. New York: G. P. Putnam's Sons.

Lutz, Harold J., and Robert F. Chandler, Jr.
    1946   Forest soils. New York: John Wiley and Sons.

Lyford, Walter H., Jr.
    1943   The palatability of freshly fallen forest tree leaves to millipeds. Ecology, 24: 252-61.

Lyon, T. L., and H. O. Buckman
    1937   The nature and properties of soils; a college test of edaphology. 3d ed.; New York: Macmillan Co.

MacArthur, John W.
    1942   Relations of body size to litter size and to the incidence of fraternal twins. Journ. Heredity, 33: 87-91.

McAtee, W. L.
    1907   Census of four square feet. Science, n.s., 26: 447-49.
    1912   Methods of estimating the contents of bird stomachs. Auk, 29: 449-64.
    1932   Effectiveness in nature of the so-called protective adaptations in the animal kingdom, chiefly as illustrated by the food habits of Nearctic birds. Smithson. Misc. Coll., 85 (7): 1-201.
    1947   Distribution of seeds by birds. Amer. Midl. Nat., 38: 214-23.

McClanahan, Robert C.
    1940   Original and present breeding ranges of certain game birds in the United States. Wildlife Leaflet U. S. Biol. Surv., BS-158: 1-21.

McClure, H. Elliott
    1939   Cooing activity and censusing of the mourning dove. Journ. Wildlife Manag., 3: 323-28.
    1942   Summer activities of bats (genus *Lasiurus*) in Iowa. Journ. Mammal., 23: 430-34.

McColloch, J. W., and William P. Hayes
    1923   Soil temperature and its influence on white grub activities. Ecology, 4: 29-36.

Macdonell, W. R.
    1913   On the expectation of life in ancient Rome, and in the provinces of Hispania and Lusitania, and Africa. Biometrica, 9: 366-80.

McDougal, W. B.
    1918   The classification of symbiotic phenomena. Plant World, 21: 250-56.

McDougall, Kenneth D.
    1943   Sessile marine invertebrates of Beaufort, North Carolina; a study of settlement, growth, and seasonal fluctuations among pile-dwelling organisms. Ecol. Monog., 13: 321-74.

Macfadyen, A.
    1948   The meaning of productivity in biological systems. Journ. Animal Ecol., 17: 75-80.

MacGinitie, G. E.
    1935   Ecological aspects of a California marine estuary. Amer. Midl. Nat., 16: 629-765.
    1939   Littoral marine communities. *Ibid.*, 21: 28-55.

McLean, Donald D.
  1930 The quail of California. Game Bull. Calif. Div. Fish and Game, 2: 1-47.

McLean, R. C., and W. R. Ivimey Cook
  1946 Practical field ecology: a guide for the botany departments of universities, colleges and schools. London: George Allen and Unwin.

Mac Lulich, D. A.
  1937 Fluctuations in the numbers of the varying hare (*Lepus americanus*). Univ. Toronto Studies, Biol. Ser., 43: 1-136.

Maier, N. R. F., and T. C. Schneirla
  1935 Principles of animal psychology. New York and London: McGraw-Hill Book Co.

Marks, John B.
  1942 Land use and plant succession in Coon Valley, Wisconsin. Ecol. Monog., 12: 113-33.

Marlatt, C. L.
  1907 The periodical cicada. Bull. Bur. Entom. U. S. Dept. Agric., 71: 1-181.

Marshall, J. F.
  1938 The British mosquitoes. London: British Mus. Nat. Hist.

Martin, A. C., R. H. Gensch, and C. P. Brown
  1946 Alternative methods in upland gamebird food analysis. Journ. Wildlife Manag., 10: 8-12.

Mason, H. L.
  1936 The principles of geographic distribution as applied to floral analysis. Madroño, 3: 181-90.
  1947 Evolution of certain floristic associations in western North America. Ecol. Monog., 17: 201-10.

Masure, Ralph H., and W. C. Allee
  1934 The social order in flocks of the common chicken and the pigeon. Auk, 51: 306-27.

Mayr, Ernst
  1935 Bernard Altum and the territory theory. Abs. Proc. Linn. Soc. New York, 45-46: 24-38.
  1942 Systematics and the origin of species from the viewpoint of a zoologist. New York: Columbia Univ. Press.
  1948 The bearing of the new systematics on genetical problems: the nature of species. Advances in Gen., 2: 205-37.

Mendall, Howard L., and Clarence M. Aldous
  1943 The ecology and management of the American woodcock. Orono, Me.: Me. Coop. Wildlife Res. Unit.

Merriam, C. Hart
  1890 Results of a biological survey of the San Francisco Mountain region and desert of the Little Colorado, Arizona. N. Amer. Fauna, 3: 1-136.
  1892 The geographic distribution of life in North America with special reference to the Mammalia. Proc. Biol. Soc. Wash., 7: 1-64.
  1894 Laws of temperature control of the geographic distribution of terrestrial animals and plants. Nat. Geog. Mag., 6: 229-38.
  1898 Life zones and crop zones in the United States. Bull. Div. Biol. Surv., U. S. Dept. Agric., 10: 1-79.

Merriam, C. H., Vernon Bailey, E. W. Nelson, and E. A. Preble
  1910 U. S. Biological Survey fourth provisional zone map of North America. Washington: U. S. Biol. Surv.

Merriam, John C.
  1911   The fauna of Rancho La Brea. Pt. I. Occurrence. Mem. Univ. Calif., 1: 197-213.
Michael, Ellis L.
  1916   Dependence of marine biology upon hydrography and necessity of quantitative
         biological research. Univ. Calif. Publ. Zool., 15: i-xxiii.
Michener, Harold, and Josephine R. Michener
  1935   Mockingbirds, their territories and individualities. Condor, 37: 97-140.
Miller, Alden H.
  1931   Systematic revision and natural history of the American shrikes (Lanius). Univ.
         Calif. Publ. Zool., 38: 11-242.
  1937   Biotic associations and life-zones in relation to the Pleistocene birds of Cali-
         fornia. Condor, 39: 248-52.
  1942   Habitat selection among higher vertebrates and its relation to intraspecific
         variation. Amer. Nat., 76: 25-35.
  1944   An avifauna from the Lower Miocene of South Dakota. Univ. Calif. Publ., Bull.
         Dept. Geol., 27: 85-100.
Miller, Milton A.
  1946   Reproductive rates and cycles in the pocket gopher. Journ. Mammal., 27:
         335-58.
Miller, Robert C.
  1922   The significance of the gregarious habit. Ecology, 3: 122-26.
Möbius, Karl
  1877   Die Auster und die Austernwirthschaft. Berlin: Wiegandt, Hempel & Parey.
  1883   The oyster and oyster-culture. Rept. U. S. Fish Comm., 1880. Pt. 8: 683-824.
         (Translation of preceding article.)
Moffett, James W.
  1943   A limnological investigation of the dynamics of a sandy, wind-swept shoal in
         Douglas Lake, Michigan. Trans. Amer. Micro. Soc., 62: 1-23.
Mohr, Carl O.
  1940   Comparative populations of game, fur and other mammals. Amer. Midl. Nat.,
         24: 581-84.
  1943   Cattle droppings as ecological units. Ecol. Monog., 13: 275-98.
  1947   Table of equivalent populations of North American small mammals. Amer.
         Midl. Nat., 37: 223-49.
Molina, E. C.
  1942   Poisson's exponential binomial limit. New York: D. Van Nostrand Co.
Moreau, R. E.
  1944   Clutch-size: a comparative study, with special reference to American birds.
         Ibis, 86: 286-347.
Moreau, R. E., and W. M. Moreau
  1938   The comparative breeding ecology of two species of Euplectes (bishop birds)
         in Usambra. Journ. Animal Ecol., 7: 314-27.
Morgan, Ann H.
  1939   Field book of animals in winter. New York: G. P. Putnam's Sons.
Morgan, M. F., J. H. Gourley, and J. K. Ableiter
  1938   The soil requirements of economic plants. Yearbook U. S. Dept. Agric. Pp.
         753-76.
Morton, Glenn M., and E. L. Cheatum
  1946   Regional differences in breeding potential of white-tailed deer in New York.
         Journ. Wildlife Manag., 10: 242-48.

Moulton, F. R. (ed.)
    1939 The migration and conservation of salmon. Publ. Amer. Assoc. Adv. Sci., 8: 1-106.

Mousley, H.
    1919 "The singing tree," or how near to the nest do the male birds sing? Auk, 36: 339-48.

Muller, Cornelius H.
    1940 Plant succession in the Larrea-Flourensia climax. Ecology, 21: 206-12.

Murie, Adolph
    1934 The moose of Isle Royale. Misc. Publ. Mus. Zool. Univ. Mich., 25: 1-44.
    1936 Following fox trails. *Ibid.*, 32: 1-45.
    1944 The wolves of Mount McKinley, Fauna Nat. Parks U. S., 5: i-xix, 1-238.

Murie, Olaus
    1935*a* Alaska-Yukon caribou. N. Amer. Fauna, 54: 1-93.
    1935*b* Food habits of the coyote in Jackson Hole, Wyo. Circ. U. S. Dept. Agric., 362: 1-24.

Murray, John, and Johan Hjort
    1912 The depths of the ocean; a general account of the modern science of oceanography based largely on the scientific researches of the Norwegian steamer Michael Sars in the North Atlantic. London: Macmillan Co.

Naumov, N. P.
    1936 On some particularities of stationary distribution of mouse-like rodents in southern Ukraine. Zool. Zhurn., 15: 675-96. (In Russian, with English summary.)

Neave, S. A.
    1910 On the birds of Northern Rhodesia and the Katanga district of Congoland. Ibis, ser. 9, 4: 78-155, 225-62.

Needham, James G.
    1948 Ecological notes on the insect population of the flower heads of *Bidens pilosa.* Ecol. Monog., 18: 431-46.

Nelson, Thurlow C.
    1921 Aids to successful oyster culture. I. Procuring the seed. Bull. N. Jersey Agric. Exper. Sta., 351: 1-59.
    1947 Some contributions from the land in determining conditions of life in the sea. Ecol. Monog., 17: 337-46.

Newcombe, Curtis L.
    1935 A study of the community relationships of the sea mussel, *Mytilus edulis* L. Ecology, 16: 234-43.
    1945 The biology and conservation of the blue crab, *Callinectes sapidus* Rathbun. Educ. Ser. Va. Fish. Lab., 4: 1-39.

Neyman, J.
    1939 On a new class of "contagious" distributions, applicable in entomology and bacteriology. Ann. Math. Statis., 10: 35-57.

Nice, Margaret M.
    1937 Studies in the life history of the song sparrow. I. Trans. Linn. Soc. N. Y., 4: i-vi, 1-247.
    1941 The role of territory in bird life. Amer. Midl. Nat., 26: 441-87.
    1943 Studies in the life history of the song sparrow. II. The behavior of the song sparrow and other passerines. *Ibid.*, 6: i-viii, 1-329.

Nichols, G. E.

1923 A working basis for the ecological classifications of plant communities. Ecology,
      4: 11-23, 154-79.

1924 The terrestrial environment in its relation to plant life. *In* Organic adaptation
      to environment. Ed. Malcolm R. Thorpe. New Haven: Yale Univ. Press.
      Pp. 1-43.

1929 Plant associations and their classification. Proc. Internat. Cong. Plant. Sci.,
      Ithaca, 1926, 1: 629-41.

1930 Methods in the floristic study of vegetation. Ecology, 11: 127-35.

1935 The hemlock–white pine–northern hardwood region of eastern North America.
      Ibid., 16: 403-22.

Nichols, J. T.

1939 Range and homing of individual box turtles. Copeia, pp. 125-27.

Nicholson, A. J.

1933 The balance of animal populations. Journ. Animal Ecol., 2: 132-78.

Nicholson, A. J., and V. A. Bailey

1935 The balance of animal populations. Pt. I. Proc. Zool. Soc. London, 1935 (2):
      551-98.

Nicholson, Arnold J.

1941 The homes and social habits of the wood-mouse (*Peromyscus leucopus nove-
      boracensis*) in southern Michigan. Amer. Midl. Nat., 25: 196-223.

Nicholson, E. M.

1931 The art of bird watching: a practical guide to field observation. London: H. F.
      & G. Witherby.

Noble, G. K.

1939 The role of dominance in the social life of birds. Auk, 56: 263-73.

Noble, G. K., and H. J. Clausen

1936 The aggregation behavior of *Storeria dekayi* and other snakes, with especial
      reference to the sense organs involved. Ecol. Monog., 6: 269-316.

Noble, G. K., and B. Curtis

1939 The social behavior of the jewel fish, *Hemichromus bimaculatus* Gill. Bull.
      Amer. Mus. Nat. Hist., 76: 1-46.

Noble, G. K., M. Wurm, and A. Schmidt

1938 Social behavior of the black-crowned night heron. Auk, 55: 7-40.

Norris, J. J.

1943 Botanical analyses of stomach contents as a method of determining forage con-
      sumption of range sheep. Ecology, 24: 244-51.

Odum, Eugene P., and Frank A. Pitelka

1939 Storm mortality in a winter starling roost. Auk, 56: 451-55.

Olson, Herman F.

1938 Deer tagging and population studies in Minnesota. Trans. N. Amer. Wildlife
      Conf., 3: 280-86.

Oosting, Henry J.

1942 An ecological analysis of the plant communities of Piedmont, North Carolina.
      Amer. Midl. Nat., 28: 1-126.

O'Roke, Earl C.

1930 The morphology, transmission, and life-history of *Haemoproteus lophortyx*
      O'Roke, a blood parasite of the California Valley quail. Univ. Calif. Publ.
      Zool., 36: 1-50.

Osborn, Ben
    1942 Prairie dogs in shinnery (oak scrub) savannah. Ecology, 23: 110-15.
    1943 Wildlife and habitats in Young County, Texas, by a new method. Journ. Wildlife Manag., 7: 241-56.

Osborn, Henry F.
    1902 The law of adaptive radiation. Amer. Nat., 36: 353-63.

Osborne, James G.
    1942 Sampling errors of systematic and random surveys of cover-type areas. Journ. Amer. Stat. Assoc., 37: 256-64.

Osgood, W. H., E. A. Preble, and G. H. Parker
    1915 The fur seals and other life of the Pribilof Islands, Alaska, in 1914. Bull. U. S. Bur. Fish., 34: 1-172.

Ostenson, Burton T.
    1947 Ecologic and geographic variation in the pelage color of the mammals in the Nebraska sandhills and adjacent areas. Univ. Mich. doctoral thesis.

Palmer, L. J.
    1944 Food requirements of some Alaskan game mammals. Journ. Mammal., 25: 49-54.

Palmer, Ralph S.
    1941 A behavior study of the common tern (*Sterna hirundo hirundo* L.) Proc. Boston Soc. Nat. Hist., 42: 1-119.

Park, Orlando
    1940 Nocturnalism—the development of a problem. Ecol. Monog., 10: 485-536.

Park, Orlando, Albert Barden, and Eliot Williams
    1940 Studies in nocturnal ecology. IX. Further analysis of activities of Panama rain forest animals. Ecology, 21: 122-34.

Park, Thomas
    1939 Analytical population studies in relation to general ecology. Amer. Midl. Nat., 21: 235-55.
    1941 The laboratory population as a test of a comprehensive ecological system. Quart. Rev. Biol., 16: 274-93, 440-61.
    1945 Life tables for the black flour beetle, *Tribolium madens* Charp. Amer. Nat., 79: 436-44.
    1948 Experimental studies of interspecies competition. I. Competition between populations of the flour beetles, *Tribolium confusum* Duval and *Tribolium castaneum* Herbst. Ecol. Monog., 18: 265-307.

Park, Thomas, Ella V. Gregg, and Catherine Z. Lutherman
    1941 Studies in population physiology. X. Interspecific competition in populations of granary beetles. Physiol. Zool., 14: 395-430.

Patterson, J. T.
    1943 The Drosophilidae of the Southwest. Univ. Texas Publ., 4313: 7-216.

Pavillard, J.
    1935 The present status of the plant association. Bot. Rev., 1: 210-32.

Paynter, Raymond A., Jr.
    1949 Clutch-size and the egg and chick mortality of Kent Island herring gulls. Ecology, 30: 146-66.

Pearl, Raymond
    1924 Studies in human biology. Baltimore: Williams and Wilkins Co.
    1925 The biology of population growth. New York: Alfred A. Knopf.

Pearl, R., and J. R. Miner
    1935 Experimental studies on the duration of life. XIV. The comparative mortality of certain lower organisms. Quart. Rev. Biol., 10: 60-79.

Pearl, Raymond, Thomas Park, and John R. Miner
1941 Experimental studies on the duration of life. XVI. Life tables for the flour beetle *Tribolium confusum* Duval. Amer. Nat., 75: 5-19.

Pearl, R., and S. L. Parker
1924 Experimental studies on the duration of life. IX. New life tables for Drosophila. Amer. Nat., 58: 71-82.

Pearl, Raymond, and Frank M. Surface
1909 Data on the inheritance of fecundity obtained from the records of egg production of the daughters of "200-egg" hens. Bull. Me. Agric. Exper. Sta., 166th Ann. Rept., 25: 49-84.

Pearse, A. S.
1914 Habits of fiddler crabs. Ann. Rept. Smithsonian Inst., 1913, pp. 415-28.
1923 The abundance and migration of turtles. Ecology, 4: 24-28.
1926 Animal ecology. New York: McGraw-Hill Book Co.
1943 Effects of burning-over and raking-off litter on certain soil animals in the Duke Forest. Amer. Midl. Nat., 29: 406-24.
1946 Observations on the microfauna of the Duke Forest. Ecol. Monog., 16: 127-50.

Pearson, G. A.
1923 Natural reproduction of western yellow pine in the Southwest. Bull. U. S. Dept. Agric., 1105: 1-144.

Pearson, Karl (ed.)
1924 Tables for statisticians and biometricians. Pt. I. 2d ed.; London: Biometric Lab., Univ. Coll.

Pearson, Oliver P.
1948 Metabolism and bioenergetics. Sci. Mo., 66: 131-34.

Pearson, Oliver P., and Anita K. Pearson
1947 Owl predation in Pennsylvania, with notes on the small mammals of Delaware County. Journ. Mammal., 28: 137-47.

Pechanec, Joseph F., and G. D. Pickford
1937a A comparison of some methods used in determining percentage utilization of range grasses. Journ. Agric. Res., 54: 753-65.
1937b A weight estimate method for the determination of range or pasture production. Journ. Amer. Soc. Agron., 29: 894-904.

Pennak, Robert W.
1946 The dynamics of fresh-water plankton populations. Ecol. Monog., 16: 339-55.

Petersen, C. G. J.
1896 The yearly immigration of young plaice into the Limfjord from the German Sea. Rept. Danish Biol. Sta., 6: 5-48.
1914 Valuation of the sea. II. The animal communities of the sea-bottom and their importance for marine zoogeography. *Ibid.,* 21: 1-44, and Appendix, 1-68.

Petersen, C. G. J., and P. B. Jensen
1911 Valuation of the sea. I. Animal life of the sea-bottom, its food and quantity. (Quantitative studies.) Rept. Danish Biol. Sta., 20: 3-81.

Peterson, Roger T.
1942 Life zones, biomes, or life forms. Audubon Mag., 44: 21-30.

Pettingill, Olin S., Jr.
1936 The American woodcock. Mem. Boston Soc. Nat. Hist., 9: 167-391.

Phillips, John F. V.
1931a The biotic community. Journ. Ecol., 19: 1-24.
1931b Quantitative methods in the study of numbers of terrestrial animals in biotic communities: a review, with suggestions. Ecology, 12: 633-49.

Pickles, Walter
 1937 Populations, territories and biomasses of ants at Thornhill, Yorkshire, in 1936. Journ. Animal Ecol., 6: 54-61.

Pickwell, Gayle B.
 1931 The prairie horned lark. Trans. Acad. Sci. St. Louis, 27: 1-153.

Piemeisel, R. L.
 1945 Natural replacement of weed hosts of the beet leafhopper as affected by rodents. Circ. U. S. Dept. Agric., 739: 1-48.

Pitelka, Frank A.
 1941 Distribution of birds in relation to major biotic communities. Amer. Midl. Nat., 25: 113-37.
 1942 Territoriality and related problems in North American hummingbirds. Condor, 44: 189-204.
 1943 Territoriality, display, and certain ecological relations of the American woodcock. Wilson Bull., 55: 88-114.

Plath, O. E.
 1935 Insect societies. In A handbook of social psychology. Ed.. Carl Murchison. Worcester, Mass.: Clark Univ. Press. Pp. 83-141.

Potzger, J. E.
 1946 Phytosociology of the primeval forest in central-northern Wisconsin and Upper Michigan, and a brief post-glacial history of the Lake Forest formation. Ecol. Monog., 16: 211-50.

Pritchard, A. L.
 1944 Return of two marked pink salmon (Oncorhynchus gorbuscha) to the natal stream from distant places in the sea. Copeia, pp. 80-82.

Rall, G. M.
 1938 Introduction to the ecology of gerbilles (Mammalia, Glires) Pallasiomys meridianus Pall. I. General remarks; dynamics of burrow activity. Vestnik Mikrobiologii, Epidemiologii i Parazitologii. Rev. Microbiol. Epidemiol. et Parasitol. (Saratov), 17: 331-63. (Quoted from Biol. Abs., 17: 8097.)

Randall, Pierce E., and Logan J. Bennett
 1939 Censusing ringneck pheasants in Pennsylvania. Trans. N. Amer. Wildlife Conf., 4: 331-36.

Ransom, R. M.
 1941 Pre-natal and infant mortality in a laboratory population of voles (Microtus agrestis). Proc. Zool. Soc. London, 111A: 45-57.

Rasmussen, D. I.
 1941 Biotic communities of Kaibab Plateau, Arizona. Ecol. Monog., 11: 229-75.

Rasmussen, D. I., and Everett R. Doman
 1943 Census methods and their application in the management of mule deer. Trans. N. Amer. Wildlife Conf., 8: 369-86.

Raunkiaer, C.
 1909 Formationsundersøgelse og Formationsstatistik. Bot. Tids. København, 30: 20-132. (English translation in Raunkiaer, 1934.)
 1918 Recherches statistiques sur les formations végétales. Det. Kgl. Danske Videnskabernes Selskab., Biol. Meddel., 1 (3): 1-80. (English translation in Raunkiaer, 1934.)
 1934 The life forms of plants and statistical plant geography, being the collected papers of C. Raunkiaer. Oxford: Clarendon Press.

Raup, Hugh M.
   1947 Some natural floristic areas in boreal America. Ecol. Monog., 17: 221-34.

Reighard, Jacob
   1920 The breeding behavior of the suckers and minnows. I. The suckers. Biol. Bull.,
         38: 1-32.
   1943 The breeding habits of the river chub, *Nocomis micropogon* (Cope). Papers
         Mich. Acad., 28: 397-423.

Renner, F. G.
   1936 Conditions influencing erosion on the Boise River watershed. Tech. Bull. U. S.
         Dept. Agric., 528: 1-32.

Reynolds, J. M.
   1945 On the inheritance of food effects in a flour beetle, *Tribolium destructor*. Proc.
         Royal Soc. London, 132B: 438-51.

Rice, T. D., and L. T. Alexander
   1938 The physical nature of soil. Yearbook U. S. Dept. Agric. Pp. 887-96.

Rich, Willis H., and Harlan B. Holmes
   1929 Experiments in marking young chinook salmon on the Columbia River, 1916-
         1927. Bull. U. S. Bur. Fish., 44: 215-64.

Richards, O. W.
   1934 Some quantitative methods for the analysis of insect associations. Proc. Linn.
         Soc. London, 146: 33-35.

Richards, P. W.
   1945 The floristic composition of primary tropical rain forest. Biol. Rev., 20: 1-13.

Ricker, William E.
   1942 Fish populations of two artificial lakes. Invest. Ind. Lakes and Streams, 2: 255-65.
   1945 Natural mortality among Indiana bluegill sunfish. Ecology, 26: 111-21.

Rickett, H. W.
   1921 A quantitative study of the larger aquatic plants of Lake Mendota. Trans.
         Wis. Acad. Sci. Arts Let., 20: 501-27.

Ridley, Henry N.
   1930 The dispersal of plants throughout the world. Ashford, Kent: L. Reeve & Co.

Riley, Charles V.
   1892 The yucca moth and yucca pollination. Ann. Rept. Mo. Bot. Garden, 3: 99-158.
   1940 Limnological studies in Connecticut. Pt. III. The plankton of Linsley Pond.
         Ecol. Monog., 10: 279-306.

Riley, Gordon A.
   1944 The carbon metabolism and photosynthetic efficiency of the earth as a whole;
         with an introduction by G. Evelyn Hutchinson. Amer. Sci., 32: 129-34.

Ritchie, James
   1940 An analysis of the influence of weather upon a migratory movement of birds.
         Proc. Royal Soc. Edinburgh, 60: 299-321.

Ritter, William E.
   1938 The California woodpecker and I. Berkeley, California: Univ. Calif. Press.

Robertson, Charles
   1928 Flowers and insects. Ecology, 9: 505-26.

Robertson, Forbes W., and James H. Sang
   1945 The ecological determinants of population growth in a *Drosophila* culture.
         I. Fecundity of adult flies. II. Circumstances affecting egg viability. Proc.
         Royal Soc. London, 132B: 258-91.

Robertson, Joseph H., and C. Kenneth Pearse
    1945   Artificial reseeding and the closed community. Northwest Sci., 19: 58-66.

Rodeheffer, Immanuel A.
    1941   The movements of marked fish in Douglas Lake, Michigan. Papers Mich. Acad.,
            26: 265-80.

Rogers, J. Speed
    1942   The crane flies (Tipulidae) of the George Reserve, Michigan. Misc. Publ. Mus.
            Zool. Univ. Mich., No. 53.

Romell, L. G.
    1930   Comments on Raunkiaer's and similar methods of vegetation analysis and the
            "law of frequency." Ecology, 11: 589-96.
    1935   Ecological problems of the humus layer in the forest. Mem. Cornell Univ. Agric.
            Exper. Sta., 170: 1-28.

Romney, Van E.
    1945   The effect of physical factors upon catch of the beet leafhopper (*Eutettix
            tenellus* (Bak.) by a cylinder and two sweep-net methods. Ecology, 26: 135-47.

Roosevelt, Theodore, and Edmund Heller
    1914   Life-histories of African game animals. New York: Charles Scribner's Sons. 2 vols.

Rossby, C. G.
    1941   The scientific basis of modern meteorology. Yearbook U. S. Dept. Agric.
            Pp. 599-655.

Rowan, William
    1926   On photoperioditism, reproductive periodicity, and the annual migration of
            birds and certain fishes. Proc. Boston Soc. Nat. Hist., 38: 147-89.

Rush, William M.
    1942   Wildlife census. Counting big game has its uncertainties—but here's the way
            it's done. Amer. Forests, 48: 20-23, 48.

Russell, Carl P.
    1932   Seasonal migration of mule deer. Ecol. Monog., 2: 1-46.

Ruthven, Alexander G.
    1920   The environmental factors in the distribution of animals. Geog. Rev., 10: 241-48.

Salisbury, E. J.
    1942   The reproductive capacity of plants. London: George Bell and Sons.

Salyer, J. Clark II, and Karl F. Lagler
    1940   The food and habits of the American merganser during winter in Michigan,
            considered in relation to fish management. Journ. Wildlife Manag., 4: 186-219.

Sampson, Arthur W.
    1914   Natural revegetation of range lands based upon growth requirements and life
            history of the vegetation. Journ. Agric. Res., 3: 93-147.
    1919   Plant succession in relation to range management. Bull. U. S. Dept. Agric.,
            791: 1-76.
    1939   Plant indicators—concept and status. Bot. Rev., 5: 155-206.

Sanders, Nell J., and Victor E. Shelford
    1922   A quantitative and seasonal study of a pine-dune animal community. Ecology,
            3: 306-20.

Saunders, Aretas A.
    1936   Ecology of the birds of Quaker Run Valley, Allegany State Park, New York.
            New York State Mus. Handbk., 16: 1-174.

Schimper, A. F. W.
  1903 Plant-geography upon a physiological basis; the authorized English translation
         by William R. Fisher. Rev. and ed. by Percy Groom and I. B. Balfour;
         Oxford: Clarendon Press.

Schjelderup-Ebbe, Thorleif
  1935 Social behavior of birds. *In* A handbook of social psychology. Ed. Carl Murchi-
         son; Worcester, Mass.: Clark Univ. Press. Pp. 947-72.

Schmidt, Johs.
  1925 The breeding places of the eel. Ann. Rept. Smithsonian Inst., 1924: 279-316. (Re-
         printed with additions from article by same title in Philos. Trans. Royal Soc.
         London, 211B: 179-208.)

Schnabel, Zoe E.
  1938 The estimation of total fish population of a lake. Amer. Math. Mo., 45: 348-52.

Schneirla, T. C.
  1946 Problems in the biopsychology of social organization. Journ. Abnorm. Psychol.,
         41: 385-402.

Schumacher, F. X., and R. A. Chapman
  1942 Sampling methods in forestry and range management. Bull. School Forestry
         Duke Univ., No. 7.

Schumacher, F. X., and R. W. Eschmeyer
  1943 The estimate of fish population in lakes or ponds. Journ. Tenn. Acad. Sci., 18:
         228-49.

Schwan, H. E., and Lloyd Swift
  1941 Forage inventory methods with special reference to big game ranges. Trans.
         N. Amer. Wildlife Conf., 6: 118-26.

Scott, J. P.
  1942 Genetic differences in the social behavior of inbred strains of mice. Journ.
         Heredity, 33: 11-15.
  1943 Differences in the social organization of mice caused by differences in fighting
         behavior (fighting of males). Genetics, 28: 88-89.
  1945 Social behavior, organization and leadership in a small flock of domestic sheep.
         Comp. Psychol. Monog., 18 (4): 1-29.

Scott, John W.
  1942 Mating behavior of the sage grouse. Auk, 59: 477-98.

Sears, Paul B.
  1932 Postglacial climate in eastern North America. Ecology, 13: 1-6.

Setchell, William A.
  1920 The temperature interval in the geographical distribution of marine algae.
         Science, 52: 187-90.

Seton, Ernest T.
  1912 The arctic prairies; a canoe-journey of 2,000 miles in search of the caribou;
         being the account of a voyage to the region north of Aylmer Lake. New York:
         Charles Scribner's Sons.
  1919 Life histories of northern animals; an account of the mammals of Manitoba.
         New York: Charles Scribner's Sons. 2 vols.
  1929 Lives of game animals. Garden City and New York: Doubleday, Doran and Co.
         4 vols.

Severtzov, S. A.
  1934 On the dynamics of populations of vertebrates. Quart. Rev. Biol., 9: 409-37.
  1940 The specific constants of reproduction of *Bison bonasus*. Trudi Inst. Evol. Morf.
         Acad. Nauk SSSR., 3: 3-31. (In Russian, with English summary.)

Shaler, N. S.
  1892 Effect of animals and plants on soils in the origin and nature of soils. Ann.
        Rept. U. S. Geol. Surv., 12: (1): 213-345.
Shantz, Homer L.
  1911 Natural vegetation as an indicator of the capabilities of land for crop pro-
        duction in the Great Plains area. Bull. Bur. Plant Industry U. S. Dept. Agric.,
        201: 1-91.
Shelford, Victor E.
  1911 Physiological animal geography. Journ. Morph., 22: 551-618.
  1913 Animal communities in temperate North America as illustrated in the Chicago
        region. A study in animal ecology. Chicago: Univ. Chicago Press.
  1918 Physiological problems in the life-histories of animals with particular reference
        to their seasonal appearance. Amer. Nat., 52: 129-54.
  1929 Laboratory and field ecology; the responses of animals as indicators of correct
        working methods. Baltimore: Williams and Wilkins Co.
  1930 Geographical extent and succession in Pacific North American intertidal
        (Balanus) communities. Publ. Puget Sound Biol. Sta., 7: 217-24.
  1931 Some concepts of bioecology. Ecology, 12: 455-67.
  1932a Basic principles of the classification of communities and habitats and the use
        of terms. Ibid., 13: 105-20.
  1932b Life zones, modern ecology, and the failure of temperature summing. Wilson
        Bull., 44: 144-57.
  1943 The abundance of the collared lemming (Dicrostonyx groenlandicus (Tr.) var.
        richardsoni Mer.) in the Churchhill area, 1929 to 1940. Ecology, 24: 472-84.
  1945 The relative merits of the life zone and biome concepts. Wilson Bull., 57: 248-52.
Shelford, V. E., and W. P. Flint
  1943 Populations of the chinch bug in the upper Mississippi Valley from 1823 to
        1940. Ecology, 24: 435-55.
Shelford, Victor E., and E. D. Towler
  1925 Animal communities of the San Juan channel and adjacent areas. Publ. Puget
        Sound Biol. Sta., 5: 53-73.
Shelford, Victor E., and others
  1935 Some marine biotic communities of the Pacific coast of North America. Ecol.
        Monog., 5: 249-354.
Sherman, Althea R.
  1924 "Animal aggregations": a reply. Condor, 26: 85-88.
Shetter, David S.
  1947 The electric "shocker" and its use in Michigan streams. Mich. Conserv., 16 (9):
        8-10.
Shirley, Hardy L.
  1945 Reproduction of upland conifers in the Lake States as affected by root com-
        petition and light. Amer. Midl. Nat., 33: 537-612.
Shoemaker, H. H.
  1939 Social hierarchy in flocks of the canary. Auk, 56: 581-406.
  1947 A laboratory study of fish populations. Trans. Amer. Fish. Soc., 74: 350-59.
Shreve, Forrest
  1925 Ecological aspects of California deserts. Ecology, 6: 93-103.
Silliman, Ralph P.
  1945 Determination of mortality rates from length frequencies of the pilchard or
        sardine, Sardinops caerulea. Copeia, pp. 191-96.

Silloway, Perley M.

    1923   Relation of summer birds to the western Adirondack forest. Roosevelt Wildlife
        Bull., 1: 397-486.

Simanton, F. L.

    1916   *Hyperaspis binotata,* a predator enemy of the terrapin scale. Journ. Agric. Res.,
        6: 197-204.

Simon, James R.

    1940   Mating performance of the sage grouse. Auk, 57: 467-71.

Simpson, George G.

    1941   The role of the individual in evolution. Journ. Wash. Acad. Sci., 31: 1-20.

Skutch, Alexander F.

    1934   A nesting of the slaty antshrike *(Thamnophilus punctatus)* on Barro Colorado
        Island. Auk, 51: 8-16.

    1935   Helpers at the nest. *Ibid.,* 52: 257-73.

    1943   The family life of Central American woodpeckers. Sci. Mo., pp. 358-64.

    1947   Life history of the marbled wood-quail. Condor, 49: 217-32.

    1949   Life history of the yellow-thighed manakin. Auk, 66: 1-24.

Smith, Harry M.

    1943   Size of breeding populations in relation to egg-laying and reproductive suc-
        cess in the eastern red-wing *(Agelaius p. phoeniceus).* Ecology, 24: 183-207.

Smith, H. S.

    1935   The role of biotic factors in the determination of population densities. Journ.
        Econ. Entom., 28: 873-98.

Smith, W. G.

    1913   Raunkiaer's life-forms and statistical methods. Journ. Ecol., 1: 16-26.

Snedecor, George W.

    1940   Statistical methods applied to experiments in agriculture and biology. Ames:
        Ia. State Coll. Press.

    1946   Statistical methods applied to experiments in agriculture and biology. 4th ed.;
        Ames: Ia. State Coll. Press.

Snyder, L. L.

    1935   A study of the sharp-tailed grouse. Univ. Toronto Studies, Biol. Ser., 40: 1-66.

    1943   The snowy owl migration of 1941-42; a report of the Snowy Owl Committee.
        Wilson Bull., 55: 8-10.

Sollberger, Dwight E.

    1943   Notes on the breeding habits of the eastern flying squirrel *(Glaucomys volans
        volans).* Journ. Mammal., 24: 163-73.

Solomon, M. E.

    1949   The natural control of animal populations. Journ. Animal Ecol., 18: 1-35.

Southern, H. N.

    1938   The spring migration of the willow-warbler over Europe. Brit. Birds, 32: 202-6.

Spalding, Volney M.

    1909   Distribution and movements of desert plants. Publ. Carnegie Inst. Wash., 113:
        i-v; 1-144.

Spencer, Herbert

    1891   The principles of biology. New York: D. Appleton and Co. 2 vols. (1st ed. in
        1864.)

Spiers, J. Murray

    1939   Fluctuations in numbers of birds in the Toronto region. Auk, 56: 411-19.

Stakman, E. C.
    1947   Plant diseases are shifty enemies. Amer. Sci., 35: 321-50.

Stebbins, G. Ledyard, Jr.
    1942   The genetic approach to problems of rare and endemic species. Madroño, 6:
           241-58.

Stebbins, Robert C.
    1944   Field notes on a lizard, the mountain swift, with special reference to territorial
           behavior. Ecology, 25: 233-45.

Stebbins, Robert C., and Harry B. Robinson
    1946   Further analysis of a population of the lizard *Sceloporus graciosus gracilis*. Univ.
           Calif. Publ. Zool., 48: 149-68.

Stebler, A. M.
    1939   The tracking technique in the study of the larger predatory mammals. Trans.
           N. Amer. Wildlife Conf., 4: 203-8.
    1944   The status of the wolf in Michigan. Journ. Mammal., 25: 37-43.

Stegeman, LeRoy C.
    1937   A food study of the white-tailed deer. Trans. N. Amer. Wildlife Conf., 2: 438-45.

Stewart, George, and Wesley Keller
    1936   A correlation method of ecology as exemplified by studies of native desert
           vegetation. Ecology, 17: 500-14.

Stickel, Lucille F.
    1946   The source of animals moving into a depopulated area. Journ. Mammal., 27:
           301-7.

Stickel, William H., and James B. Cope
    1947   The home ranges and wanderings of snakes. Copeia, pp., 127-36.

Stock, Chester
    1929   A census of the Pleistocene mammals of Rancho La Brea, based on the collec-
           tions of the Los Angeles Museum. Journ. Mammal., 10: 281-89.

Stoddard, Herbert L.
    1931   The bobwhite quail; its habits, preservation and increase. New York: Charles
           Scribner's Sons..

Stoddard, L. A., and A. D. Smith
    1943   Range management. New York and London: McGraw-Hill Book Co.

Stoner, Dayton
    1942a Behavior of young bank swallows after first leaving the nest. Bird-Banding, 13:
           107-10.
    1942b Bird study through banding. Sci. Mo., 55: 132-38.

Storer, Tracy I., Francis C. Evans, and Fletcher G. Palmer
    1944   Some rodent populations in the Sierra Nevada of California. Ecol. Monog., 14:
           165-92.

Stuewer, Frederick W.
    1943   Raccoons, their habits and management in Michigan. Ecol. Monog., 13: 203-57.

Sudworth, George B.
    1908   Forest trees of the Pacific slope. Forest Service, U. S. Dept. Agric.

Sukachev, V. N.
    1926   Plant associations. (Quoted from Formozov, 1928.)

Summerhayes, V. S.
    1941   The effect of voles (*Microtus agrestis*) on vegetation. Journ. Ecol., 29: 14-48.

Sumner, E. L.
  1935 A life history study of the California quail, with recommendations for conservation and management. Calif. Fish and Game, 21: 167-256, 275-342.

Sumner, Francis B.
  1915 Review of: Joseph Grinnell, 1914. An account of the mammals and birds of the Lower Colorado Valley, with special reference to the distributional problems presented. Science, n.s., 41: 65-69.
  1932 Genetic, distributional and evolutionary studies of the subspecies of deer mice (*Peromyscus*). Biblio. Genetica, 9: 1-106.

Sumner, W. G., and A. G. Keller
  1927 The science of society. New Haven: Yale Univ. Press.

Sverdrup, H. U., Martin W. Johnson, and Richard H. Fleming
  1942 The oceans: their physics, chemistry, and general biology. New York: Prentice-Hall.

Sweetman, Harvey L.
  1936 The biological control of insects; with a chapter on weed control. Ithaca, New York: Comstock Publ. Co.

Swellengrebel, N. H.
  1940 The efficient parasite. Science, 92: 465-69.

Talbot, M. W., and H. H. Biswell
  1942 The forage crop and its management. *In* The San Joaquin experimental range. Bull. Univ. Calif. Agric. Exper. Sta., 663: 13-49.

Talbot, M. W., H. H. Biswell, and A. L. Hormay
  1939 Fluctuations in the annual vegetation of California. Ecology, 20: 394-402.

Talbot, Mary
  1943 Population studies of the ant, *Prenolepis imparis* Say. Ecology, 24: 31-44.

Tansley, A. G.
  1935 The use and abuse of vegetational concepts and terms. Ecology, 16: 284-307.
  1939 The British Islands and their vegetation. Cambridge: Cambridge Univ. Press.
  1946 Introduction to plant ecology; a guide for beginners in the study of plant communities. London: George Allen and Unwin.

Tansley, A. G., and T. F. Chipp
  1926 Aims and methods in the study of vegetation. London: Brit. Empire Vegetation Comm.

Taylor, Griffith
  1919 The settlement of tropical Australia. Geog. Rev., 8: 84-115.

Taylor, Walter P.
  1934 Significance of extreme or intermittent conditions in distribution of species and management of natural resources, with a restatement of Liebig's law of minimum. Ecology, 15: 374-79.
  1935a Some animal relations to soils. *Ibid.*, 16: 127-36.
  1935b Significance of the biotic community in ecological studies. Quart. Rev. Biol., 10: 291-307.
  1941 Ecological classification of the mammals and birds of Walker County, Texas, and some adjoining areas. Trans. N. Amer. Wildlife Conf., 5: 170-76.

Taylor, Walter P., and D. M. Gorsuch
  1932 A test of some rodent and bird influences on western yellow pine reproduction at Fort Valley, Flagstaff, Arizona. Journ. Mammal., 13: 218-23.

Taylor, Walter P., and Daniel W. Lay
  1944 Ecologic niches occupied by rabbits in eastern Texas. Ecology, 25: 120-21.

Taylor, Walter P., Charles T. Vorhies, and P. B. Lister
1935 The relation of jack rabbits to grazing in southern Arizona. Journ. Forestry, 33: 490-98.

Taylor, W. S.
1932 The gregariousness of pigeons. Journ. Comp. Psychol., 13: 127-31.

Test, Frederick H.
1945 Substrate and movements of the marine gastropod *Acmaea asmi*. Amer. Midl. Nat., 33: 791-93.

Tevis, Lloyd, Jr.
1947 Summer activities of California raccoons. Journ. Mammal., 28: 323-32.

Thienemann, A.
1926 Der Nahrungskreislauf im Wasser. Verh. deutsch. Zool. Ges., 31: 29-79. (Also Zool. Anz. Suppl., 2: 29-79.)

Thompson, W. R.
1922a Etude de quelques cas simples de parasitime cyclique chez les insectes entomo-phages. C. R. Acad. Sci. Paris, 174: 1647-49.
1922b Theórie de l'action des parasites entomophages. Accroissement de la proportion d'hôtes parasites dans le parasitisme cyclique. *Ibid.*, 175: 65-68.
1923 La théorie mathématique de l'action des parasites entomophages. Rev. Gen. Sci., 34: 202-10.
1928 A contribution to the study of biological control and parasite introduction in continental areas. Parasitology, 20: 90-112.
1931 On the reproduction of organisms with overlapping generations. Bull. Entom. Res., 22: 147-72.
1939 Biological control and the theories of the interactions of populations. Para-sitology, 31: 299-388.

Thomson, A. L.
1926 Problems of bird-migration. London: H. F. and G. Witherby.

Thomson, George M.
1922 The naturalization of animals and plants in New Zealand. Cambridge: Cam-bridge Univ. Press.

Thomson, J. Arthur, and Patrick Geddes
1931 Life: outlines of general biology. London: Williams & Norgate. 2 Vols.

Thornber, J. J.
1909 Vegetation groups of the Desert Laboratory domain. Publ. Carnegie Inst. Wash., 113: 103-12.

Thornthwaite, C. Warren
1931 The climates of North America according to a new classification. Geog. Rev., 21: 633-55.
1933 The climates of the earth. *Ibid.*, 23: 433-40.
1941 Atlas of climatic types in the United States, 1909-39. Misc. Publ. U. S. Dept. Agric., 421: 1-7.

Thorpe, W. H.
1940 Ecology and the future of systematics. *In* The new systematics. Ed Julian Hux-ley; Oxford: Clarendon Press. Pp. 341-64.

Tiffany, Loel, and Hanford Tiffany
1944 One of the apostles. Chicago Nat., 7 (4): 75-80.

Timmons, F. L.
1941-42 The rise and decline of cactus in Kansas. Bienn. Rept. Kans. State Bd. Agric., 33: 37-46.

Tinbergen, L.
    1946 De Sperwer als Roofvijand van Zangvogels. Ardea, 34: 1-213 (In Dutch, with
          English summary.)

Tinbergen, N.
    1935 Field observations of East Greenland birds. I. The behavior of the red-necked
          phalarope (*Phalaropus lobatus* L.) in spring. Ardea, 24: 1-42.
    1939 On the analysis of social organization among vertebrates, with special reference
          to birds. Amer. Midl. Nat., 21: 210-34.

Tompkins, Grace
    1933 Individuality and territoriality as displayed in winter by three passerine species.
          Condor, 35: 98-106.

Toumey, James W., and C. F. Korstian
    1937 Foundations of silviculture upon an ecological basis. 2d ed; New York: John
          Wiley and Sons.

Transeau, E. N.
    1926 The accumulation of energy by plants. Ohio Journ. Sci., 26: 1-10.

Treherne, R. C., and E. R. Buckell
    1924 Grasshoppers of British Columbia. Bull. Dept. Agric. Dom. Can., n.s., 39: 1-47.

Trippensee, R. E.
    1948 Wildlife management; upland game and general principles. New York: McGraw-
          Hill Book Co.

Truog, Emil
    1938 Soil acidity and liming. Yearbook U. S. Dept. Agric. Pp. 563-80.

Turesson, Göte
    1922a The species and the variety as ecological units. Hereditas, 3: 100-113.
    1922b The genotypical response of the plant species to the habitat. *Ibid.*, 3: 211-350.
    1925 The plant species in relation to habitat and climate. Contributions to the knowl-
          edge of genecological units. *Ibid.*, 6: 147-236.

Turrill, W. B.
    1946 The ecotype concept. A consideration with appreciation and criticism, espe-
          cially of modern trends. New Phytol., 45: 34-43.

Tutin, T. G.
    1941 The hydrosere and current concepts of the climax. Journ. Ecol., 29: 268-79.

Twomey, Arthur C.
    1945 The bird population of an elm-maple forest with special reference to aspection,
          territorialism, and coactions. Ecol. Monog., 15: 173-205.

Udvardy, Miklós D. F.
    1947 Methods of bird sociological survey, on the basis of some Tihany communities
          investigated. Arch. Biol. Hungarica, ser. 2, 17: 61-89.

Uttendörfer, O.
    1930 Die Rolle des Sperbers in der Natur. Ber. Ver. Schles. Ornithol., 16: 27-31.

Uvarov, B. P.
    1931 Insects and climate. Trans. Entom. Soc. London, 79: 1-247.

Van der Klaauw, C. J.
    1948 Ecological morphology. Biblio. Biotheoretica, 4: 25-111.

Varley, G. C.
    1947 The natural control of population balance in the knapweed gall-fly (*Urophora
          jaceana*). Journ. Animal Ecol., 16: 139-87.

Varshavski, S. N.

    1938 Fluctuations in the fertility of the little ground-squirrel (*Citellus pygmaeus* Pall.). Plant Protection, Leningrad, 17: 3-13. (In Russian, with summary in English.)

Verrill, A. E.

    1873 Report upon the invertebrate animals of Vineyard Sound and adjacent waters. Rept. U. S. Comm. Fish and Fisheries, 1871-72, Pt. 1, pp. 295-778.

Vestal, Arthur G.

    1913 Local distribution of grasshoppers in relation to plant associations. Biol. Bull., 25: 141-80.

    1914 Internal relations of terrestrial associations. Amer. Nat., 48: 413-45.

    1931 Plant ecology. Ecology, 12: 232-39.

    1938 A subject index for communities, including vegetation-components. Ecology, 19: 107-25.

Vestal, Arthur G., and Mary F. Heermans

    1945 Size requirements for reference areas in mixed forest. Ecology, 26: 122-34.

Volterra, Vito

    1928 Variations and fluctuations of the number of individuals in animal species living together. Journ. conseil internat. pour l'explor. mer., 3: 3-51. (Reprinted in Animal Ecol., by R. N. Chapman, 1931: 409-48.)

Vorhies, Charles T.

    1945 Water requirements of desert animals in the Southwest. Tech. Bull. Ariz. Agric. Exper. Sta., 107: 487-525.

Vorhies, Charles T., and Walter P. Taylor

    1933 The life history and ecology of jack rabbits, *Lepus alleni* and *L. californicus* ssp. in relation to grazing in Arizona. Tech. Bull. Univ. Ariz., 49: 472-587.

Voronov, A. G.

    1935 Some observations on the activity of the social vole (*Microtus socialis* Pall.) on the pastures of the Dagestan foothills. Bull. Soc. Nat. Moscow, Sec. Biol., 44: 314-23, 391-406. (In Russian.)

Wagner, Helmuth O.

    1946 Food and feeding habits of Mexican hummingbirds. Wilson Bull., 58: 69-93.

Waksman, Selman A.

    1927 Principles of soil microbiology. Baltimore: Williams and Wilkins Co.

    1936 Humus: origin, chemical composition, and importance in nature. Baltimore: Williams and Wilkins Co.

    1945 Soil microbiology as a field of science. Science, 102: 339-44.

Wallace, Alfred R.

    1880 Island life; or, the phenomena and causes of insular faunas and floras, including a revision and attempted solution of the problem of geological climates. London: Macmillan Co.

Wallace, G. J.

    1941 Winter studies of color-banded chickadees. Bird-banding, 12: 49-67.

Warming, E.

    1899 On the vegetation of tropical America. Bot. Gaz., 27: 1-18.

    1909 Oecology of plants. An introduction to the study of plant-communities. Oxford: Clarendon Press.

Watt, A. S.

    1919 On the causes of failure of natural regeneration in British oakwoods. Journ. Ecol., 7: 173-203.

1923 On the ecology of British beechwoods with special reference to their regeneration. *Ibid.*, 11: 1-48.

Weaver, J. E.
1919 The ecological relations of roots. Publ. Carnegie Inst. Wash., 286: i-vii, 1-128.
1920 Root development in the grassland formation, a correlation of the roots systems of native vegetational and crop plants. *Ibid.*, 292: 1-151.
1926 Root development of field crops. New York: McGraw-Hill Book Co.
1943 Replacement of true prairie by mixed prairie in eastern Nebraska and Kansas. Ecology, 24: 421-34.

Weaver, J. E., and F. W. Albertson
1943 Resurvey of grasses, forbs, and underground grass parts at the end of the great drought. Ecol. Monog., 13: 63-117.

Weaver, J. E., and Frederic E. Clements
1938 Plant ecology. 2d ed.; New York: McGraw-Hill Book Co.

Weaver, J. E., and R. W. Darland
1944 Grassland patterns in 1940. Ecology, 25: 202-15.

Weaver, J. E., and V. H. Hougen
1939 Effect of frequent clipping on plant production in prairie and pasture. Amer. Midl. Nat., 21: 396-414.

Weaver, Richard L.
1940 The purple finch invasion of northeastern United States and the maritime provinces in 1939. Bird-banding, 11: 79-105.

Weese, A. O.
1924 Animal ecology of an Illinois elm-maple forest. Ill. Biol. Monog., 9 (4): 1-93.
1939 The effect of overgrazing on insect population. Proc. Okla. Acad. Sci., 19: 95-99.

Weiner, J. S.
1946 Some remarks on physical anthropology. Man, 46: 90-91. (Reprinted in Year-book Phys. Anthropol., 1946: 22-23.)

Welch, Paul S.
1935 Limnology. New York: McGraw-Hill Book Co.
1948 Limnological methods. Philadelphia and Toronto: Blakiston Co.

Welter, Wilfred A.
1935 The natural history of the long-billed marsh wren. Wilson Bull., 47: 3-34.

Went, F. W.
1942 The dependence of certain annual plants on shrubs in southern California deserts. Bull. Torrey Bot. Club, 69: 100-14.
1949 Ecology of desert plants. II. The effect of rain and temperature on germination and growth. Ecology, 30: 1-13.

Wesenberg-Lund, C.
1930 Contributions to the biology of the Rotifera. II. The periodicity and sexual periods. D. Kgl. Danske Vidensk. Selsk. Skrifter, Naturvidensk. og. Mathem. Afd., ser. 9, 2: 1-230.

Wessel, John P., and W. Henry Leigh
1941 Studies of the flock organization of the white-throated sparrow. Wilson Bull., 53: 222-30.

Westermarck, Edward
1891 The history of human marriage. London: Macmillan Co.

Wetmore, Alexander
1943 The birds of southern Veracruz, Mexico. Proc. U. S. Nat. Mus., 93: 215-340.

Wheeler, William M.
   1910   Ants: their structure, development and behavior. New York: Columbia Univ. Press.
   1923   Social life among the insects. New York: Harcourt, Brace and Co.
   1926   Emergent evolution and the social. Science, 64: 433-40. (Reprinted as small book under same title in 1927, by Kegan Paul, Trench, Trubner and Co., London.)

Whiting, P. W.
   1947   Some experiments with *Melittobia* and other wasps. Journ. Heredity, 38: 11-20.

Wight, Howard M.
   1939   Field and laboratory technic in wildlife management. Ann Arbor: Univ. Mich. Press.

Williams, C. B.
   1930   The migration of butterflies. Edinburgh and London: Oliver and Boyd.

Williams, Eliot C., Jr.
   1941   An ecological study of the floor fauna of the Panama rain forest. Bull. Chicago Acad. Sci., 6: 63-124.

Williams, Laidlaw
   1942   Interrelations in a nesting group of four species of birds. Wilson Bull., 54: 238-49.

Williams, Roger J.
   1946   The human frontier: a new pathway for science toward a better understanding of ourselves. New York: Harcourt, Brace and Co.

Wilson, P. W.
   1937   Symbiotic nitrogen fixation by the *Leguminosae*. Bot. Rev., 3: 365-99.

Winterbottom, J. M.
   1943   On woodland bird parties in Northern Rhodesia. Ibis, 85: 437-42.

Wolcott, George N.
   1937   An animal census of two pastures and a meadow in northern New York. Ecol. Monog., 7: 1-90.

Wolfe, John N., Richard T. Wareham, and Herbert T. Scofield
   1943   The microclimates of a small valley in central Ohio. Trans. Amer. Geophys. Union, 1943: 154-66.

Wolfenbarger, D. O.
   1946   Dispersion of small organisms: distance dispersion rates of bacteria, spores, seeds, pollen, and insects; incidence rates of diseases and injuries. Amer. Midl. Nat., 35: 1-152.

Woodbury, A. M.
   1933   Biotic relationships of Zion Canyon, Utah, with special reference to succession. Ecol. Monog., 3: 148-245.
   1941   Changing the "hook-order" in cows. Ecology, 22: 410-11.

Woodbury, A. M., and Ross Hardy
   1940   The dens and behavior of the desert tortoise. Science, 92: 529.
   1948   Studies of the desert tortoise, *Gopherus agassizii*. Ecol. Monog., 18: 145-200.

Wright, Sewall
   1931   Evolution in mendelian populations. Genetics, 16: 97-159.

Wulff, E. V.
   1943   An introduction to historical plant geography. Waltham, Mass.: Chronica Botanica Co,

Yapp, W. B.
    1934 The rook population of West Gloucestershire. Journ Animal Ecol., 3: 77-80.

Yeatter, Ralph E.
    1934 The Hungarian partridge in the Great Lakes region. Bull. School Forestry and Cons. Univ. Mich., 5: 1-92.

Yerkes, Robert M.
    1943 Chimpanzees; a laboratory colony. New Haven: Yale Univ. Press.

Zenkevich, L. (ed.)
    1931 Fish-food in the Barents Sea. Repts. 1st Sess. State Oceanographical Inst., Moscow, 4: 1-60. (In Russian, with English summary.)

INDEX